SPECIAL MILLENNIUM EDITION

# BOTTOM LINE YEAR BOOK 2000

BY THE EDITORS OF

**Bottom Line**
PERSONAL

Copyright © 1999 by Boardroom® Inc.

First Printing
10  9  8  7  6  5  4  3  2  1

Boardroom® Classics publishes the advice of expert authorities in
many fields. The use of a book is not a substitute for legal,
accounting or other professional services. Consult a competent
professional for answers to your specific questions.

**Library of Congress Cataloging in Publication Data**
Main entry under title:

Bottom Line Yearbook 2000

    1. Life skills—United States.    I. Bottom line personal.
ISBN 0-88723-195-0


Boardroom® Classics is a registered trademark of
Boardroom®, Inc.
55 Railroad Avenue, Greenwich, CT 06830


Printed in the United States of America

# Contents

## 7  •  BUSINESS AND CAREER SMARTS

## 8  •  DOCTOR'S, HOSPITALS AND YOU

## 9  •  SIMPLE SOLUTIONS TO COMMON HEALTH PROBLEMS

## 10  •  THE WINNING EDGE

## 11 • INVESTMENT WISDOM

## 12 • RETIREMENT PLANNING STRATEGIES

## 13 • THE SMART CONSUMER

## 14 • BETTER ESTATE PLANNING

## 15 • VERY, VERY PERSONAL

## 16 • DIET, NUTRITION AND EXERCISE

## 17 • NATURAL HEALING

## 18 • EDUCATION SMARTS

## 19 • MAKING THE MOST OF YOUR LEISURE TIME

## 20 • YOUR CAR

## 21 • SELF-DEFENSE

# 1

# Staying Healthy

## Secrets of Maximum Longevity

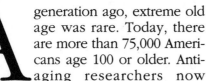 A generation ago, extreme old age was rare. Today, there are more than 75,000 Americans age 100 or older. Anti-aging researchers now predict that humans may soon be living to age 120…or even 150.

What determines life span? Luck plays a role. So does heredity. But emerging research demonstrates the critical importance of three other factors—each of which lies completely within our control…

●**Healthful lifestyle.** Given a good diet and regular exercise, someone with average "longevity genes" can expect to live to roughly age 75.

●**Nutritional supplements.** People who consume optimal levels of key vitamins and minerals can expect to live an extra 10 to 15 years.

●**Hormone therapy.** For decades now, postmenopausal women have been taking estrogen to cut their risk for heart disease, osteoporosis…and now dementia.

Other forms of hormone therapy look promising, too. In recent studies, animals given certain hormones and other drugs lived 20% to 30% longer than animals not given these drugs. In human terms, that's 120 years.

### EATING FOR LONGEVITY

Nutritionists have long recommended minimizing the consumption of caffeine, sugar, fat and salt…while eating at least five servings per day of fresh fruits and vegetables.

That's good advice—as far as it goes. But some foods are especially conducive to longevity…

●**Soy foods.** Soybeans are rich in antioxidants. These compounds neutralize *free radi-*

Ronald Klatz, MD, DO, president of the American Academy of Anti-Aging Medicine, 1341 W. Fullerton, Suite 111, Chicago 60614. He is coauthor of *Stopping the Clock: Dramatic Breakthroughs in Anti-Aging and Age Reversal Techniques*. Bantam.

*cals,* substances that accelerate aging by causing cellular damage.

One antioxidant in soy, *genistein,* has been shown to prevent cancer. It also blocks formation of fatty deposits along artery walls.

This process, known as *atherosclerosis,* is the main cause of heart attack and stroke.

*Optimal intake:* 50 mg to 75 mg of soy protein per day. That's equal to one cup of soy milk or three servings of tofu.

●**Garlic.** In addition to boosting immune function and lowering levels of LDL (bad) cholesterol, garlic helps prevent cancer and acts as an antibiotic.

It's even a mild anticoagulant, so it helps reduce the risk for stroke and heart attack.

*Optimal intake:* Two or three cloves…a teaspoon of garlic powder…or four 300-mg garlic capsules three times a day.

●**Onions.** Red and yellow varieties contain *quercetin,* an antioxidant that deactivates carcinogens and prevents blood clots. It also boosts levels of HDL (good) cholesterol while lowering levels of both LDL cholesterol and triglycerides.

*Optimal intake:* One medium-sized red or yellow onion per day.

It's also essential to drink lots of water—ideally eight eight-ounce glasses each day.

### THE LONGEVITY LIFESTYLE

A nine-year study completed recently at Stanford University found that most people who live past age 100…

●**Sleep seven to eight hours a night.**

●**Always eat breakfast.**

●**Avoid smoking.**

●**Exercise regularly.**

●**Consume little or no alcohol.** Moderate drinking—no more than two drinks per day with meals—helps prevent heart disease in older people. But if you're younger than 45, the risk of alcohol-induced liver trouble or other illness outweighs the benefits to the heart.

Anyone who has a history of liver damage should avoid alcohol.

●**Avoid excessive weight gain or loss.** Men should weigh no more than 20% over

their ideal weight, women no more than 10% over their ideal weight.

●**Eat sugary snacks infrequently, if at all.** They can cause blood sugar levels to fluctuate, and that can contribute to blood sugar abnormalities.

### VITAL ANTIOXIDANTS

Many doctors maintain that vitamin and mineral supplements are unnecessary, as long as one eats a wholesome diet. Recent research suggests otherwise.

*Finding I:* In a Harvard Medical School study of 14,000 physicians, high doses of vitamins C and E and beta-carotene cut the risk for heart disease by nearly 50%.

*Finding II:* In a recent study from Australia, the survival rate was 12 times higher among breast cancer patients who consumed high levels of beta-carotene than among breast cancer patients who consumed low levels of beta-carotene.

What level of supplementation is best? Recent studies point to the following daily dosages…

●**Vitamin C…**500 mg to 1,500 mg of *calcium ascorbate.*

●**Vitamin E…**100 international units (IU) to 400 IU of mixed tocopherols.

●**Beta carotene…**10,000 IU.

●**Selenium…**100 micrograms (mcg) to 200 mcg.

People who rarely eat cereal or nuts should add a magnesium supplement—200 mg to 300 mg per day.

People age 50 or older should add 30 mg of *coenzyme Q-10* a day. This key nutrient helps prevent heart attack.

### HORMONE THERAPY

The slow physical decline associated with aging is caused in part by falling levels of estrogen, testosterone, human growth hormone (hGH) and other key hormones.

Via hormone therapy, it's possible to raise these hormones to their youthful levels.

●**Testosterone replacement therapy** (TRT) boosts the sex drive and strengthens bones in men and women alike.

But TRT is suspected of raising the risk for prostate enlargement and prostate cancer.

•**Human growth hormone therapy** can smooth wrinkles, strengthen a weak libido and reverse a low muscle-to-fat ratio.

Unfortunately, hGH has been implicated as a cause of carpal tunnel syndrome and arthritis.

•**Melatonin therapy** has been shown to extend the life span of mice by up to 25%.

Melatonin lowers LDL cholesterol levels and shows promise as a treatment for diabetes, cataracts and Alzheimer's disease.

•**DHEA therapy** boosts immune function and seems to fight cancer, heart disease, Alzheimer's disease, diabetes and osteoporosis.

***Caution:*** Hormone therapy should be strictly supervised by a physician. For help in locating a qualified practitioner, write the American Academy of Anti-Aging Medicine (see page one for address)...or fax your request to the Academy at 773-528-5390.

---

# Over-the-Counter Drugs: Some Are Much Safer And More Effective Than Others

Michael B. Brodin, MD, assistant clinical professor of dermatology at New York University School of Medicine in New York City. He is author of *The Encyclopedia of Medical Tests* and *The Over-the-Counter Drug Book*, both published by Pocket Books.

---

There are now 300,000 over-the-counter (OTC) medications on the market. How does one make a smart selection?

Select products with only a *single active ingredient*—one that's been shown to be safe and effective for your primary symptom.

***Reason:*** Each active ingredient carries its own side effects. Don't subject yourself to these side effects unless you really need the medication.

Doctors and pharmacists tend to talk about brand-name products, but it makes sense to opt for the generic equivalent whenever one is available. Generics are just as safe and effective. They're also less costly.

Here are the best OTC products for nine common ailments...

### ACHES AND PAIN

The *acetaminophen* in Tylenol is your best bet. While it doesn't combat inflammation, it's less likely than aspirin or nonsteroidal anti-inflammatory drugs like *ibuprofen* (Advil) to cause stomach upset or ulcers.

Acetaminophen is safe for children, too. Aspirin can cause a potentially fatal disorder known as Reye's syndrome when given to children under age 16.

Acetaminophen is also the best OTC drug for lowering fever.

### CONSTIPATION

Many people continue to take *senna* (Ex-Lax) or another stimulant laxative. But there's now ample evidence that "bulk-forming" laxatives are effective—and less likely to result in dependency.

Bulk-forming laxatives absorb liquid and swell in the gut. The resulting increase in stool size stimulates the muscles of contraction and evacuation.

Different bulk laxatives contain different active ingredients—*psyllium* in Metamucil, *methylcellulose* in Citrucel, *malt soup extract* in Maltsupex and *calcium polycarbophil* in FiberCon. They're all approximately equivalent in performance.

### COUGH

The best OTC medication for cough depends upon the kind of cough you have.

•**Productive cough**—one that produces phlegm. Your best bet is the expectorant *guaifenesin,* which is found in Robitussin. By helping to liquefy mucus, guaifenesin seems to shorten the duration of a productive cough... and make the cough less painful.

•**Dry, hacking cough.** Use *dextromethorphan,* which is found in Benylin Adult Cough Formula and similar products. A morphine derivative, dextromethorphan is more effective at suppressing coughs than *diphenhydramine* (Benadryl), an OTC antihistamine that's often used as a cough suppressant.

Dextromethorphan does not cause drowsiness…but diphenhydramine can.

### CUTS AND SCRAPES

Choose an antibiotic ointment that contains only *bacitracin* or a combination of bacitracin and polymycin.

The *neomycin* found in Neosporin and similar products can cause an allergic reaction.

### DIARRHEA

*Loperamide,* found in Imodium and similar products, is safe and easy to take. It works by curbing the muscular contractions that lead to defecation.

Loperamide is more effective than adsorbent compounds—*attapulgite* (Kaopectate) and *kaolin/pectin* (Kao-Paverin). It's also more effective than *bismuth subsalicylate* (Pepto-Bismol).

### HEARTBURN

Most OTC antacids contain sodium, calcium, magnesium or aluminum—or a mixture thereof.

The best choice for most people is a magnesium-aluminum combination, like that found in Riopan and similar products.

People with kidney disease should not take aluminum or magnesium. For these individuals, calcium carbonate—found in Tums and similar products—is a good substitute.

### NASAL CONGESTION

*Pseudoephedrine,* found in Sudafed and similar products, is the best option for daytime use. It reduces congestion by narrowing blood vessels, helping shrink swollen tissues.

Since pseudoephedrine has a mild stimulating effect, it should be avoided for at least four hours before bedtime.

For controlling congestion at night, diphenhydramine is often a better choice. Besides drying mucous membranes, it has a mild cough suppressant effect.

***Caution:*** Consult a doctor before taking diphenhydramine or any other antihistamine if you have glaucoma, heart disease, thyroid disease, diabetes, high blood pressure or an enlarged prostate.

### SORE THROAT

The best way to soothe throat pain is with a saltwater gargle…or with the natural painkiller *menthol.* One good source of menthol is Halls Mentho-Lyptus Ice Blue Cough Suppressant drops.

Each drop contains 12 mg of menthol—more than most competing cough drops.

### YEAST INFECTION

The four leading antifungal medications are *clotrimazole* (Gyne-Lotrimin, Mycelex-7), *miconazole* (Monistat 7), *butoconazole* (Femstat 3) and *tioconazole* (Vagistat-1).

These products are so similar as to be virtually interchangeable. Buy the one that you find most convenient to use.

---

# Melanoma Is on the Rise

Catherine Poole, a journalist and melanoma survivor who lives in Glenmoore, PA. She and DuPont Guerry IV, MD, director of the melanoma program at the University of Pennsylvania Comprehensive Cancer Center in Philadelphia, are the authors of *Melanoma Prevention, Detection & Treatment.* Yale University Press.

Most forms of cancer are on the decline, but the incidence of melanoma is rising. Between 1990 and 1995, the number of cases of this deadly skin cancer rose by 2.5%. Researchers theorize that the continuing depletion of the atmosphere's ozone layer—which blocks cancer-causing ultraviolet light—plays a role in this rise.

I was age 38 when I learned I had melanoma. I happened to glance at the back of my right leg and saw what looked like tiny black bubbles coming out of a mark that I had assumed to be a harmless mole.

Aware that an obvious change in a mole can be a sign of skin cancer, I consulted a dermatologist. She ordered a biopsy, which confirmed our suspicions.

I was lucky—my melanoma hadn't yet spread to my lymph nodes or to any organs. I underwent surgery to remove the cancerous cells. Today—eight years later—I'm cancer-free.

### PREVENTING MELANOMA

Melanoma is rarer than the other two forms of skin cancer, *basal cell carcinoma* and *squamous cell carcinoma.*

These cancers—characterized by pink bumps or raised, scaly patches—can usually be eradicated via outpatient surgery.

Because it tends to spread (metastasize), melanoma is far deadlier. Fifteen percent of those who get it ultimately succumb to it—despite recent advances in treatment.

*To reduce your risk:* Minimize your exposure to the sun. Whenever you head outdoors, wear a broad-brimmed hat and sunscreen with a sun protection factor (SPF) of at least 15… and seek shade when sunlight is brightest (between 11 am and 3 pm).

### CALCULATING YOUR RISK

Melanoma affects Caucasians almost exclusively. The more likely you are to freckle and/or burn, the greater your risk.

*Other risk factors…*

• **Excessive sun exposure**—especially before age 10.

• **A personal or family history** of any type of skin cancer.

• **A large number of moles…**or the presence of big, flat moles. Many people think moles are present at birth. In fact, they appear in childhood—in reaction to sun exposure.

Odds are slim that any given mole will turn cancerous, but every mole on your body should be monitored.

### DANGER SIGNS

Consult a doctor at the first sign that you might have a melanoma. *The ABCDs of what to look for…*

• **Asymmetry.** With a typical melanoma, half of the spot looks different than the other half.

• **Border irregularities.** Melanomas tend to have notched rather than round or oval borders.

• **Color variation.** Normal moles are usually of one color. Melanomas are often blends of tan, brown, dark brown, pink, black, white—even blue.

• **Diameter in excess of one-quarter inch.** Ordinary moles seldom grow larger than that. If the spot is three-eighths of an inch or larger, have a doctor evaluate it.

Since some melanomas are raised, melanoma specialists recently added an *"E"* (for elevation) to the melanoma alphabet. Any mole that develops a bump or becomes elevated should be checked out right away.

### EARLY DETECTION IS KEY

As part of *every* routine examination, your doctor should perform a comprehensive visual exam of your skin. If your doctor skips this exam—many do—remind him/her to do it.

If your melanoma risk is very high, you may need to have skin exams four times per year—preferably by a dermatologist.

To find a good dermatologist in your area, contact the American Academy of Dermatology, 930 N. Meacham Rd., Schaumburg, Illinois 60173. 888-462-3376. www.aad.org.

*Also essential:* Skin self-exams *between* doctor visits. For most people, occasional self-exams are adequate. If you're at high risk, the self-exams should be done monthly.

Do the exams in a brightly lit room, using a full-length mirror, a handheld mirror and a flashlight.

Examine every inch of your body, including your shoulders, underarms, the back of your neck and the soles of your feet.

If you have a partner, ask him/her to help you check hard-to-see areas of your body.

If a self-exam turns up a suspicious spot, see a doctor at once.

### DIAGNOSIS AND TREATMENT

The best way to check suspicious tissue is via an *excision* biopsy, in which the entire lesion is removed and examined.

If the lesion is on the face or another cosmetically sensitive area, a less extensive *punch* or *incisional* biopsy will suffice.

If you do have melanoma, treatment depends on how advanced it is…

• **Stage I and II melanomas** haven't yet spread. They can usually be cured via surgical removal of the affected tissue.

The five-year survival rate for early melanoma is 95%.

• **Stage III melanoma** has spread to nearby lymph nodes. Treatment involves surgical removal of the melanoma and the affected lymph node or nodes, often followed by chemotherapy.

The five-year survival rate for stage III melanoma is about 50%.

●**Stage IV melanoma** has spread to distant organs. Treatment involves surgical removal of all metastases in the region, combined with chemotherapy using a relatively new drug called *alpha interferon.*

The five-year survival rate for stage IV melanoma is about 5%.

For information on state-of-the-art melanoma care, contact the National Cancer Institute at 800-422-6237. http://rex.nci.nih.gov.

# Protecting Your Gums Can Save Your Life

Alan Winter, DDS, periodontist and partner, Park Avenue Periodontal Associates, 532 Park Ave., New York 10021.

Tooth decay is fast becoming a thing of the past, thanks mostly to fluoridated water. But people keep losing their teeth—to periodontal disease.

Sooner or later, 80% of adults develop this disease, also known simply as gum disease. It's caused by *Porphyromonas gingivalis* and other plaque-forming bacteria that work their way below the gum line.

Good dental hygiene helps keep these bacteria in check. If allowed to flourish, however, these nasty microbes attack gum tissue.

Once this tissue erodes, teeth slowly loosen and ultimately may need to be extracted.

*Extra danger:* The same bacteria that cause gum disease are now thought to contribute to heart disease and pregnancy complications.

### DO YOU HAVE GUM DISEASE?

Early gum disease is characterized by chronic bad breath and red, swollen gums that bleed when teeth are brushed. Or—spaces may form between teeth and teeth may become loose.

*Caution:* Some people develop severe gum disease *without* obvious symptoms. For this reason, it's essential to have your gums professionally examined—and your teeth professionally cleaned—*at least twice a year.*

Gum disease progresses slowly in some individuals, rapidly in others. Psychological stress can aggravate the condition by releasing hormones that bacteria feed on.

Gum disease can also be aggravated by smoking...by systemic diseases like diabetes ...and by eating sugary foods. The gums can also be affected by calcium channel blockers, *phenytoin* (Dilantin) and certain other drugs.

### REGULAR EXAMS ARE KEY

While semiannual dental exams are sufficient for most people, those with existing gum trouble should have their teeth examined and cleaned four times a year.

*Reason:* Bacteria carve out tiny pockets between gums and teeth. When these pockets exceed three millimeters (about one-eighth inch) in depth, the bacteria change from a comparatively harmless form to a virulent form.

This transition occurs after the bacteria have been growing for eight to 12 weeks.

If your teeth are professionally cleaned every three months, the bacteria will be disrupted before they cause significant damage to your gums.

### PROPER BRUSHING TECHNIQUE

Brush your teeth twice a day for 30 to 60 seconds. Use an old-fashioned manual brush with soft nylon bristles and a small head.

Hard bristles—especially those of horsehair or another natural fiber—are too abrasive.

What about electric toothbrushes? They don't really clean any better, although they can add an element of fun, motivating some people to brush more frequently.

Irrigating devices that use pressurized water do *not* remove bacterial plaque—only food particles.

### THE IMPORTANCE OF FLOSSING

Flossing is even more important than brushing. Most periodontal disease starts *between* teeth, in areas that are out of the reach of toothbrush bristles.

*Best approach:* Floss once a day with unwaxed dental floss. Slide the floss into the space between teeth, then move it gently under the gum line.

Once bacteria have established themselves in deep pockets, the only way to get rid of them is to have your teeth professionally cleaned.

### DENTAL SCALING

If professional cleaning isn't doing the trick, you may need dental scaling. In this process, a dentist or dental hygienist uses a special instrument to go farther below the gum line than is possible in a regular cleaning, scraping away bacterial plaque and mineral deposits (tartar) from the roots of the teeth.

Scaling renders teeth less hospitable to bacteria. It also causes the pockets in which they live to shrink.

Three or four 60-minute visits are required. *Total cost:* $400 to $1,000.

### GUM SURGERY

If gum disease is advanced—or if it persists after scaling—surgery may be necessary.

In the typical procedure, diseased areas of gum are peeled back in flaps, exposing the roots of the teeth so that they can be thoroughly cleaned.

Once the tooth roots are smoothed and free of plaque, the pockets should shrink.

Two to four 60- to 90-minute procedures are required. *Total cost:* $3,000 to $6,000.

### ANTIBIOTICS

Although antibiotics are often helpful for controlling bacterial growth during or after surgery, they're no substitute for gum surgery when it is necessary.

***Trap:*** If tooth roots aren't smoothed and the pockets corrected, the bacteria—and the gum disease—recur quickly once antibiotics are discontinued.

Remember, gum disease is a *chronic* condition. Even if you have surgery, you must remain extremely vigilant.

# Simple Secrets of Making Your Skin Look Young Again

Arthur K. Balin, MD, PhD, clinical professor of dermatology and research professor of pathology at MCP Hahnemann School of Medicine in Philadelphia, and director of the Sally Balin Medical Center for Dermatology and Cosmetic Surgery in Media, PA. He is coauthor of *The Life of the Skin: What It Hides, What It Reveals, and How It Communicates.* Bantam Books.

What's the best way to rejuvenate skin that's starting to look its age? Dr. Arthur K. Balin explains the most common aging-related skin problems and the best way to correct each one…

### MINOR SUN DAMAGE

Years of exposure to the sun can leave skin looking lined and wrinkled.

For minor sun damage, the prescription cream *tretinoin* (Retin-A) is often the best bet.

Although it can take several months for the effect to be noticeable, tretinoin helps eliminate fine wrinkles by causing the skin to "slough off" old cells. Tretinoin also promotes the growth of new elastic tissue in the dermis, the second layer of skin.

It can even turn certain precancerous cells back to normal.

***Caution:*** Tretinoin can cause skin irritation. To minimize the problem, decrease the frequency of application…use a mild facial cleanser once a day…and apply a moisturizer.

### SEVERE SUN DAMAGE

When lines and wrinkles are too numerous or too deep to be repaired with tretinoin, a skin peel may be necessary.

A skin peel involves the application of acid to "burn off" the damaged outer layer of skin. This eliminates not only lines and wrinkles, but also age spots and other forms of sun damage.

Dermatologists use a variety of acids, depending on the extent of the damage…

•**Glycolic acid peels** are fine for moderate wrinkling. These "lunchtime" peels take just a few minutes in a doctor's office. They require no recuperation time.

The typical patient requires six to 12 monthly treatments.

•**Trichloroacetic acid or phenol peels** are better for more severe wrinkling. These stronger acids take off more layers of skin.

*Drawback:* Strong acid peels can be painful. They can leave the skin raw and red for many days. To avoid embarrassment, most people "hole up" at home for up to one week after having a strong acid peel.

The most effective way to remove wrinkles—and the best option for especially severe sun damage—is a technique known as *laser resurfacing.*

In this technique—which involves up to two weeks of recovery time—the doctor uses laser light to vaporize outer layers of skin. This eliminates wrinkles, brown spots and precancerous cells, too.

*Bonus:* Laser resurfacing causes the underlying layer of skin to shrink. As the skin heals, it looks significantly tighter—almost as if you had had a face-lift.

### EXPRESSION LINES

To eliminate laugh lines, frown lines, crow's feet and other "expression lines," many doctors now opt for *botulinum toxin* (BoTox) injections.

BoTox paralyzes the tiny muscles that cause these deep wrinkles to form. With the muscle inactive, furrowed skin has a chance to become smooth and unlined once again.

One BoTox injection can minimize the appearance of expression lines for up to six months. At that point, your doctor can administer new injections.

*Caution:* Too much BoTox can temporarily paralyze the muscle used to raise the eyelid, causing the eyelid to droop for about a week.

### AGE SPOTS

For people with light-colored skin, these brown or yellow spots can usually be eliminated by freezing them or by burning them off with acid applied directly on the spot.

*Trap:* As the skin heals, it can become lighter in color than the surrounding skin. This can be a problem for African-Americans and others with dark complexions.

*Alternative:* Removing the age spots with laser light. Spots removed via laser heal without any lightening of the skin.

### SAGGING SKIN

Double chins, "turkey-wattle" neck, loose skin on the upper arms, etc., are typically the result of excessive subcutaneous fat…or skin that has lost its elasticity.

•**Double chin.** This is usually treated with liposuction to remove the excess fat. The neck is then bandaged so the loose skin can reattach to the underlying tissue of the chin.

Recovery is immediate—you can go back to work the following day. You'll have to wear a chin strap constantly for about one week to reduce swelling and enhance the tightening effect. After that, you'll need to wear it at night for another month or so.

•**Loose skin.** The best solution for this problem is surgically removing the extra skin.

This outpatient procedure takes about 90 minutes. Stitches come out in a week or two.

As with all surgical procedures, these operations carry risks of infection and scarring. Make sure the surgeon is certified by the American Society for Dermatologic Surgery or the American Academy of Cosmetic Surgery.

### SPIDER VEINS

Spider veins can occur on the face or legs. They can form at any age—in part because of sun damage. They're most troublesome for women.

Lasers work well for tiny spider veins on the face. Injections of a salt solution or another "sclerosing agent" work better for large leg veins.

Some veins may need to be treated more than once—to get rid of the "roots." Once they're destroyed, however, the veins don't come back.

### VARICOSE VEINS

Compression stockings can keep varicose veins from getting worse. But the only permanent solution is surgery or treatment with a sclerosing agent.

Large varicose veins can be removed through a tiny hole in the skin—about one-eighth of an inch in diameter. The doctor inserts a thin hook through this opening, grabs the vein and pulls it out.

This form of surgery, known as ambulatory phlebectomy, does not affect circulation—and creates no significant scarring.

### AVOIDING SKIN PROBLEMS

Both sunlight and tobacco smoke are known to cause wrinkles and other problems. Be careful to avoid both.

To detect skin cancer in its earliest stages—when effective treatment is still possible—it's a good idea to have a head-to-toe skin exam at least once a year, beginning at age 18.

If your dermatologist determines that you're at high risk, more frequent skin exams may be recommended.

# How to Get a Good Night's Sleep

James B. Maas, PhD, professor of psychology at Cornell University in Ithaca, NY. He is author of *Power Sleep.* Villard.

If you're having trouble sleeping, you are probably well acquainted with the basic recommendations for sound sleep…

●Avoid caffeine and alcohol near bedtime.

●Avoid nicotine. If you smoke, quit.

●Take a warm bath or shower just before turning in.

●Get regular exercise and eat a wholesome diet.

●Avoid sources of stress late in the evening.

If insomnia persists despite your best efforts to follow these strategies, the culprit could be your bedroom. Here's how to set up your "sleep environment" for a restful night of sleep…

●**Make sure your home is secure.** You will sleep better knowing that your family is protected against fires, burglary and other threats.

In addition to smoke detectors and good locks, consider investing in a burglar alarm.

●**Choose bedroom decor carefully.** Sky blue, forest green and other "colors of nature" are especially conducive to sleep. So are paintings of landscapes…or family photos taken on a favorite trip.

***Bedroom office trap:*** Looking at stacks of bills or other paperwork makes it hard to fall asleep. If your home lacks a den or study, find a hallway or another place in your home to set up your office.

●**Eliminate light "pollution."** The easiest way to keep light from disturbing your sleep is to wear light-blocking eyeshades. You can pick up a pair at a drugstore.

If you find eyeshades uncomfortable, rid your bedroom of illuminated clocks, nightlights and other sources of light.

If streetlamps or other light sources shine in through your bedroom windows, fit your windows with light-blocking "blackout" curtains.

●**Silence environmental noise.** Any sound louder than 70 decibels (the equivalent of a dripping faucet) is disruptive to sleep. If you cannot eliminate a particular sound, block it using these strategies…

●Furnish your bedroom with heavy drapes and thick carpeting. If you're building a new home, make sure walls and ceilings have good sound insulation.

●Wear sound-blocking earplugs. Several types are available at drugstores. They cost only a dollar or two a pair.

●Use a "white noise" generator. White noise is high-frequency sound like that produced by rainfall, surf, rustling leaves, etc. It masks other, more intrusive sounds…and helps lull you to sleep.

***Low-cost white-noise generator:*** A bedside FM radio tuned between stations to static. Alternatively, you can play compact discs containing recorded nature sounds…or use an electronic sound-masking device like those sold by The Sharper Image and other retailers.

●**Keep your bedroom cool.** An overheated bedroom can set off the body's wakeup call in the middle of the night. It can trigger nightmares, too.

***Best temperature:*** Sixty-five degrees Fahrenheit.

●**Maintain ideal humidity.** Most people sleep best when relative humidity stays between

60% and 70%. Check it occasionally using a humidity indicator. This simple gauge is available at hardware stores for about five dollars.

If humidity regularly falls outside this range, a humidifier or dehumidifier can help. These devices are sold at department and hardware stores. They cost from $50 to $200.

● **Buy the best mattress you can afford.** If you like innerspring mattresses, spring count is crucial. A mattress for a full-size bed should have more than 300 coils...a queen, more than 375...a king, more than 450.

If you prefer the feel of a foam mattress, make sure the foam density is at least two pounds per cubic foot.

Whatever kind of mattress you pick, be sure to "test-drive" it at the store. You and your partner should have at least six extra inches of leg room.

*Mattress maintenance:* Once a month, rotate the mattress so that the head becomes the foot. Flip the mattress, too.

For more information on mattresses, contact the Better Sleep Council, 501 Wythe St., Alexandria, Virginia 22314. www.bettersleep.org.

● **Pick good sheets and bedclothes.** If you wear pajamas or a nightgown to bed, be sure the garment is soft to the touch—and roomy. Cotton and silk are more comfortable than synthetics.

When purchasing sheets, opt for cotton, silk or—best of all—linen. It feels smooth against the skin and absorbs moisture better than other fabrics.

● **Avoid overly soft pillows.** People often pick pillows that are too soft to provide proper support for the head and neck.

Down makes the best pillow filling. If you're allergic to down, polyester microfiber is a good second choice.

Some people troubled by insomnia find that a pillow filled with buckwheat hulls is particularly comfortable. These pillows are sold in department stores.

● **Don't be a clock-watcher.** The last thing you want during the wee hours is a visible reminder of how much sleep you're losing.

If you wake up in the middle of the night, don't even glance at the clock. If necessary,

get rid of the clock...or turn it to face away from you before you turn in for the night.

● **Keep a writing pad on your nightstand.** To avoid ruminating on fears or "to do" lists as you try to fall asleep, jot them down as soon as they arise. Vow to deal with any problems or obligations the following day.

If worries keep you awake anyway, read or watch television until you feel drowsy. If you sleep with a partner, get a lamp designed for reading in bed—ideally one with a gooseneck and a dimmer switch.

---

# Amazing New Ways to Control Rheumatoid Arthritis

James F. Fries, MD, professor of medicine and rheumatology at Stanford University School of Medicine in Stanford, CA. He is coauthor of *The Arthritis Helpbook*. Perseus Books.

---

If you're among the two million Americans who have rheumatoid arthritis (RA), there's good news.

New treatment strategies are proving to be much more effective than the strategies that were considered state of the art just a few months ago.

*Implication:* If you have RA but haven't seen a doctor recently, your current treatment regimen may not be optimal.

An autoimmune disease, RA occurs when the immune system attacks the body's own cells as if they were invaders.

This attack causes the joints to become swollen and warm to the touch. Enzymes produced in the joints as a result of this inflammation slowly digest adjacent tissue, causing permanent damage to bone and cartilage.

Joint damage begins earlier in the disease process than many RA patients—and even some doctors—realize. For this reason, it's crucial that treatment be initiated without delay.

*Important:* Consult a rheumatologist. Especially given all the recent advances, few primary-care physicians are up to date on rheumatoid arthritis treatments.

### DRUG SEQUENCING

The most important recent advance in the treatment of RA is in the way medications are "sequenced." Traditionally, doctors prescribed potent *disease-modifying antirheumatic drugs* (DMARDs) only after nonsteroidal anti-inflammatory drugs (NSAIDs) proved ineffective.

***New thinking:*** It's more effective to prescribe DMARDs first. Doing so ensures that the disease is brought under control as quickly as possible.

Ironically, *naproxen* (Naprosyn), *ibuprofen* (Advil) and other NSAIDs don't quite live up to their reputation for mildness.

Recent research indicates that NSAID-induced gastrointestinal problems and other serious side effects cause more than 16,000 deaths and 100,000 hospitalizations each year.

*Methotrexate* (Rheumatrex), *hydroxychloroquine* (Plaquenil) and other DMARDs now appear to be no riskier than NSAIDs, and are more effective.

***Bottom line:*** Virtually every rheumatoid arthritis patient should be taking a DMARD. With early and consistent use of DMARDs, lifetime disability can be cut by up to two-thirds.

### COMPLETE PAIN RELIEF

The old approach to treating RA was simply to keep pain levels tolerable. But since pain stems from tissue damage, even mild discomfort means the disease process is continuing.

***Better:*** Treat the disease until pain and stiffness disappear. Speak up if you feel pain. Don't put up with it…and don't assume that it is normal.

Becoming pain-free may take time. Some drugs take up to six weeks to work. If one DMARD doesn't work, the doctor may try another…or may try a combination of drugs.

### NEW MEDICATIONS

If older, established DMARDs don't work—or if they cause severe side effects—you may be a candidate for one of the new medications.

The Food and Drug Administration recently approved several new medications for the treatment of rheumatoid arthritis…

•***Leflunomide*** (Arava) slows the rate of cell division, inhibiting the reproduction of joint-damaging inflammatory cells. It's often a good option for people who cannot tolerate methotrexate, which can cause mouth ulcers, liver problems and other side effects.

•***Etanercept*** (Enbrel) and *infliximab* (Remicade) work by blocking *tumor necrosis factor* (TNF), a naturally occurring compound that activates the inflammatory response.

•**COX-2 inhibitors,** such as *celecoxib* (Celebrex) and *rofecobix* (Vioxx) are less toxic versions of conventional NSAIDs.

Most conventional NSAIDs block the action of *both* members of a pair of enzymes known as *cyclooxygenases* (COX-1 and COX-2). COX-1 protects the gastrointestinal system from damage. COX-2 causes inflammation.

As a result of this dual action, NSAIDs block inflammation but open up the gastrointestinal tract to severe damage.

COX-2 inhibitors inhibit only COX-2, so inflammation is decreased without any gastrointestinal upset.

### THE ROLE OF EXERCISE

Exercise cannot cure RA, but it can be highly effective at reducing joint pain and improving flexibility. Nearly everyone benefits from a walking program.

To prevent morning stiffness, do gentle stretching before going to bed at night…and before getting out of bed in the morning. Spend extra time stretching any joint that has become "frozen."

Include hand and wrist exercises, since those joints are often affected by RA. One particularly effective hand exercise is the thumb walk.

***What to do:*** Keeping your wrist straight, touch your index finger to your thumb, forming an "O." Straighten and spread your thumb and fingers. Then touch your middle finger to your thumb. Repeat for all fingers.

Choose exercises on the basis of which joints are affected and how well the disease is controlled. Discuss the matter with your rheumatologist.

Don't do any exercise that puts excessive force on an inflamed joint.

# Corticosteroid Caution

People taking corticosteroids for arthritis, asthma or other ailments may lose up to 20% of their bone mass in the first six months. *To fight steroid-related osteoporosis:* Ask your physician for the lowest possible corticosteroid dose…do weight-bearing exercise regularly …consider physical therapy…talk with your doctor about taking extra calcium and vitamin D. *Also:* Ask your physician about diuretic drugs—which can help keep calcium in the bones—and about medications that stop bone loss.

Barbara Lukert, MD, director, Osteoporosis Clinic, University of Kansas Hospital, Kansas City.

# Saint-John's-Wort Trap

Individuals who take the mood-boosting herb Saint-John's-wort along with a prescription antidepressant risk developing confusion, twitches, loss of muscle coordination and other symptoms. These symptoms—known collectively as "serotonin syndrome"—are caused by the buildup of the neurotransmitter serotonin in the brain. *To avoid trouble:* Take Saint-John's-wort only under medical supervision. Do *not* take it along with an antidepressant.

James J. Stockard, MD, PhD, associate professor of psychiatry and neurology, Northwestern University Medical School, Chicago.

# Why Women Live Longer than Men

Royda Crose, PhD, associate director of the Fisher Institute for Wellness and coordinator of the Center for Gerontology, both at Ball State University in Muncie, IN. She is author of *Why Women Live Longer Than Men…and What Men Can Learn from Them.* Jossey–Bass.

As far as longevity is concerned, men are clearly the weaker sex. On average, women live about seven years longer.

Men lead the way in each of the top causes of death—from heart disease, cancer and stroke to suicide and homicide.

A portion of this longevity gender gap can be traced to biological differences between men and women. Female hormones, for instance, protect women against heart disease. But much of the gap appears to be linked to differences in lifestyle.

### GENDER DIFFERENCES

Although there are exceptions, men generally prefer to "tough out" their problems…and find it harder than women to admit weakness.

These tendencies are largely responsible for lifestyle habits and behavioral patterns that shorten men's lives…

•**Bad eating habits.** Men know less about nutrition than do women. They're also less weight conscious.

Men eat fruits, vegetables and whole grains less often than do women. They also eat more meat, fat, dairy products and eggs. Consumption of these foods has been linked with heart disease and cancer.

Most people gain weight as they grow older, but men start adding pounds an average of 10 years earlier than women. The weight goes on differently, too.

Men tend to add fat at the waist…women at the hips. The familiar male "apple" shape poses a far more serious threat to the heart than the "pear" shape that's widely seen among females.

***Solution:*** Men should be more concerned about weight control…and educate themselves about nutrition.

•**Sedentary lifestyle.** Young men tend to be more active than young women. They play sports, run and hike more. They also tend to have more physically demanding jobs.

As men reach middle age, however, they grow increasingly sedentary. Women's activity levels stay the same.

***Solution:*** Men should make a conscious effort to *stay* physically active.

•**Substance abuse.** Smoking, drinking and using illicit drugs are known to shorten life. Men are far more likely than women to indulge in these vices.

Men are twice as likely as women to die of cirrhosis of the liver, which is often caused by alcohol abuse.

Men frequently turn to alcohol or drugs to blunt their emotional distress and numb painful emotions. Women are less likely to resort to substance abuse because it's acceptable for them to *discuss* their emotions.

*Solution:* Men must find healthier ways to express their feelings—tender feelings as well as sadness and anger. Fighting back tears is not a good idea.

•**Accidents and violence.** Men are three times more likely than women to die in car accidents. They drive faster and are less likely to use seat belts.

In addition, men are victims of homicide four times as often as women.

*Solution:* Men need to consider whether their "macho" attitudes toward risk are rational.

They should also learn safer ways of venting anger—working it out through exercise, gardening, writing, etc.

### THE HEALTH CARE GAP

In part because of their monthly cycles, women are highly aware of their bodies. Men tend to be oblivious to bodily changes —unfamiliar sensations, changes in bowel habits, etc.—that can be the very first signs of disease.

When they do notice symptoms, men ignore them longer. They act as if it isn't "manly" to seek help. When they feel ill, they're likely to continue working...or simply go home rather than seek medical care.

Men also neglect the regular checkups that can catch heart disease and other serious illness in early stages, when effective treatment is still possible.

In a recent survey of more than 1,000 men and women, only 60% of men had undergone a physical exam sometime during the previous year. Seventy-six percent of women had undergone one.

The researchers estimated that 8% of the men hadn't undergone a physical for a *decade* or longer.

*Solution:* Men should go to the doctor on a regular basis...and should take action if pain or any other symptom surfaces.

### SOCIAL SALVATION

It's been well established that people with strong, close relationships have a lower death rate...and are better able to survive bouts of serious disease.

But many men depend exclusively on their wives for personal support—outside the family they're loners. And men tend to base their self-worth almost entirely on their careers.

So when a man loses his wife or his job, he's likely to fall victim to severe depression. Suicide is much more common among white males over age 65 than for members of any other demographic group.

*Solution:* Men should work to develop close friendships outside of marriage...and get involved in worthwhile activities outside of work.

# Have *Your* Homocysteine Levels Been Tested?

David W. Freeman, editor, *Bottom Line/Health*, Boardroom Inc., Box 2614, 55 Railroad Ave., Greenwich, CT 06836-2614.

There's now solid evidence that too much *homocysteine*—an amino acid that forms in the body after consumption of meat and dairy foods—means a heightened risk for heart disease and stroke.

Yet few doctors are urging their patients to have their homocysteine levels checked.

Why is that? According to Kilmer McCully, MD—the Providence, Rhode Island, pathologist who originated the homocysteine theory of heart disease—many doctors are unaware of the studies showing how dangerous *hyperhomocysteinemia* can be.

Others fail to recommend the test because they think it's too costly...or because the necessary apparatus isn't available at the diagnostic lab they use.

*No more excuses.* Two new homocysteine tests have been introduced that use standard lab apparatus. Doctors don't have to track down a new lab, and the cost of testing should fall to only $25 to $30.

Testing makes sense for anyone age 65 or older...as well as anyone over age 50 who has a family history of heart trouble.

In some cases, a high homocysteine level is caused by underlying illness—which needs treatment. More often, the problem is simply eating too much meat and dairy products and not enough fruits and veggies.

It's often possible to keep homocysteine low by eating right and perhaps taking three B-vitamins—folic acid (1 mg), B-6 (10 mg) and B-12 (0.1 mg). Higher doses may be needed to lower an elevated level.

If you could benefit from homocysteine testing and your doctor has never mentioned the test to you, ask him/her about it. Don't let a doctor who's out of date place your life in jeopardy.

# Grape Juice and Aspirin

Purple grape juice boosts the heart-protective effects of daily aspirin therapy. Aspirin helps guard at-risk individuals against heart attack by preventing blood clots. But adrenaline produced by exercise or during periods of psychological stress can counteract this clot-inhibiting effect. *Result:* Reduced protection from heart attack. *Good news: Flavonoids* in grape juice—as well as in dark beer and red wine—block the effects of adrenaline. *Best:* 10 to 12 ounces of grape juice per day.

John Folts, PhD, professor of medicine and director, coronary thrombosis research and prevention laboratory, University of Wisconsin Medical School, Madison.

# Blood Pressure Eye Trap #1

High blood pressure can lead to macular degeneration, the potentially blinding eye disease. *Recent finding:* The incidence of macular degeneration was 4.7 times higher among people whose diastolic pressure (the "lower" number) was at or above 100 than among people whose diastolic pressure was normal (below 85).

Debra Schaumberg, OD, MPH, and Umed Ajani, MD, PhD, associate epidemiologists, Brigham and Women's Hospital, Boston. Their study of 18,053 physicians was presented at a recent meeting of the Association for Research in Vision and Ophthalmology.

# Blood Pressure Eye Trap #2

Take medications that result in lower blood pressure in the *morning* if your doctor says you can. *Reason:* If the drugs are taken at night, when blood pressure normally drops, the additional medication-induced drop can trigger serious eye problems. *Among the drugs that lower blood pressure:* Some prostate drugs...Hytrin...beta-blockers, calcium channel blockers, ACE inhibitors and other antihypertensive drugs.

Sohan Singh Hayreh, MD, PhD, professor of ophthalmology, University of Iowa College of Medicine, Iowa City. His study was published in the *American Journal of Ophthalmology.*

# Best Pill Timing

Timing is critical for medications to work as intended.

Always ask your physician and pharmacist when you should take any prescribed medicine and follow the accompanying instructions. *Correct times to take some commonly used drugs...*

• *Aspirin:* To prevent heart attacks—first thing in the morning, when arising. For common wear-and-tear arthritis (osteoarthritis)—take aspirin in the latter half of the day and at night, before going to sleep.

• *Anticholesterol drugs:* At bedtime.

●*Corticosteroids:* When arising, unless your doctor says otherwise.

●*Ulcer drugs:* At bedtime.

William J.M. Hrushesky, MD, senior clinical investigator, Stratton VA Medical Center, Albany, NY.

# On-Line Medical Information Trap

On-line medical information can be hazardous to your health—and life. A review of information on the World Wide Web about childhood diarrhea—a potentially life-threatening condition—found that many recommendations were dangerous. And misinformation was found even on sites of major academic medical centers. *Important:* Review all on-line medical information with a qualified professional before taking action.

H. Juhling McClung, MD, associate professor of pediatrics at Ohio State University and chief of pediatric gastroenterology at Children's Hospital in Columbus.

# Subtle Stroke Signs

The telltale symptoms of stroke include weakness or numbness on one side of the body, difficulty speaking and/or vision loss.

These symptoms often go unrecognized. In fact, only 25% of stroke victims know they're having a stroke.

If you notice suspicious symptoms, seek immediate medical attention. If you wait, you may be unable to benefit from new "clot-busting" drugs, which minimize brain damage.

Linda S. Williams, MD, assistant professor of neurology, Indiana University School of Medicine, Indianapolis. Her study of 67 stroke patients was published in *Stroke,* American Heart Association, 7272 Greenville Ave., Dallas 75231.

# Adult-Onset Diabetes

Richard Jackson, MD, medical director of the outpatient intensive treatment program at the Joslin Diabetes Center and assistant professor of medicine at Harvard Medical School, both in Boston.

Diabetes can lead to heart disease, stroke and blindness. It can also interfere with blood flow to the extremities, a problem that sometimes necessitates the amputation of fingers and toes.

*Good news:* With proper treatment, these problems can almost always be avoided.

Unfortunately, only half of the estimated 12 million Americans who have the more common adult-onset (type II) form of the disease know that they're ill.*

Of those who know they have diabetes, only a tiny fraction are getting aggressive treatment.

### UNCONTROLLED BLOOD SUGAR

In a healthy person, insulin keeps the level of glucose (blood sugar) within the normal range —60 mg per deciliter (mg/dl) to 140 mg/dl.

In individuals with type II diabetes, the pancreas fails to produce enough insulin to keep glucose levels in check.

In most cases, the problem is *not* that the production of insulin declines. It's that cells become resistant to the glucose-lowering effects of insulin.

The more resistant the cells become, the higher glucose levels rise. The higher the glucose levels, the greater the risk for long-term complications.

What's the secret to avoiding long-term complications of diabetes? Keeping glucose levels under control *at all times.*

### WARNING SIGNS

Type II diabetes usually strikes after age 40. *It causes...*

●**Excessive thirst**

●**Frequent urination**

●**Blurry vision**

●**Increased hunger**

●**Unexplained weight loss**

*One million Americans have the other form of diabetes, type I (juvenile-onset). It occurs when the pancreas fails to produce any insulin at all.

- **Skin infections**
- **Fatigue**
- **Vaginal infections**

These symptoms are often extremely mild. The only way to be sure you don't have diabetes is via a blood sugar test.

Insist on having this test as part of each annual checkup.

If your blood sugar is ordinarily above 140 mg/dl—or your fasting blood sugar is above 120 mg/dl—your doctor should perform additional tests.

*Especially helpful:* The glucose tolerance test. This involves fasting overnight, then having your blood sugar checked before and after drinking a glucose mixture.

### HEMOGLOBIN A1-C TEST

If you have diabetes, it's important to monitor your blood sugar levels closely.

Many diabetics continue to believe that daily do-it-yourself blood-sugar tests are all that are needed. They're wrong. These daily finger-prick tests reveal only what your blood sugar level is at that particular moment. The only way to know whether your blood sugar has *consistently* been within safe levels is to have a doctor test your blood for *hemoglobin A1-C.*

This simple $45 test reveals the average blood-sugar level over the preceding eight weeks. The test should be used every three months.

In a recent National Institutes of Health study of 1,400 diabetics, half of the participants received standard diabetes care—dietary planning, drug therapy and exercise combined with daily blood-sugar testing. The other half received more intensive care aimed at lowering the hemoglobin A1-C level.

*Result:* Diabetics who lowered their hemoglobin A1-C had 70% fewer complications than those who didn't.

### DIET AND EXERCISE

Mild cases of type II diabetes can usually be controlled via careful eating habits and regular exercise—and, of course, carefully monitoring blood sugar and hemoglobin A1-C levels.

Since the body uses bread, pasta and other carbohydrates to make glucose, some doctors urge diabetics to limit their carbohydrate intake severely.

Yet many diabetics do fine on a high-fiber, moderate-carbohydrate diet—as long as they space their meals carefully. It's essential to check blood sugar to follow the effects of your diet.

*Aim:* To spot any increases in glucose levels.

If you drink alcohol, do so in moderation—and only when your diabetes is under control. Diabetics should *never* drink alcohol on an empty stomach.

*Best:* Work with a doctor *and* a nutritionist to develop a workable meal-planning strategy...and an appropriate regimen of walking or another aerobic exercise.

Getting aerobic exercise for 20 to 45 minutes, four days a week, is usually very effective at controlling glucose levels.

*Best time to exercise:* Sixty to 90 minutes after eating, when blood sugar levels are highest.

### ANTIDIABETIC MEDICATION

Even if they're diligent about eating right and exercising regularly, about one-third of all type II diabetics need medication to help control glucose levels.

Several classes of medication are available...

- **Sulfonylureas.** These drugs squeeze a little extra insulin out of the pancreas...and boost the body's sensitivity to insulin.

Common sulfonylureas include *glyburide* (Micronase), *glipizide* (Glucotrol) and *glimepiride* (Amaryl).

- **Metformin (Glucophage).** Like sulfonylureas, this relatively new drug boosts the body's sensitivity to insulin. Since it also triggers weight loss, metformin is often a good choice for overweight diabetics.

- **Acarbose (Precose).** This drug works by slowing the digestion of carbohydrates.

- **Troglitazone (Rezulin).** This drug boosts the body's sensitivity to insulin. Anyone who takes it should have periodic liver-function tests.

If glucose levels remain elevated despite the use of one or more of these drugs—or if the drugs lose their effectiveness—insulin injections may be necessary.

### CHECKUPS TO PREVENT TROUBLE

As insurance against complications, diabetics should have regular checkups. The goal is to catch complications as early as possible.

**Daily:** Check feet for redness, swelling or sores that aren't healing. Diabetes-related circulation problems render the feet unusually vulnerable to infection.

**Yearly:** A doctor should test your blood pressure and cholesterol levels...and your microalbumin level (to test kidney function). Also—an ophthalmologist should check your eyes for signs of diabetic retinopathy, a condition that can lead to blindness.

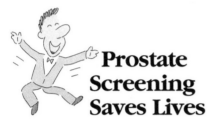

# Prostate Screening Saves Lives

Prostate cancer screening really does pay off. The death rate from prostate cancer among men who had a prostate-specific antigen (PSA) blood test and a digital rectal exam (DRE) was 69% lower than among men who weren't screened. None of the screened men died of prostate cancer before age 65. Fifteen percent of the unscreened men did. *Bottom line:* All men age 50 or older should have an annual PSA test and DRE.

Fernand Labrie, MD, director of research, Laval University Medical Center, Quebec City, Canada. His eight-year study of 46,193 men 45 to 80 years of age was presented at a recent meeting of the American Society of Clinical Oncology.

# Hormone Replacement Therapy

Women doctors are twice as likely as their nonphysician peers to use hormone-replacement therapy (HRT). Studies linking estrogen to a slight rise in the risk of developing breast cancer have scared many women away from HRT—including many women who stand to benefit. *Recent survey:* Forty-eight percent of postmenopausal women doctors—who should be better able to weigh

medical risks and benefits than the average woman—are on HRT. Nationwide, 24% of postmenopausal women are on HRT.

Sally E. McNagny, MD, MPH, assistant professor of medicine and epidemiology, Emory University School of Medicine, Atlanta.

# Allergy Shots Are No Quick Fix

It usually takes several months for shots to begin working—and they do not work at all in some people.

*Situations in which shots can be particularly effective:* Allergy to bee, wasp, yellow jacket or hornet stings...seasonal pollen allergy...well-documented sensitivity to dust mites or cat dander. Results are much less predictable with sensitivity to dog dander or for mold allergy.

Harold Nelson, MD, senior staff physician, National Jewish Center for Immunology and Respiratory Medicine, Denver.

# Aspartame Has Side Effects

The popular artificial sweetener aspartame can cause symptoms that are identical to those associated with hyperthyroidism—which is also called Graves' disease.

*Symptoms:* Heart palpitations, anxiety attacks, headaches, hypertension, hair loss, enlarged eyes.

The symptoms appear most often in people who are dieting and on vigorous exercise programs.

Nan Kathryn Fuchs, PhD, nutrition editor, *Women's Health Letter,* 7100 Peachtree Dunwoody Rd., Atlanta 30328.

# Antacid Trap

I f you're taking any prescription drug, consult a doctor before taking an antacid that contains aluminum. Aluminum blocks absorption of the ulcer medication *ranitidine* (Zantac) and other prescription drugs for up to two hours.

Bruce Yaffe, MD, an internist and gastroenterologist in private practice in New York City.

# How to Minimize Mosquito and Tick Annoyances

Richard Pollack, PhD, a public health entomologist at the Harvard School of Public Health, 677 Huntington Ave., Boston 02115.

• **Choose a lotion/cream repellent that contains no more than 35% DEET.** Apply sparingly. DEET can cause adverse reactions—particularly skin rashes—when it has higher concentrations. It is, however, the most effective repellent available—and it can be used safely.

***Recommended:*** Use the lowest effective concentration possible—generally no more than 35% for adults…and no more than 15% for children. Apply the repellent sparingly. Wash with soap and water when the protection is no longer needed. Treat clothes, rather than skin, whenever possible.

***Important:*** The repellent you choose should be registered by the Environmental Protection Agency (EPA). Look for one that has an EPA registration number on the label. These repellents are under strict regulation.

• **Apply a permethrin spray to the outside of clothing.** Especially effective at killing ticks, these sprays may also work with mosquitoes and other biting flies. Spray only enough to moisten the material. Let clothes dry before wearing. Hardware and garden-supply stores sometimes carry brands such as *Duranone* and *Permanone*. These sprays can also be obtained through SCS Ltd., 800-749-8425.

• **Don't assume that the "natural" formulas are better.** Many of the "natural" non-DEET formulas on the market don't specifically claim to repel insects, and may not be registered with the EPA. Consumers have no idea what's in them—or how safe and effective they are.

***Other ways to reduce exposure to biting insects and ticks and the pathogens they may transmit:*** Wear long sleeves and pants when possible…perform a tick check at the end of each day…get proper medical attention if you have been bitten by a tick.

# 2

# Travel Secrets

## How to Avoid Jet Lag

Jet lag is rarely a problem following a short flight. But anyone who flies across three or more time zones is likely to experience days of fatigue, fuzzy thinking and stomach upset.

Jet lag is caused by the sudden disruption of the body's internal clock. The key to minimizing this disruption is to begin shifting over to the "new" time zone well in advance of your departure.

### USING A TRAVEL WATCH

As soon as your travel plans are finalized, consult an atlas to determine the number of time zones you'll be crossing. That's how many days prior to departure you should begin your jet lag avoidance program.

*Example:* If you'll be flying from New York City to Bombay (across 10 time zones), you should begin your program 10 days before takeoff.

During this period, bedtime, wake-up time, meals, etc., should be scheduled not according to your regular watch...but according to a second "travel" watch. On this watch, time must be adjusted each day until your departure.

*Eastbound travel:* On the first day of your jet lag prevention program, your travel watch should be set to the same time as your regular watch. Each day until your departure, advance the travel watch one hour. On the day of your departure, your travel watch should be on the same time zone as your destination.

*Westbound travel:* Start your program with your travel watch at the same time as your regular watch. Then, as you are traveling, set your travel watch back one hour a day until you reach the time zone of your destination.

For distant destinations, of course, your jet lag program will put you significantly out of sync with your home time.

*Solution:* Begin by setting your travel watch ahead or behind by just 15 minutes a day.

Charles B. Inlander, president, People's Medical Society, 462 Walnut St., Allentown, PA 18102. He is author or coauthor of more than 20 books, including *62 Natural Ways to Beat Jet Lag*. St. Martin's.

Switch to the full one hour per day when you're halfway to your departure date.

### LIGHT AND DARKNESS

To shift your body clock while you are still in your home time zone, you will need to manipulate your light exposure, activity patterns and diet. *Here's how...*

*Eastbound travel:* Expose yourself to bright light in the early morning hours—before sunrise, if necessary. After sunrise, spend a few hours outdoors. If that's impossible, sit near a bright lamp...or go to a brightly lighted building.

After mid-afternoon, you should avoid sunlight and other bright light. Once it's bedtime according to your travel watch, you should avoid all sources of light.

*Westbound travel:* Avoid bright light in the morning. You may need to wear a light-blocking eye mask until it's wake-up time according to your travel watch.

Wear wraparound sunglasses until midday. Try to get as much late afternoon light as possible, then use artificial light to "extend" your day.

### WHAT TO EAT—AND WHEN

Keep mealtimes consistent, using the times on your travel watch. If you vary your mealtimes, you'll throw your digestive system out of whack...and that sets you up for an even worse case of jet lag.

*Eastbound travel:* You'll be eating one hour earlier each day. At breakfast and lunch, have mostly protein-rich foods—beans, fish and low-fat meats and dairy products. Proteins are energizing.

For dinner, focus on vegetables, grains and other carbohydrates. Carbohydrates are calming.

*Westbound travel:* You'll be delaying meals by an hour a day. Eat carbohydrates for breakfast, proteins for lunch and dinner.

### ACTIVITY LEVELS

Whenever your jet lag plan calls for exposure to light, try to engage in physical activity. If you cannot be active at that time, read...or do a crossword puzzle.

When you're supposed to avoid light, be sure to rest or sleep.

### DURING THE FLIGHT

If you've followed your jet lag plan carefully, your body clock will be in sync with the new time zone when you take off.

Once airborne, continue to follow your light/darkness schedule. If you're supposed to be getting light exposure, keep the window shade up and use the reading light.

If you're supposed to be avoiding light, keep the window shade pulled down and wear your eye mask as much as possible.

*Also important:* Rest or sleep according to the time at your destination.

What about eating? Emphasize proteins when you need to be alert...and carbohydrates when you need to wind down.

### FOLLOWING YOUR ARRIVAL

Schedule all of your meals and activities according to the new time zone—even if your body hasn't yet fully adjusted.

Avoid the urge to nap, even on your first day. Drinking caffeinated beverages can be helpful. If you absolutely cannot stay awake, nap for one hour or less.

Go to bed when the natives do. If you wake up early the next morning, stay in bed until the clock says it's time to get up.

### MELATONIN

Jet lag medication is unnecessary as long as you followed your pretrip jet lag program. If you failed to follow the program, ask your doctor about using melatonin.

The usual protocol calls for three doses—one the day before travel, a second on your travel day and a third dose on arrival day.

*Caution:* Melatonin is off-limits to pregnant or breastfeeding women...children...and many others.

---

# Cheaper Air Travel

If you and your travel companion are willing to sit separately, mention that to the airline reservationist—it could result in big savings.

***Reason:*** If advance seating assignments are available, the computer will search for all of the individual cheap seats on the flight. However, if you do not *specifically mention* that you and your family members are willing to split up, the computer will search for the least expensive *group of seats* large enough to accommodate all of you. That could be more expensive than individual seats or several groups of two or three seats.

***Best:*** Add up the cost and decide whether you want to sit together or are willing to be a few seats apart.

Louise Weiss, travel writer and author of *Access to the World: A Travel Guide for the Handicapped.* Henry Holt.

# Consumer Advocate Ed Perkins on Cutting Travel Costs

Ed Perkins, consumer advocate, American Society of Travel Agents, 1101 King St., Alexandria, VA 22314. He is former editor of *Consumer Reports Travel Letter.*

## Saving Money on Planes and Hotels

With travel spending in the US at an all-time high—it surpassed $500 billion last year—more people than ever are looking for the best deals.

Here are the questions people ask me to help them save money in the air, on the ground —and in lodgings…

**What are the best ways to find the best airline and hotel deals?** The Internet has scores of sites devoted to travel, but some are better than others. The really good ones bring you the big bargains.

Travelocity (www.travelocity.com) and Microsoft Expedia (www.expedia.msn.com) are both good at tracking down the lowest airfare rate. They don't include ticket consolidator rates.

Consolidators offer low-cost airline tickets— if you are willing to accept restrictions. They are usually nonrefundable…and you don't earn frequent-flier miles. For consolidator rates, you'll still have to call a consolidator directly

…find a travel agent who deals with such companies…or check www.1travel.com, one of the biggest sites for consolidator fares.

Finding the best hotel rates is more challenging. I've yet to see this information reliably pulled together in one site on the Web.

Hotel Reservations Network (800-964-6835) and Quickbook (800-789-9887) are the equivalent of consolidators for the hotel business. Call them to find their best room rates.

**How can travelers find travel agents who will save them the most money?** Most people find a travel agent through word of mouth, and they don't think much about the agent's skill until problems occur. Key factors to consider when shopping for an agent who will get you the best deals…

•**Access to a good preferred-rate hotel program.** Hotels often make deals with travel agencies for room rates that are better than those the hotels advertise. These preferred rates can save you up to 40%.

•**Sources for consolidator airline tickets.** Ask your travel agent for examples of both consolidator prices and list prices. Make sure the consolidators' rates are significantly better than the regular fares—enough to compensate you if you do not get frequent-flier miles or are subject to other restrictions. Otherwise, it may not be worth putting up with them.

•**Samples of hotel rates and airfares associated with cities you want to visit.** Check with a few travel agents, and compare what they find.

**How can I accumulate and use frequent-flier miles without driving myself crazy?** The number of ways to earn frequent-flier miles both on the ground and in the air is increasing —and increasingly complex. Here's how to get, and spend, those miles…

•**Trade miles for ease of use.** If you want to avoid the typical restrictions associated with frequent-flier miles, you can almost always get what you want by using additional miles.

***Example:*** The typical award ticket costs 25,000 miles for a domestic flight. But it is subject to blackout dates and severe seat restrictions. Most frequent-flier programs will waive these restrictions if you'll ante up 40,000 or 50,000 miles—assuming there's still an open seat on the plane.

•**Be flexible.** As frequent fliers are no doubt aware, airlines severely restrict the number of seats that are initially allocated to award-ticket travelers on any given flight. You may be able, though, to take advantage of the bonus seats that often are available seven to 10 days before flight time.

Airlines often release additional seats to award-ticket travelers in the week to 10 days immediately preceding the flight, if they determine that the flight wouldn't otherwise be full.

*Obstacle:* Few travelers' plans are flexible enough to wait until the last week to see if these tickets will be available.

*Solution:* If no frequent-flier seats are available when you first check, buy a ticket for as low a price as you can find. Then, between seven and 10 days ahead of flight time, check in to see if there are any new frequent-flier seats available. If there are, get the award seat and trade in the ticket you bought earlier. You'll pay an exchange fee—usually $50 to $75—but if it's an expensive ticket, it is worth trying.

Make certain that the tickets you purchase are redeemable. Most tickets are. Certain international tickets, and some tickets purchased through discounters—businesses that sell consolidator tickets to consumers—might not be.

•**Do the arithmetic.** Tempting as it is, using a hotel chain or car rental agency that is associated with your airline's frequent-flier program may not make financial sense.

*Problem:* You'll rarely earn more than 500 miles for a hotel stay or car rental. Since 500 miles is worth no more than $10, it might not be worth your trouble. And—bonus miles often aren't available on discounted rates. So if there's a discount rate available that will save you more than $10, it's a better deal than earning miles.

**How can travelers avoid penalties when their plans change at the last moment?** One solution is travel insurance, which is available through any travel agency, typically for 5% to 5.5% of the cost of the trip. This will cover your expenses should you become ill or meet some other misfortune, such as a fire or flood that destroys your home.

Unfortunately, there is no travel insurance that will cover your loss if you simply decide not to go on the trip, or if business contingencies force you to cancel.

*Helpful:* If you're worried that business concerns may force you to cancel a trip, it is usually best to prepay *as little as possible* and avoid airlines, hotels and other travel businesses that have no-refund policies.

---

**More from Ed Perkins...**

## Car Rental Smarts

Many car rental companies allow you to return the car as much as 59 minutes late without incurring charges for an extra hour—or even an extra day. But some companies begin charging extra if the car is brought back as little as 30 minutes late. *Caution:* The grace period can vary from location to location within the same company. *Self-defense:* Always ask about the grace period before driving off. If you will be on a tight schedule, shop around for the longest possible grace period before reserving a car. It may pay to go with a slightly more expensive per-day rate, if you will be able to avoid a late penalty.

---

# Beware of Frequent-Flier Brokers

Frequent-flier brokers buy miles from one person's account, obtain tickets and sell them at a deep discount. The person selling the miles and the one buying the low-cost ticket may both think this is a good deal. But these brokerage deals violate airline frequent-flier program rules—and airlines are using tracking software to be sure tickets are legitimate.

If you hold a broker's ticket, it may be confiscated at the gate. If you sell miles, you risk having your entire balance confiscated by the airline.

Randy Petersen, publisher, *InsideFlyer*, 4715-C Town Center Dr., Colorado Springs 80916. He is also editor of *The Official Frequent Flyer Guidebook*. Randy Petersen Publishing.

# Better Ticket Buying

Get on-time performance data for airline flights before you book. Ticket and travel agents can call up arrival performance on their computers. Records are kept for all flights on the 14 largest US airlines.

*Example:* An eight means the flight landed within 15 minutes of schedule between 80% and 89% of the time during its last monthly reporting period…seven means 70% to 79% of landings were within 15 minutes.

*The Fearless Flyer* by Cherry Hartman, clinical social worker specializing in treatment of anxiety, Portland, OR. Eighth Mountain Press.

# New Airline Ticket Alert

Many carriers are now buying seats on other airlines and then selling them to passengers for more money—without telling consumers. This practice, known as "code-sharing," is on the rise, resulting from an increase in alliances between airlines. Typically, with code-sharing, two airline carriers are listed at the departure gate.

*Key:* Before booking a flight, ask your travel agent or airline if the ticket you want to buy is a "code-share" flight. If it is, ask *which airline is selling the cheaper ticket.*

Terry Trippler, editor and publisher of *Rules of the Air,* www.onetravel.com/rules/rules.cfm, a Web site that provides information on airline rules and regulations.

# Making the Most Of a Layover

Consider airline layovers an opportunity. They can give you time for a brief tour of the area around the airport—so you have memories of something besides a frustrating delay. If a delay is too short for you to leave the air-port, try a micro-vacation inside the terminal. Go to airport stores and find clues about the region based on the special items for sale. Try to find offbeat shops or areas, such as the secondhand bookstore in the Minneapolis airport or the corridor filled with changing light and music in Chicago's O'Hare.

Rose Moss, novelist and short-story writer, writing in *The New York Times.*

# Travel Smarts from Charles Leocha

Charles Leocha, a Boston–based travel writer. He is author of *Travel Rights.* World Leisure Corp.

## Travel Rights Galore

In 21 years as a travel writer, I have learned that travelers can get a lot more satisfaction from airlines, rental-car firms and other companies than they ever expected. *You just have to know what your rights are…*

•**On-the-spot compensation if you're involuntarily bumped** from a flight in the US or Europe. You get…

•**One-way fare to your destination** if you arrive more than one hour late—two hours on international flights. The maximum is $200.

•**200% of the one-way fare, with a $400 maximum,** if you are more than two hours late domestically—or are more than four hours late internationally.

In both cases, you can keep your original ticket and use it on another flight—or get a refund.

*Important:* This is the *minimum* amount the airline must pay you. You have 30 days to negotiate more.

*Example:* Because being delayed meant I missed a connection and arrived late, the airline also gave me 1,500 frequent-flier miles.

•**Compensation even if your flight is merely delayed for an hour.** An airline will usually give you a voucher for lunch or dinner, worth about $10…or a seat on another airline …or put you on a flight to a nearby city.

**Helpful:** If your flight is canceled, or if you just miss it, and you can't get another flight until the next day, ask customer service to book you a "distressed passenger" rate at a local hotel. I did this in Denver during a snowstorm, and a room that cost $100 per night dropped to $39.

•**Return-date flexibility.** The outbound segment of a round-trip ticket is generally chiseled in stone. But airlines may allow you to change your return date without a penalty *if* travel space is available...and the Saturday-night-stay requirement is met.

•**Vouchers for basics**—clothing, toiletries and sports-equipment rental—if the airline loses your luggage.

**Example:** I once had to attend a formal dinner and my luggage didn't arrive. The airline paid for a tuxedo rental.

If your luggage is lost, the airline is liable for provable consequential damages of up to $1,250 on domestic flights and $9.07 per pound on international flights.

You can submit claims to your homeowner's insurance company if your loss is more than $1,250 or you are having a problem with the airline, and let them go after your air carrier for reimbursement.

**Helpful:** The US Department of Transportation offers a Web site that tells you how to register a complaint (www.dot.gov/ost/ogc/subject/ consumer/aviation/publications/telljudge.html). In some cases, the government may contact the airline on your behalf.

•**Ability to use one airline's discount coupon on another carrier.** I recently received a coupon from a shopping mall for a round-trip flight on Continental Airlines anywhere in the US for $150. I wanted to visit my family in South Carolina, but Continental didn't have the flights I wanted, and my frequent-flier miles were on US Airways.

**Solution:** US Airways agreed to honor the coupon. If a carrier flies to a destination, it usually will accept a competitor's coupon.

•**Ability to avoid paying collision damage and loss damage insurance** for rental cars by paying with the right credit card.

**Best:** Diner's Club, 800-234-6377, which provides full-value, primary insurance coverage worldwide for up to 31 days.

MasterCard BusinessCard, MBNA, 800-358-9088, provides similar coverage.

If you plan to rent an SUV, minivan or luxury car, make sure the credit card you use covers these "exotic" cars.

•**Refund on taxes you pay on purchases abroad...**

**Canada:** Get back your 7% Goods and Services Tax (GST) by mailing in a refund form from the store within 60 days after purchase. If your claim is for less than $500 (Canadian), make your claim at the border.

You must provide originals of all receipts. You can get a refund on the cost of hotel rooms, but not on gasoline, tobacco, alcohol, meals or car rentals.

**Europe:** Look for stores that are part of the European Tax-Free Shopping Network. Call its US office at 800-566-9828 for more information. You'll have to submit only one form to the network, regardless of how many countries you've been in, to get a refund of the Value Added Tax (VAT). Otherwise, you have to fill out a form for each country.

Ask the salesperson to fill out a check for a VAT refund. When you leave the country, get the check stamped by customs officials.

Then cash it at one of the 3,000 windows at most airports and many border crossings in Europe. Funds are converted into US dollars or credited to your credit card. There are no network refund booths in the US.

---

**More from Charles Leocha...**

## Senior Fares for Children

Some airlines allow senior citizens who are traveling with a child under age 11—and using special low-cost senior coupon books—to use a senior coupon for the child's fare, too. And—senior fare reductions are often available to seniors' companions as well. Airline rules vary so check with each carrier.

---

# Safest Seat on the Plane

The safest seat on a plane is an aisle seat near an exit. The location of exits varies according to aircraft and carrier. When obtaining your advance seat assignment, ask the airline or travel agent where the exit rows are …and, if there is a last-minute equipment change, ask again.

*Flying Blind, Flying Safe* by Mary Schiavo, former inspector general, US Department of Transportation, and a licensed pilot. Avon Books.

# Seats to Avoid on Planes

On planes you'll want to avoid coach seats that don't recline and those near lavatories.

**Strategy:** When booking a seat, ask for one that reclines fully. Avoid 747s—they have the highest number of nonreclining seats. *Better:* 777s and L-1011s.

**Beware:** 767s, A300s and MD-11s have the highest number of seats near lavatories…747s, 777s and DC-10s have the fewest.

Laurie Berger, editor, *Consumer Reports Travel Letter*, 101 Truman Ave., Yonkers, NY 10703.

# Baggage Self-Defense When Traveling by Air

When traveling by plane, use soft-sided luggage—hard luggage is more likely to split open when handled roughly. Stay within airline limits on weight and size—otherwise, baggage handlers may be less than gentle with your belongings. Avoid unique baggage, which can be singled out for damage or theft. Put your name and phone number inside each piece of luggage, not just outside—outside

tags can be lost. Take off detachable handles and straps before checking luggage through.

From Fodor's *How to Pack: Experts Share Their Secrets* (Fodor's Travel Publications), by Laurel Cardone, reported in *New Choices*, 28 W. 23 St., New York 10010.

# Benefits of Frequent Guest Programs

To get a better hotel deal even in these times of high occupancy, join a frequent-guest program—even if you are not a frequent guest. As soon as you join, programs give benefits like free fitness center use, express checkout, late check-in and—sometimes—room upgrades. *Also:* Do not accept the first rate you are quoted. Keep asking for a lower one. *Examples:* A special weekend rate…a package including breakfast or free parking. *And:* Ask to have high phone surcharges—such as a $2 per call long-distance access fee—removed. Many frequent-guest programs waive the surcharges automatically.

Wendy Perrin, travel columnist, writing in *Condé Nast Traveler*, 4 Times Sq., New York 10036.

# Little-Known Things a Concierge Can Do for You

Holly Stiel, who was a concierge for 16 years and now conducts seminars on customer service for companies, Mill Valley, CA. She is author of *Ultimate Service: The Complete Handbook to the World of the Concierge*. Prentice Hall.

Besides confirming airline reservations and getting you theater tickets, hotel concierges can provide many other free services. Here's what even mid-priced hotel concierges will do if you fax them requests in advance…

•**Make special occasions more special.** Concierges are a great source of ideas for special occasions.

**Examples:** Set up a candlelit birthday dinner for two on the beach…fill your room with bouquets of fresh flowers…buy presents for your spouse and gift wrap them.

●**Get you into popular places.** The concierge may be able to provide access to places that are booked.

*Examples:* If you want to play golf in Hawaii, the concierge can tell you which public course is best, find you partners and perhaps get you into a private club. If you're interested in visiting a museum, the concierge might be able to set up a private tour.

●**Save the day when you're in a jam.** Concierges are very resourceful and can turn around almost any disaster.

*Examples:* If you need a necktie…tear a pair of stockings…or break your reading glasses, the concierge may be able to help.

●**Customize your itinerary,** from a day trip …to places off the beaten path…to a romantic weekend.

*Example:* In San Francisco, the concierge can set up a trip through the Napa Valley, with stops at private wineries.

●**Get your chores done.** The concierge can do everything from having film developed to buying items you might have forgotten. If you don't have the time to ship your souvenirs home, the concierge will have it done for you.

*Remember:* For a concierge who has gone out of his/her way to accommodate your stay, it is appropriate and appreciated to compensate him with a gratuity. *Example:* $20 or more.

# David and Linda Glickstein on How to Pick The Best Travel Agent

David and Linda Glickstein, editors, *The Discerning Traveler*, 504 W. Mermaid Ln., Philadelphia 19118.

### Questions to Ask When Choosing a Travel Agent

●Can you or someone from your office be reached 24 hours a day? Do you charge extra for requests outside routine working hours?

●Do you have a Web site…an automated booking system…E-mail?

●Are your preferred carriers those that I fly most often?

●With which hotels do you have preferred rates? And are they within my price range?

●Can I see a list of references?

**More from David and Linda Glickstein…**

## Lower Travel Costs

To keep travel costs down, use only travel agents whose computers have software that constantly scans for lower fares (and better seats) so you can get a refund if the ticket price falls before you travel. If you own a company —even a small one—negotiate lower fees. If you do not change tickets often, ask for a smaller per-ticket purchase fee in exchange for a larger ticket-change fee. If you are a frequent traveler, negotiate a discount by promising a certain amount of business over the course of a year.

# Hotel Bumping

Hotels bump people, too. They call it *getting walked*—you have a guaranteed reservation but are told your room is not available. *Self-defense:* Reconfirm reservations twice by fax or phone—once before leaving home and again on your day of arrival. Tell the hotel what time you will arrive. If you are told upon your arrival that you will be walked, ask to see the hotel manager. If no rooms are available in the category you reserved, ask for an upgrade at no extra cost. If none are available at any price, most places will pay for your room at a different hotel and transport you there free.

Scott Ahlsmith, certified travel consultant and owner, TRAVA Travel Agency, Glen Ellyn, IL.

# ATMs vs. Traveler's Checks

Travelers are using fewer traveler's checks and making more use of ATMs. *Advantage of ATMs:* A more favorable exchange rate

...and the amount of local currency you want. The Cirrus network, linked to MasterCard, and Plus, linked to Visa, have extensive ATM networks overseas. Both offer leaflets at US member banks to help travelers locate machines. *Caution:* Carry some traveler's checks as backup, in case the only ATM in town is out of cash or out of order.

Betsy Wade, travel columnist, *The New York Times.*

## Travel Self-Defense

Accidents pose a greater threat than infectious disease to tourists who go abroad.

*Theory:* Because tourists are in a "holiday" state of mind, they take risks that would be unthinkable at home—such as riding a motorcycle without a helmet.

*Self-defense:* Take the same safety precautions while traveling as you would at home.

Paul Prociv, MD, PhD, associate professor of parasitology, University of Queensland, Brisbane, Australia. His study of fatalities among Australians traveling overseas was presented at a recent Australian Tropical Health and Nutrition conference in Brisbane.

## Tropical Travel Ahead?

Before traveling to the tropics, consult with your physician about preventive measures for...

*Malaria:* Prevalent in rural areas of Asia, Central and South America, and especially dangerous in sub-Saharan Africa, even in cities. *Self-defense:* Pre-exposure drugs, such as *chloroquine*...DEET repellent on skin...permethrin insecticide on clothing.

*Dengue fever:* Caribbean, Latin America, Southeast Asia, India, Africa. Disease has flu-like symptoms with a high fever and rash. *Self-defense:* Protect against mosquito bites—there is no vaccine.

*Hepatitis A:* Risk in all underdeveloped countries. *Self-defense:* Get your hepatitis vaccine at least two weeks before travel.

*Travelers' diarrhea:* High risk in all underdeveloped countries. *Self-defense:* Eat only well-cooked foods and drink only bottled water. Take along a standby antibiotic such as *Floxin.*

*Other precautions:* Make sure all your routine shots are up-to-date...buy a travel insurance policy to cover emergency air ambulance evacuation. *Cost:* $3 to $5 a day.

Stuart Rose, MD, president, Travel Medicine, Inc., 351 Pleasant St., Northampton, MA 01060

## First Aid for Air Travelers

Air travelers should pack a bottle of baby aspirin in their carry-on baggage. Aspirin isn't always included in the medical kits aboard commercial airliners—even though its clot-busting effect can be lifesaving in case of a heart attack. If you think you're having a heart attack—aboard an airliner or anyplace else—chew one of the 81-mg tablets while seeking emergency medical assistance.

Victor S. Sloan, MD, clinical assistant professor of medicine, University of Medicine and Dentistry of New Jersey, New Brunswick. His suggestion was published in the *Annals of Internal Medicine,* Sixth St. at Race, Philadelphia 19106.

## Useful Items for Travel

Net bag for shopping, laundry, etc....tube of concentrated shampoo—it can be used for hand laundry, too...old-fashioned rubber galoshes...multipocketed safari vest, with zippers on some pockets...padlock for lockers at health clubs or hostels...masking tape and rubber bands.

*Tips for the Savvy Traveler* by Deborah Burns, travel writer based in Williamstown, MA, who has circled the globe and visited every state in the US. Storey Publishing.

# Better Fitness While Traveling

Take a jump rope…a stretchy elastic rubber band that works with resistance…and a long rubber tube with handles on each end. All are available at sports stores.

***Warm-up:*** Jump rope lightly in your hotel room.

***Arms and shoulders:*** Sit in a chair. Place one end of the rubber band in each hand… raise hands so they are in front of your face, with arms extended…pull the band out to the sides, then back in. Repeat 12 to 15 times.

***Biceps:*** Stay seated…put one foot on the rubber tube…with palms up, elbows at sides, pull handles up toward shoulders. Repeat 12 to 15 times.

***Legs:*** Climb stairs—two at a time going up, one at a time going down.

*Patrick Netter, independent sports and fitness equipment consultant, 333 Bonhill Rd., Los Angeles 90049.*

# Travel Savvy From Jens Jurgen

*Jens Jurgen, editor,* Travel Companions, *Box 833, Amityville, NY 11701.*

## Don't Get Lost When Traveling

Rent a car with a satellite navigation system when in an unfamiliar city. These use the Global Positioning Satellite system to determine exactly where you are at any moment, and how to get to where you want to go. Navigational systems can give directions both on a map and by "voice" direction, such as by saying "turn right." With the system, you will never have to fear getting lost. Navigation systems are available from major car rental agencies for a modest extra fee—about $6 per day.

## Airline Fare Frenzy

When a fare sale is announced, airline phones are often tied up.

***Better:*** Call the reservation number on your frequent-flier card or mileage statement instead.

***Reason:*** You will usually get through more readily—and the agents who answer those numbers are generally the best and most experienced.

***Alternative:*** Work with a knowledgeable travel agent who can compare availability on airlines that may be matching the reduced fares.

# Save with CityPass

Half-price CityPass coupons are a great buy for visitors to Boston, New York, San Francisco, Seattle or Philadelphia. The coupon books—currently available only for those five cities—contain admission tickets to six of each city's most popular attractions. Prices vary by city. Passes are good for nine days.

***Information:*** www.citypass.net or 707-256-0490.

# Enjoy Disney World… At Much Lower Prices

*Bob Sehlinger, author of* Mini Mickey: The Pocket-Sized Unofficial Guide to Walt Disney World. *Macmillan Travel.*

Although almost everyone loves Disney World, not everyone loves the cost of enjoying the experience. To cut those costs next time…

### ACCOMMODATIONS

•**Know where to find hotel discounts.** Save money by ordering the free Orlando MagiCard (407-363-5872). It offers 10% to 50% discounts at 75 local hotels and area attractions.

*The Exit Information Guide* (352-371-3948) also provides bargain rates at hotels throughout Florida. *Cost:* $3.

●**Stay at a Disney World hotel—and pay less.** The advantages to staying on the property include free transportation to sites…early entry to parks…priority seating for lunch, dinner and character meals…baby-sitting and child care…free parking…and preferential treatment for tee times at golf courses.

### TO BRING DOWN THE HIGH COST

●**Magic Kingdom Club membership** is offered free by many employers, credit unions and trade associations. Or you can purchase the membership directly from Disney (714-781-1550). The two-year membership can save you 10% to 20% on lodging…and up to $15 on park admissions during off-peak times. *Cost:* $65 ($50 for seniors and Disney stockholders).

●**Use AAA or other auto club membership,** and cut your hotel bill by 10% to 20%.

●**Stay during the "off" season**—Generally from January 1 to February 11…and August 29 to December 24.

### THEME PARKS

Don't overbuy theme park admission tickets. Many people waste money at Disney World by buying package deals that give them more tickets than they have the energy to use.

To get a sense of how long you'll want to stay at each park, take your family on a dry run to a state or county fair or a similar sprawling activity. You'll get a good sense of everyone's stamina.

### FOOD

The best way to save on food is to avoid all full-service Disney restaurants. *Alternatives…*

●*Have breakfast at a diner off the property…* lunch at food stands in the parks …and dinner at a restaurant off the property.

●*Pack your own food.* You can keep a cooler in your hotel room or rent a refrigerator for $5 per night.

●*Ethnic restaurants at Epcot Center* are a good deal—if you eat your main meal at lunch. Portion sizes are the same as at dinner, but prices are much lower.

### SHOPPING AT EPCOT

Much of the merchandise in Epcot's World Showcase shops is overpriced and available elsewhere on the property for less. But some shops are really special…

●*Yong Feng Shangdian* in the China pavilion. Crafts, rugs, carvings and furniture.

●*Mitsukoshi Department Store* in the Japan pavilion. Porcelain, bonsai trees, pearls.

●*Village Traders,* located between the China and Germany pavilions. Kenyan wood carvings for about the same price you would pay at the carving center in Mombasa, where they're made.

---

# How to Enjoy the Great National Parks For a Lot Less Money

David L. Scott, a professor of finance at Valdosta State University in Valdosta, GA. Mr. Scott is coauthor of *Guide to the National Parks Area: Western States, Guide to the National Parks Area: Eastern States* and *Complete Guide to the National Park Lodges,* all published by Globe Pequot Press.

---

The cost of vacationing in national parks has soared—with rooms at some lodges in Yosemite and Grand Teton now going for more than $200 a night.

The federal government, which operates the 54 parks,* offers very limited senior or other discounts—but you can still find bargains…

●**Go to less-frequented parks.** *Examples…*

●While a room at fabulous Yosemite's Ahwanee lodge costs $237 a night, lodging at Voyageur Park's Kettle Falls Hotel, in Minnesota's beautiful lake country, is only $60 a night.

●At Texas's Big Bend National Park, with its steep-walled canyons, desert and mountains alongside the Rio Grande, you can reserve one of the Chisos Mountains Lodge's six stone cottages (with adobe walls) for $73 per night in high season.

●Yellowstone and Yosemite each charge $20 per car to enter the park…North Cascades National Park, in northern Washington, charges nothing to enjoy the park's glaciers and snow-

*The US National Park Service, part of the US Department of the Interior, operates 378 areas—54 national parks and hundreds of historic sites, battlefields, campgrounds, monuments and other areas.

covered peaks. Most smaller parks charge only $3 to $10 per car for entrance.

● **Buy an annual entrance pass for $50** instead of paying up to $20 per vehicle each time you enter any one of the parks.

A Golden Eagle Passport is good for one year of entrance to all US National Park Service parks, historic sites and recreation areas.

*Better:* Get a lifetime entrance permit for $10 if you are a US citizen age 62 or older (Golden Age Passport)...or for free if you are permanently disabled (Golden Access Passport). These permits also entitle you to 50% off all user fees, such as fees for camping. Passports are available at any park entrance, or by contacting the National Park Service at 202-208-4747.

● **Take advantage of free or inexpensive activities.** Every national park offers hikes, tours or history and nature programs.

*Some free activities...*

● **Canyonlands National Park,** located in southeastern Utah, offers free tours of native American petroglyphs and incredible sandstone landscapes shaped by nature over 300 million years. 435-259-7164.

● **Dinosaur National Monument,** near Vernal, Utah, has free exhibits showing life-sized replicas of Tyrannosaurus rex and more. 970-374-3000.

● **Isle Royale National Park,** in Lake Superior, east of Grand Portage, Minnesota, offers free tours of its old copper mine. Or, pick blueberries in the summer. 906-482-0984.

*Some free annual festivals...*

● **Shenandoah National Park,** in the Blue Ridge Mountains of Virginia, about 70 miles west of Washington, DC, features games and various craft demonstrations during July and August. 540-999-3500.

● **Gettysburg National Military Park,** Gettysburg, Pennsylvania, hosts the Bluegrass and Apple Blossom Festival in May...the Civil War Heritage Festival in June and July...antiques shows in May and September...and a celebration on the anniversary of Lincoln's Gettysburg Address every November 19. 717-334-1124.

● **Stay outside the park the night before you enter the park, and the night you leave it.** Look for rooms within a two-hour radius of the park entrance. You'll enjoy a full day in the park at both ends of your vacation without paying high rates on park grounds...or at the lodgings right outside them.

*Example:* We spent the night before we entered Yosemite 100 miles away at a Best Western Inn in Fresno, California. *Cost:* $60 a night—half the cost of the Yosemite Lodge...about a quarter of the Ahwahnee's. The next morning, we got up early and were in the park by 9 am.

*Alternative:* Stay at one of dozens of US Forest Service campsites, just outside the parks —for $8 to $12 per site per night. For a list of campsites, call 202-205-1027, or check out www.fs.fed.us/recreation/states/us.html.

Or, camp out in the parks themselves, for about $10 to $20 per night per site. Reserve on-line at http://reservations.nps.gov, or call 800-365-2267.

● **Camp out in a park cabin.** About half a dozen of the national parks have cabin accommodations that give you the feel of adventure —but with more luxury (linens and electricity) than a tent. *Cost:* Less than $50 a night. *Write:* The Department of the Interior, National Park Service, Office of Public Inquiries, Box 37127, Room 1013, Washington, DC 20013-7127. Specify the park you are interested in. *Examples...*

● **Hawaii Volcanoes National Park** is known for its rare plants and craters of red-hot lava. The Namakani Paio cabins are at a safe, 4,000-foot elevation. *Cost:* A total of $40 a night for four, including linens, towels, soap, blankets, electricity and a barbecue grill. 808-967-7321.

● **Grand Teton National Park** in Moose, Wyoming. Western-style adventure, including rubber rafting on the Snake River. The Colter Bay canvas-and-log tent cabins have a woodstove and two double-decker beds. *Cost:* $30 per night, double occupancy, per cabin...$3 for each additional person over age 12. 800-628-9988.

● **Travel in the off-season.** Spring or fall is the only time that you can get popular lodgings at a reasonable price. *Example...*

● **Virgin Island National Park,** on St. John's, US Virgin Islands. The Cinnamon Bay campground has 40 cottages located two minutes from the beach. Each of the cement-and-canvas cabins has twin beds, a terrace, charcoal grill, picnic table and electricity. Community bathroom. *Cost:* $70 per night per unit from May 1 to December 1...price goes up nearly 50% from December through April. 800-539-9998.

# 3

# Your Family and Your Home

## What Busy Parents Can Do To Raise Intelligent Kids

The great challenge for any parents is to help their kids do the best they can in school.

**Key:** How well children do in school determines so much of their future—college versus high school...good schools versus bad.

Here, Philip Bigler, a national Teacher of the Year, gives his award-winning motivational suggestions on what parents can do to excite their children about school and learning...

●**Promote a culture of reading at home.** Reading is the gateway to all knowledge and fundamental to academic excellence and ideas. Computers are wonderful tools, but they cannot replace books. Reading stimulates the imagination and encourages creative thinking.

*Helpful:* Read with your children, and discuss the books and articles in the car...while walking to school...and at the dinner table.

It's also important to set aside time for reading, making sure children view this time as a joy, not as a chore or a punishment.

One way to turn reading into a pleasurable event is to take children to the library and/or a bookstore once a week. Give them an allowance, and let them choose the books they want without questioning what they've chosen.

*Important:* Don't insist that children always read "educational" material. When I was a kid, I read the Hardy Boys mysteries all the time, and I think that's where my lifelong love of reading started. I still set aside one hour to read each night before bed.

●**Stimulate your children's curiosity.** Children need to be encouraged to ask,

Philip Bigler, who teaches 11th-grade history and humanities at Thomas Jefferson High School for Science and Technology in Alexandria, VA. In April 1998 he was named Teacher of the Year, a national award sponsored by the Council of Chief State School Officers and Scholastic Inc. Mr. Bigler has won 12 teaching awards and written four books, including *Hostile Fire: The Life and Death of First Lt. Sharon Lane*. Vandamere Press.

"Why?" when they don't understand something. Learning is a constant process, and children think this process is over once they have an answer. They need to be taught to probe and push for more answers.

*Helpful:* When children ask, "Why?" don't turn them off or respond with pat answers. Even when you know the answer, it is more stimulating to ask, "What do you think? Why do you think that's so?" Or, "I'm not sure, let's look it up."

Your questions will show them that wondering "why" is an important part of learning.

*Aim:* To spark their curiosity in a spontaneous way so that it becomes fun—not a lesson or lecture.

*Examples:* Make up trivia games that you both can play regularly, even when you're on the run…help kids become active participants in the learning process by giving them chances to experiment around the house with measuring, cooking, fixing and other activities that require finding and using information.

•**Know what's going on in school.** Attend school events, send notes to teachers at the opening of the school year to express your availability to them and ask if you may phone them whenever you have questions or concerns.

Also, get involved with your kids by asking for detailed descriptions of what they're studying in school.

*Helpful:* Encourage teachers and schools to print out an informational sheet on what children are studying week to week.

I have a Web page that the parents of my students can access to see what the class assignments are—and when they are due. More and more teachers I know are doing this now.

It's also important to become involved in school activities. Even if you can attend only a few events, your presence shows your children that you're interested in their school life and value its importance.

•**Establish a sense of ethics in children.** It's critical that parents have the courage to say "No" when children's interests are in conflict with what is acceptable.

As your children get older, continue to uphold firm, clear limits but gradually give them more opportunities to make choices and live with the consequences.

It is easier to establish these standards in first- and second-graders than in preteens. However, there are ways to encourage preteens to adhere to standards of behavior.

*Examples:* In school, we teach students to say, "Thank you" and write thank-you letters to speakers who visit. We teach a sense of helping others through a strong mentoring program in which better students tutor others. We teach them stories of justice. We try to teach kids that there is right and wrong.

•**Celebrate the thinking process,** not just the ability to retain information. Inquisitive, active learners have social skills that have been nurtured by parents and teachers. Those skills include listening, thinking, sharing information and clearly expressing themselves.

*Helpful:* If your child is not a particularly good listener, get down to his/her eye level, touch his shoulder and look him in the eye before speaking. When he talks to you, give him your full attention.

Listening to children closely gives them practice in expressing themselves. Whenever they come home with a problem, don't hand them a solution. Ask them to tell you more about it.

Let them explain and talk through possible solutions—this is an important exercise for problem-solving.

These social skills are the underpinnings for success in school and in life.

---

# When Your Child Dislikes School

If a young child dislikes school, spend several hours—at different times and on different days—observing his/her classroom and talking at home about what might be bothering him. Try having him draw a picture of his classroom for clues to what is troubling him.

*Common problems and their solutions…*

*Trouble with transitions and limits*—find ways at home to help him get used to changing activities and waiting his turn.

***Personality conflict with teacher***—try filling in the teacher on your child's likes and dislikes to find some common ground.

***Separation anxiety***—try reminding him of after-school plans and put loving notes in his book bag.

Fred Provenzano, PhD, psychologist in private practice specializing in family and school issues, and clinical instructor at the University of Washington, Seattle.

# Nancy Samalin Tells How to Help Your Kids Build the Right Kind of Friendships with The Right Kind of Kids

Nancy Samalin, founder and director of Parent Guidance Workshops, 180 Riverside Dr., New York 10024. She is author of several books on parenting, including *Loving Your Child Is Not Enough: Positive Discipline That Works.* Penguin. The book was recently updated and reissued after having sold more than 100,000 copies.

Parents have much more influence than they think over their children's choice of friends.

But in our attempt to protect our children, it is important to recognize that peer relationships are vital to children's development. It's the arena in which they learn to make decisions, to lead or follow, to become considerate and loyal and to recover from mistakes.

How to have a positive influence over your children's choice of friends…

•**Deemphasize popularity.** Many parents unwittingly push kids to make friends. They fret if their children aren't invited to every birthday party. They are devastated whenever their kids are rejected by the "in" crowd.

But when you push for more popularity, your children get the message there is something wrong with them.

Encourage quality over quantity. The number of friends your children have is less important than if they have one or two good friends. And if you emphasize popularity or being part of the clique, your children may become followers who go along blindly with the crowd.

If children are left out—or picked on by their peer group—help them recognize that it is not necessarily their fault. Instead, reassure them that it is normal, though painful, to be "in" one week and "out" the next.

I've found that these popularity contests are more upsetting to parents than to kids. Most kids are more resilient than we give them credit for. Try to ride the waves of friendship fads, remembering that kids are fickle and peer groups are constantly in a state of flux.

•**Don't interfere without good reason.** Unless your children's friends are leading them into potentially hazardous situations, resist meddling in their relationships.

If you suspect that risky behavior is involved, remind your children about your clear, firm rules.

***Example:*** When my kids wanted to go along with peer pressure, a phrase we used was, "Safety is a nonnegotiable issue in this family."

Otherwise, allow children opportunities to negotiate their own issues and differences. Kids need time among themselves to learn how to develop their own rules, to share and take turns, to play fair and square, to recover from bruised egos.

Certainly there are times and places for adult supervision, but try to intervene selectively.

•**Listen to your child.** The stronger your children's self-confidence, the better they'll be able to resist negative influences of peers.

Help strengthen children's egos by listening attentively when they're having trouble with friends.

Don't jump right in with ready-made solutions or criticism. Invite children to tell you what happened before you overreact…and listen. They're not likely to open up if you go through the roof.

***Example:*** Your son comes home in tears because his friends ridiculed him for backing out of a scheme to shoplift.

Don't immediately yell, "You're not spending time with those kids ever again." Instead, listen to his anguish about being ridiculed. Encourage him to talk about his feelings, and praise him for being strong and taking an unpopular stand.

You might say, "I know that was tough. It took a lot of courage not to go along with the guys. I'm wondering, though, if these are kids you *really* enjoy being with."

Try to determine whether your child is afraid of being left out. If that's the problem, help build up his self-confidence by praising him when he shows independent thinking.

•**Encourage individuality.** Keep in mind that you and your child have different tastes and opinions.

He may be attracted to people to whom you don't relate at all, just as you and he probably don't share the same tastes in food, music or movies.

Try to respect your children's differences even when you don't like the friends they keep.

*Helpful:* Encourage children to make choices and solve problems...ask their opinions about people you meet, TV shows and articles and books you read together.

When your child mentions a new best friend, don't grill him with lots of intrusive questions. Withhold your judgment.

Even if you don't like his choice of friends, don't automatically denigrate him, especially without any evidence of harmful behavior.

•**Encourage children to stick up for themselves.** Help your children practice this skill by allowing them to disagree with you in reasonable ways. That doesn't mean tolerating sassy back talk or outright defiance, but it does mean supporting their self-expression.

*Example:* When your daughter insists that she must have a pair of expensive sneakers because all her friends are wearing them...or when she begs you to let her stay out with peers past her curfew...give her a chance to express her reasons for asking.

You don't have to agree, but show respect for her opinions. You might say, "Well, I'm ready to listen—try to convince me..." or "Let me hear your point of view..."

Even if you disagree with her, you are giving her opportunities to think for herself and evaluate her options.

If you decide that your child should not stay out past her curfew or that you cannot afford to buy her those expensive sneakers, reassure her that she can still be part of the group.

Point out that the other kids will still invite her to play basketball in her old sneakers or that she'll be able to go off with her friends on other excursions—even though she must be home by 9 pm on this particular night.

By supporting children in voicing and defending their opinions, you help them practice a skill that they can also use with their peers.

They will become more confident about saying no the next time friends try to lead them toward misbehavior or toward values that are unacceptable to you.

---

# Better Photos of Young Children

Use natural light for more realism—and to avoid startling a child with a flash. Move in close. Keep the camera at the child's level. Use ISO 100 or 200 film for outdoor shots...and ISO 400 for indoor shots without a flash. Take lots of pictures—you will need many shots of a scene to get one outstanding one. Be creative—try a shot of your baby's hand next to yours or a close-up of the child sleeping.

*Capturing Childhood Memories* by Samuel Thaler, professional photographer, Santa Cruz, CA. Berkley Books.

---

# The Right Questions to Ask to Find the Right Summer Camp

Richard Kennedy, director of Kieve Science Camp for Girls, Nobleboro, ME. He has been a sleepaway camp director since 1959 and is author of *Choosing the Right Camp,* available at local libraries.

Parents looking for the right summer camp for their children need to begin the investigative process early.

Questions to ask the camp director that go beyond the obvious and reveal the most telling information...

●**What is the greatest success the camp has ever had? What is the greatest problem?** Actually, the first question is just to get the camp director talking. The answer to the second question is more important. Any camp director who has been in the business for five years or more will have dealt with a serious problem.

*Examples:* Perhaps a child ran away from the camp or a counselor was discovered using drugs.

If a camp director says he/she never had a serious problem at the camp or talks about a problem that sounds lightweight, I would tend not to believe him.

I wouldn't send my child to a camp where I couldn't completely trust the camp director to be honest with me.

●**How do you handle troublesome children?** If a camp director hesitates when answering this question, there probably isn't an official policy.

I like to hear camp directors say that their process of dealing with troublemakers involves not just the camp director but also the camper, his parents and the counselor.

Whatever the policy, make sure it is official and written down...provided to all campers and their parents...and enforced consistently.

●**What percentage of campers come back for another year?** Anything over 50% is a good sign. This is one of the best ways to judge whether children are likely to enjoy their time at the camp.

While it's impossible to know for sure whether you're being told the truth, you can ask for the names and numbers of five campers who returned last year. Then call those campers' parents and ask whether their child's friends came back too. If they did, there were probably a large number of returning campers.

It also pays to ask campers' parents for the camp's biggest faults. Even if their answers are slight and do not justify ruling out the camp, it's better to know about even the small problems in advance.

●**What percentage of your counselors started out as campers at your camp?** If more than 50% of the counselors were campers,

it's a good indication that the camp's culture is positive and nurturing.

Ask for the names and numbers of five counselors. Then ask these counselors about their academic and personal backgrounds as well as their aspirations. Think of the conversation as if you were interviewing people for a job.

●**How is the staff trained?** At least three to five days of counselor training is necessary, in my experience.

One of the most important skills is the ability to understand the subtle differences when working with children of different ages.

*Example:* You can't deal with an eight-year-old the same way that you deal with a 12-year-old and expect to get the same results.

Ask the camp director whether such issues are covered during counselor training.

●**How do you deal with homesickness?** When homesickness develops, good camps assign a counselor as a "case manager." This counselor then makes it his responsibility to see that the homesick child fits in with the group. Usually, the counselor will do this by enlisting the help of a second camper.

He will explain to the second camper that the homesick camper is feeling a bit down. Then he'll ask the second camper to go out of his way to be a friend.

---

# What Parents Need to Know About Children's Nutrition Now

William V. Tamborlane, MD, professor of pediatrics and chief of pediatric endocrinology at Yale University School of Medicine, New Haven, CT. He is editor of *The Yale Guide to Children's Nutrition*. Yale University Press.

Modern living creates special challenges for busy parents who are concerned about their children's food choices and eating habits.

Pediatrician William V. Tamborlane, MD, answers some important questions on children's nutrition...

●**What can parents do to get children to eat a good breakfast when they say they're not hungry in the morning?** Some children *aren't* hungry when they first wake up. Their appetites surface around midmorning.

Don't insist that children eat breakfast before they leave the house. It's a losing battle. Instead, pack snacks for them to eat in the car or on the bus on their way to school or at around 9 am or 10 am.

A low-fat granola bar and a juice box is an excellent morning snack. So is cheese with crackers and a piece of fruit.

●**Should parents of picky eaters let their kids eat what they want and hope they'll get the nutrition they need?** There's no need to micromanage your child's eating. All children have an internal food regulator that tells them what and when to eat. Much of our appetite is actually genetically programmed and operates on a subconscious level.

I wouldn't worry if a child's appetite seems small or if he/she insists on eating the same foods over and over again. Such food fads will change or disappear over time.

Even though there may be day-to-day variations in food intake, almost all kids, left to their own devices, will satisfy their nutritional needs over the course of a few days to a week. Research also indicates that children's day-to-day variations in appetite probably relate to their calorie expenditures the day before. If they were very active yesterday, they're likely to be ravenous today.

*My best advice:* Stock your kitchen with a variety of nutritious foods...provide balanced meals...and let your children eat as they desire. Forcing them to eat foods they don't like only makes them more resistant.

●**What can I do when children object to eating vegetables?** Substitute fruit, or try giving them more selections from the grain, cereal, rice and pasta group. This will provide some of the minerals, trace nutrients and fiber they are missing by not eating vegetables.

I still suggest, however, that you offer children vegetables at most meals—especially in combination with foods they like. You could also offer raw instead of cooked vegetables with or without sauces. Or simply serve the one favorite vegetable they will eat over and over again.

*Example:* My teenage son only eats salad, so we make sure to have that with dinner every night.

●**How many sweets a day should I allow my child?** Don't exclude cookies or candy from a child's diet. But—don't use them as a reward for good behavior. Those rules only make these "forbidden" foods more attractive.

The goal is to make sweets a small but acceptable part of a total diet. I think a few cookies a day to satisfy the sweet tooth is fine. Also encourage your children to get more physical activity. Have them get out and play...ride bikes...jump rope...hike...or play team sports.

An active lifestyle helps children manage their weight and increases the chance that they'll be hungry come dinnertime.

You, too, should get into the habit of exercise if you don't already work out. You have a wonderful opportunity to help your youngsters learn good eating and exercise habits by setting a good example.

●**Do children need a daily multivitamin supplement?** For children who eat varied and balanced diets, vitamin supplements are not necessary.

However, if children are finicky eaters or they won't eat breakfast, it won't do them any harm to give them a multivitamin/mineral supplement.

Any of the leading brands of children's vitamins is fine, but be sure the supplement you choose contains iron and calcium. These are two minerals in which children's diets may be deficient.

Give the supplement at breakfast or dinner. Food helps the body to better absorb vitamins and minerals.

# Better Bedtimes

Help children sleep better by being firm about bedtime. Children whose parents do not enforce discipline are more likely to delay bedtime, wake up often during the night and have daytime behavior problems. *Average sleep needs for kids:* Ages three to seven, 10 to 12 hours per night...older children, nine to 10 hours per night.

Judith Owens, MD, director, Pediatric Sleep Disorders Clinic, Hasbro Children's Hospital, Providence, RI.

## Better Baby-Sitting Alternative

Swap baby-sitting with friends. The cash cost is zero—and you will have the peace of mind of knowing that your children are happy playing with their friends.

Robin Gagliardi, contributing writer, *The Pocket Change Investor*, Box 78, Elizaville, NY 12523.

## Sports Benefit Teen Girls In Many Ways

Benefits of sports for teen girls extend well beyond exercise and physical fitness. Teenage girls who play sports tend to start sexual activity later...and are less than half as likely to get pregnant during the teenage years as girls not involved in sports.

**Possible reason:** They have higher self-esteem and are more confident making sexual choices that further long-range goals.

**But:** Teenage *boys* who participate in sports do not show a significant change in sexual behavior.

Don Sabo, PhD, project director, Women's Sports Foundation Teen Pregnancy Study, East Meadow, NY.

## Secondhand Smoke and Ear Infections

Children whose parents smoke are *twice* as likely as other kids to have chronic ear infections. The link between secondhand smoke and ear infection (otitis media) has long been controversial. But a recent study is the fifth since 1995 to support a connection. *Bottom line:* If you smoke and have young children, quit. If you can't quit, at least make sure that your home and car are smoke-free.

Carol E. Adair, PhD, pediatric epidemiologist, Child Health Research Unit, Alberta Children's Hospital, Calgary, Alberta, Canada.

## How to Make Rooms Seem Larger

If you want to make a small room appear larger, get rid of draperies so more light gets in...add a skylight...get rid of an acoustic ceiling, and replace it with a plain white one, to reflect more light. If a room has a blank wall that faces east, south or west, consider adding windows. Even a horizontal window strip near the ceiling or narrow vertical bands in corners will expand the room visually. *To add special character as well as light:* Consider a bay window, which has three faces...or a *bow* window, which has any number of faces arranged in an arc.

Arrol Gellner, architecture columnist, writing in the *Chicago Tribune.*

## Home Savvy from Real Estate Attorney David Schechner

David Schechner, real estate attorney, Schechner & Targan, 80 Main St., West Orange, NJ 07052.

### Better Remodeling...

When remodeling, you, not the contractor, should be in control of the money. *How...*

•**Have a complete written job description**—including start, finish and milestone dates. Release 90% of the money due only when milestones are met to your satisfaction. This creates a 10% cushion to secure final work.

●**Pay suppliers directly,** rather than giving money to the contractor to give to them. If that is not possible, insist that no payment be made unless the contractor supplies an affidavit that all supplies have been paid to date. If you pay the contractor and he/she fails to pay suppliers, they can put a lien on your home.

***When remodeling is completed:*** Do not pay the withheld 10% unless you receive lien releases or fully paid receipts from all suppliers and subcontractors—and the general contractor, too. If the work costs more than $10,000, you probably should have a lien search done by a local agency for peace of mind.

More from David Schechner...

## Shrewder Home Selling

Buyers often want to sign a "contingent contract," which says that if their home cannot be sold by a certain date, the agreement to buy is null and void and they will get their deposit back.

***Result:*** Lost time if the buyer backs out of the deal.

***Self-defense:*** Consider having an attorney add a "kick-out" clause to the contract. That allows the seller to continue marketing the home. If a second buyer is interested, the first buyer has a set amount of time—usually not more than 24 hours—to remove the contingency clause and keep the contract alive.

# Pools Make Poor Investments

Most home owners recover only half of what they spend to install a pool. Some homes, however, are expected to have them—particularly expensive houses and those located in places like southern California and Florida. *Costs:* $20,000 to $25,000 for an average-size pool, plus another $1,500 or more for

fencing. Pool services cost several hundred dollars a season. *Important:* Be sure you have enough homeowner's or umbrella liability insurance to cover any accidents.

Stephen Elder, home inspector and home-repair columnist, Pittsboro, NC.

# How to Win the Bidding War for Your Perfect Home

Ralph Roberts, president of Ralph R. Roberts Real Estate, Inc., in Warren, MI. He is author of *Walk Like a Giant, Sell Like a Madman*. HarperBusiness.

With mortgage rates low and buyers hunting for larger homes, sellers are able to hold out for higher offers.

How to improve your odds of winning a bidding war...

●**Offer a bigger down payment.** Rather than offer more for the house, offer a larger deposit or a heftier down payment. Buyers making a larger down payment stand a much better chance of being approved by mortgage lenders.

And...you can improve your odds by offering more in the form of services rather than money.

***Examples:*** If you are an attorney, offer to draw up a will for the seller at no charge. If you are a florist, offer to deliver fresh flowers every Monday morning for the next six months.

●**Write a letter to the seller.** Money isn't everything. Sometimes a personal note can make all the difference, especially when the bid amounts are close.

***Example:*** Someone wrote, saying, "I'm a single parent with an eight-year-old daughter, and I know your house is in the best school district. I really love your house, and I hope you'll sell it to me."

The letter writer won. People want to know they're selling to a nice person, to someone who really cares about the house.

●**Offer free rent or 30 days free occupancy to the seller.** If you are flexible, it could make a big difference. Delaying the closing would cause problems. By letting them stay even after you take title, you could clinch the deal.

●**Be preapproved for a mortgage.** You can't lock in a mortgage rate until you have an actual address to put on the loan document. But you can apply for a loan and use the certificate of preapproval as part of your offer, giving the seller one less thing to worry about.

With two similar offers, all other things being equal, most sellers will take the offer with a preapproved mortgage.

●**Be available immediately after your agent presents the offer.** Just being available to raise your bid, should that become necessary, may do the trick.

If another few thousand dollars will make the difference and two other agents can't reach their clients but yours can reach you, you stand a good chance of being the winner.

# Real Estate Expert Robert Irwin on Home Purchase and Sale Strategies

Robert Irwin, a real estate investor and broker in Los Angeles and one of the country's top authorities on residential home purchase and sale strategies. He is author of more than 50 books, including *Tips & Traps When Buying a Home.* McGraw–Hill.

## Few Real Estate Agents Are as Helpful As They Could Be

With mortgage rates low and employment up, growing numbers of people are able to buy homes. So, there now are more house buyers than sellers.

*Trap:* In the race to keep up with demand, some real estate brokers may not tell you the full story about the homes you're seeing.

Here's what you need to learn on your own, and how to get the information…

●**Find out if the neighborhood is safe.** Most agents won't tell you if a neighborhood is unsafe…because under the 1988 Fair Housing Act, it's unsafe for them to tell you.

The act bars agents from steering people away from neighborhoods because of racial, religious or other characteristics. If they say a neighborhood is bad, it could later be interpreted as steering.

Agents also will not tell you that a neighborhood is safe. If a buyer is later the victim of a crime, the agent could be open to a lawsuit.

*Helpful:* Call the local police department's community relations officer and ask for local crime statistics, which are public record. A modern computerized department will be able to break down neighborhoods by blocks, and tell you how frequently police are called and what crimes have been reported.

●**Usually the seller will take less than the asking price.** If you are dealing with the seller's agent, the agent has a fiduciary responsibility to get the highest possible offer…and to keep the lowest price the seller will accept confidential.

Ask the agent for a list of all comparable sales in the area over the past six months. Check out homes that are similar in size, amenities and location for an indication of the recent market price of the home you are considering.

Also, compare asking prices to sales prices. That will tell you by how much sellers are typically cutting their price to make sales.

Another option is to talk to the seller directly. Since a seller's bottom-line price is often a function of how much time he/she has to sell the house, innocuous questions can reveal important information. *Ask directly…*

●Why are you selling this house? (A divorce or other pressing family situation can make a seller eager to sell.)

●How soon do you have to move?

●Have you found a new house yet?

●**Determine whether the home will increase in value.** Agents don't like to offer opinions on the future value of the home you are buying. They don't want you to come back to them later, saying, "You said it would go *up* in price. Instead it went down."

*Helpful:* Past history is an excellent way to size up how the home will appreciate. *Ask the agent for...*

• The price history of homes in the area over the past five years.

• The average time it has taken to sell a home—30 to 60 days is reasonable in a good market.

• The average difference between asking price and selling price, which tells you whether sellers are getting their price, or that they have to discount deeply to get a sale.

• Whether the mean price of homes in the area has moved up, and if so, how quickly.

• **Evaluate whether the home inspector is biased.** A good real estate agent will recommend a thorough home inspection to protect you. But an agent in search of a quick sale might recommend an inspector who passes over things to speed up the process.

Home inspectors are not licensed in most states, so performance varies.

*Better:* Get referrals to an inspector who is independent of the agent.

Don't use an inspector recommended by a real estate agent unless he is a member of a recognized trade group, such as the American Society of Home Inspectors.

Before signing with any inspector, insist on getting a list of three previous inspections conducted within the last year. Call those home buyers and ask them if they've found any problems that the inspector didn't detect or mention.

Most big problems crop up within six months of a move into a new home.

• **Find out whether there's a problem with the house.** In 28 states, sellers are not required by law to provide disclosure statements to buyers at or near the time the parties sign a purchase agreement.

In all 50 states, however, agents are required to pass along whatever problems the seller has disclosed, as well as to disclose problems that they themselves can see.

But unless they are required to give information about a problem, sellers and agents may not do so.

*Helpful:* Call the local building department and ask to see the full permit reports of the house, which are public record. They will reveal major work done.

Check heaters, air conditioners and other equipment for labels pasted on by repair companies. Call those companies to see what work was done. They keep records of jobs. These records could form the basis of a claim for a seller's or agent's failure to disclose a problem.

Also, ask the agent to disclose any known defects in writing. If the agent fails to disclose a problem that he knew about or should have known about, it could later help in pressing a claim against the agent as well as the seller.

---

**More from Robert Irwin...**

# When to Reconsider The Deal

When buying or selling a home, remember that finding the right house —or buyer—is just the first step. *What's left:* Negotiating a deal you can live with. Deals you *shouldn't* live with...

### SELLER BEWARE

• **Buyer wants the purchase to be contingent on the sale of his/her old house.**

*Best:* Walk away. *Reason:* If you agree, you now have two houses to worry about selling— yours and the buyer's.

In general, you can walk away with no strings attached only before everyone has signed the purchase contract.

*Alternative:* Insist on the right to show your house and accept other offers...but give this buyer first refusal if another offer comes in.

• **Buyer puts up a smaller deposit than you want...or no deposit at all.**

*Best:* Walk away. *Reason:* Buyer may back out, feeling he has little to lose.

*Alternative:* Often the buyer is simply wary of the home's condition. Ask him/her to increase the deposit after he approves the inspection and disclosures.

• **Buyer insists on right at final walk-through to refuse to buy your home for *any* reason.**

**Best:** Walk away. *Reason:* This means that when you're ready to close, the buyer can disapprove of the house and not buy it.

The *final* walk-through should be used just to check that the home is in the same condition as when the contract was signed. Beware of language that allows the buyer to back out without a reasonable cause.

**•Buyer has no loan preapproval.** Maybe he can get financing, maybe not.

**Best:** Give the buyer two weeks to secure lender approval. You're tying up your home for only a short time, and he may turn out to be a good buyer.

**•Buyer wants you to offer financing.** That means you'd give him a mortgage.

**Best:** Walk away—unless you planned to put the money from the sale in the bank anyhow. If so, give the buyer a higher than market interest rate loan after approving his credit/income history.

### BUYER BEWARE

**•Seller wants to eliminate the mortgage contingency clause,** which makes your promise to buy the house dependent on getting an acceptable mortgage.

**Best:** Walk away. If you can't get a mortgage, you could lose your deposit. You need this protection.

**•Seller refuses to allow inspection or provide disclosures.**

**Best:** Walk away. The seller may be hiding serious defects.

**•Seller wants to sell "as is."** That means that he won't fix anything.

**Best:** Insist that seller make full disclosure and allow for inspection. You may still want to buy the house if it's not too bad…and the seller reduces the price.

**•Seller will not agree to a liquidated damages clause.** Liquidated damages are money amounts that the parties have agreed are payable for a breach of the contract. If the seller won't agree to liquidated damages if you default, he's reserving the right to take legal action if you can't complete the deal…in addition to keeping your deposit.

**Best:** Walk away. It will be too hard to get out of the deal if you need to.

**Alternative:** Offer to increase your deposit if seller will agree to a liquidated damages clause.

**•Seller refuses to allow a contingency on the sale of your home, and you haven't sold it.**

**Best:** If you can't pay two mortgages at once, walk away. If you can, and this is truly the house for you, buy the new home without selling your existing property.

---

**Self-Defense from Robert Irwin…**

## New Home-Buying/Selling Trap

Some brokers have introduced transaction fees—also called document fees—to offset the cost of paperwork. Ranging from $110 to $150, fees are due at closing from whoever signs a brokerage contract, which means buyers and sellers both get hit.

**Self-defense:** Not all brokerages charge the fees. Find one that does not…or ask to have fees taken out of the contract.

---

# Keith Gumbinger On Mortgages

Keith Gumbinger, vice president of HSH Associates, a publisher of mortgage information, 1200 Rte. 23, Butler, NJ 07405.

---

## Mortgage Borrowers Beware

More and more lenders are setting interest rates according to the borrower's credit score. The worse your score, the higher the rate. Lenders do not reveal the formula they use for "risk-based lending," and they may not specify the rate until after the approval process. *Self-defense:* Check your rating with the major credit bureaus *before* you apply for a mortgage…correct any errors…and close any unused credit lines. And—be prudent in your use of credit to keep your record clean.

**More from Keith Gumbinger...**

## Private Mortgage Insurance Alternatives

Alternatives to paying Private Mortgage Insurance (PMI) for people putting down only 10% of the cost of a home...

•*Piggyback loans,* also called 80-10-10 loans, include a 10% down payment, an 80% first mortgage and a 10% second mortgage at a higher rate.

•*Prepaid PMI* includes a lump-sum payment up front for PMI—which lenders require for loans of more than 80% of home value. The payment can be financed as part of the total loan.

**Keith Gumbinger on How to Choose a Mortgage...**

## Shopping for Your Mortgage

Mortgage brokers are independent agents who currently originate about half of all mortgages. Depending upon who pays for the service, they may work for you or for the lenders they represent. Unscrupulous brokers may take advantage of unsuspecting borrowers by bumping up the bank's interest rates or fees and pocketing the difference. *Self-defense:* Comparison shop. First determine what loan program you need and what fees you can afford to pay, then have each broker and lender you contact spell out all the terms for you.

# Better Mortgage Shopping

Find out how and by whom the mortgage broker is paid. Before applying for a loan ask the loan officer to choose one of the following three disclosures...

•I represent you and will charge you a fee...

•I do not represent you, but will be paid as an employee or agent of a lender...

•I arrange mortgage financing and may be paid by both lenders and borrowers.

A broker who agrees to represent you—and who can deliver the best rate and terms—is your best financial choice.

Peter G. Miller, real estate broker and author of *Buy Your First Home Now.* HarperCollins.

# Before You Sign Your Lease

While rental agents may be quick to say problems with an apartment or house will be fixed, once you have signed the lease, management has no incentive to follow through.

***Strategy:*** Don't sign anything—an application or a lease—that doesn't include a contingency clause basing the lease on the problem being fixed to your satisfaction before the starting date of the lease. Make the cutoff date enough in advance so you can find a suitable alternative space. The clause should state that the execution of the lease is contingent upon the work being completed within a set period of time. If the work isn't completed, the contract should state that your deposit will be returned in full on the spot.

Ed Sacks, a landlord–tenant relations columnist for the *Chicago Sun-Times* and a certified mediator with the Center for Conflict Resolution in Chicago. He is author of *The Renters' Survival Kit.* Dearborn Financial Publishers.

# 4

# Better Money Management

---

## Money Mistakes We Can't Afford to Make Anymore

**P**eople work hard so they can retire in comfort and provide for their heirs. But far too often, upon attaining that goal, they take a financial misstep that causes them enormous harm.

One very obvious mistake is being inadequately protected against a market crash. *There are many others...*

### YOU AND YOUR ADVISER

•**Perils of turning over cash.** I've heard so many horror stories about investors who handed cash to a financial "professional" and lost everything. Don't do it!

•**Never ever sign blank papers or documents that you don't understand.** If you're not sure what something means, ask your lawyer or accountant to review the document.

•**Understand how a broker or financial planner makes money.** He/she may charge a flat fee, hourly rate, percentage of assets or commissions—or all of the above. Sometimes, the compensation method can cause an adviser to do things that are not in your best interest.

•**Never select an adviser without first checking** with the National Association of Securities Dealers (NASD) Disclosure Program (800-289-9999). The NASD will tell you if the adviser's background checks out and whether he has been subject to any disciplinary actions or criminal investigations.

•**Only sign an account agreement** giving the adviser investment power when you absolutely trust him—*and* when the adviser is not compensated by commissions.

•**Monitor financial statements closely** to be sure your assets are where you think they are.

•**Calculate your annual return at least four times a year.** If you're badly lagging the overall market, be sure to find out why.

---

Suze Orman, a certified financial planner in Emeryville, CA, and author of *You've Earned It, Don't Lose It* (Newmarket) and the national best-seller *The 9 Steps to Financial Freedom* (Crown).

***Bottom line:*** You can never ask too many questions, only too few. If the explanation is unsatisfactory or the disappointing performance continues, consider switching advisers.

### MORE THAN A WILL

You don't have to be rich to need a *trust.* Often, it's people who aren't rich who need one most.

***Problem:*** Say you live in California and own a home worth $200,000. Your will leaves the home to your daughter. When you die, your daughter can't get the home until she pays probate fees of $10,300 (4% to 5% in most states). If she doesn't have the money, she'll have to sell the home.

***Solution:*** A *revocable living trust.* It allows your heirs to avoid probate fees, as well as the hassle and cost of court. With this type of trust, you retain control of the assets. *Required:* A lawyer who specializes in trusts.

***Cost:*** Less than $1,500, higher if you have many assets (multiple homes, etc.).

***Key:*** You can change the trust at any time by paying a small fee.

### THE A-B TRUST

If you have substantial assets you may need an *A-B trust.*

A revocable living trust eliminates probate fees, court costs and delays, but does not by itself reduce estate tax liability.

An A-B trust, though, can double the amount you and your spouse can leave to beneficiaries free of estate tax. By 2006, you will be able to shelter up to $2 million from estate tax.

***How it works:*** Assume the first spouse dies in 1999. His half of a $1.3 million estate passes into the B trust rather than directly to the surviving spouse. It is not taxed because it is equal to the applicable $650,000 exclusion amount (the exclusion amount in 2000 rises to $675,000). The surviving spouse can be the trustee and receive all the income, and in many circumstances the principal, the trust provides. The rest of the assets remain in the A trust and qualify for the estate tax marital deduction.

When the second spouse dies, the B trust passes directly to the beneficiaries. It is never part of the surviving spouse's estate, so it isn't subject to estate taxes. (The second spouse's estate, which includes the A trust, also has the benefit of an applicable exclusion amount to reduce or entirely avoid taxes.)

***Cost:*** $1,000 to $2,000. *Note:* A testamentary A-B trust (one that is incorporated into your will) would still have to be probated, so you may not want to do it that way.

### JOINT TENANCY TRAPS

Joint tenancy can sometimes cause huge problems.

***Trap 1:*** To avoid probate, a widow might decide to hold her home in joint tenancy with her only child. If the child injures someone—for instance in a car accident—that person could sue. The home would then be considered part of the child's assets. If he lost the case, his mother could lose her house.

***Trap 2:*** A widow remarries and then buys a new home, which she leaves to her children in a will. So, if she holds the home in joint tenancy with her new husband, that legal fact overrides her will if she dies first. The house passes to the spouse, not to her beneficiaries.

A solution to this would be to put the title of the house in a QTIP (Qualified Terminable Interest Property) trust, which will allow her spouse to live in the house for as long as he wants. Upon his death, the house passes immediately to the children.

---

# Where to Look for Money You Didn't Know You Had

David W. Folsom, author of *Assets Unknown: How to Find Money You Didn't Know You Had.* Two Dot Press.

---

Thousands of people die every day with assets their heirs never know about. And about 95% of unclaimed assets have no statute of limitations. If you think you might be an heir to hidden assets—you can track them down on your own.

### FAMILY TREES

Often a person wills his/her estate to someone who doesn't know he is an heir. If the heir dies before the estate can track him down, then that person's heirs may have a claim against the original estate.

### STEPS TO A SUCCESSFUL SEARCH

•**Check death records.** Deaths are first recorded by the county where the person died and by the state's office of vital statistics within 12 months.

•**Check probate records.** They are available to the public in all states. Ask for a list of the deceased person's estate inventory. The list may contain information about stocks or privately held companies through which he owned other assets.

•**Establish heirship.** That's necessary for access to many types of personal data, including bank accounts and financial records. You need proof of heirship to make a claim to an estate.

*To prove heirship:* You need certified records, not photocopies, that link you with the deceased relative. Usually only the original issuing agencies can provide certified records.

*Examples:* Birth and death certificates, marriage licenses and military identification.

•**Track down the relative's Social Security number.** The number usually becomes public information upon death and is sometimes found on death certificates.

The IRS requires banks and other institutions to list the Social Security number on all accounts. Since many states put Social Security numbers on driver's licenses, the easiest way to learn the number is simply to find the relative's license.

*Inside maneuver:* If you have trouble finding a deceased person's Social Security number, ask your auto insurance agent to check the person's name through the company's computer database that it uses to check on driving records.

•**Look through bank records.** When you produce proof of heirship, banks generally let you go through the deceased relative's canceled checks. They can be useful clues to other assets, such as insurance policies, brokerage accounts and out-of-state property.

•**Check the state's unclaimed property office.** If your claim is uncontested and your proof of heirship is in order, most offices will turn the assets over to you within 30 to 45 days.

To claim other property, go to the probate court in the jurisdiction where your relative died. Here the procedure usually takes three to four months.

Since most probate court clerks will help you fill out the appropriate forms, you probably won't need an attorney.

But if the estate is complex, it may be wise to consult a lawyer. If you do retain an attorney, most states limit lawyer's fees to 10% of the estate's value.

During your search, don't be overly concerned if you discover other legitimate claimants. At worst, you may have to share the estate with them.

---

# New Money-Management Rule

The long-standing money-management rule of thumb—keeping assets you plan to spend within three years *out* of the stock market and *in* cash or cash-equivalent holdings like money market funds—is no longer valid.

*Better:* If you plan to sell an investment within *four to five years* to pay tuition...to make a down payment on a home, etc., consider moving that money to a conservative alternative.

*Reason:* When the market dips, you won't be tempted to bail out of stocks and then figure out when to get back in.

*Ray Martin, CFP, a principal in State Street Global Advisors, a global investment firm in Quincy, MA, and a financial contributor to* NBC Today.

---

# All About Cash and How to Protect It

William E. Donoghue, author of *Mutual Fund Super-Stars*, publisher of *Donoghue's WealthLetter* and chairman of W.E. Donoghue & Co., Inc., registered investment advisers, Box 623, Milford, MA 01757. He is also author of *The Millennium Advantage: 100% Income Tax-Free Wealthbuilding*. Elliott & James.

If you intend to park your cash for a year to stay clear of the stock market, there are more profitable places to put it than bank CDs…

●**Pay down your outstanding credit card balances.** This may seem like an odd suggestion for cash. But if you have money to spare and have an unpaid balance on your credit card, paying off that balance is the best use of cash.

The interest you pay on such debts can be as high as 19%. Eliminating this nondeductible debt is the equivalent of making an investment that yields 30%. No investment today can beat that rate…without subjecting your investment to great risk.

●**Keep money in a money market mutual fund—at virtually no risk.** No consumer has ever lost money in a modern money fund, so they are extra-safe accounts. They are also very convenient. Many financial services firms offer telephone exchange from your money fund when you are ready to reenter the stock or bond markets.

●**Stay away from most bond funds.** Bond funds can have load, volatility and yield risks. When interest rates are this low, even a 3% load is a very high price to pay for a government bond fund.

Just how many governments did your broker research for you to conclude that you should be in a US government bond fund?

While the trend of interest rates is down, it would not take much of an increase in rates to erode significantly a long-term bond portfolio's market value.

●**Be especially wary of insured municipal bonds,** which are only as good as the insurance companies that back them.

A study of these insurance companies indicates that the companies are grossly overrated.

If the insurance companies are overrated, the bonds that rely on their ratings for credibility are overpriced. A realistic valuation by the marketplace could cause investors to lose market value. Many insurance companies today would have a mediocre rating of BBB if they were rated realistically.

With three million bond issuers out there, it's difficult to get accurate information on each one. There is also no reliable secondary market if you want to sell before your insured municipal bonds mature. It will be especially difficult to sell if the bonds' ratings are lowered.

●**Try a high-yield (junk) bond fund—if you can stomach a bit more volatility.** Junk bond funds offer attractive returns and appreciate as the economy recovers and their issuers' credit ratings improve.

*Top choices…*

●*Northeast Investors Trust,* a five-star Morningstar high-yield bond fund with a low Morningstar risk ratio and a high Morningstar return ratio, is an excellent choice. It clearly stands out among bond funds as a great value. 800-225-6704.

●*Fidelity Capital & Income Fund.* 800-544-8888.

●*T. Rowe Price High-Yield Fund.* 800-638-5660.

●*Vanguard Fixed Income Securities Fund–High Yield Corporate Portfolio.* 800-523-7731.

# Biggest Mistakes People Make with Financial Windfalls

William G. Brennan, CPA/PFS, CFP, Columbia Financial Advisors, LLP, 1730 Rhode Island Ave. NW, Suite 800, Washington, DC 20036. Mr. Brennan is a widely quoted expert who has written extensively on income tax and investment planning.

People are coming into large financial windfalls every day in many different ways.

**Problem:** Few people have experience handling large sums of money. Just one stupid move could wipe out what should have been a lifetime of financial security.

*Key mistakes to avoid if you want your windfall to remain intact...*

**Mistake 1: Leaping into investments without first making a comprehensive financial plan.** *Example:* You may be tempted to rush out and buy annuities with your money because you've heard tax is deferred on the income. *Catch:* Once you've put your money in an annuity, steep surrender charges make it difficult to get out. This is something you need to know before you invest in an annuity.

*Defense:* Learn as much as you can about your investment options before you commit your money. While you're studying, though, put your windfall to work for you right away.

*Best choice:* A money market mutual fund where you'll earn interest and not have to pay anything to transfer your funds to other investments once you settle on a financial strategy.

Keep in mind that it could take you six months to devise an investment plan that makes sense to you.

*Alternative temporary investment:* Treasury bills of one year or less. You'll earn interest without tying up money for a long time.

**Mistake 2: Taking bad advice.** People who come into windfalls get advice whether they ask for it or not. The neighbor at a cocktail party, the barber or a cousin may be quick to steer you into one type of investment or another.

*Defense:* Ask a financial adviser, who is an expert in individual tax and finance. The adviser will take an overall view of your new financial picture and chart a course to follow. The consultation can be a one-time thing or the start of an ongoing arrangement to monitor your investments.

Some people may be hesitant to pay for financial advice. But you can easily lose far more than the amount of the fees by following unsolicited advice of friends, family and coworkers.

**Mistake 3: Being too conservative with investments.** Some people who come into unexpected wealth are overly concerned with

preserving capital. They may seek only fixed-income investments, such as Treasury bonds, that guarantee return of principal. The result often is that their investment returns, after inflation and taxes, do not meet their personal and financial goals.

*Defense:* Invest a significant portion (the size of the portion varies with a person's age, risk tolerance and other factors) in equities. It's generally a good idea to use mutual funds for equity investments since the funds have professional management. If your windfall is big enough, you could hire a personal investment manager.

For those who are uncomfortable committing large sums all at once or are anxious to reduce short-term risk, consider "dollar cost averaging." This is simply an investment approach that commits a small amount on a regular basis with the thought that fluctuations in the price of the stock or mutual fund will average out over the long run.

*Example:* Someone with $250,000 can dollar cost average with monthly investments of about $20,000 over the course of one year. It's easier, and in a volatile market more prudent, for someone to commit to a $20,000 investment than to a $250,000 investment. And it gives the person the opportunity to monitor each month how the investment is doing.

**Mistake 4: Investing in mutual funds that produce significant income tax liability.** People who come into windfalls may never have had to be concerned with income taxes before. They may have been in a lower tax bracket and never had much investment income. Now, taxes on investment income will need to be considered.

*Defense:* Invest in "tax sensitive" mutual funds that generate little or no dividends or capital gains because the fund manager does not turn over the portfolio frequently or balances recognized gains with losses.

These types of funds stress long-term growth. To generate cash, you can always sell some shares—hopefully at favorable long-term capital gains rates. One example of a "tax sensitive" mutual fund is an "index fund," one that tracks the Dow or the S&P 500.

The same reasoning holds true for investments in stocks. Plan to buy and hold for long-term growth.

***Mistake 5:*** **Aggressively making gifts to reduce the size of your taxable estate.** It's true that people with windfalls may have estate tax concerns that they never had before. And making gifts up to the annual exclusion ($10,000 per recipient, or $20,000 if a spouse consents to such a gift) will reduce the estate. But rushing ahead with a gift-giving program can leave the windfall recipient short on income.

***Defense:*** Devise a financial plan that projects how much income is necessary to support the standard of living you desire. After investments are in place to produce this income, estate planning with gifts can be explored.

An aggressive gift-giving program for a couple in their 40s who inherit $1 million may not be advisable since they can expect to live for another 40 years or so. In contrast, such a program should certainly be advisable for a couple in their 70s who inherit $10 million.

Once it's determined that gifting is a good idea, you need to decide how best to do it. Making $20,000 spousal gifts to children each year into a custodial account set up under the Uniform Gifts to Minors Act (UGMA) or the Uniform Transfers to Minors Act (UTMA) may be the simplest way to meet your goals.

***Caution:*** At age 18 (or age 21, depending upon state law), the child will have unfettered control of the funds which, in 10 years of smart investments such as with growth mutual funds, could easily double in value from $200,000 to $400,000.

***Option:*** If that thought frightens you, consider setting up a trust to receive your $20,000 annual gifts. The terms of the trust can control under what circumstances the child can receive distributions. But be careful. Restricting your children's access to the funds, once they legally become adults, could jeopardize your annual gift tax exclusion.

# Credit Card Savvy From Robert McKinley

Robert McKinley, president, CardWeb, Inc., Box 3966, 1270 Fairfield Rd., Suite 51, Gettysburg, PA 17325. He is also publisher of *CardTrak*, a newsletter listing the best credit card deals in the US.

## New Credit Card Tricks and Traps

When switching credit cards, watch out for the hidden penalties and restrictions that card issuers are increasingly adding to boost their revenues.

*Here are the biggest traps now—and ways to avoid them...*

### DISCLOSURE-BOX RED FLAGS

***Trap:*** **Not reading the disclosure box.** It's on the back of all credit card applications. Fewer than 10% of consumers read these boxes. If you don't, you can end up paying unexpected fees if you violate a card company's agreement.

***Trap:*** **No mention of a grace period in the disclosure box.** More than 90% of credit card issuers offer a grace period of about 25 days, which means that you have 25 days to pay without being charged interest.

***Caution:*** Stay away from any card that doesn't mention a grace period. When there is no grace period, interest starts the day you make a purchase—and you are charged interest on all charges...even if you pay in full.

***Trap:*** **High annual fees.** Today, it's easy to find a no-fee credit card with a decent interest rate...or a low-fee card with a very good interest rate.

***Exception:*** If the issuer does charge a high fee, determine if there are enough benefits to justify the rate.

***Example:*** Airline rebate cards charge annual fees of $35 to $100. To make the deal worthwhile, you must charge $1,750 to $5,000 a year on the card...not carry a balance...and use all of your miles *before* they start to expire.

***Trap:*** **Very low interest rate.** If the rate is lower than 10%, it could be an introductory rate offered only for a short time.

The card issuer must disclose how long the rate lasts…and what the rate *will be.* A 5.9% rate that jumps to 18.4% after six months is a bad deal—unless you're sure you'll pay all charges before the high rate kicks in.

*Smart move:* If the difference between a card's introductory rate and its long-term rate is greater than six points, look for a better deal.

*Trap:* **Any type of penalty interest.** Beware of disclosure boxes that tell you a higher interest rate kicks in if you don't meet your account's requirements, which are not always clearly spelled out. You may not learn that your rate has increased—until you get a bill that includes the new rate.

*Self-defense: Before* signing up, call the issuer to ask about penalties.

*Trap:* **A "two-cycle average daily balance" method.** If this phrase appears on the disclosure box, throw the application away. This method is the sum of the average daily balances for two billing cycles.

More than 85% of the industry uses a method that calculates the balance by adding all new purchases to the outstanding debt and then dividing by the number of days in the billing cycles. This is the preferred method.

### CARDS WITH FAVORABLE TERMS

At press time, these cards offer some of the lowest rates—and none of the problems cited above…

•**AFBA Industrial Bank** (800-776-2265) has a variable rate based on the prime rate—currently 11.40%…and no annual fee.

•**People's Bank** (800-426-1114) offers a fixed rate of 13.9%. *Annual fee:* $25/standard card…$40/gold card.

•**Wachovia First Year Prime** (800-241-7990). Current introductory rate is 7.75% for the first year. Then it rises to prime plus 6.90%. There's no annual fee.

---

**More from Robert McKinley…**

## Low Long-Term Credit Card Rates

There are some new, lower credit card rates that are not just teasers that expire in a few months. Some card issuers are now promising long-term low rates. *Examples:* Major card issuers Capital One and First USA both offer no-annual-fee cards with fixed rates of less than 10% a year—for customers with excellent credit and payment records. *More information:* Capital One, 800-738-9717…First USA, 800-451-2491.

---

**High Interest Rate Self-Defense from Robert McKinley…**

## Don't Accept Higher Interest Rate

If your credit card issuer announces a rate increase, tell the issuer in writing that you refuse to accept the higher rate. You can then keep making payments at the old rate until your account is paid off. *Caution:* Any new purchases will be charged the higher rate. Refusal of the rate change means you are, in effect, closing the account—but with 7,000 card issuers in the US, it should not be hard to get a new one…at an attractive rate.

---

## 🐟 How to Beat Credit Card Companies At Their Own Game

Ken McEldowney, executive director of Consumer Action, a consumer education and advocacy group, 717 Market St., San Francisco 94103.

---

Fueled by the booming economy, credit card companies are rolling out ways to land new customers—and to make money off existing ones. *Here's how to avoid the troubles that credit cards may trigger…*

•*Trap:* **Your low introductory rate jumps 10 percentage points in six months.** Many people who transfer their debt to a low-rate credit card believe they will pay the debt off before the rate expires—but are often not able to do so.

*Better:* Look for cards that promise the same low rate until the balance you transferred is paid. You won't have to renegotiate rates or switch cards again in a few months.

●*Trap:* **You respond to mail that says you were preapproved for a low interest rate— but you wind up with a higher rate.** Credit issuers are allowed to rescreen your application after "preapproving" you, and may renege on a low-rate offer if you recently lost your job, moved, accepted another credit card or paid your bills late.

*Self-defense:* Get a copy of your credit report from a credit bureau such as Experian (800-301-7195). *Cost:* $8. Review the report for credit problems, and correct errors.

If your report is unblemished and nothing in your life has recently changed, you should be eligible for the low rate. Call the card issuer. Ask for the supervisor and explain that you were turned down for the card, even though your credit report is clean. Ask him/her to issue you the low-rate card.

*Important:* Never use a preapproved card without first reading your contract to determine the interest rate and other fees and conditions. Once you use the card, you've automatically agreed to its terms.

●*Trap:* **Being charged a "penalty" interest rate for a late payment on a new low-rate card.** If you make a late payment, many card issuers will bump up your interest rate to a higher "penalty" rate—even during an introductory low-rate period.

*Self-defense:* Before accepting any low-rate card, check out the issuer's penalty rate policy in the letter it sent you. Calculate how much a higher interest rate will add to your typical bill. If it's not a better deal than your current card, don't accept the new one.

●*Trap:* **Being charged for late payments.** In the past, you had a grace period of a few days after the due date before you were charged a late fee. Now some companies charge a fee if you're one day late.

*Self-defense:* Mail your check to the card company at least seven days before the payment due date.

●*Trap:* **Winding up with debt while trying to rack up frequent-flier miles.** Charging

everything you buy may seem a fast way to build up cash rebate points or frequent-flier miles. But you risk paying high interest charges on a sizable balance you can't pay off quickly.

*Example:* If you put a $700 suit on a 16% credit card, but do not pay it off for six months, the suit will cost you about $735.

Many cards limit the amount of points that can be earned per month. High annual fees and interest charges could cancel out any "free" tickets you finally earn.

●*Trap:* **Applying for more than one card to get the lowest rate.** The more cards you apply for—even preapproved ones—the less likely you are to get any.

*Reason:* More than one credit card "inquiry" on your credit report within a six-month period reduces your creditworthiness.

And—having cards with unused credit lines can affect your ability to get a loan. Lenders interpret credit lines as potential "outstanding" unpaid debts.

---

# How to Lower The Interest Rate on Your Credit Card

Todd Bierman, vice president of Credit Insider, a fee-based service that helps consumers correct credit problems, 164 Ogden Ave., Jersey City, NJ 07307. He is coauthor of *The Fix Your Credit Workbook: A Step by Step Guide to a Lifetime of Great Credit.* St. Martin's Press.

Whenever you apply for credit, your billing history, payment history and other data that appear on your credit report are analyzed by a computer.

*Result:* A *credit score,* which is the basis for your interest rate. *To improve your credit score before applying for a credit card...*

●**Order credit reports.** Review them carefully, and notify the credit bureaus* in writing if there are changes that need to be made.

*To receive your credit report or to dispute information, contact Experian, 800-301-7195...Trans Union, 800-916-8800...and Equifax, 800-685-1111.

●**Make sure credit bureaus have your correct address.** If credit bureaus have more than one address or an incorrect address, they will think that you move around a lot, which in turn can lower your score.

●**Don't use a post office box.** This signifies transience to credit-scoring companies.

●**Reduce the number of open credit lines.** Cancel cards you no longer use, even if you have paid off your balance in full.

●**Beware of mail offers that "guarantee" low introductory rates.** The standards that card issuers use to choose you as a candidate are far easier than those that come into play when you actually apply for the card.

Being rejected after applying for a card can hurt your credit score. Even if you are approved, once the introductory rate expires, your score will trigger a higher rate.

●**Once rejected, don't reapply for at least 45 days.** This allows time for changes to be made to your credit report before you reapply.

●**Question your score.** Call the issuer and ask for the person who can negotiate fee waivers and reduced rates.

# Fixed Credit Card Rates Can Go Up

All card issuers reserve the right to amend rates by giving cardholders 15 days' notice. Some cardholders find that their rates go up 50% from one billing period to the next—even though there has been no change in their credit status.

***Self-defense:*** Read bill inserts carefully for notices of changes in your cardholder agreement. Also watch out for separately mailed notices—they may look like junk mail. If your rate is raised, call and negotiate a lower one.

David Masten, publisher, *Credit Insider Magazine*, 164 Ogden Ave., Suite 203, Jersey City, NJ 07307.

# Credit Cautions

Gerri Detweiler, education adviser, Debt Counselors of America, a nonprofit organization, Box 8587, Gaithersburg, MD 20898. She is coauthor of *Invest in Yourself: Six Secrets to a Rich Life* (John Wiley & Sons) and *Debt Consolidation 101: Strategies for Saving Money and Paying Off Debts Faster* (Good Advice Press).

## Canceled Credit Card Danger

Canceled credit cards may stay active for several months—at least. Card issuers often use a so-called *soft close* to make it easy for customers to reopen accounts. Simply using the old card again reactivates the account. *Caution:* This can lead to fraud if a thief manages to reactivate an account you thought you closed. *Self-defense:* Watch credit card statements carefully and report any discrepancies. If you move within a year of closing an account, contact the card issuer to be sure you will get a statement if anyone reactivates it fraudulently.

**More from Gerri Detweiler...**

## Zero-Interest Trap

Zero-interest, deferred-payment plans offered by many retailers can be costly. In some stores, more than half of the shoppers who take advantage of these offers miss the payment deadlines.

***Result:*** Consumers are hit with very high interest rates that can be higher than most bank credit cards. The deals are also blamed for inducing shoppers to purchase high-ticket items that they wouldn't otherwise buy.

# On-Line Banking Can Be Costly

Banking on-line can cost more than regular banking.

***Reason:*** All the usual checking account fees apply—on top of electronic account fees. So—if your balance drops below a minimum, you could pay the monthly checking fee *and* a separate on-line account fee.

**Best:** Use an on-line bank (reachable over the Internet or a dial-up network) if you need minute-by-minute balance information or if you travel a lot...and if you find one of the many on-line banks that currently offer accounts with no monthly fee and unlimited access and bill paying.

*Sara Campbell, senior vice president, Bank Rate Monitor, a company that tracks rates at more than 2,500 banks nationwide, Box 088888, North Palm Beach, FL 33408.*

# Electronic vs. Manual Banking

Paying bills electronically may take longer than sending a traditional check via US mail. Two-thirds of bill-payment orders sent by computer or phone to electronic bill-paying services are actually paid using paper checks sent by mail.

**Bottom line:** Find out how payments are made and allow enough time for payments to arrive.

*Edward Mrkvicka, Jr., president, Reliance Enterprises Inc., 22115 O'Connell Rd., Marengo, IL 60152.*

# Much Cheaper Checking

*Robert K. Heady, a nationally syndicated personal finance columnist. He is coauthor of* The Complete Idiot's Guide to Managing Your Money. *Macmillan.*

Banks are charging their customers more fees than ever before—for using a teller, calling for an account balance, etc.

Smart strategies to save you money on a checking account now...

● **Shop for a better deal.** You can save $200 to $300 a year by shopping around for the lowest fees that match your banking behavior. Call your current bank and at least six other banks to request their "fee disclosure documents." Compare the relevant numbers, and ask yourself, "How do I use my account? How often do I write checks? Use the ATM?"

**Example:** If you bounce checks or make overdrafts on a regular basis, it can cost you up to $30 in penalty fees each time. Look for a bank with low fees in these areas.

**Beware:** If you switch to a cheaper bank, your original bank will keep charging you monthly maintenance fees, unless you officially close the account. Send a letter to your bank with your name, address, phone number, account number and Social Security number. Request a check for the remaining balance. And—keep a copy of the letter.

● **Negotiate with the bank to lower—or waive—fees.** One of the best-kept secrets in banking is that many banks will negotiate fees.

Banks don't want to lose your business— they know that checking account customers are potential buyers of other revenue-producing services for the bank, including mortgages and estate planning.

Discuss the charges with the branch manager or officer, not a teller.

**Helpful:** If you have a five-figure or more balance in your savings or checking account, you have clout and may be able to get fees waived altogether.

● **Be a shrewder ATM user.** During the last two years ATM fees have risen between 5% and 10%. Most banks charge $1 to $1.75 per transaction to non-account holders to use their ATMs. And increasingly, banks are charging ATM fees to their *own* customers.

Some states are considering legislation to prohibit banks from charging excessive ATM fees. Meanwhile, there is only one way to save money on ATM use—withdraw more money, less often.

● **Consider a credit union.** Credit unions are nonprofit institutions and charge much lower service fees on their share-draft (checking) accounts. They also have much lower balance requirements—sometimes as low as $1. They charge less for checks, too. More than 70 million Americans belong to credit unions. For more information, visit www.ncua.gov.

•**Find out if you're eligible for an "alternative" account.** Many banks have cheaper accounts for senior citizens, students, the disabled, even people who write very few checks. But they rarely advertise them. You must ask.

•**Look into stockbrokers' cash-management accounts.** Some deep-discount brokers may charge lower fees than banks. If you're paying high monthly bank fees now, this could be a very good deal, especially if you find the convenience of the accounts' other features beneficial.

•**Consider money market funds and mutual funds.** In most cases, there is a limit of five checks per month, with a minimum of $250 per check.

## Free-Checking Traps

Free checking can result in: Ultrahigh fees for bounced checks, stop payments, certified checks, etc....and limitations on service. Canceled checks may not be returned to you. You may not be able to use any teller services—just the ATM and your checks. You'll probably get the best no-fee deal from a smaller financial institution, either a local or regional institution or a credit union. To determine what's best for you, estimate how many checks and deposits you average each month (many no-fee accounts have limits)...whether you are likely to incur high-fee charges...and, if the bank requires a sizable balance, how much you could earn on that sum elsewhere.

Bill Anderson, publisher, *Bank Rate Monitor's 100 Highest Yields,* Box 088888, North Palm Beach, FL 33408.

## Better Bank Shopping

To find the best bank for you, spend some time at lunch visiting area banks. That is usually a bank's busiest time of day, so you can get a clear picture of how bank personnel work under pressure. Are there enough tellers to handle the crowds? Do the waits seem reasonable? Are staff members friendly and willing to answer questions?

Carolina Edwards, personal-finance writer based in New York and coauthor of *The Rookie's Guide to Money Management.* Princeton Review.

## When a Small Bank Is Better

Smaller banks are *not* likely to give better deals than big ones on personal matters—checking accounts...mortgages...etc. But they can help a small business.

*Key:* At small banks you are more likely to be dealing with a high-level officer who can make decisions fast and probably takes more time to understand your needs. If a supplier checks your credit, this closer relationship may come across as a vote of confidence in you and your business.

Edward Mendlowitz, CPA, partner, Mendlowitz Weitsen LLP, CPAs, Two Pennsylvania Plaza, Suite 1500, New York 10121. He is author of eight books on taxes, including *A Practical Guide to Transferring Your Business to the Next Generation.* Practical Programs, Inc.

## Family and Money Don't Mix

Making loans to relatives can cause many more problems than it solves. Before you lend money, help relatives look for alternative cash sources, such as a home-equity loan or salary advance. If you do make a loan, attach conditions making repayment more likely. *Example:* If the borrower needs to pay off credit card debt, insist on seeing future months' credit card statements. Consider drawing up a formal promissory note through a lawyer or use the boilerplate form available on legal software. *Important:* Charge interest at market rates so the IRS does not label the loan a gift.

Lewis J. Altfest, CFP, president of the financial planning firm of LJ Altfest & Co., 116 John St., New York 10038.

# How to Get the Most from Your Most Valuable Asset

Your home does not count as a real estate investment for the purpose of diversifying your investment portfolio. But it's a valuable asset.

**Smart planning:** If you own a home, you should have a big mortgage on it. Too many retirees consider having a mortgage risky, which it was decades ago when banks could foreclose at will to obtain funds. But today, having a mortgage is actually the safer, smarter thing to do. Owning your home free and clear is nice, but it doesn't help put food on the table.

**My advice to clients:** Never pay off your mortgage. Instead, invest that money.

If you are a preretiree, you should either refinance or take out a home-equity loan of $100,000 and invest that money to provide income that you can use to pay the mortgage and other living expenses. You'll also enjoy the tax advantage of deducting mortgage or home-equity interest payments.

Ric Edelman, founder and chairman, The Edelman Financial Center, Inc., 12450 Fair Lakes Circle, Suite 200, Fairfax, VA 22033. He is author of *The Truth About Money* and *The New Rules of Money*, both published by HarperResource.

# Savings over Earnings

You don't pay taxes on savings. If you cut expenses by $1, you save a full dollar. But to make enough to *spend* $1, you must earn $1.43—*if* your total federal and state income taxes add up to 30%. In higher brackets, you must earn even more.

**Result:** Small savings add up. If you pay 30% in taxes—spend 20 minutes a week clipping grocery coupons for items you would buy anyway...and save $20 as a result. That is the equivalent of a raise of $28.60 per week.

Diane Rosener, editor, *A Penny Saved*, Box 3471, Omaha, NE 68103.

# Is a Medical Savings Account for You?

Don't open a Medical Savings Account (MSA) unless you are young, healthy and affluent. MSAs combine a health insurance plan with a tax-deferred savings account from which money can be withdrawn to pay the deductible and other medical-related expenses.

**Who is eligible:** Self-employed individuals or people working for small companies that offer MSAs.

**Major MSA drawback:** The deductible is high—$1,500 to $2,250 for an individual...and $3,000 to $4,500 for a family.

Ginny Povall, employee benefits specialist at The Kooper Group, a consulting firm, New York.

# 5

# Insurance Strategies

## How to Get Your HMO to Pay Your Claims Fast

The larger the dollar amount of a claim filed with an HMO, the less likely the HMO is to pay for all—or even most—of it. No matter how frustrated you become with the HMO, don't give up. Managed-care companies count on most people to accept their decisions on claims, even if the companies are wrong.

Here's how to get satisfaction on your medical claims...

•**Take an active role in the claims process.** Unlike conventional—or indemnity—insurance policies, in which you personally file your claims, HMOs handle your claims for you.

But if anything goes wrong—such as an HMO doctor's office neglecting to file the right forms or paperwork being improperly filled out—the HMO may deny the claim or delay payment for it. *Helpful...*

*If your case is not routine:* Ask the HMO to send you copies of all claims filed on your behalf. Review them, and promptly forward any missing information to the HMO's home office.

Don't be afraid to telephone the claims examiner assigned to your case. Ask him/her to explain any decision you believe is unfair. If you're not satisfied, move up the chain of command and contact the examiner's supervisor.

***With a complex medical problem that will require ongoing treatment:*** Establish a personal relationship with the case manager (who oversees the examiner) in charge of your paperwork.

As a participant in the HMO, you have the right to see how the case manager has written up your problem—and what the HMO has recommended to your physician. When HMO

William M. Shernoff, senior partner in the law firm of Shernoff, Bidart, Darras & Arkin, which represents policyholders who are seeking claims payments from insurance companies and HMOs, 600 S. Indian Hill Blvd., Claremont, CA 91711. He is author of *Fight Back & Win: How to Get Your HMO and Health Insurance to Pay Up.* Capital Books.

employees know that you are taking an active role in your care, they are less likely to put up roadblocks.

**•Don't take the company's first *no* as the final answer.** File an immediate appeal in writing.

*Important:* Carefully follow the complaint procedure outlined in your HMO handbook.

Explain why you feel your benefits were wrongfully denied…and clearly state what action you want your HMO to take.

To protect your future legal rights, include the following sentence in every letter that you write to the HMO…

"This appeal relates only to the denial of the benefits in question. It does not constitute and shall in no way be deemed an admission that I am limited in my right to pursue a 'bad faith' remedy in state court."

Send your complaint letter by registered mail, return receipt requested—even if you are not required to do so. It's amazing how often HMOs claim they never received communications from patients…so you should have proof to the contrary. Request a written response within 30 days.

Set up a folder for all the paperwork on the grievance, and track on a calendar each step of the complaint process and when the HMO's responses are due.

**•Go straight to arbitration if you feel you are not getting a fair hearing.** The *internal* appeal procedures set up by HMOs may not be as impartial as they seem.

Some are biased in favor of the health plan because decision makers in the appeals process are not likely to disagree with their fellow employees.

The HMO's appeals process is not your only remedy. You also have the right to arbitration, an independent process conducted by third parties who are not usually beholden to the HMO. The sooner you can get your appeal heard in this setting, the better. Your HMO handbook lists the arbitration entity.

**•Get another medical opinion from doctors outside your HMO.** If your HMO doctor is reluctant to order a costly or experimental test or procedure that you're convinced you need, get a second, or even a third, opinion—even if you must pay for it out of your own pocket.

If these outside doctors agree with you, ask them to write to the HMO on your behalf. The aim is to establish a written record that supports your case, should you later appeal.

**•Get documentation for using a nonaffiliated emergency room.** Most people who seek care in an emergency room that is not affiliated with their HMO network do so when they are away from home.

If you must visit a nonaffiliated emergency room, request a letter from the facility documenting that you had a real medical emergency. The letter should also state that you could not be transferred to a facility in the HMO network without endangering your health.

**•Make as much noise as possible.** Start in your own company's human resources department with the person who is the official liaison with the HMO.

Then contact local consumer hot lines and consumer affairs reporters at television stations and newspapers.

Also complain to your local, state and federal elected officials—your mayor, state representatives and US senators. It's also wise to contact your Better Business Bureau and state attorney general.

***Complain to the regulators.*** Contact the appropriate state regulatory agency—usually the Department of Insurance or the Department of Corporations—and ask about the procedures for filing a complaint against the HMO. Many states have waiting periods, but in some emergency cases a complaint may be filed and heard within 72 hours. Be sure to let your HMO know that you are contacting the state regulator.

If you are covered by both an HMO and Medicare, you can appeal to the Center for Health Dispute Resolution (1 Fishers Rd., Pittsford, New York 14534. 716-586-1770).

If the Center for Health Dispute Resolution rules in your favor, you can then have the HMO provide appropriate care and treatment or have the HMO pay for the care and treatment you received in the interim.

If you lose, you can file a complaint with the Administrative Law Justice division of Medicare.

●**Seek legal redress if necessary.** If your claim is modest, file a claim in small-claims court. You don't need a lawyer, and the odds of winning are good. Your case will probably be heard within six months.

If you have a major claim, look for a lawyer who specializes in "bad faith" cases against insurance companies and HMOs. You're best off hiring an attorney who works on a contingency basis. This means the attorney gets nothing if you lose but takes at least one-third of any amount you recover from the HMO.

## Get More From Your HMO

The one true benefit of HMOs to patients is their disease-management programs.

These increasingly popular programs provide coordinated team care to people with such conditions as asthma, diabetes or heart disease.

Teams usually include the patient's personal physician, a specialist, a pharmacist and other professionals, such as nurses and social workers.

Within one year after one diabetes-management program started, hospital admissions decreased by 75%...emergency room visits went down by 70%...and sick days lost from work were reduced by 65%.

Large HMOs and some smaller ones offer these programs, which patients can choose to join at no extra cost. If yours doesn't, urge it to do so.

*Charles B. Inlander, president, People's Medical Society, 462 Walnut St., Allentown, PA 18102. He is author or coauthor of more than 20 books, including* This Won't Hurt (And Other Lies My Doctor Tells Me). *People's Medical Society.*

## Health Insurance Trap

Medicare patients who expect to be dropped by their HMOs—a growing trend—should apply now for traditional Medicare insurance. Also apply for Medicare gap insurance (Medigap). That may take as long as three months to be in force. *Downside:* Paying $30 to $50 a month for Medigap. *Upside:* More choice among medical practitioners...and an opportunity for better care than from a cost-cutting HMO. *Note:* Nobody can be turned down for Medicare.

*Frank Darras, a partner at Shernoff, Bidart, Darras & Arkin, a law firm in Claremont, CA, that specializes in handling cases against health insurers.*

## How to Know If Long-Term-Care Insurance Is for You

*Joseph Matthews, JD, an attorney in San Francisco. He is author of* Beat the Nursing Home Trap: A Consumer's Guide to Choosing & Financing Long-Term Care. *Nolo Press.*

Many insurance companies now pay nursing home reimbursements for geriatric conditions. And home health care coverage now is part of all good long-term-care policies.

But does it pay to buy a policy?

### WHEN COVERAGE IS A WASTE

A good policy's premiums run as high as $700 a year for people in good health who are 50 years old—and $3,000 a year for people age 70. Such a policy will pay a $100 maximum daily benefit for three years—with a *100-day deductible*. If you can afford to pay 20 to 30 years of annual premiums, you probably don't need long-term-care insurance.

***Reason:*** You can afford nursing home or home health care if it becomes necessary.

A person's odds of spending a long period in a nursing home are relatively low. So—most people who purchase this insurance collect few, if any, benefits because they simply don't need a long stay at a nursing facility.

**Better:** Consider investing the money you would spend each year on premiums in a separate investment account. This way, if you don't need long-term care, you will have the assets for other things or for inclusion in your estate.

### THE IDEAL CANDIDATE

Even though the likelihood you'll need a lot of long-term care is low, coverage may make more sense for some people than for others.

**Examples:** People in their 60s and 70s who can't afford care...or have a small family that wouldn't be able to care for them...or have family members who live far away.

When considering coverage, remember that national health care costs rise faster than inflation, and your policy may not keep up with the cost.

**Helpful:** Be sure your policy includes inflation protection, although rapidly rising health costs may require you to pay more out of pocket when you need care.

---

# If My Income Stopped Today...Would I Be Able To Pay My Bills?

Ric Edelman, founder and chairman, The Edelman Financial Center Inc., 12450 Fair Lakes Circle, Suite 200, Fairfax, VA 22033. He is author of *The Truth About Money* and *The New Rules of Money,* both published by HarperResource.

---

Since illness or injury could cause your income to drop, leaving you with an insufficient level of cash to pay your bills, you probably need to buy disability insurance.

### SIGNS OF A GOOD POLICY

•**Consider supplementing employer insurance with individual insurance.** Many people are covered by an employer disability policy. But often employer disability coverage is taxable and limited to total disability. In such cases, it's advisable to buy your own policy that covers partial disability.

•**Look for a policy that covers 40% to 60% of your *take-home* pay.** The benefits received from disability policies are tax free. Trying to find a policy that exactly matches your gross pay is a waste of money.

If your company insurance covers just 40% of pay, consider finding a policy that will provide another 20% of your take-home pay.

•**Consider policies that cover only your working life.** If you've already planned financially for retirement, there's no need to spend more than you need for additional disability coverage.

After you turn 65, you shouldn't have to worry about lost wages.

•**The policy should refer to your own occupation.** And make sure your policy says that your doctor—rather than the insurance carrier's doctor—decides whether or not you are disabled.

**Example:** Is a surgeon who breaks a finger disabled? He can teach or practice medicine—but not perform his specialty.

Be sure the policy covers *partial disabilities*—defined as lost time or a reduction in pay from your current occupation due to disability. Maybe you can do some work, but if you're still suffering a loss of earning power, you need to be protected.

•**The waiting period before benefits kick in should be 90 to 120 days.** This will be much cheaper than a policy with a shorter waiting period.

### FINDING A POLICY

Getting a good disability policy isn't as easy as it used to be. The best way is to hire an independent financial adviser who can comparison shop a variety of disability contracts for you. Fake claims and other fraud have spurred the industry to trim the benefits and charge much more for the most desirable provisions.

**Important:** Avoid paying extra for plans that return all premiums when the policy expires if you never filed a claim. You pay a big price for this privilege. The extra fees you pay over the years aren't worth it.

---

# How to Save Money on Liability...Home...and Auto Insurance

David L. Scott, PhD, professor of accounting and finance at Valdosta State University in Valdosta, GA. He is author of *The Guide to Buying Insurance: How to Secure the Coverage You Need at an Affordable Price.* Globe Pequot Press.

---

The biggest insurance expenses people face each year are premiums on health and life policies. But hidden expenses in liability, homeowner's and auto insurance can also be substantial. Here are ways to hold down the costs of these important policies...

### LIABILITY INSURANCE

**•Don't assume that the state-mandated minimums on auto liability are adequate.** Many people need liability insurance well beyond the state mandates. In some states, for example, the required minimum coverage is $10,000 per injured person riding in the vehicle, $25,000 total for persons injured outside the vehicle and $10,000 for damage to property. In many states, the minimums haven't changed for years.

But if you are responsible for an accident in which you maim a young person, $10,000 will not go far toward compensation. And your insurance company will not compensate you for any more than your coverage. Here's what to do...

**•The more you have to lose, the more liability coverage you need.** In most cases, the more assets you have, the less insurance you need because your assets will protect you if they must be liquidated. Liability insurance protects your assets against claims by those who charge you with wrongdoing. In the case of liability, the more assets that you have, the more liability coverage you need.

**•With considerable assets—consider an umbrella liability policy.** This type of policy gives you liability protection over and above what is provided by your auto and homeowner's policies. Before you can purchase such a policy, you must have a minimum amount of protection in place.

*Example:* You might need auto liability insurance that includes $100,000 per injured person in the vehicle, $300,000 total for persons outside the vehicle, $50,000 for property damage and $100,000 in homeowner's liability. If so, you can buy an *umbrella policy* that will give you $1 million in coverage in all areas for a very reasonable rate—perhaps $150 per year.

### HOMEOWNER'S INSURANCE

**•Take a personal inventory of what you own.** If you suffer a loss, this personal inventory will help you to be accurate in your report. You'll also be able to prove that you owned what you say you're missing, which usually speeds up the claims process.

Take photographs or a short video. If there is a fire or burglary, you will not only have the proof of ownership that you need but also be reminded of the things you have lost. Many people have trouble remembering without a list or photos.

*Important:* Keep this record in a fireproof safe or a bank safe-deposit box.

**•If you rent, you still need insurance to cover your possessions.** A lot of renters are under the impression that the owner of the property has insurance that covers the contents. That's not the case. Whenever there is an apartment fire and the tenants are interviewed, we learn that only a very small percentage have any insurance at all. Renters' insurance is relatively cheap, so it's a worthwhile expenditure if you can't afford to replace the things you would lose.

Like homeowner's insurance, it covers property you own even if it is in your car or at some other location. It also offers some liability protection and pays some living expenses if your apartment is uninhabitable because of a fire or some other disaster. Be sure to check what your policy does and does not cover. Depending on the coverage, you may want to take extra coverage for items like jewelry, computers or collectibles.

**•Be wary of insuring keepsakes.** You may have inherited a silver set or some jewelry from your mother. While you are fond of it, you probably wouldn't—or couldn't—

replace it if it were stolen. In that case, buying insurance is not a good use of your money.

On the other hand, if you have an expensive computer at home that you need for your work, get a special policy rider to insure it.

**Rule of thumb on a rider:** Get one for things you need but couldn't afford to replace if they were destroyed or stolen.

● **The liability portion of your homeowner's or renter's policy provides important coverage.** This coverage protects you if your child breaks a neighbor's antique vase or your dog bites someone walking on the street. A lot of people don't file claims for these things because they don't think they're covered.

### AUTO INSURANCE

● **Think about the car you're buying.** The type of car you buy will affect your insurance costs. Some cars have insurance surcharges because they're more likely to get stolen or be involved in an accident. Others have discounts because they are less likely to be stolen.

**Strategy:** Once you've narrowed your choices to several vehicles, ask your agent for premium quotes on each one. Also ask for damage studies on those models. Some cars are subject to greater damage in accidents and, therefore, cost more to repair. These damage studies are based on statistics compiled from previous or similar models. It is also beneficial to call a few insurance companies to see what they charge for the same models.

● **Save 35% to 40% by canceling collision and comprehensive insurance.** Consider canceling this coverage when the car is six to seven years old. Older cars don't have a great deal of value if destroyed, and insurance is expensive for the coverage you get.

**Example:** I own a 1980 Datsun 280Z. It's a great car, but probably worth only $2,000 to $2,500. I've canceled all auto insurance except liability, for which I pay a significantly reduced premium every six months. Collision and comprehensive coverage would more than triple the cost.

● **Before you submit a small claim, consider the possibility that doing so will increase the policy's premiums.** This is one of the frustrating aspects of insurance. Most people think the purpose of insurance is to collect on claims—and they rush to submit even the smallest ones.

But you can end up paying more in extra premiums than you would have if you had paid the original repair bill.

**Strategy:** Call and ask your insurance agent how a claim will affect your premium. If you have a small claim—such as one for a small dent—it might be better to pay it out of your own pocket.

Some companies will not increase the premium until the second or third claim. Ask your agent if your insurer adheres to this policy.

● **Consider raising your deductible.** Though you will have to pay for some damages on your own, you will still come out ahead since you will have greater insurance coverage when problems occur. Choose a deductible that you would be able to cover with your savings if you had an accident.

● **Items stolen from your car are covered by your homeowner's policy, not your auto policy.** Many people are confused on this point. An auto policy will cover a broken car window. But if someone steals camera equipment from the trunk, you must turn to your homeowner's policy, which covers your belongings anywhere in the world. Even if your suitcase is stolen in an out-of-town airport, your homeowner's policy should pay.

# Homeowner's Insurance: Big Opportunities/ Big Traps, Too

Steve Slepcevic, damage assessment appraiser and vice president of West Coast Paramount Construction Inc., one of the nation's largest independent insurance restoration contracting firms, 13030 Inglewood Ave., Suite 105, Hawthorne, CA 90250.

Few people think twice about homeowners insurance—until disaster strikes. Here's what you can do now to make sure you aren't shortchanged—and strategies to use when filing a claim...

### WHAT TO DO NOW

•**Read your policy very carefully.** Do it as if your home has just been damaged and you need to file a claim now. See if you are covered for *actual* cash value...or *replacement* cost value...

•**Replacement cost value.** This type of coverage is ideal. Under this policy, you'll be paid the amount it costs now to *replace* damaged or destroyed property.

•**Actual cash value.** This type of coverage has a lower premium than that for replacement cost value, but it pays only the cash value of your property.

*Problem:* You might receive only $50 for your 10-year-old dryer—even though a new one would cost $400 now.

•**Look for specific items that are covered.** *Example:* Your policy may cover water damage caused by a broken pipe, but not the plumbing repairs themselves.

If you are not covered as well as you had thought, look into paying a higher premium for the supplemental coverage.

•**Lower the size of your annual premium by raising the amount of your deductible.** Ask your agent to work up a table comparing how larger deductibles would lower your premium.

•**Check your policy annually.** Contact your agent each year and ask about policy limits and coverage.

•**Spend an hour or more videotaping your home and its contents.** Be thorough—don't just scan rooms. Focus on each object, the brand and the model number.

At the beginning and end of each tape, focus on the front page of that day's newspaper and the date at the top. This will serve as proof of when you taped your property.

Update the tape as you make any major purchases, and write down serial numbers of all major electronics and appliances. Store the tape in a bank safe-deposit box.

### WHEN DAMAGE OCCURS

•**Document the damage to your home before you begin to clean it up.** It may not be practical to put off cleaning up for the days or even weeks that it takes an insurance adjuster to arrive.

Before cleaning up, take pictures or videotape the damage. Be sure to take *close-ups* of damaged items. Damage always looks less severe from a distance in pictures and on tape.

•**Keep track of the time you spend cleaning.** Most policies reimburse policyholders for the labor costs involved in cleanup and repair—including *your* labor.

•**Once you have determined the extent of the damage,** file your claim with your agent if the damage exceeds the deductible amount. It is not uncommon for insurance agents to discourage the filing of smaller claims.

Do not be misled by an agent who tells you that it is not worth filing a claim at all...or that doing so could get your policy canceled.

*Reality:* Policy cancellation is unlikely, especially if it is your first claim. If the damage exceeds your deductible, it is always worth filing a claim.

# Common Life Insurance Mistakes—and What to Do About Them

•*Not matching policy length to need.* If you have small children, buy a policy that keeps you covered at least until they graduate from college.

•*Buying based only on price.* The features and the financial strength of the company are always important—even at higher cost.

•*Mistaking "reentry" rates for renewal rates.* After the level term expires, attractive reentry rates are available only if you're still healthy. If you are not in top health, rates will skyrocket.

Byron Udell, owner, AccuQuote.com, life insurance quote service, Northbrook, IL.

# Term Insurance Strategies From Consultant Glenn Daily

Glenn Daily, a fee-only insurance consultant, 234 E. 84 St., New York 10028.

## Comparison Shop For Insurance

Cut term-insurance premiums by shopping for a new policy. Rates continue to fall for healthy buyers due to the strong competition. A new policy may cost less than one that you purchased a few years ago. You can seek a new policy from your current insurer or any other.

*Caution:* Do not drop your current policy before being accepted for a new one at lower cost. If a health exam turns up problems, the original insurer must continue your current coverage. But if you drop the policy, you may have to pay much more for a new one—or may be unable to get one.

---

**More from Glenn Daily...**

## Term Life Insurance For All Ages

Term life insurance is so inexpensive now that even people in their 50s and 60s—previously considered too old for this insurance—should consider it if they need a policy. Most term insurance sold is for 10, 15 or 20 years. You can lock in low guaranteed rates and convert to a cash-value policy if the marketplace changes and cash-value policies become the better deal. *My favorite companies now:* Ameritas (800-552-3553)...Lincoln National Life (800-254-6265).

# How Safe Is Your Life Insurer?

It is very important now to check on an insurer's soundness before signing up for a new policy...and to assure yourself about an existing policy.

*Risk:* In the early 1990s, about two million US policyholders could not get their money out of whole-life policies written by failed companies, and they wound up having to accept 50 cents on the dollar or inferior policies.

*One warning sign:* Increasingly heavy investment in junk bonds.

*Helpful:* Ask the company or agent to verify that the insurer is top rated by at least two rating services.

*Five largest, top-rated life insurers...*

- *Northwestern Mutual*/A+.
- *State Farm Life Insurance*/A+.
- *Teachers Insurance and Annuity Association of America*/A+ (limited to education-sector employees and their families).
- *New York Life Insurance*/A.
- *Metropolitan Life Insurance*/A-.

Martin Weiss, chairman, Weiss Ratings Inc., which rates the safety of banks and insurance companies, and editor, *Safe Money Report,* Box 109665, Palm Beach Gardens, FL 33410.

# Sell Instead of Cancel

If you're not satisfied with your life insurance policy, don't just cancel it. If you no longer need the coverage...or can now buy the same coverage much cheaper...*sell* the policy—you can get at least 5% and up to 60% of the death benefit—and buy a more suitable one. *Example:* A 73-year-old woman paying $43,000 a year for a $2 million policy exchanged it for another $2 million policy costing $5,000 less per year and received more than $100,000 for the old policy. A broker can put you in contact with institutions interested in buying policies from healthy people over age 65...and those over age 50 with health problems.

Bruce Burns, president of Wholesale Life Insurance Brokerage Inc., 3 N. River St., Suite B, Batavia, IL 60510.

# Robert Hunter on Better Car Insurance

Robert Hunter, director of insurance, Consumer Federation of America, 1424 16 St. NW, Suite 604, Washington, DC 20036. He is the former insurance commissioner for the state of Texas.

## The Good Revolution In Car Insurance

Insurance companies are passing along to car owners some of the savings they have received as a result of the reduction in the number of auto accidents.

Here's how to determine if the premium you're paying is high—and how to find the lowest rate in your area…

●**Call insurers with reputations for providing good service.** Insurers that get high marks in consumer satisfaction also tend to have low rates.

*Examples:* Amica (800-242-6422) requires a perfect or near-perfect driving record…USAA (800-531-8100) requires a family member to have been in the military.

Call your state insurance department to find out the insurers with the lowest complaint ratios in your area or the ratios of the companies you are considering.

●**Get quotes from two different types of companies,** so you can compare the rates in your area…

●**A *direct* policy writer sells directly to the public and has no agents.** Try Amica (800-242-6422), GEICO (800-841-3000) or USAA (800-531-8100).

●**A company such as Nationwide or State Farm sells coverage through *captive* agents.** Ask an independent agent to beat the lowest quote. Check the phone book for a regional office.

Quotes from different types of companies will provide good benchmarks for comparing rates—and will help you find the best policy in your area.

●**Use an independent buying service,** if available. *Consumer Reports* (800-808-4912) will search its database of almost 200 companies in 15 states and provide the 25 lowest cost companies.

*Cost:* $12 for the first vehicle in your family…$8 for each additional vehicle.

*Another possibility:* Call Progressive Auto Insurance (800-288-6776), which will give you its rate and the rates of up to three major competitors in 27 states, including Allstate and State Farm. It is a free service, but may not cover every single bargain.

●**Factor in the impact of dividends.** "Mutual" companies, such as State Farm and USAA, are owned by policyholders and pay dividends of as much as 25% of the cost of the policies. This reduces your net cost of coverage.

*Example:* You may be better off buying a $1,000 policy from a mutual company that pays a 20% dividend—cutting your effective cost to $800—than buying a $900 policy from a publicly traded company that shares its wealth with shareholders.

●**Start early—at least 60 days before your insurance policy is due to expire.** Don't wait till the last moment. You'll need time to do your homework. All insurers need time to do a background check on you before they accept you as a policyholder.

*Important:* Don't drop your current policy until you are approved for the new one.

### OTHER STRATEGIES

●**Take as high a deductible as you can afford.** Boost your deductible—the amount you must pay out of your own pocket before the insurance company steps in—to $500 or higher. You'll save about 20% on the collision and comprehensive portions of your coverage. Also—pay for minor fender benders yourself.

*Reason:* Most insurers penalize you for how often you submit claims—not how big the claims are. Chances are an insurer won't refuse to renew your policy if you have a serious accident—but it might refuse to renew if you submit claims for a bunch of little scrapes.

●**Drop collision on older cars.** Pass on collision coverage if the premium costs more than one-tenth the value of the car. The average driver has an accident only once every 11 years, and usually it is much less than a total loss.

**•Don't skimp on liability coverage,** which protects you against claims if you injure others while driving. Liability is the most important part of your auto insurance since such claims can climb into the millions of dollars. The minimum liability coverage required by most states is usually $10,000 to $20,000—but you should try to purchase at least $300,000.

*Strategy:* Supplement your underlying auto coverage with an umbrella policy that protects you for an additional $1 million to $2 million. An umbrella policy can be purchased through your car or home insurer. The cost for such extra coverage is fairly modest—usually no more than a few hundred dollars a year.

**•Decline options for peripheral coverage.** Many policies offer coverage for towing, car rental when your car is in the shop and other "nice to have" but nonessential services. You usually pay much more for such protection each year than you'll ever receive in actual claims reimbursements.

Also, consider declining the medical payment option if you have good medical insurance through your health plan.

---

**More from Robert Hunter...**

## Beat Auto Insurance Trap

If you don't ask when shopping around, insurance companies won't tell you about *surcharges*—how much the premium may increase if you have an accident.

The usual increase is 10% to 20% for the first accident, more for the next.

And they won't tell you how fast surcharges increase with multiple claims...how long after an accident you have to pay extra...and under what circumstances a policy is automatically canceled.

*To minimize surcharges:* Take the biggest deductible you can afford, so you won't be filing small claims. It will save you money on your base premium, too.

*Be aware:* In some states, companies can slap on a surcharge even when an accident is not your fault. Even where this is prohibited, a surcharge may be imposed until fault has been determined—and you may have to keep after the company to get it removed and reimbursed.

---

# Insurance for the Adopting Family

Adoption insurance reimburses the policyholder for all the birth mother's living and medical expenses incurred during her pregnancy should she decide against giving up her child for adoption. Supporting a birth mother can easily cost $20,000 or more. And while the policy can't insure against the emotional loss, it can help to absorb most of the financial loss. *One company that offers adoption insurance:* Kemper Adoption Cancellation Services (800-833-7337). *Cost:* $750 for a minimum policy size of $5,000.

Mark McDermott, adoption attorney based in Washington, DC.

---

# 6

# Tax Savvy

## Hot New Legal Rights Under the New Tax Law

The *IRS Restructuring and Reform Act of 1998* creates new legal rights for taxpayers and expands key existing legal rights. The major benefits are outlined below...

### INNOCENT SPOUSE RELIEF

The new law makes it easier for a spouse who signs a joint return, unaware of the other spouse's wrongdoing, to avoid personal liability for the taxes incurred. *How...*

●**By letting a spouse limit liability.** Joint filers who are divorced, legally separated or living apart for at least 12 months may limit their liability for unpaid taxes on a joint return by electing to allocate items of income and deductions as if they had filed using "married, filing separately" status.

This election must be made within two years from the date the IRS begins collection efforts on a return.

●**By eliminating dollar thresholds.** The new law eliminates dollar amounts that had to be met under prior law to qualify for innocent spouse relief. It also makes relief available for tax liabilities resulting from "erroneous" items on a tax return, instead of "grossly erroneous" items as under old law. These changes make it easier for a person who is currently married to claim innocent spouse relief.

The new law further authorizes the IRS to relieve a spouse of liability, even if he/she does not otherwise qualify, if it would be inequitable to hold him liable for any unpaid tax or deficiency.

●**By allowing the Tax Court to hear claims for innocent spouse relief.** *The difference:* To have a claim heard in District Court, one must pay the disputed tax and sue for a refund. But Tax Court will hear a case without the tax being paid first.

Phil Brand, partner and director of tax controversy services, KPMG LLP, 2001 M St. NW, Washington, DC 20036. Mr. Brand was formerly Chief Compliance Officer of the IRS, responsible for managing all IRS administrative and criminal enforcement activities worldwide.

## BURDEN OF PROOF

Normally, the IRS position in tax disputes is presumed to be correct. It's up to the taxpayer to refute it. The new law *reverses* this in court proceedings and places the burden of proof on the IRS once a taxpayer introduces "credible evidence."

**Limits:** The shift of the burden of proof applies only in court proceedings, not in audits. *To shift the burden in court, the taxpayer must...*

- Substantiate the item.
- Maintain records.
- Cooperate with reasonable IRS requests for documents, meetings, etc.
- Exhaust all administrative remedies before going to court.

Also, only individuals and small businesses worth less than $7 million, and having no more than 500 employees, can benefit from this change.

## TAX ADVISER PRIVILEGE

The new law extends the protections of attorney–client privilege to all tax professionals who are authorized to practice before the IRS—including accountants, enrolled agents, actuaries and so on. Thus, documents and recorded communications held by these advisers may be protected from the IRS—which under old law could summon and examine them.

**Limits:** The privilege applies only to non-criminal *federal* tax matters—not to the states (unless the state provides tax adviser privilege). Also, the privilege does not apply to written communications between tax advisers and corporations promoting tax shelters.

**Caution:** Don't rely on the new privilege without examining the law. *There are many exceptions...*

- Communications between adviser and client heard or witnessed by a third party are not privileged.
- Having an *attorney* prepare your tax return does not create a privilege for return-related matters.

Extending privilege to persons authorized to practice before the IRS will let taxpayers decide on a tax adviser without worrying that some have privilege and some don't.

**Effective date:** The privilege applies only to communications made on or after July 22, 1998.

## EXPANDED TAX COURT

The jurisdiction of Tax Court is expanded in several areas...

- **Small Case Division** now can hear cases involving as much as $50,000—up from $10,000.

If your case involves an amount just over the limit, concede the excess amount and go to the Small Case Division. If you are fighting a $60,000 tax bill, you can concede $10,000 and contest the remaining $50,000 as a "small case." (You'll recover some of the $10,000 through reduced legal fees.)

- **Tax Court now can review decisions** by the IRS Appeals Division that are adverse to taxpayer protests of IRS levies.

- **Taxes improperly collected by the IRS** during any period when it is barred from assessing or collecting tax can be ordered refunded by the Tax Court.

**Example:** Filing a bankruptcy petition automatically stays any IRS collection activity—but the IRS sometimes takes further collection actions anyhow. The Tax Court now can refund any taxes so collected.

The new law also requires that all IRS deficiency notices state the last day on which the taxpayer can respond to the notice by filing a case in Tax Court. *Key:* A taxpayer who misses the 90-day deadline for responding to a deficiency notice is barred from going to Tax Court, regardless of the merits of the case.

## DAMAGES AND ATTORNEY'S FEES

The new law makes it easier to collect damages and attorney's fees when the IRS acts in an outrageous manner.

- **Damages.** The new law lets taxpayers sue the IRS for up to $100,000 of damages caused by an IRS employee who "negligently" disregards provisions of the Code or regulations in connection with collecting taxes.

This is in addition to the current provision that lets you sue for up to $1 million in damages caused by an IRS employee who "recklessly or intentionally" disregards the law.

Also, the new law lets the IRS be sued for up to $1 million if it violates the automatic bankruptcy stay against collection actions.

Finally, third parties (i.e., persons other than the taxpayer) may sue for civil damages for unauthorized collections actions.

●**Attorney's fees.** You can collect attorney's fees and related costs—such as expert witness fees—if you prevail in a case in which the court determines that the IRS acted without "substantial justification." *The new law...*

●**Increases the basic maximum rate for attorney's fees** to $125/hour, and indexes the rate to inflation.

●**Makes it easier to receive an award of fees at a higher rate** if you needed to pay more to employ an attorney with special expertise.

●**Increases the amount of prelitigation expenses that qualify for reimbursement.** Fees now can be awarded from the date of a 30-day letter issued at the end of an audit, instead of from the later date of a deficiency notice or a determination by the IRS Appeals Court.

●**Says the IRS may be deemed to have acted "without substantial justification"** if it brought the case after losing a similar case in a Court of Appeals—deterring it from relitigating the same issue after it loses in court.

●**Gives the taxpayer legal fees and costs** if he makes a pretrial settlement offer that the IRS refuses, but that is larger than the actual amount the IRS wins at trial.

---

# Attorney Sidney Kess On How to Win The Tax Game

Sidney Kess, attorney and CPA, 10 Rockefeller Plaza, Suite 909, New York 10020. Over the years he has taught tax law to more than 600,000 tax professionals. Mr. Kess is consulting editor of *Financial and Estate Planning* and coauthor of *1040 Preparation, 2000 Edition,* both published by CCH Inc.

---

## Your New Rights as a Taxpayer

The third Taxpayer Bill of Rights is designed to make the IRS more user-friendly, setting up new protections for taxpayers who have to do business with the IRS. *Your new rights...*

### WHAT THE IRS MUST TELL YOU

One of the main criticisms aimed at the IRS and its procedures has been its disregard for a taxpayer's right to know and/or obtain specific information about his/her case. To end the frustration, the following requirements will be in effect...

●**Right to representation.** The IRS is now required to clearly inform you in a *rewritten* IRS Publication 1, *Your Rights as a Taxpayer,* of your right to be represented by an accountant, attorney or other tax professional.

●**No solo interviews.** If you have a representative, you can't be interviewed alone by the IRS without your consent.

●**Right to a clear explanation of the process.** Along with the first letter you get of a proposed tax deficiency, you must be given a clear and complete explanation of the administrative process from the audit through appeals to the collection of taxes.

●**Right to help from a Taxpayer Advocate.** You must be informed that you can get help from an IRS Taxpayer Advocate.

●**Right to know why a refund was disallowed.** If your request for a refund is denied, you must be given an explanation of the reasons for the disallowance (in whole or in part).

●**Right to continuity of contacts.** Also, to the extent practicable, the IRS is supposed to assign one person to a particular case so that you have continuity of contact in resolving your issues.

●**Right to have the name of an IRS contact.** All personal notices and correspondence from the IRS must contain the name, telephone number and identifying number of an IRS employee you can contact.

●**Right to an annual statement of balance due.** If you've made an installment agreement with the IRS, it must send you an annual statement of the initial balance owed, the payments made by you during the year and your remaining balance.

### AUDITS AND COLLECTION

In testimony before Congress, some of the most outrageous IRS conduct related to audits and collection tactics. New limits on IRS authority should help to protect taxpayers…

●**Right to adequate notice of levy.** Taxpayers must be given sufficient notice of a levy on their property and the opportunity to contest it.

●**Right not to face "economic reality audits."** Audits using financial status or economic reality techniques are barred. The IRS can audit a taxpayer this way only if there is a reasonable likelihood that income has been underreported.

●**Right to know beforehand that the IRS is contacting third parties.** Reasonable advance notice of IRS contact with third parties must be given to a taxpayer (other than in criminal matters, jeopardy situations or if a taxpayer consents to such contact).

●**Right to prevent a levy during a refund suit.** Levy on property is barred during a refund proceeding. This would apply where a refund suit could be brought without the full payment of tax.

●**Right to keep a roof over your head.** The IRS may not seize real property used as a residence to satisfy an unpaid liability of $5,000 or less (including interest and penalties). Also, before a home or business assets can be seized, the IRS must first exhaust all other payment options. Further, before a home can be levied upon, a judge or magistrate of a US district court must approve the levy in writing.

●**Right to pay in installments.** The IRS must consent to an installment agreement if the liability is $10,000 or less (excluding interest and penalties), full payment will be made within three years and other requirements are met. Also, new rules make it easier to enter into an offer in compromise.

### TAKING THE IRS TO COURT

If you believe you're right and the IRS is wrong in a particular matter, you don't have to settle—you can take your case to court. The new law makes it easier to do so…

●**Greater access to small case procedures of Tax Court.** Small Case Division Tax Court cases just got bigger. The ceiling on using the simplified small case procedure has been raised from the current $10,000 proposed

deficiency to $50,000. Using small case procedures means swifter resolution of your case. *Plus:* You don't need an attorney to represent you. *Downside:* You can't appeal a decision from this court.

●**Recovery of damages in cases of IRS abuse.** Civil damages up to $100,000 can be recovered where an IRS officer or employee negligently disregards the Code or regulations in connection with the collection of tax. The limit increases to $1 million if damages are caused by a willful violation of the Bankruptcy Code relating to automatic stays or discharges.

●**Bigger recovery of your legal fees.** If the IRS was not substantially justified in going after you and you win, you'll be able to recover more of your attorney's fees. The new law raises the hourly recovery cap to $125 (as adjusted annually for inflation). Also, in determining whether the IRS was substantially justified, the fact that the IRS lost in other appellate courts on the same issue will be taken into account.

### PENALTIES AND INTEREST

Penalty and interest charges remain, but have gotten fairer…

●**Equalization of interest rates.** The interest rate paid by the IRS on overpayments to taxpayers (other than corporations) is now the same rate as the interest rate taxpayers must pay on underpayments.

●**Reduced penalties for failure to pay an installment on time.**

●**Suspension of penalties and interest in certain cases.** Penalties and interest must be suspended after 18 months if the IRS fails to send a notice of deficiency within 18 months following the later of the original due date of the return or the date a timely return was actually filed (other than in cases of fraud or criminal penalties). Interest and penalties can resume 21 days after the notice is sent. This change means that interest and penalties won't be racked up because of IRS delays in pursuing an underpayment. The 18-month period will be cut to one year starting in 2004.

●**Right to have penalty calculations explained.** After the year 2000, the IRS will be required to explain to taxpayers how penalties have been computed, along with the name of the penalty and the Tax Code section authorizing it. A similar rule applies to interest.

---

More from Sidney Kess...

## Tax-Wise Ways to Handle Stock Market Losses

Use the tax rules to minimize the impact when you have stock market losses. *Key rules...*

• Capital losses can be used to offset capital gains dollar for dollar.

• Up to $3,000 of losses in excess of gains can be written off against salary and other income each year.

• Losses above these amounts can be carried forward indefinitely to be used against gains in future years.

*To maximize the benefit of these rules...*

• Be sure to realize enough capital losses to offset all your short-term capital gains, which are taxed at up to 39.6%.

• In addition, have $3,000 of capital losses in excess of gains to use against salary and other income.

• Minimize your taxable gain—or maximize your loss—by telling your broker exactly which shares of a company's stock (or mutual fund) to sell. Sell the shares with the highest tax cost first to minimize gain, or lowest tax cost to maximize loss. Be sure your broker confirms in writing your order to sell specific shares.

• Take losses in retirement account investments and improve portfolio holdings. *Note:* Losses in IRAs and 401(k) plans are not deductible.

• Take a tax write-off for securities that became worthless during the year. Nail down a deductible loss by selling the securities for a dollar before year-end.

---

Sidney Kess on the Nanny Tax...

## It Pays to Pay the Nanny Tax...Believe It or Not

According to the IRS, only about one in 13 taxpayers who have domestic workers pay employment taxes for these workers.

*Problem:* Nonpayment of this tax, if detected by the IRS, can result in big penalty and interest payments.

But how will the IRS ever find out that you didn't pay? They find out when the employee, who probably told you he/she wanted to be "off the books," turns around and...

Applies for Social Security...applies for unemployment benefits...or is injured on the job and applies for workers' compensation.

Then, the IRS finds out quickly, and you get a bill—which may well be steeper than the taxes you should have paid.

Here's what you need to know about taxes and household workers...

### PAYING THE TAX

• **Income tax.** You are *not* required to withhold income tax on wages paid to a household employee unless the employee requests withholding. In that case, you must give your worker IRS Form W-4, *Employee's Withholding Allowance Certificate.* You use this form to figure the amount of tax to withhold.

• **Social Security and Medicare taxes.**

• You must pay the employer's portion of Social Security and Medicare taxes—if you pay your employee $1,100 or more in 1999.

  ☐ Employer's share of Social Security tax: 7.65% on wages up to $72,600 in 1999.

  ☐ Employer's share of Medicare tax: 1.45% on all wages (for this tax there is no ceiling).

• You must also pay the *employee's share* of Social Security and Medicare taxes—the amounts are the same as the employer's share—unless you withhold the employee's share from your worker's wages.

If *you* pay the employee's share of the taxes, it is treated as additional wages—so your employee is taxed on this income, too. But it is not subject to additional Social Security and Medicare taxes.

• **FUTA tax.** In addition to Social Security and Medicare taxes, you must also pay FUTA tax (tax under the Federal Unemployment Tax Act) if wages paid to all workers in any calendar quarter this year (or last year) are $1,000 or more.

This obligation is only on you, not on your worker. And students under age 18 are not exempt from FUTA (they *are* exempt from Social Security and Medicare taxes).

**Paying the tax.** New law permits you to pay employment taxes as part of your individual income tax.

*Warning:* Under new law you must include these taxes as part of your estimated tax payments to avoid penalties for underestimating tax.

*What to do:* If you have a job, increase your own salary withholding to cover employment taxes. If you are self-employed or do not work, increase your quarterly estimated tax payments.

### REPORTING REQUIREMENTS

*Paying* the Nanny Tax is only half the battle—the other half is complying with the reporting requirements for household workers...

•**Form SS-4.** You must get an employer identification number (your Social Security number is not good enough) by filing Form SS-4, *Application for Employer Identification Number,* with the IRS.

•**Form I-9.** The employee must fill out the Immigration and Naturalization Service's (INS) Form I-9, *Employment Eligibility Verification,* to prove he/she is either a US citizen or an alien who can legally work here. To get a form and the *Handbook for Employers,* call the INS at 800-870-3676. *Caution:* It's unlawful to hire an unauthorized alien.

•**Schedule H.** Report employment taxes on Schedule H, *Household Employment Taxes,* that you file with your Form 1040. Even if you don't have to file Form 1040 (because your income is low), you must file Schedule H for your household employees.

•**Form W-2.** You must give your household employee Form W-2, *Wage and Tax Statement,* by January 31 of the year following the year of payment.

•**Copy A of Form W-2 and Form W-3.** Send to the Social Security Administration Copy A of Form W-2 along with Form W-3, *Transmittal of Income and Tax Statements.* The 1999 form is due by February 29, 2000.

*More information:* To learn more about federal employment tax rules for household employers, get a copy of IRS Publication 926, *Household Employer's Tax Guide,* by calling 800-TAX FORM or going to the IRS Web site at www.irs.ustreas.gov/prod/forms_pubs/index.html.

•**State taxes.** There are also state obligations for unemployment insurance, workers' compensation and, where applicable, state income tax withholding.

### BOTTOM LINE

In many instances, employees don't want these taxes paid because they don't report their earnings. Talk them into it or find someone else.

Employers don't want to pay these taxes, all of which are nondeductible, because they add significantly to the cost of employment. But paying a relatively small amount of tax now may save you bigger penalties and interest later.

---

# Eight Shrewd Ways to Take Advantage of the New Tax Laws

Laurence I. Foster, CPA, PFS, tax partner, personal financial planning practice, KPMG LLP, 345 Park Ave., New York 10154. Mr. Foster is former chairman of the estate planning committee, New York State Society of Certified Public Accountants.

---

Congress has passed several new tax laws in the past several years that create new tax-saving opportunities for individuals. Here are eight ways to take advantage of them.

### NEW OPPORTUNITIES

**1. Use new education tax breaks for yourself and your children.** New tax breaks that help finance the cost of education...

•**Hope scholarship tax credit** is worth up to $1,500 of the cost of the first two years of postsecondary schooling incurred by a taxpayer, a spouse or a child.

•**Lifetime learning credit** gives a tax credit equal to 20% of up to $5,000 of the cost of any instruction at a higher educational institution.

•**Interest on student loans** is now deductible, up to $1,500 in 1999 ($2,000 in 2000).

•**Education IRA** is a new kind of savings vehicle that can accept nondeductible contributions of up to $500 annually for a beneficiary under age 18. Distributions are tax free if used to pay qualified education costs.

•**Tax-favored state college savings plans** are authorized by Congress. Rules vary by state, so check with your state.

*Note:* These new tax benefits have different qualification rules and "phase out" ranges for high-income individuals, so be sure to check with your tax adviser.

**2. Set up a home office.** Home office deduction rules were liberalized by Congress starting in 1999.

You can now deduct a home office if you need it to maintain records for your business because you have no other office, even if you do not actually work in the home office.

Before 1999, a home office was deductible only if it was the principal place where you conducted a business or if you met customers or clients in it on a regular basis.

*Example:* A doctor works at several hospitals without having an office at any of them. So he keeps his records at home. In 1998, he could not deduct a home office—but starting in 1999, he could.

*Extra benefits:* Having a home office can help you claim other deductions as well…

•**Travel between home and work** locations is nondeductible commuting. But travel between two work sites is deductible, so a first stop in your home office to review your files may give you a new deduction for travel from home to other work sites.

•**Business deductions for work equipment,** such as computers, fax machines, phone lines and so on, are often much easier to justify to the IRS when they are located in a deductible home office.

*Note:* Even if you have a regular full-time job with an office, a sideline job can support a home-office deduction.

**3. Use capital gains.** The tax rate on long-term capital gains has been lowered to 20%—only 10% for those in the 15% tax bracket for assets held more than one year. *Opportunities…*

•Adjust your portfolio to earn more long-term-gain income and less ordinary income taxed at rates as high as 39.6%.

•Reduce the family tax bill by giving long-term-gain assets to children or other low-tax-bracket family members and having them cash in the gains to pay their own expenses.

*Example:* If you plan to cash in stock to help pay a child's college costs, having the child cash them in may cut the gain tax to only 10%. The gift to your child can be protected from tax by the larger annual gift tax exclusion (see below).

•Make gifts to charity of long-term-gain assets. You'll get a deduction for their full market value without ever having to pay gain tax on them.

*Contrast:* If instead you make a gift of cash and keep the gain property, you will face a future gain tax.

*Private foundations:* New law permanently restores the full-market-value deduction for shares of publicly traded stock donated to a private foundation. Setting up a foundation lets you control how your gift is spent and obtain publicity for it.

*Community trust:* If your gift isn't large enough to justify setting up a private foundation, you can get similar benefits by donating to a *community trust.* The foundation won't be legally bound to follow your instructions, but it probably will try to please you and can publicly acknowledge your gift.

**4. Make tax-free gifts to family members.** The annual gift tax exclusion is still $10,000 in 1999. But the new law allows for increases due to inflation after 1998. With low inflation, it is expected to take several years until an adjustment is made.

You can make tax-free gifts of this amount to as many recipients as you wish each year. The exclusion is $20,000 when you make gifts jointly with a spouse. *Annual gift-giving benefits…*

•Sharply reduce your future taxable estate. Five gifts a year by a married couple can reduce your estate by $100,000 annually and move future appreciation of the gift property out of your estate.

•Reduce the family's income tax bill by shifting income-producing assets to family members in lower tax brackets.

**Best:** Make such gifts early in the year to shift as much income as possible.

**5. Make larger tax-free bequests.** Revise your will and estate plan to take advantage of the fact that the new law increases the amount that an individual can leave to heirs tax free— $650,000 in 1999, $675,000 in 2000...and increasing to $1 million by 2006.

**Key:** With the right planning, a married couple can use *two* of the new larger exempt amounts to pass assets to heirs tax free. But without proper planning, the couple may easily forfeit some or all of one of their exempt amounts.

**6. Take tax-free gain on a home.** New tax law lets you take *totally tax-free* gain of up to $250,000 ($500,000 on a joint return) on the sale of a home that has been your primary residence for two of the prior five years.

Also, if you are forced to move in less than two years due to work or medical reasons, you can take a tax-free gain in an amount proportional to the amount of time you resided in the home.

**Example:** Up to $125,000 (or $250,000 on a joint return) of gain if you resided in the home for one year.

**Second-residence opportunity—***if it has appreciated in value:* You can sell your current home tax free, move into the second home for two years and then sell it—and take a total of up to $500,000 (or $1 million on a joint return) of gain tax free in just over two years.

**7. Use your IRA to finance the down payment on a home or education expenses.** Individuals now can make penalty-free withdrawals before age 59½ of up to $10,000 from any IRA to help a "first-time home buyer" purchase a home...or from a traditional IRA to pay for qualified higher education expenses. But withdrawals may be subject to tax.

**8. Contribute more as a couple.** One spouse is no longer precluded from making a deductible IRA contribution because the other spouse is covered by an employer's qualified plan.

The spouse who is not a participant in an employer plan can make a $2,000 deductible IRA contribution, provided joint income does not exceed $150,000.

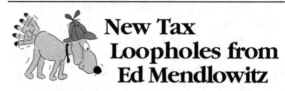

# New Tax Loopholes from Ed Mendlowitz

Edward Mendlowitz, CPA, partner, Mendlowitz Weitsen, LLP, CPAs, Two Pennsylvania Plaza, Suite 1500, New York 10121. He is author of eight books on taxes, including *A Practical Guide to Transferring Your Business to the Next Generation.* Practical Programs, Inc.

## Lifesaving Loopholes In the New Tax Law

Every tax law contains loopholes. Some are planned by legislators...some exist by accident.

The 1998 tax law contains several new special provisions meant to *help* taxpayers. Use these loopholes and provisions to cut your tax bill...

### CAPITAL GAINS LOOPHOLES

The new law reduces the holding period to more than 12 months. The 1997 tax law lowered the top tax rate paid on long-term gains to 20%...10% if you are in the 15% tax bracket.

**•Loophole:** You can donate long-term capital gain stocks to charity. This creates a tax-saving opportunity by allowing you to deduct the full market value of the stocks without being taxed on their appreciation.

**•Loophole:** Use capital gains to minimize the cost of the *kiddie tax.* That taxes the investment income of a child under age 14 at the rate paid by the child's parents.

By placing a child's investments in capital gain property rather than in income-producing property, you reduce the tax rate owed on the income they produce.

Even better, you can *time* receipt of income by choosing when to cash in gains.

You may avoid the kiddie tax entirely by not cashing in gains until the child reaches age 14, when the child's own low—perhaps zero—tax rate will apply.

### HOME OFFICE LOOPHOLES

When you sell a home you've lived in for at least two out of the prior five years, the new law lets you take a *tax-free* gain of $500,000 on a joint return or $250,000 on a single return.

•*Loophole:* Persons who use part of their homes for *business* are not prevented from claiming the exclusion as long as they meet the primary residence requirements. But depreciation taken on a home office needs to be taken into account…

•**Before May 7, 1997,** it merely reduces your basis in your home. This increases gain when the home is sold—but the gain *can* be sheltered from tax by the $500,000/$250,000 exclusion. So a big tax saving may result compared to the old law.

•**After May 6, 1997,** the depreciation you've taken is taxed at a 25% rate when you sell your home. But *only* the amount of this depreciation is taxed. Appreciation in the value of your home allocable to your home office *does* qualify for exclusion from income, again saving tax compared to the old law.

*Important:* Keep careful records of depreciation claimed for your home office before and after May 6, 1997.

•*Loophole:* If you are required to move before living in your house for two years, for certain specified reasons such as certain job transfers, the tax benefit is not lost—it is prorated. The portion of time owned and lived in the house divided by two years is multiplied by the $500,000 or $250,000 exclusion.

•*Loophole:* An owner of a family-run C corporation can have the corporation *rent* part of his/her home. This is a way of getting money out of the business without owing all the employment taxes due on salary.

You can't depreciate the part of your home that the company rents—but this also means no tax will be due on recaptured depreciation when you sell the home.

*Key:* Under the new law's rules, such business use of part of your home does not disqualify any gain on a subsequent home sale from the $500,000/$250,000 exclusion, provided that you at least meet the two-out-of-five-years test.

### NEW EDUCATION LOOPHOLES

The new tax law created a new Hope Scholarship tax credit that is worth up to $1,500 per year. It also created a Lifetime Learning tax credit worth up to $1,000 per year for college education.

In addition, the law created a new deduction for up to 60 months of interest paid on student loans. The maximum deduction is $1,500 in 1999, $2,000 in 2000 and rises to $2,500 in 2001. It is available for refinancings of old loans as well as for new loans.

•*Loophole:* You can combine these tax breaks by borrowing to pay college costs that qualify for an education credit and deducting the interest paid on the loan. You'll get a tax credit and a deduction for the same funds.

*Limit:* The student loan interest deduction is phased out as modified Adjusted Gross Income (AGI) rises from $60,000 to $75,000 on a joint return…or from $40,000 to $55,000 on a single return.

However, if your income is over the limit, you may be able to get the same combined benefit of tax credit and interest deduction by financing education expenses with a home-equity loan.

### NEW IRA LOOPHOLES

The new law creates new ways to use an IRA.

•*Withdrawal loopholes:* The new law provides more ways to take money out of an IRA before age 59½ without penalty. Penalty-free withdrawals can be taken to…

•**Pay higher education costs** for yourself, a spouse, child or grandchild.

•**Meet medical expenses** that exceed 7.5% of AGI.

•**Pay health insurance premiums** if you are unemployed for more than 12 weeks.

•**Help meet home-purchase costs** of a first-time home buyer, including yourself, a child or a grandchild. *Lifetime limit:* $10,000.

These new withdrawal loopholes are steps toward being able to use your IRA as a tax-favored savings account.

You can also take penalty-free early distributions in the form of "substantially equal" annuity payments calculated to last over your lifetime or in the event of disability or death.

•*Contribution loophole:* The new law says a spouse remains eligible to make fully *deductible* contributions to an IRA even if the other spouse participates in a qualified retirement plan, provided their joint AGI is less than $150,000.

•*Roth IRA loopholes:* Perhaps best of all, the new law creates a new, nondeductible Roth IRA.

•**Amounts contributed to a Roth IRA** can be withdrawn tax free and penalty free after five years. So you can tap it before age 59½ for tax-free funds.

•**Retirement distributions from a Roth IRA** will be totally tax free, provided the five-year holding period is met.

•**Mandatory distributions are not required** from a Roth IRA at age 70½.

These rules mean a Roth IRA effectively can be used as a flexible *tax-free investment account.*

You can make a full $2,000 contribution to a Roth IRA if AGI is less than $150,000 on a joint return...or less than $95,000 on a single return. You may also be able to convert existing IRAs to Roth IRAs by paying tax on their current value.

---

**More from Ed Mendlowitz...**

## Contrarian Tax Loopholes

Playing by the IRS's rules isn't always the best way to go. In some instances, you can save money by deliberately going about things the wrong way. *Best contrarian tax strategies...*

•*Loophole:* **Turn down an inheritance.** Property received by will is estate tax free to surviving spouses because of the marital deduction. But the property is taxed in the estate of the second spouse to die.

Tax may be avoided by disclaiming—that is, giving up—the inheritance. Let the property revert to charity or other beneficiaries.

*Example:* Instead of inheriting an IRA, a spouse disclaims it in favor of a charitable remainder trust named in the will or the IRA forms as alternate beneficiary of the IRA. The trust pays income for life, and the property goes to charity at death. *Amount of tax saved:* 55% in estate tax plus income tax owed on distributions from the IRA. Some tax will be due on annual distributions from the trust.

•*Loophole:* **Deliberately underpay withholding and estimated taxes.** *Advantage:* When you underwithhold or pay less in esti-

mated taxes than the IRS requires, you have use of the tax money for the entire year.

To avoid the IRS's underpayment penalty at year-end, take a distribution from your IRA at the end of the year (the IRS lets you withdraw money from your IRA, as long as it is replaced within 60 days).

When you take the money out of your IRA account, request that income tax be withheld. The withholding is credited to your IRS tax account as if it had been paid in equal amounts over the entire year, pushing the total withheld up to the required amount.

*Caution:* Return the *full* amount that you withdrew from the IRA, not the amount that you received after income taxes were withheld, to avoid the early withdrawal penalty.

•*Loophole:* **Don't liquidate your corporation after you sell the business.** When you sell a C corporation, operate the defunct corporation as a personal holding company instead of liquidating it. *Reason:* When you liquidate a corporation, you owe capital gains taxes on the liquidating dividends you receive.

*Contrast:* When you keep the equity, you pay no tax on the money left in the holding company.

*Example:* You receive $5 million when you sell your manufacturing corporation, and have $3 million left after taxes are paid. The $3 million is distributed to you by the corporation, and you pay an additional tax of $750,000.

You can avoid the second tax by keeping the $3 million in a holding company.

*Caution:* Don't forget to consider the tax cost of the personal holding company penalty.

***Best way to invest that money:*** Common stock or preferred shares, because 70% of the dividends received by corporations are exempt from tax.

•*Loophole:* **Make a tardy generation-skipping transfer election.** In general, grandparents who set up trusts for grandchildren can take a $1 million lifetime exemption (adjusted annually for inflation) for their collective gifts.

For timely filed returns, the value of the gift is determined when the gift was made. When a late election is made, the value is determined when you elect to offset the gift's value against the lifetime exemption, not when the transfer is actually made. Therefore, making a late, post-April 15 election saves money when the value of the gift is less at the later date.

*Example:* When the premium is paid on a whole-life insurance policy owned by a generation-skipping trust, part of the premiums paid accumulates as cash value and part is used to cover costs. With some policies, cash payments aren't credited for as long as one year. So, you could easily pay premiums in excess of the policy's cash value.

*Caution:* Stiff penalties can apply if the form is not filed. To avoid them, prepare and file your late election at least a day late, on April 16 and hope you don't die before the IRS receives it.

**•*Loophole:* Disagree with the IRS.** When you take a position contrary to an IRS rule, you are required to disclose your position. You can file Form 8275, which explains the reasoning supporting the position you took on your return…or you can attach a sheet to your tax return with the same information.

*Best:* Attach a written explanation to your return instead of filing the official IRS form, decreasing your chances of being selected for audit. *Reason:* All the Forms 8275 are automatically reviewed.

**•*Loophole:* Elect out of installment sales.** When you sell property and receive the proceeds over two years or more, the transaction is treated as an installment sale. You owe taxes only on the prorated portion of the profit attributed to each year's payment.

However, you can elect to have the entire gain taxed in the year of the sale. Do this when you are in a lower tax bracket that year than you will be in subsequent years.

**•*Loophole:* Pay tax immediately on grants of restricted stock.** The usual tax advice is to defer paying taxes as long as possible. Not so when you receive restricted shares. Consider making a Section 83(b) election—it lets you pay tax immediately on the value of the stock when received, even though you are not yet entitled to the shares.

*Reason:* You pay tax on the full fair market value of the shares, which presumably will be less than the value when the restrictions are lifted. In effect, you convert all future appreciation to capital gains.

**•*Loophole:* Don't wait to exercise incentive stock options (ISOs).** People who hold ISOs often wait until the final date to exercise their options and pay the tax. But the difference between the value of the ISO on the exercise date and the price paid is subject to a steep Alternative Minimum Tax (AMT).

*Better:* Exercise ISOs regularly so your AMT doesn't exceed your regular income tax (whenever possible).

**•*Loophole:* Set up an intentionally defective trust.** When you create what is called an "irrevocable grantor trust," you give the trust assets along with any income the assets generate, plus their appreciation in value, to a family member or other beneficiary. If you make the trust "defective," you become liable to pay the taxes on its income, further reducing your estate.

*Full tax impact:* You remove assets from your taxable estate. By paying annual income taxes, you shrink your estate and allow income to accumulate in the trust during your lifetime.

*Example:* Donald T. transfers $650,000 to a defective trust earning 10% annually for his daughter Alexandra. The $65,000 earned by the trust is taxable to Donald but is accumulated in the trust for Alex. Donald, who pays taxes in the 40% bracket, owes $26,000 of taxes on the trust income each year.

When Donald dies, his estate will save $14,300 ($26,000 times a top federal estate tax rate of 55%) for every year he paid the tax on the trust income.

---

Ed Mendlowitz Gives the Bottom Line on…

## Basis Loopholes

To minimize capital gains taxes, you need to know your "basis," that is, your cost for tax purposes in assets you are selling.

*Reason:* You have to pay tax on the difference between your basis in the property and its selling price. If your basis is high, your taxable gains will be low, and vice versa.

Here are some ways to use basis to your advantage…

### INHERITED PROPERTY

A beneficiary's basis in *inherited* property is its fair market value at the date of the owner's death, or six months later, depending on which date is selected by the executor of the estate.

The basis in property given as a *gift* is generally the donor's original cost...if the property has appreciated in value.

***Flip side:*** If the gift property has dropped in value, the recipient's basis is the market value on the date of the gift.

**•*Loophole:* Give your heirs the benefit of a step-up in basis.** Property that has greatly appreciated in value should not be given away during your lifetime. Instead, you should leave such property to your heirs through your will. Your heirs will then get what is known as a "stepped-up basis," taking over the property at its value on the date of your death. If they immediately sell the property, they will pay no tax at all on the appreciation that built up while you owned it.

***Contrast:*** When you give appreciated property to your heirs during your lifetime, and they sell it, they owe capital gains tax on the value that built up in the property since you bought it.

**•*Loophole:* Shift capital gains to low-bracket family members.** If you are supporting people in lower tax brackets, such as elderly parents or college students, make them gifts of appreciated property rather than selling the property and giving them the sales proceeds.

***Reason:*** They can sell the gift and pay taxes on the gains at their lower rates. The capital gains rate for a person in the 39.6% tax bracket is generally 20%. A person in the 15% bracket, on the other hand, pays only a 10% tax on such capital gains.

***Warning:*** You may owe gift tax if you give a person in any one year property worth more than $10,000 ($20,000 per recipient if your spouse joins you in making the gift). Also, this won't work for children under age 14 who are subject to the "kiddie tax."

**•*Loophole:* Last-minute tax planning.** Give appreciated property to a spouse who is terminally ill. When you subsequently inherit the property back from your deceased spouse, you'll owe no estate tax on it because of the unlimited marital deduction. And you get a

stepped-up basis to the property's value at date of death, reducing future capital gains taxes you'll pay when you sell the property.

***Note:*** To capture this tax break your spouse must survive the transfer of the property by at least one year.

### STOCK OPTIONS

Your basis in *incentive stock options* issued by your employer is the cost of the shares when you exercise the options.

**•*Loophole:* Shorter holding period.** You only have to hold the stock for more than one year before selling it, to have your gain taxed at favorable long-term rates.

***Trap:*** The difference between the option's exercise price and its market value is considered a *"preference item"*—an item that receives preferred treatment under regular tax law. Preference items are included in your income for the purpose of calculating your Alternative Minimum Tax (AMT) liability.

Your basis in stock options that are *not* incentive stock options is zero if they are issued by your employer.

***Impact:*** You are fully taxed on the difference between its fair market value and the amount paid for the stock.

**•*Loophole:* New basis.** The amount you are taxed on is added to your basis in the shares. This becomes your new tax cost to calculate what you owe when you eventually sell the shares.

**•*Loophole:* Make a Section 83(b) election within 30 days of receiving restricted stock**—stock that only becomes yours after a number of years of employment, for example. Ordinarily you are fully taxed on the stock when the restriction period ends. But if you make a Section 83(b) election when you get the stock, you will be taxed on the value of the shares when received, not when the restrictions lapse.

Your basis is the amount that you were taxed on originally. When the restricted shares finally are sold, the difference between the basis and the amount received is taxed as long-term gain if the shares are held for more than 12 months.

### ESOPs

•*Loophole:* **Tax-free rollover of company stock.** When at least 30% of your company stock is sold to an ESOP (Employee Stock Option Plan), the proceeds can be rolled over within one year into other securities of other domestic companies completely tax free.

You will not be taxed on the original sale until the substituted securities are eventually sold. Your basis in the substituted shares is equal to your basis in the stock originally sold to the ESOP.

### PARTNERSHIP INTERESTS

Your basis in a partnership is the amount you contributed plus your proportionate share of the partnership's liabilities.

•*Loophole:* **Mortgages on partnership property become part of your basis.** This has the effect of allowing you to deduct a bigger share of losses.

*Difference:* Your basis in an S corporation is the amount you invest in the company plus loans you make to the company. It does not include amounts for which individual shareholders are personally liable, as it would in a partnership.

### MUTUAL FUNDS

Your basis in mutual fund shares is the price you paid plus any reinvested dividends. Sales loads are built into the share price. Any brokerage commissions are added to your basis in the fund.

The amount of capital gains or losses generated when you sell mutual fund shares depends on the price you paid for them. If, like many investors, you bought shares in a fund at various times and paid different prices, you can cut your tax bill by selling the shares with the highest basis—and, therefore, lowest taxable gain.

*Strategy:* When you sell, you must identify in writing on the sales confirmation the shares you are selling. You must say you are selling, specifically, those shares that you bought on such and such a date.

Keep a record of each mutual fund purchase you make, including the date, total amount paid, price per share and number of shares. Keep a running tally of shares owned, and keep all your confirmation slips.

If you don't specifically identify shares, or use one of two IRS-sanctioned averaging methods, you must use FIFO (first in, first out) to calculate your gain or loss.

The FIFO method assumes you are selling the first shares you acquired—usually the most costly alternative because shares generally tend to increase in value over long periods of time.

*Example:* You buy 100 shares in a mutual fund for $10 per share. Five years later, you buy 100 more shares for $15. When you subsequently sell 25 shares for $20, your taxable gain equals $125 if you identify the shares with the $15 basis. Otherwise, you owe tax on $250.

---

Ed Mendlowitz Discusses…

# Big! Beautiful! Helpful! Substantiation Loopholes

One day, the IRS may ask you to prove a deduction you took on a recent tax return. Here's what you need to know to survive an audit—along with loopholes to give you the upper hand…

### JOB AND BUSINESS EXPENSES

In general, you must have receipts to substantiate travel and entertainment costs, as well as job hunting and unreimbursed business expenses.

*Receipts for T&E must include:* The name of the person you met with, the business you discussed, the place you met, the date and amount of the expenses. *Best:* Write the person's name and the business purpose of the meeting on the back of the receipt.

*Loophole:* The IRS doesn't require receipts for cash expenses of less than $75 if you record them in a business deduction diary at the time that they were incurred.

### CHARITABLE DONATIONS

A canceled check isn't sufficient proof of charitable donations of $250 or more.

You need to get a receipt from the charity by the due date of your return. You need receipts for donations of $75 or more if you receive something from the charity in return for your donation, such as a benefit performance or an umbrella. The receipt must state the value of what you received.

***Loophole:*** The rules requiring receipts apply to individual donations, not the full amount donated to a charity over a year's time.

***Example:*** You give $100 weekly to your church. The IRS views that as 52 gifts of $100, not one $5,200 annual gift, so no receipts are required.

When you donate *property* worth less than $5,000, all you need is a receipt from the organization. For gifts of property worth more than $500 (but not over $5,000), you also need to complete IRS Form 8283, *Noncash Charitable Contributions,* and attach it to your tax return.

When you donate property (except marketable securities) worth more than $5,000 (more than $10,000 for certain nonpublicly traded securities), you must get an appraisal by an independent appraiser. You must attach an appraisal summary (IRS Form 8283, Part B) to your return.

***Caution:*** The appraisal must be done no earlier than 60 days before you make the donation and no later than the due date of your tax return.

***Loophole:*** When you make a gift of appreciated property, you can deduct its full market value as long as the charity uses the property in its exempt function.

***Example:*** You give a print collection to a college for use by art students.

***Trap:*** If the charity tells you when the gift is made that it will sell or otherwise dispose of it, you can deduct only your cost, not the gift's market value.

***Example:*** You give a valuable coin collection to a hospital that wants ready cash, not old coins.

### CASUALTY LOSSES

Your deduction for property that is destroyed in a fire, flood or other casualty is limited to the lesser of your cost or the property's market value.

***Loophole:*** When the property is very old and you've misplaced the original receipts, you can use affidavits from people who saw it before it was destroyed, along with estimates of your acquisition cost.

### DEDUCTIBLE DRIVING COSTS

You can deduct your actual mileage costs when you use your car for business purposes.

As a general rule, you must keep a diary in which you write down the beginning and ending odometer readings for each trip, as well as the purpose of each trip.

***Loophole:*** The diary entry is sufficient to prove your deduction if you're taking the IRS standard mileage rate for driving costs. You don't need to collect receipts for gasoline, repairs, insurance and other automobile expenses unless you're deducting your actual driving expenses rather than the IRS rate.

### SOUR LOANS

When you lend money to friends or family and you're not repaid, you can recover part of the bad debt through tax deductions.

***Loophole:*** You can deduct bad loans to family or friends as "nonbusiness bad debts" on Schedule D of your tax return.

***Warning:*** You must have formal loan papers and have made a legitimate effort to collect the money, such as talking to an attorney or filing a lawsuit.

### STOCK AND MUTUAL FUNDS

When you sell investments, you owe capital gains tax on the difference between the sales proceeds and your tax cost. You must have written proof of your cost (basis).

That means—confirmation slips, dividend reinvestment and stock split information.

***Loophole 1:*** When you know the approximate date you acquired the shares, you can reconstruct your cost by using price information published in newspapers.

***Loophole 2:*** Under Section 1244 of the Tax Code, you can deduct money you lost on the sale of stock in a small business corporation.

***Bonus:*** You can deduct up to $100,000 of any Section 1244 losses against your ordinary income on a joint tax return even *if one spouse owns all the shares.* The amount over $100,000 is deductible as a capital loss.

### HOBBY LOSSES

In general, losses from sales of collections of stamps, coins and other collectibles are not deductible.

***Loophole:*** Capital gains on collectibles are taxed at 28% (not 20%). Keep receipts proving the cost of collectibles, to keep taxes down.

**GIFTS**

When you receive property as a gift, your cost basis for tax purposes is the donor's cost. Ask the donee for records that will prove your cost when you sell the gift.

*Loophole:* Giving property by your will rather than as a gift during your lifetime.

When you do, no substantiation is needed for any capital gain property. Your heir's cost basis in the inherited property equals its market value on the date of death or six months later, depending on which value is used by the executor who prepares the estate tax return.

---

Ed Mendlowitz on
**What You Need to Know About...**

 **Tax-Free Exchange Loopholes**

The IRS generally frowns on bartering by taxpayers, preferring to view swaps as sales and subsequent purchases (which makes them taxable). But the Tax Code clearly authorizes tax-free exchanges of some types of assets...

•**Real estate.** When you exchange a piece of real estate for "like-kind" property, taxes are deferred.

*Example:* You pay no tax when you exchange a motel in Virginia for an apartment building in Sacramento. This is a tax-free like-kind exchange. You can also exchange a warehouse for an office building tax free.

*Caution:* You cannot swap unlike property tax free, e.g., vacant land for an office building.

*Strategy:* Tax-free transfers happen even if the property is sold, as long as the funds are held in trust, the exchanged property is identified within 45 days and the exchange is completed in 180 days.

•**Life insurance.** You can exchange one type of life insurance for another without owing tax.

*Example:* You can swap a whole-life policy that requires large payments for another contract with the same insurer with lower payments.

*Opportunity:* If you surrender an insurance policy or annuity contract of a financially troubled company and reinvest the entire cash proceeds within 60 days in another company's policy, the transaction is tax free.

•**IRA rollovers.** You can roll over distributions from a qualified retirement account into an IRA tax free.

*Best:* Ask the plan trustee to move the money directly into an account with the IRA provider.

*Caution:* If you take the money yourself, you must get it into an IRA within 60 days or you'll be taxed. *Limit:* Once a year. *Contrast:* There's no limit on how many "trustee-to-trustee" transfers you can make.

•**Charity.** When you transfer appreciated assets to a charitable remainder trust in exchange for lifetime income payments, the transfer is tax free. However, you would possibly owe tax on any payments you received from the trust.

*Opportunity:* You can deduct in the year you set up the trust the present value of the remainder interest the charity will get when you die.

•**Private annuities.** You can exchange assets tax free for a private annuity—a promise by someone not in the insurance business, such as your children, to make annual payments for the rest of your life in exchange for certain assets, such as shares in the family business.

*Benefit:* You remove the assets from your taxable estate, which enables you to avoid both gift and estate tax. You do have to pay income tax on a portion of the annual payments you receive.

*Trap:* If you outlive your life expectancy at the time of the transfer, you receive far more in annual payments than what the business or other asset was worth when the annuity was established—and the payments are taxed as ordinary income.

•**Divorce.** Property transferred from one spouse to another because of a divorce settlement is tax free. There is no limit to the amount of property you can transfer tax free under these circumstances.

*Opportunity:* Limited partnership interests with accumulated losses that create "phantom income" can be transferred tax free to a spouse you're divorcing. Normally, you would owe tax on the phantom income.

●**Reimbursements for casualty losses** are tax free to the extent the money is spent on replacement property. *Caution:* Generally, the replacement property must be purchased within two years.

### BONDS

●**US savings bonds.** Series EE bonds can be rolled over tax free into Series HH bonds. Ordinarily, when you cash Series EE bonds at maturity, you owe tax on the accumulated interest. But, when exchanged for Series HH bonds, you defer the tax until the HH bonds are sold.

*Caution:* You receive taxable interest payments semiannually on the full value of Series HH bonds.

●**Municipal bond exchanges.** Any exchange of tax-free government bonds pursuant to a refunding (in which the governmental issuer changes the nature of the bond) is tax free to the bondholder.

*Example:* A bond funding a school project may be used instead to finance a hospital.

### STOCKS

●**Transfers to controlled corporations.** Transfers of assets to controlled corporations in which the person transferring owns 80% or more of the corporation's stock immediately after the transfer are tax free.

*Example:* When you transfer nearly fully depreciated equipment to a controlled corporation that you own, you don't have to pay tax on the difference between the market value of the equipment and its tax basis.

●**Stocks received as the result of a merger or spin-off**—where one company's shares are received in exchange for another's—are generally tax free.

●**Corporate recapitalizations.** Your stock is exchanged for shares of preferred stock during recapitalization. Preferred shares generally pay much bigger dividends than common shares.

*Trap:* When you sell preferred shares received in a corporate recapitalization before the company is sold or during your lifetime, the gain is taxed at ordinary income rates.

---

**Ed Mendlowitz Tells How to...**

## Give to Your Children And Save

You can cut capital gains taxes on appreciated stock in half by giving the stock to a low-tax-bracket child age 14 or older and having the *child* sell it.

A gift of $10,000 per year—$20,000 from a married couple—is free of gift tax. If you make a gift of appreciated stock and a child in the 15% tax bracket sells it, he/she will pay only 10% capital gains tax.

---

**How to Give Your Car to Charity From Ed Mendlowitz...**

## Profitable Donation

Donating your old car to charity may be profitable for you—and save you the hassle of selling it yourself. A charitable donation of a used car gives you a tax deduction equal to the lower of the fair market retail value of the car or your purchase price. You can find the fair market price—also known as the "Blue Book" value—on the Web at www.kbb.com. Calculate the value of the deduction to you (the deduction multiplied by your top tax rate), and compare it with how much you could get for the car if you actually sold it (including any advertising costs).

---

# Big New Threat From the Alternative Minimum Tax

Michael E. Mares, Esq., CPA, tax member of Witt Mares & Company, PLC, 11742 Jefferson Ave., Suite 300, Newport News, VA 23606. Mr. Mares is chairman of the tax executive committee of the American Institute of Certified Public Accountants. He is coauthor of three books, most recently *Guide to Limited Liability Companies.* Practitioners Publishing Co., Inc.

---

Increasing numbers of taxpayers are being snared by the Alternative Minimum Tax (AMT)—a tax that was designed to ensure that corporate and high-income noncorporate taxpayers pay at least some tax, regardless of their deductions.

The AMT for individuals is a two-tiered tax. The first $175,000 of AMT income is taxed at 26%, the rest is taxed at 28%.

**Problem:** The AMT net has suddenly grown much bigger.

As a result of the *Taxpayer Relief Act of 1997,* far more people will be subject to the AMT in the years ahead. They will see their tax liabilities rise as exemptions, deductions and credits throw them into the AMT where they are sliced away.

**Big numbers:** The staff of Congress's Joint Committee on Taxation projects that by 2008, about 8.8 million returns, or 6.5% of those filed, will include an AMT liability. That's up from 414,000, or 0.4% in 1995.

**Most likely targets:** Taxpayers with incomes above $100,000. About a quarter of those with incomes between $100,000 and $200,000 and more than 40% with incomes of $200,000 and over could be hit by the AMT.

Not all is lost, though, if your accountant tells you that you had an AMT liability on your return or are likely to face one this year. *Here's how to make the best of a bad situation—or to prevent its recurrence...*

●**Time the payment of state and local taxes.** Although state and local income, real estate and personal property taxes are normally itemized deductions on your federal return, they are *not* deductible for AMT purposes.

**Planning:** If you are likely to face an AMT liability in 1999, but not in 2000, it would be beneficial to delay paying these taxes until 2000, if possible. *Caution:* In some cases a delay would result in a penalty.

Conversely, if you are not likely to face AMT this year but may in 2000, you may want to accelerate payments of state and local taxes into 1999.

●**Consider paying down home-equity loans.** Interest on home-equity loans is generally deductible. Therefore, a taxpayer in the 31% bracket with a 9% home-equity loan is effectively paying 6.2% interest. But this is

another of the deductions that the AMT does not allow.

So, if you are liable for the AMT, unless you are earning an after-tax return above 9% on the borrowed money, it might be a good idea to pay down the loan.

●**Create an accountable reimbursement plan,** if you have your own business. Unreimbursed employee business expenses are a miscellaneous itemized deduction and, again, are not allowed under the AMT.

Small businesses are often set up so that the owner is employed by the business. If you are in such a situation, create an accountable reimbursement plan and the business will pay you back for those expenses. The business will not incur extra payroll taxes or fringe benefits, as it would if it simply increased salaries to offset the expenses.

●**Time the exercise of incentive stock options.** The bargain element of incentive stock options is considered income for AMT purposes, so while you do not want the tax tail to wag the economic dog, do ask your accountant what the tax consequences will be before you exercise options.

●**Change your tax-exempt bond holdings.** "Private activity bonds" (i.e., tax-exempt bonds issued after August 7, 1986, for a private purpose) are subject to AMT. Switch to other tax-exempt bonds if you know you're going to be subject to the AMT.

●**Know the AMT consequences of a deal *before* you go ahead with it,** especially if you're buying or selling a business.

The only way to be sure you are not blindsided by the AMT is to ask your accountant to project whether an AMT liability would result from the proposed transaction. Consider that when weighing your projected economic return and deciding whether to proceed.

●**Pull income forward into an AMT year.** If you cannot avoid an AMT liability at 26% or 28% this year, it may be beneficial to bring any income you can into 1999, rather than recognizing it in 2000—when you might have to pay regular rates of 36% or 39.6%. Again, this is a complex matter to discuss with your accountant.

●**If you are eligible for the AMT credit,** be sure you take advantage of it in a year when you face regular tax liability. Most AMT taxpayers are not eligible for the credit because their problem results from exclusion items, such as state taxes. However, if the liability resulted from a timing or deferral item, you will get a credit.

***What about the new child and education credits?*** Unfortunately, there is no way out for middle-income taxpayers who are thrown into the AMT because they claimed the new child tax credit, the Hope Scholarship credit or the Lifetime Learning credit. The only defenses are to project next year's taxes and to be prepared.

# Tax-Filing Smarts

For an extra chance to correct errors on your tax return penalty-free, get a filing extension *even if you plan to file early.*

***Benefit:*** If you file a return by April 15 and then discover you made a big mistake on it, you can correct the error on an amended return. The IRS treats an amended tax return as an original return *if* it is filed before the due date of the extension.

***Example:*** An error on an original return was large enough to involve an additional statute of limitations—of six, not three, years—giving the IRS extra time to audit. But because the error was corrected before the extended due date, the entire return—including other, smaller errors—was safe from audit after three years.

*IRS Service Center Advice 1998-024.*

# Inside the IRS From Ms. X, Esq.

Ms. X, Esq., a former IRS agent who is still well connected.

## When to File Separate Returns

The Tax Code provides that both spouses are liable for the entire tax, interest and penalties on a jointly filed return even though only one spouse had income. If it appears that it is unlikely that a liability owed to the IRS will ever be paid—say the working spouse lost a high-paying job and will not be able to replace that income—it generally makes sense to file separate income tax returns. *Benefit:* The assets of the spouse who earned no income will be protected from IRS claims. *Downfall:* Couples in this situation often file joint returns anyway, well aware of the pitfall, to save the few thousand dollars that filing jointly saves them.

More from Ms. X...

# The 15-Minute Audit

Every now and then, a revenue agent will signal that he/she doesn't want to spend a lot of time examining your books and records. Perhaps the agent is being pressed by his group manager to close more cases. Or perhaps he is getting ready for a two-week vacation and wants to think about his travel plans. If the agent suggests that it might be possible to agree to make a few changes to your travel and entertainment deductions and close the case quickly, you should graciously accept his offer. If the agent is highly motivated to close the case, you won't have to give up much. A modest concession will be enough.

Self-Defense Against IRS Trap from Ms. X...

# Collection Division Tricks

Be wary of certain information requested by collection division personnel on the telephone. Volunteering information about who your employer is, or at which bank your checking account is maintained, means that you've given the IRS an available levy source in case they decide to grab your money fast. *Best defense:* When you owe the IRS money, don't ever call the collection division yourself. Hire a tax professional to make the initial telephone contact with the division. An experienced practitioner should know how to avoid answering such questions without having to say, "I refuse to answer your questions."

---

**Divorce Tactic from Ms. X...**

## The Tax-Wise Divorce

Taxpayers who expect to owe the IRS more money than they will ever be able to repay often transfer their assets to their spouse via property settlements in divorce proceedings. *How it works:* As long as the property settlement occurs before the IRS files a federal tax lien, a house or other asset can be transferred free of IRS claims. *Caution:* The IRS may assert in court that the divorce and property settlement was really just a way to make a fraudulent conveyance of the property and will seek to have ownership restored to the name of the taxpayer who owes the tax. *Trap:* Taxpayers who have transferred assets in a property settlement and continue to live with their ex-spouses in the "marital" home after the divorce are targets for IRS legal action to reverse a fraudulent conveyance.

---

**Ms. X Tells How to...**

## Get a Bad IRS Employee Fired

Until recently, an IRS employee who lied or harassed a taxpayer was rarely reprimanded. But the *IRS Restructuring and Reform Act of 1998* says that the IRS must terminate an employee who provides a false statement under oath with respect to a material matter...or violates the Tax Code, regulations or the IRS manual "for the purpose of retaliating against or harassing a taxpayer." *Best protection:* Keep detailed records of any evidence whatsoever of retaliation or harassment by IRS employees.

---

**Cash Caution from Ms. X...**

## Cash Trap

Beware of leaving the country with too much cash. A currency transaction report must be signed when you leave the US with more than $10,000 in cash. *New trap:* Individuals who meet a certain profile will be stopped before boarding international flights and asked to complete a declaration of the amount of cash they have with them. After signing the form, the person and his/her luggage will be searched. A false statement will result in immediate arrest and the initiation of a proceeding to force the traveler to hand over the cash. Furthermore...it is likely that the IRS will start an investigation to determine if the individual has committed any tax crimes.

---

# Helpful Tax Tactics from Attorney James Glass

James Glass, Esq., a longtime writer for *Tax Hotline,* Boardroom Inc., Box 2614, 55 Railroad Ave., Greenwich, CT 06836-2614, and an authority on tax Web sites.

---

### How to Use the IRS Web Site to Cut Taxes...Save Money

The IRS's rapidly growing Web site at http://www.irs.ustreas.gov/ is proving to be a valuable resource for individuals, businesses and tax professionals, too.

The IRS Web site can help anyone save a lot of the time and work that goes into planning for taxes. And everything on it is free—including much that you'd have to pay for elsewhere, if you could get it at all.

#### WHAT YOU'LL FIND ON THE WEB

•**Inside information.** Learn what an IRS auditor will be looking for before he/she calls.

•Audit Guides. Get a copy of the same audit guide an IRS auditor will use in examining your business. The IRS has drafted dozens of these, focusing on particular businesses—such as lawyers, architects, restaurant owners and so on. Use the one written for your business to head off an audit.

•IRS Training Materials on Independent Contractor Disputes. One of the hottest areas of dispute between the IRS and businesses today involves the tax treatment of independent contractors. Get the same materials that the IRS uses to train its auditors on this issue. See if the auditor who visits you follows the IRS's own new rules for these cases.

●Collection Financial Standards. Find out how the IRS decides how much a taxpayer can afford to pay when settling an overdue tax bill. These rules spell out the process.

●Internal Revenue Manual (IRM). This is the instruction book that IRS agents follow when doing their jobs. You can read it and learn the IRS's procedures for conducting undercover operations, among many other things.

*Key:* The IRM may reveal in advance how IRS agents will conduct business in your case—and whether they are following their own rule book.

All this and much more "inside" information is on the IRS Web site at the "Tax Professional's Corner," at http://www.irs.ustreas.gov/bus_info/tax_pro/.

There's also a great deal of other useful information at the same location.

*Examples:* Advance notice of new IRS rulings and procedures, tax calendars, current interest rates used by the IRS and so on.

●**Local news you can use.** There's probably a lot of useful information you don't know about your local IRS office—but it's all available at the IRS Web site. *Examples...*

●Local "IRS Problem Solving Days" are listed for all 50 states in the US by city, street address and hours at http://www.irs.ustreas.gov/hot/prob-solv.html.

●Who to call regarding particular kinds of problems and where to go for local assistance are listed at http://www.irs.ustreas.gov/where_file/. This includes phone numbers and addresses for IRS offices nationwide—including the local Problems Resolution Office nearest you, which can help you cut through IRS red tape.

●Special programs offered by your local IRS office are at the same address. *Examples:* Volunteer counseling for the elderly, braille tax materials, live telephone assistance (also for the hearing impaired), small business workshops and much more.

●**Answers to tax questions.** If you have a tax question, the answer may be at the IRS Web site. Hundreds of commonly asked questions are answered there. *Useful...*

●The IRS's Frequently Asked Question (FAQ) list, answering 192 of the most commonly asked questions of the IRS.

●Tax Trails. An interactive program that asks you questions about your situation, and as you answer "yes" or "no" steers you to the answer to your tax problem.

●Personal answers by E-mail. If you can't find an answer to your question anywhere else on the IRS Web site, you can submit your question directly to the IRS through the Web site and receive a personal response by E-mail.

All these resources are available through the IRS's "Help" page at http://www.irs.ustreas.gov/help/.

●**Tax law research.** The IRS Web site provides a great deal of tax research material formerly available only in law libraries or the offices of high-charging tax professionals—all for free.

The Web site's search engine can help you find useful information quickly and easily, just by typing in related words. You don't need the knowledge of a librarian to find what you are seeking.

*Payoff:* If you use a paid tax adviser, you'll get better results for the fees you pay if you know more about the issues facing you. You may even give your adviser a head start by providing helpful rulings or citations that you find at the IRS Web site. *Valuable resources...*

●The Internal Revenue Code, the tax law itself.

●Treasury Regulations, rules issued by the government to interpret and apply the Code.

●Regulations in Plain English. An IRS program to explain regulations in language that persons other than lawyers and accountants can understand.

●The Internal Revenue Bulletin (IRB). This is the publication in which the IRS publishes all its official Revenue Rulings and Procedures, as well as news releases and other documents.

Suppose you read about a new IRS Revenue Ruling, new procedure or news release that sounds helpful to you. You can download a copy from the IRS Web site and give it to your tax adviser. You'll save the fee he'd charge for looking it up himself if you just told him about it, and he'll get to work quicker using it to help cut your taxes.

● **Making filing easier.** The IRS Web site can make tax filing season easier on everyone.

Tax returns and other tax forms can be downloaded from it ready to be printed, filled out and filed. And IRS publications on dozens of topics can be downloaded as well.

There's no more need to go to an IRS office and wait in line for tax forms (and maybe realize later that you forgot something) or to call the IRS's 800 phone number, wait for ages and hope forms arrive in time through the mail.

You can also arrange to file your return electronically to obtain a refund in half the time—19 million individuals do so now—and to receive your refund by direct deposit straight into your bank account, so there's no risk of your check being delayed or lost in the mail.

Learn about the IRS's growing number of electronic services at http://www.irs.ustreas.gov/elec_svs/index.html.

● **See the future and give your opinion.** At the same location the IRS also lists 45 additional electronic initiatives to make managing taxes easier in the future—and invites your comments on them.

● **Stay informed.** The IRS Web site is constantly changing, as is the tax law and the IRS's administration of it.

Keep informed by signing up for the IRS's electronic mailing lists…

● Digital Dispatch announces what's new on the IRS Web site, new IRS tax forms, new publications and news releases, and includes reminders about approaching important tax dates. Subscribe at http://www.irs.ustreas.gov/help/newmail/maillist.html.

● Local News Net is an electronic mailing list providing local IRS news for your particular area. It's designed for tax professionals, but anyone can subscribe at the same address above.

***Point:*** The information E-mailed to you can be very practical and useful—such as a recent notice about an error on the IRS form used to compute gain on home sales.

***Helpful tips:*** The IRS Web site is complicated. A "Site Tree" feature lists all the topics covered on the site and provides a short description of each—as well as links. Use the site's "Text Only Version" for speediest navigation.

**More from James Glass…**

## International Travel Tax Trap

An IRS tax deficiency notice must be answered in 90 days if you wish to protect your right to go to Tax Court instead of paying the tax. But the time limit is extended to 150 days if you are out of the country.

***Key:*** The time limit that applies is determined on the day the notice is delivered.

● You *don't* get the extra time if the notice is delivered the day before you leave on a long-planned trip.
*Robert Roberts,* TC Memo 1998-301.

● You do get the extra time if the notice is delivered on the actual day you leave the country, because you are out of the country on that day (even though you are also in the country).
*Gregory Wade,* TC Memo 1998-235.

***Important:*** If you receive a tax notice just before leaving the country for an extended time, arrange to have a tax professional handle it while you are gone.

# Deductions and More From Randy Bruce Blaustein, Esq.

Randy Bruce Blaustein, Esq., senior tax partner in the accounting and auditing firm of Blaustein, Greenberg & Co., 155 E. 31 St., New York 10016. Mr. Blaustein is author of several books, including *How to Do Business with the IRS.* Prentice Hall.

## IRS Interest Relief

The *Taxpayer Bill of Rights 2* enables you to seek relief from interest charges that are added to your tax bill due to the IRS's unreasonable delay of your case. *Examples:* After the beginning of an audit...

• **The IRS loses your records** and the case is delayed until the records are found or reconstructed.

• **The IRS auditor becomes ill** and goes on sick leave, and the IRS neglects to assign another auditor to your case.

If the interest on a tax bill that you owe has been increased by unreasonable IRS delay in such a manner, make a case to the auditor you are dealing with—or to the auditor's manager—that the interest should be waived.

---

Randy Bruce Blaustein on How to
Make the Most of...

## Home Office Deductions

As of January 1, 1999, a home-office deduction is allowed if the office is used for administrative or management activities for business and no substantial administrative or management activities are conducted at another fixed location.

*Other ways of getting a home-office tax deduction:* Set up your office in a separate structure—such as a detached garage—and use the office *regularly* and *exclusively* for business. If no separate building is available, you can still meet IRS requirements by using it regularly and exclusively as a principal place of business or to meet clients, customers or patients. Telephone meetings do not count.

---

More Deductions
From Randy Bruce Blaustein...

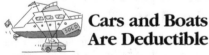

## Cars and Boats Are Deductible

Personal-property taxes on cars and boats are deductible if you file an itemized federal return. But they must meet specific requirements. They must be based on *value*, not—for example—on the weight of the vehicle. They must be assessed on a yearly basis, even if collected at a different interval.

# How to Stand Up to the IRS from Tax Attorney Frederick Daily

Frederick W. Daily, Esq., tax attorney, 302 Warren Dr., San Francisco 94131. He is author of *Stand Up to the IRS* and *Tax Savvy for Small Business*, both published by Nolo Press.

## How to Keep Your Secrets From the IRS...Legally

The IRS probably doesn't know as much about you as you think. And if you know your rights, you may be able to keep it from learning more than you want. *To keep secrets—legally—from the IRS...*

### FUNDAMENTALS

The first thing to realize is that the IRS is not the all-knowing agency many taxpayers think it is...

• **Many IRS computer systems are obsolete.** This makes it hard for IRS agents to get information about you from its files. If you're called for an audit, it's likely the only information the auditor will have about you will be your tax return and information returns (W-2, 1099s, etc.) for the year in question.

*Result:* An IRS auditor who needs extra information to pursue an audit may have to get it from you. By not volunteering information, you contain your audit risk.

• **You do not have to produce information just because an IRS auditor requests it.** In the majority of cases, not responding to an auditor's request for information will simply result in the disallowance of the deduction to which the information relates—and nothing worse than that.

*Strategy:* It can be the better part of valor to accept the loss of a deduction by not providing requested information that might point the auditor to other trouble areas on your return.

• **IRS auditors have limited resources and are under pressure to close cases.** They are very unlikely to force you to produce information, even when they have the legal right to do so, if it will slow down the processing of your case without leading to any real payoff for them.

This means that you can negotiate most IRS information requests. And you don't have to fear retaliation from the IRS—such as its expanding the audit—if you try to contain the IRS's information requests.

*Key:* Expanding an audit means *slowing it down.* This is counterproductive to the auditor—so he/she is unlikely to do it out of spite.

The only time an auditor will expand an audit is if he has a specific idea of how it will lead the IRS to a bigger tax assessment—and if he already has that idea, it is even more important that you not provide the information requested and accept paying the extra tax.

### CONTAINING AN AUDIT

IRS auditors have no right to fish through your tax records, but many of them will try to do so nonetheless.

IRS audit notices typically ask the taxpayer to bring to an audit the tax returns filed for the years *before* and *after* the year being examined.

But the IRS's own rules say auditors are supposed to ask only for information relevant to the specific tax year or tax issue currently under examination.

*Strategy:* In my practice, I ordinarily do not provide other years' returns to the IRS. If a specific item, such as a depreciation schedule, relates to more than one year, I will provide the relevant *part* of another year's return, not the whole return.

Declining to provide the extra years' tax returns has *never once* resulted in the IRS retaliating by opening another year for examination.

And while auditors can get other years' tax returns from storage, this is so slow a process that they rarely do.

*Result:* The auditor never sees the other years' returns, and fishing expeditions through them are averted.

*More ways to contain the IRS...*

●**Have an auditor place all requests for information *in writing*.** This tends to deter him from making an overbroad, burdensome or repetitious request. And if you do receive

such a request, you can appeal it to the auditor's supervisor.

*Also:* Written requests avert misunderstandings that can lead to needless conflict with the auditor, and provide a record if you appeal the audit's results.

●**Have a professional represent you at an audit instead of attending yourself.** This is a right you have under the *Taxpayer Bill of Rights.*

*Benefits:* You can't inadvertently volunteer information if you aren't there. Your representative will know how to minimize the auditor's requests. Because requests must be relayed to you through your representative, they slow down the audit—which will deter the auditor from making "speculative" requests.

●**Never bring full records to an audit for the auditor to thumb through.** Bring only what the auditor has requested. If the auditor wants other records, ask for another written request.

### SPECIAL CASES

Even when an auditor puts a request for records in writing, you do not have to comply if you are willing to have the related deduction disallowed.

The only time you are *legally required* to produce records is if the IRS serves you with a summons—a court order requiring you to produce them.

But, in reality, the IRS *rarely* issues summonses in audits of individuals—and when it does, it rarely goes to court when taxpayers don't comply.

*Reason:* Again, the IRS is short of resources—IRS attorneys don't want to deal with summonses without very good reason for doing so.

*Result:* Even if you receive a summons, you usually can negotiate with the IRS to reduce its scope by complaining that it is overbroad, burdensome or repetitive.

*Special legal defenses:* The following defenses can defeat any IRS information request or summons...

●The *right against self-incrimination* applies if records sought by the IRS include information that could be incriminating. Because a criminal matter must be involved, you should speak with an attorney before making this claim.

● *Attorney–client privilege* allows clients to claim that tax-related communications they make to their lawyer are protected from disclosure. Since 1998, the privilege applies to such communications to both attorney and accountant.

**Example:** If you believe that a planned tax transaction is likely to put you in court against the IRS, your lawyer's and accountant's work on it will be privileged.

**Note:** The privilege does not apply to all communications—you can't claim privilege for communications related to tax preparation. Privileged documents must relate to actual or anticipated litigation.

Also, the accountant–client privilege applies only to noncriminal matters. In criminal matters, only those communications between client and lawyer are privileged.

### PROTECTING ASSETS

You may wish to keep the IRS from knowing about the assets you own, in case you get into future tax trouble.

You can achieve this goal by legally transferring ownership of your assets—such as real estate, investments, vehicles, a safe-deposit box, etc.—to other legal entities that you control, to family members or to close associates.

You may transfer assets to a corporation, family limited partnership, life insurance trust or other trust. *Such a transfer may...*

●Legally insulate the assets from the IRS, if the other entity is not legally responsible for your taxes.

●Construct an information barrier that prevents the IRS from learning the assets exist. If they aren't held in your name, the IRS may not find them when it conducts a search to identify all the assets that are in your name.

**Important:** Such transfers are legal if made well before a tax problem arises.

**Helpful:** Have such a transfer also serve a nontax-related purpose—say, related to estate planning or investments.

**Caution:** If you make such a transfer after a problem with the IRS arises, the courts may set it aside as a fraudulent transfer.

More from Frederick Daily...

# If You Can't Pay The Tax Bill... Practical Options

If you owe the IRS more than you can pay, you may be able to pay in installments... buy extra time...even reach an agreement with the IRS to pay less than the full amount that you owe. *But you've got to know what you're doing...*

●**File for the right to pay for the bill in installments.** You can do this when you file your tax return. File IRS Form 9465, *Installment Agreement Request.* Indicate the amount you propose to pay each month, and the period over which you plan to pay the tax. *If you owe...*

●$10,000 or less, expect the request to be granted if your other taxes are current and you agree to pay within 36 months.

●More than $10,000, the IRS will request information about your personal finances to be sure that you are proposing to pay all you can.

●**You can request an installment plan by phone**—*if* you receive a tax bill after you file your return and it does not exceed $10,000. Call the IRS's automated Voice Balance Due (VBD) system, 800-829-8815, using a push-button phone.

**Rule:** You can use the VBD system even if the IRS rejected a Form 9465 request filed with your return.

**Strategy:** Interest and penalties charged by the IRS on installment payments currently total 11%. Consider borrowing elsewhere at a lower interest rate.

●**Ask the IRS to reduce or eliminate penalties and interest.** The IRS removes about one-third of all tax penalties it imposes. You must show that you had "reasonable cause" for incurring them.

*Excuses the IRS may accept as "reasonable cause":* Mistaken advice from a tax professional...loss of tax records that was beyond your control.

To have interest charges abated, you must show they were mistakenly calculated...or that they resulted from the IRS's unjustified delays in handling your case.

***To request an abatement:*** File IRS Form 843, *Claim for Refund and Request for Abatement.* Explain why you feel an abatement is justified.

● **Make an offer in compromise (OIC).** If you won't *ever* be able to pay all taxes owed, you can offer to settle the tax bill with the IRS for less than the total amount.

The IRS accepts about 25% of all offers—sometimes taking as little as pennies on the dollar in full payment of taxes owed.

***Hitch:*** You must convince the IRS you won't ever be able to pay the tax, and prove this with current financial statements. *Also, you must offer...*

● **More than the IRS could recover** by seizing/selling your assets in a "quick sale"—at a price about 20% below fair market value.

● **More than the IRS would receive** through a five-year installment agreement.

Make an offer to the IRS by filing IRS Form 656, *Offer-in-Compromise,* along with IRS Form 433-A or 433-B, *Collection Information,* which details your finances.

● **Declare bankruptcy as a last resort.** Consult with an attorney first. *Two benefits...*

● **Bankruptcy filing immediately stops** the IRS from taking further actions to collect tax.

● **Bankruptcy may result in the discharge** —wiping out of personal liability—of some taxes, or provide payment terms more generous than the IRS would typically grant.

***Downside to declaring bankruptcy:*** Black mark on your credit report.

***Two kinds of bankruptcy:*** *Liquidations* that eliminate debts (Chapter 7)...*reorganizations* (Chapters 11, 12 and 13) in which as many debts as possible are paid off over time.

***Caution:*** Filing for bankruptcy does not automatically eliminate all back taxes. Taxes resulting from tax evasion or fraud or payroll taxes cannot be discharged by a bankruptcy filing.

# Shrewd Tax Planning For Mutual Fund Investors

Dennis A. Ito, partner in charge, Personal Financial Planning, Western Area, and Rande Spiegelman, manager of Personal Financial Planning, KPMG LLP, 3 Embarcadero Center, Suite 2000, San Francisco 94111.

Tax planning can help you keep more of what your mutual funds return. And recent changes in the tax rules for capital gains make it even *more* important to identify which funds are best for different accounts.

What you need to know now...

### YOUR GOALS

Mutual fund investments are taxed at *two* levels...

● **You, the investor, face a capital gain—or loss—**when you sell your shares in a mutual fund.

● **The mutual fund *itself* realizes taxable investment income...**in the form of the capital gains, dividends and interest it earns during the year. This income is distributed to its shareholders through a dividend paid before year-end.

***Trap:*** Fund shareholders *owe the tax* on these gains—a fact that they often overlook in their planning. If a fund reports high investment gains and the gains are subject to high tax rates, your after-tax return from the fund will be *lower* than it appears.

Your two tax goals as a fund investor should be to...

● **Manage your own shareholdings** to minimize capital gains tax due on them.

● **Select funds for your portfolio that are *tax efficient,*** meaning portfolio turnover is low.

***Payoff:*** With smart planning, just one percentage point added to your *after-tax* investment returns will compound over time to significantly increase future wealth.

## MINIMIZE CAPITAL GAINS

Gains are taxed depending on how long you hold the investment...

•**Short-term gains** on assets held one year or less are taxed at ordinary rates of up to 39.6%.

•**Long-term gains** on assets held more than one year are taxed at a top rate of only 20%—10% if you are in the 15% tax bracket.

You may own shares in a fund that you've purchased at different times and prices—giving you different amounts of gain and holding periods. If you sell *some* shares, you need a way to determine the amount and nature of your gain.

The IRS allows you to select from among *four* different methods of determining gain from the sale of mutual fund shares (see IRS publication 564, *Mutual Fund Distributions*)...

•**First-in, first-out** (FIFO) accounting treats your shares as being sold in the order in which you acquired them. The IRS presumes the use of FIFO unless you elect another method.

•**Average cost method** computes your gain on a sale using the average cost of all the shares you own. Most mutual funds will compute this number for you, saving you work. But this method often fails to produce the best possible tax result.

•**Average cost double category method** is rarely used. It allocates shares to long- and short-term holding periods according to the overall ratio of such holdings.

•**Specific share method** lets you select particular shares from among your holdings for sale.

***Best option in most cases:*** The *specific share* method. It lets you choose among all your shares and select for sale the particular ones that produce the best tax result.

☐ You can sell your highest-cost shares to minimize taxable gain.

☐ If you have a capital loss elsewhere, you can sell your lowest-cost shares to maximize gain and use the loss to offset the gain from tax.

☐ You may even be able to generate a deductible loss when you've made a big profit on your shares overall.

The snag with the specific cost method is that you must have cost records for every share you own.

And...when you sell shares, you must notify the fund *in writing* that you are using the method to identify the shares you are selling and their cost.

***Self-defense:*** From the day you set up your account with a fund, keep all the account records that the fund provides you, including trade confirmations and year-end statements.

Choose the best accounting method for you from the beginning. Once you use one of the four methods for a particular fund, you can't change it without IRS approval.

***Dividend shares trap:*** Pay special attention to record keeping for shares acquired with reinvested dividends. These shares are *taxed* when you receive them and increase the cost basis of your total holdings. But many people forget to increase their tax basis to account for reinvested distributions and pay tax on the shares again when they sell them.

## CUTTING TAXES

You control the taxable capital gains *you* report, but not the amount of taxable dividend income a mutual fund will distribute to you. So it's important to consider this income and the effect it has on a fund's total return.

***Fund selection strategy:*** First look for funds that will meet your real investment needs. Then, among those, invest in the funds that have the lowest tax cost.

***Beware:*** The most actively traded funds generally produce the largest taxable distributions—including short-term gains taxed at rates as high as 39.6%.

***Contrast:*** Index funds that don't trade at all produce the smallest taxable distributions—near zero.

Some funds seek to trade "tax efficiently" by offsetting gains with losses and holding investments long enough to qualify as "long term."

Before buying a fund, study its prospectus—for its trading philosophy and the record of gains it has produced.

***Caution:*** Its pattern of performance may change, unless its prospectus states otherwise.

***Helpful:*** Consider holding funds that produce taxable distributions in tax-favored retirement accounts, such as Roth IRAs and 401(k) plans, while holding "tax-efficient" funds in taxable accounts.

***Trap:*** If you buy a fund and the market falls from its current high level, the fund may distribute taxable gains to you even as you take a loss on your investment.

***How that happens:*** As the value of your shares falls, the fund will be cashing in its appreciated gains to pay redemptions—and its gains will be taxed *to you* as a shareholder.

Some major fund groups are now making provisions against this event—so ask before investing.

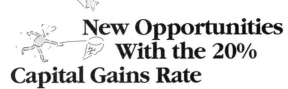

# New Opportunities With the 20% Capital Gains Rate

S. Timothy Kochis, CFP, president, Kochis Fitz, a wealth management firm, 450 Sansome St., Suite 1600, San Francisco 94111. Mr. Kochis is also chairman of the International CFP Council.

The *Taxpayer Relief Act of 1997* lowered the maximum tax on capital gains from 28% to 20%, on assets held more than 12 months. This creates new opportunities for investors.

## BUILD UP STOCK INVESTMENTS

● **Stocks beat bonds** by a wider margin now. As an investment, equity (stocks) is generally preferable to debt (bonds) provided that you…

   ● Diversify your holdings.

   ● Stay in for the long term.

Now that the tax on any long-term gains has been cut to 20%, individual stocks and stock mutual funds look even better.

***Implication:*** Increase the percentage of your total portfolio that is allocated to stocks.

***Caution:*** Don't be quick to switch from stocks to bonds as you near retirement. Today, you're better off keeping your money invested in equities and meeting your income needs by selling stocks, than using bonds to generate income.

***Reason:*** Under the new law, you pay a very low tax when you sell appreciated securities.

Bond interest, on the other hand, can be taxed at rates as high as 39.6%.

● **Borrowing to buy stocks or real estate makes more sense.** The after-tax cost of borrowing remains the same as it did before the law was changed, while your after-tax gains may be greater now.

***Example:*** You take a $10,000 margin loan to buy stocks, paying 8% ($800) per year in deductible investment interest. In a 39.6% tax bracket, your net cost will be $483 per year.

Suppose the stocks you buy go up 10% ($1,000). Under prior law, your gain would have been $720, after paying capital gains tax at 28%. Now, your after-tax gain is $800 a year…at a cost of $483.

### REVISE RETIREMENT STRATEGIES

● **Retirement plans are still good** but not as great. You need a commitment to higher returns now (perhaps by investing more in stocks) and longer holding periods for investments inside deductible IRAs, 401(k)s, SEPs, etc.

***Problem:*** All money coming out of such retirement plans will be taxed at your top marginal rate (currently as high as 39.6%), no matter how that income was derived. By holding the investments inside a retirement plan, you lose the benefit of the low capital gains tax rate.

***Strategy:*** The longer you defer taxes, the better a retirement plan will work. The plans remain particularly effective if you'll have a holding period of 20 years or more.

Tax brackets count, too. If you think you'll be in a lower bracket when you withdraw your money, perhaps after you retire, tax-deferred plans still can be very big winners.

● **Think twice about variable annuities** …at least for now. These insurance company vehicles are burdened with costs that stack the deck against investors. Now, they deprive you of your 20% capital gains tax rate on investment gains, too.

***Bottom line:*** Don't put new money into variable annuities. Wait and see if issuers come out with lower cost, higher quality products.

***Strategy:*** If you already have a variable annuity, wait until you no longer owe any surrender charges and switch to another contract via an *Internal Revenue Code* Section 1035 tax-free exchange. With this maneuver, the appreciated value of your old contract becomes the guaranteed death benefit of your new one, no matter how your investments subsequently fare.

*Example:* You invested $50,000 in a variable annuity in 1991. At your death, your heirs will receive at least $50,000. By now, the surrender charges have lapsed and your contract value is $100,000, say. If you exchange it for a new variable annuity, you'll have that $100,000 "floor" under your contract.

### MUTUAL FUNDS GAIN FAVOR

•**Mutual funds are the place to have your money now.** Funds must pass through to shareholders the gains they realize on sales each year. The shareholders owe taxes immediately on these distributions of gains whereas the tax on the gains on individual stocks are postponed until the investor decides to sell. Now, many of those mutual funds' gains distributions will be taxed at 20% instead of 28%. This significantly reduces the tax burden.

*Strategy:* So, if you've been trying to decide between mutual funds and direct stock purchases, the new law could tip the balance toward funds, especially when you consider other fund advantages such as diversification and access to opportunities that are difficult for individual investors to reach, such as international markets.

### BALANCING ACT

•**An inside–outside investment strategy makes clearer sense now.** Many investors try to decide which investments to hold inside tax-deferred retirement plans and which belong outside, in taxable accounts.

*Strategy:* First decide on an ideal asset allocation to meet your goals. If taxable bonds or bond funds are in the mix, hold them inside a retirement plan. This will enable you to hold more stocks outside the plan, where long-term gains qualify for the 20% tax rate.

What if virtually all your money is in stock? Then you should hold high-turnover, short-term stocks inside the plan, and low-turnover, long-term stocks outside.

You can keep large-company stocks outside your retirement plan, especially if you invest through low-cost, tax-efficient index funds.

*Strategy:* Index funds are great vehicles for holding large-company stocks outside of a retirement plan. Generally, turnover is low so few capital gains are passed through to the investors.

### KIDDIE TAX BREAK

•**The new law has a bargain 10% capital gains rate for taxpayers in the 15% bracket.** In 1999, that includes single filers with up to $25,750 in taxable income ($43,050 filing jointly).

*Strategy:* If you're using appreciated securities to pay college bills, give them to your children for them to sell. As long as your kids are older than 13, they likely can sell the shares and pay tax at just 10%, netting more for college costs.

*Loophole:* You and your spouse can give away $20,000 worth of assets per year, *per recipient,* with no gift tax consequences.

In addition to $10,000/$20,000 annual gifts, you can give any amount directly to an institution for a child's education gift tax free.

*Strategy:* If you are helping to support low-bracket elderly parents, give them appreciated securities instead of cash. Your parents can sell the securities and pay tax at a bargain 10% rate.

•**Diversification may come easier.** Your portfolio may be overweighted in shares of your employer's stock, stock options, or shares of one company given to you by family members. Selling some of those shares reduces the risk of tying up too much money in one stock but may generate large capital gains.

Now, under the new tax-rate structure, rebalancing your portfolio becomes less expensive because you'll owe only 20% of the gain on assets held more than 12 months.

### SHRINKING TAX ADVANTAGES

•**The benefit of holding on to assets** so that your heirs can inherit them and get a basis step-up to date-of-death value has been diminished.

*Example:* You have a portfolio of stocks you bought for $100,000, now worth $500,000. If you die tomorrow and your son inherits, his basis in those shares moves up to $500,000. He can sell them for $500,000 and owe no capital gains tax.

The value of this tax break is smaller now (an $80,000 savings at a 20% rate) than it was under prior law (when the savings would have been $112,000, at a 28% rate).

Formerly, many investors were frozen in place. They held on to appreciated assets until death, so their heirs would get the basis step-up. Now that this tax break has been devalued, you can take some gains, pay tax at 20%, and reinvest the net proceeds where opportunities seem greater.

●**Charitable giving also has been devalued.** Since you now pay so little tax on assets you sell, there's less incentive to give them to charity to save taxes.

Charitable giving now depends even more on your philanthropic objectives and not as much on tax savings.

## Tax-Saving Technique For Investors

Suppose you need cash for college costs, medical bills or some other major expense. You can sell appreciated shares, but you'll likely wind up paying 20% of your profits in tax (higher after factoring in state income tax). Instead, *borrow* against those securities. Interest rates on margin loans have been between 8.5% and 9% and such interest may be deductible against your investment income.

Robert Willens, CPA, managing director, Lehman Brothers Inc., 3 World Financial Center, New York 10285.

## How to Win with Savings Bonds

Series EE Savings Bonds grow in value on a tax-deferred basis. You don't owe tax on the accumulated interest income until you cash them in, at which time ordinary income tax rates apply—fortunately the income is free of state and local taxes.

**Snag:** If you've accumulated a lot of bonds over your life, cashing them in all at once could push you into a higher tax bracket and result in a big tax bill. This is also true if the bonds are cashed in by your estate or heirs.

**Option:** After retirement, when you may be in a lower bracket, exchange Series EE bonds for Series HH bonds that pay interest in cash semiannually. *Advantages...*

●You'll get spendable income that EE bonds don't provide.

●The income will be taxed at your lower, postretirement tax rate.

**Alternative:** You can elect to have interest on the Series EE bonds taxed every year. But this election must cover all Series EE bonds you presently own or may purchase in the future. All income already accumulated on bonds that you own is taxed in the year you make this election.

William G. Brennan, CPA/PFS, CFP, Columbia Financial Advisors, LLP, 1730 Rhode Island Ave. NW, Suite 800, Washington, DC 20036.

## Picking the Right Tax Professional

An accountant or enrolled agent can satisfactorily represent you in dealing with the IRS if the audit involves tax record-keeping, interpretations of the tax law or just honest mistakes.

**But beware:** Hiding income from the IRS is *fraud*...and that is a crime.

So if you feel you may be vulnerable on an unreported income issue, hire a tax attorney to represent you.

Your discussions with an attorney are protected by attorney-client privilege, so the meetings in which you discuss your tax problems will be confidential.

**Trap:** No such privilege applies between accountants and clients in criminal matters—so in a criminal case, your own accountant can be called upon to testify against you.

In such cases, an attorney can also best advise you whether or not to cooperate with the IRS.

In a normal civil tax dispute, it's usually best to cooperate with the IRS to determine your accurate tax liability and get the matter behind you within a reasonable period of time. An accountant or enrolled agent can handle this for you.

But if there is a potential criminal problem, an attorney can best protect your interests.

Seymour Goldberg, Esq., CPA, senior partner, Goldberg & Goldberg, PC, 666 Old Country Rd., Suite 600, Garden City, NY 11530. Mr. Goldberg is author of *How to Handle an IRS Audit* and *Pension Distributions: Planning Strategies, Cases and Rulings,* both published by the *CPA Journal.*

# Douglas Brundage On Taxes and Your Car

Douglas O. Brundage, CPA, partner, Arthur Andersen LLP, 115 Broad Hollow Rd., Melville, NY 11747.

## Maximizing Auto Deductions Made Simple...Very Simple

If you drive a car for work, or use company-owned cars in your business, you'll want to get the best tax treatment for business driving. *Here's how...*

### BIGGEST DEDUCTIONS

Proprietors of unincorporated businesses and members of partnerships can deduct their business driving costs on their own returns (on Schedules C and E, respectively). They get a full deduction for their actual documented costs or a mileage rate of 31 cents per mile for business travel on or after April 1, 1999 (32.5 cents per mile for business travel before April 1, 1999). [*Note:* That's right, it's gone *down* 1.5 cents].

But for employees—including owner/executives of corporations—the situation is different. They may deduct their driving costs on their own tax returns or the company can pay the costs and deduct them.

Larger deductions generally will be available *overall* if the company deducts business driving expenses. *Why...*

● **Some employees may not be able to deduct driving at all.** Employee business expenses are an itemized deduction—so employees who don't itemize will get no deduction.

● **For those who do itemize, employee business expenses are counted among miscellaneous expenses,** which are deductible only to the extent they exceed 2% of Adjusted Gross Income (AGI). So their deductions may be reduced.

● **When high-income individuals have AGI exceeding $126,600 for 1999,** their total itemized deductions are reduced by 3% of the excess—further reducing the value of deductions taken on a personal return.

As a result, both the company and its employees may come out ahead if the company deducts driving costs, claims larger total deductions and shares the tax savings with employees—perhaps through adjusted compensation packages.

### HOW TO DO IT

The simplest way for the company to deduct driving costs is to reimburse employees for driving their own cars for work.

Reimbursement may be provided at the IRS's standard mileage rate of 31 cents per mile, plus tolls and parking.

Alternatively, reimbursement can be based on employees' actual documented driving costs.

*Note:* If employees receive a cents-per-mile reimbursement that is less than their actual driving cost, they can treat the *difference* as an employee business expense on their personal returns.

A reimbursement program has the added advantage of assuring that employees keep adequate records of their business driving—those who don't won't be reimbursed, so they have an incentive. In contrast, employees who are provided with a company car may be lax about recording their business driving.

*Snag:* Requiring employees to drive their own cars for work may not be practical. Some may not own cars, others may have families that need their cars for personal use, or may own vehicles unsuitable for business. So it may be that the company will have to provide cars for business driving.

### COMPANY CARS

Company cars can be either bought or leased. *Tax consequences...*

●**Buying.** A purchased car can be depreciated at the following rates…

- ●**Year 1:** 20%.
- ●**Year 2:** 32%.
- ●**Year 3:** 19.2%.
- ●**Years 4 & 5:** 11.52%.
- ●**Year 6:** 5.76%.

*Limit:* Deductions are restricted for cars costing more than $15,500 in 1999. For such cars placed in service in 1999 the maximum depreciation deductions are…

- ●**Year 1:** $3,160.
- ●**Year 2:** $5,000.
- ●**Year 3:** $2,950.
- ●**Later years:** $1,775, until cost is fully depreciated.

*Note:* At the time of writing, figures for cars in service in 2000 have not been released.

●**Leasing.** A company that leases a car can deduct the full lease payment as a business expense, no matter how large. But when a car's value exceeds $15,500, an amount is added back into the company's income, partially offsetting the lease payment deduction.

The amount added back is based on the value of the car and determined from IRS tables found in IRS Publication 463. Obtain a copy by calling 800-TAX-FORM, or from the IRS Web site, http://www.irs.ustreas.gov/.

### TAXABLE INCOME

The complication of providing company cars to employees is that the cars' value must be included in employees' income. *Two ways this is done…*

●**The entire value of company-provided cars can be reported in employee income,** with employees claiming offsetting business expense deductions for the cost of driving the cars.

This is the simpler method for the company —but many employees may be unable to deduct some or all of their business expenses, for the reasons described previously.

●**The company can allocate into each employee's income a portion of the car's value** that corresponds with personal use.

This requires that a record-keeping system be set up under which employees report their business and personal use of each car, and the company computes the appropriate amount to be included in each employee's income.

The value of personal use of a car also can be figured using the IRS standard mileage rate, but only if the car's value does not exceed $15,500 in 1999.

### RECORD KEEPING

No matter how the company organizes its business driving, the key to getting the best deductions for driving costs is good record keeping.

Drivers must keep records of the mileage they drive for business and nonbusiness purposes, the date and purpose of business driving and out-of-pocket expenses incurred.

Without these records, tax breaks for business driving will be in jeopardy no matter how business driving is arranged.

*Key:* Records of business driving no longer have to be contemporaneous, but the sooner they are compiled, the more persuasive they will be. The best plan in most cases is simply to have drivers keep a daily log of their business driving.

"Keep good records" may seem like mundane advice—but failure to do so is the number-one cause of lost deductions.

### TRADE-IN TRAPS

Owners of business vehicles should consider the tax consequences of selling cars as well as buying them.

When an old car is traded in toward the price of a new one, "like-kind exchange" rules apply and no current gain or loss is reported on the sale.

This is good if the seller would recognize a taxable gain on the sale of the car. But it is bad if the seller would recognize a deductible loss.

*Key:* Because of the annual depreciation deduction limit that is imposed on business autos, expensive cars often will have a tax basis that exceeds their market value—so a deductible loss would result from their sale. But the deduction won't be available if the car is traded in. Instead, the loss will be deferred with the new car's basis being increased by the basis remaining in the old car.

*Strategy:* When the basis in a business vehicle is greater than its market value, sell it for cash, take a loss deduction and then reinvest the cash in a new vehicle.

---

**More from Douglas Brundage…**

## The New Law on the Auto Luxury Tax

The 1997 tax law changes phase out the luxury tax imposed on autos costing more than $36,000. (*Note:* This may change in 2000.)

The tax is set at 6% in 1999 and will decline by 1% annually until it reaches 3% by 2002.

*Snag:* Many people overlook the fact that the law imposes the same tax on parts and accessories bought for a luxury car within six months after the car has been purchased. This provision is meant to prevent purchasers from avoiding the luxury tax by buying a "stripped down" car for less than $36,000 and buying expensive accessories later.

*Example:* You buy a car for $34,000, then spend $5,000 by adding a sunroof, stereo system and other accessories. The expenditures are added to the price of the car, which becomes $39,000—with $3,000 subject to tax.

The new law applies the tax to "parts and accessories" only when their purchase prices total $1,000 or more, up from $200 under old law.

*Opportunity:* It's possible to avoid the luxury tax by buying a "sport-utility vehicle" that weighs more than 6,000 pounds. Vehicles that are over that weight are considered "trucks" rather than autos under the Tax Code, and aren't subject to the general restrictions imposed on automobiles.

---

## Deductible Mortgage

If you do not own a second home yourself, but cosigned your child's home loan, you can make mortgage payments on that child's home and then deduct the mortgage interest portion of the payments on your own taxes.

This will free up the cash your children would otherwise have to use for mortgage payments…and they can then use it to pay for a car, a child's college tuition or anything else they wish.

*Bonus:* It removes money from your estate.

A similar strategy can be used to make gifts to elderly parents or certain other family members. Discuss the rules with your tax adviser.

Sean Smith, enrolled agent and tax accountant in the Washington, DC, area and author of *101 Tax Loopholes for the Middle Class.* Broadway.

---

# Mortgage Payments Can Now Be Deducted on a Home You Don't Own

A recent Tax Court decision shows how to save a mortgage interest deduction when one family member helps another obtain a home, and mortgage payments are not made by the person whose name is on the mortgage.

*Facts:* A married couple found they could not obtain a mortgage on the home they wanted to buy. The husband's brother then bought the home and let the couple live in it. The couple made all the mortgage payments on the house, even though the mortgage and title to the home both were in the brother's name.

The couple also paid all other ownership-related expenses, such as property taxes, utilities and so on, and acted in all ways as the owners of the home.

But when they tried to deduct the mortgage interest they paid, the IRS disallowed the deduction because they weren't legally obligated to pay the mortgage.

*Tax Court:* The couple were legally obligated to pay the mortgage because if they failed to do so, the brother would have a cause of action to evict them, and they would lose the home.

Because they had assumed all the rights and obligations of home ownership, and the brother hadn't taken the mortgage deduction, they could take the deduction.

*Saffet Uslu,* TC Memo 1997-551.

# Home Sale Tax Trap

When you sell a home that has greatly appreciated in value, you might pay a larger tax bill than you think—in spite of the new tax law that lets up to $500,000 of home-sale gain be taken tax free on a joint return ($250,000 on a single return).

*Trap:* Not all states allow the same exemption that is allowed on the federal tax return. So you may incur a significant tax on your gain at the state or local level.

Moreover, if you do owe a large state and local tax bill that you deduct on your federal return, you may increase your federal tax bill as well.

This is because a large deduction for state and local taxes can make your federal return subject to the AMT (Alternative Minimum Tax) —a special tax computation that may increase your federal tax bill.

*Safety:* Before selling an appreciated home, examine all the tax consequences with an expert.

C. Clinton Stretch, tax principal and director of tax policy, Deloitte & Touche LLP, 555 12 St. NW, Washington, DC 20004.

# Tax Write-Off When Refinancing

If you refinance a second time, all points left over from the first refinancing—ones not yet deducted on your taxes—can be written off immediately.

*Example:* Say you paid $3,000 in points to refinance and have so far written off $500. If you refinance again this year, the remaining $2,500 in points is deductible on your taxes for the year of refinancing.

Ed Slott, CPA, E. Slott & Co., CPAs, 100 Merrick Rd., Rockville Centre, NY 11570. Mr. Slott is publisher of *Ed Slott's IRA Advisor.*

# To Lower Property Taxes...

Don't just grumble and accept a property tax assessment you believe is too high. Appeal for a reduction...

• **Take advantage of any tax breaks for which you qualify.**

*Examples:* Senior citizen...veteran...disabled...low income...owner occupied.

• **Check the accuracy of the assessment.** Go to the assessor's office and look for errors in the description of the property.

• **Compare your assessment with your neighbors'.**

• **Check the records of recent home sale prices** in the neighborhood that suggest you are overassessed.

• **Put all your facts and figures in order** so that you can make a compelling case to the appeals officer.

*Important:* If the figures suggest you may be *under*assessed, don't push your luck.

Frank Adler, a Miami businessman and author of *How to Reduce Your Property Taxes.* HarperBusiness.

# Foreign Tax Havens Don't Work

Forget about foreign tax havens. US citizens—even those living abroad—and US residents cannot use them.

*Reason:* US taxes are based on worldwide income. Tax loopholes of the past have been plugged. Income (interest, dividends, etc.) must be reported when it is earned—whether the investments are in your name or an offshore holding company.

*Narrow exception:* Profits from a legitimate business operated in a tax haven are not taxed until the money is remitted to you.

Gideon Rothschild, Esq., CPA, a frequent lecturer on estate planning and a partner in the law firm Moses & Singer LLP, 1301 Avenue of the Americas, New York 10019.

# Gambler's Heaven

A couple won a state lottery's grand prize that was paid out over 20 years. They enjoyed it by traveling to various gambling locations and gambling extensively.

***IRS private ruling:*** Each of the couple's 20 annual prize payments are "gains from wagering," so they can *deduct* against them any wagering losses that they may incur.

*Letter Ruling* 9808002.

# Latest Way to Make More Money for Yourself... By Giving It Away

Stanley S. Weithorn, Esq., Roberts & Holland, Worldwide Plaza, 825 Eighth Ave., New York. Mr. Weithorn also has offices at Fennemore Craig, 10019 North Central Ave., Suite 2600, Phoenix 85012. He specializes in charitable tax planning and sophisticated estate planning.

One of the most exciting methods for charitable giving is the Deferred-Payment Gift Annuity (DPGA). Few financial planning techniques offer so many advantages...

• **An immediate deduction** on your income taxes.

• **The equivalent of tax-free buildup** on investment capital.

• **Income deferral,** perhaps until you're retired and in a lower tax bracket.

• **The ability to lock in capital gains now** while deferring the tax obligation for many years.

• **Guaranteed lifetime income for yourself** and perhaps your spouse.

• **Removal of assets from your taxable estate** with no gift tax consequences.

• **Satisfaction from making a charitable contribution** and, if desired, the recognition that comes with it.

## GIVE NOW, TAKE LATER

With a DPGA, you make a gift now to a charity (a religious organization, cultural group, etc.)

and receive the promise of a fixed annual payment sometime in the future.

***Example:*** Bill Smith gives $200,000 to the March of Dimes in 1999, when Bill is age 55. The March of Dimes agrees to pay Bill an annuity starting in 2009, when Bill is 65 and plans to retire.

Bill can receive this annuity...

• For a fixed number of years.

• For the rest of his life.

• For the rest of his life as well as the life or lives of others.

Typically, married donors choose a joint-and-survivor annuity that pays as long as either spouse is alive.

***Trap:*** If you name someone other than your spouse as an annuitant or co-annuitant, you may trigger a gift tax liability.

***Tax-free buildup:*** The amount transferred is compounded annually, at a predetermined interest rate, during the deferral period. The annuity is then based on the total sum.

***Example:*** When Bill gives $200,000 to the March of Dimes, the annual buildup rate is just over 7%. With a 10-year deferral, the annuity will be based on a $400,000 total sum rather than $200,000. In essence, Bill is locking in a return based on his money doubling in 10 years.

***Payoff:*** Annuity payments are based on the annuitant's life expectancy. Because Bill will be 10 years older when he starts receiving payments, he'll receive a higher percentage of his contribution and only a portion of each year's annuity will be subject to tax.

***Details:*** Bill chooses a joint-and-survivor annuity with his wife, Bonnie, who will be 62 when the payments begin. At that point, they can expect to receive $45,200 per year—an 11.3% payout rate based on a total sum of $400,000.

If they had taken their joint annuity immediately, when their ages were 55 and 52, they would only have received $12,800 per year—a 6.4% payout on their actual $200,000 transfer.

***Bottom line:*** Deferring the annuity increases the Smiths' annual payments by about 250%. They may be in a lower tax bracket, too, after Bill retires.

## DEDUCING THE DEDUCTION

Even though Bill and Bonnie won't start receiving payments until 2009—and the March of Dimes may not receive a dime for another 20 or 30 years—Bill and Bonnie get a tax deduction in 1999, the year of the contribution.

*Here's how they figure their income tax deduction...*

•**Step 1.** The value of the annuity is calculated under IRS tables.

•**Step 2.** This value is subtracted from the sum contributed.

•**Step 3.** The difference is immediately deductible.

*Example:* Using current interest rates, the value of the annuity payable to Bill and Bonnie is nearly $160,000. Because they contributed $200,000 in 1999, they're entitled to an immediate charitable deduction of more than $40,000.

*Trap:* There are limits on the amount of contributions you can deduct in one year. Excess amounts may be carried forward for five years. *Caution:* Don't file more than you can deduct over a six-year period.

### A CAPITAL IDEA

The above examples assume that Bill donates $200,000 in cash. *Better:* Bill donates appreciated assets.

*Example:* Bill funds his DPGA with $200,000 worth of securities that he bought for $100,000 several years ago. If he sells these securities, he'd net $180,000, after paying a 20% capital gains tax. By donating them instead, he benefits from a $200,000 fund rather than from the lesser sum of $180,000.

*Spreading the gain:* As mentioned, Bill has a $100,000 basis in his $200,000 worth of donated assets—a 50% ratio. The value of the annuity payable to Bill and Bonnie is calculated at $160,000. Thus, the capital gain is determined to be $80,000...50% of $160,000.

At ages 65 and 62, their joint life expectancy is 23 years. Their $80,000 capital gain is, for tax purposes, spread evenly over 23 years. (If someone else had been named as an annuitant or if the contract was assignable, the entire $16,000 [$80,000 x 20%] tax would be owed immediately.)

*Tax-free income:* The remainder of each annuity payment (beyond the portion subject to capital gains tax) will be part ordinary income and part tax-free return of capital,

under an IRS formula. If either Bill or Bonnie outlives their 23-year life expectancy, all subsequent annuity payments will be fully taxed as ordinary income.

In addition to the advantages described, DPGAs are easy to create and free of administrative costs.

Many charities are glad to set up specific annuity arrangements for contributors. The annuity payments are the legal liability of the charity issuing the contract, so ongoing payments are secure as long as you deal with a reputable and substantial organization.

# Frequent-Flier Miles...and Taxes

Randy Petersen, publisher, *InsideFlyer,* 4715-C Town Center Dr., Colorado Springs 80916. He is also editor of *The Official Frequent Flyer Guidebook.* Randy Petersen Publishing.

Frequent-flier miles are so widespread these days that they seem like another form of money. They've even become an issue in divorce settlements and in estate planning. The federal government's knee-jerk reaction, of course, is to tax frequent-flier miles.

*The current situation on frequent-flier miles and taxes...*

### NOT TAXABLE INCOME

Despite all the talk, there is presently no chance that the act of cashing in frequent-flier miles will be treated as income, subject to income tax. *Reasons...*

•The IRS has studied the matter and decided that the expense of monitoring and enforcing a tax on frequent-flier miles would be greater than the revenue that would be brought in by such a tax.

•Imposing an income tax on frequent-flier miles would be extremely unpopular with the 10 million travelers (voters) who cash in miles every year. With the federal budget in surplus now, there's no need for any politician to take the risk of proposing such a tax.

## CAUGHT BY A NEW SURTAX

Realizing that a direct tax on frequent fliers wouldn't be popular, Congress found an indirect way to tax them. The *Taxpayer Relief Act of 1997* included a *hidden tax* on frequent-flier miles.

**Background:** Whenever you buy an airline ticket you pay a surtax. Revenues from this tax are earmarked for airport improvements, security measures, etc.

But when you cash in frequent-flier miles, you do not pay this surtax. This means that millions of airport users—those traveling on frequent-flier miles—avoid paying the airport usage tax each year.

In an attempt to plug this loophole, the 1997 Act imposed a 7.5% surtax on "miles," though not on frequent fliers themselves.

**Who pays:** This tax is imposed on "industry partners," such as hotel chains and car rental companies that offer miles to customers.

When those customers cash in miles for airline tickets, the companies owe tax on the value of the transaction.

**Point:** There is no surtax if the miles are redeemed for hotel rooms, rental cars and so on. So the clear purpose of the law was to tax air travel.

**Result:** Some frequent-flier partners—hotels, for example—are eating the tax while others are passing it on to users. Those who are passing it on may or may not be disclosing the fact.

**What to do:** Don't alter your travel plans. The amounts involved are tiny, less than 1% of the cost of a room, for example, not worth switching hotel chains or car rental companies for.

## GIFT OF MILES FROM THE IRS

The big news about frequent-flier miles relates to taxes—but not to the taxation of miles.

The IRS has announced that taxpayers will be able to pay their taxes with credit cards. American Express, Discover and MasterCard already have signed on, with Visa likely to follow.

Especially for those who pay quarterly estimated taxes, this is a great opportunity to put thousands of dollars on a credit card and earn thousands of frequent-flier miles.

**Catch:** The program will be administered by private entities, which charge fees for their efforts. If fees are 2% to 3%, as expected, it won't be worth using a credit card for your tax bill just to earn miles.

Nevertheless, the opportunity to charge your taxes may be welcome if you're short on cash. Being able to earn miles as well can make a good deal even better.

# Family Home Saved from IRS...By a Trust

A couple put their home in a trust benefiting their five-year-old son, then continued living in it. Later, the IRS tried to seize the house for back taxes. It said the trust was fraudulent because the couple owed a tax debt when it was set up, and the trust was a sham because the couple still used the home as their own.

**Court:** The trust had a genuine purpose, to assure the house would pass to the son. The tax debt that had existed when it was set up had been paid, so the trust hadn't been set up to avoid taxes. And the trust's terms restricted how the couple could use the home, so it was not a sham. Thus, the trust was valid—and the home was beyond the reach of the IRS.

*In re: Eugene T. Richards, Jr.,* Bankr ED Pa., No. 97-14798DWS.

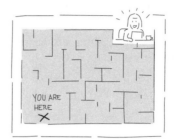

# 7

# Business and Career Smarts

## Starting Your Own Business with Just $10,000 Down

**B**y investing as little as $10,000, you can be part of an already established company—and be your very own boss.

Experience isn't usually required when you buy a franchise, and most high-quality franchisers will train you. But you'll dramatically increase your odds of succeeding if you buy into a chain that puts its responsibility to serve its franchisees first...and its desire to sell new franchises second.

To improve the odds that your investment will pay off...

●**Consider franchisers whose trademarks are well established.** Many entrepreneurs-to-be underestimate the power of a known brand name to generate sales. They think they can get the same results with a lesser-known competitor that offers a lower franchise fee.

*Reality:* A little-known franchise is often much more challenging and less rewarding than a large brand-name one.

That's because copycat franchises generally don't have the well-developed training and support programs that helped put their bigger-name predecessors on the map.

*Special opportunity:* If you discover a small chain that you are convinced is the next market leader, make sure that its franchise fee is much lower than the market leader's.

It may be worthwhile to ask an experienced franchise lawyer to compare the numbers.

●**Look for a strong, independent franchisee association.** At the best companies, organized groups of franchisees play a big role in shaping the franchise system. These groups

---

Robert Purvin, CEO and chairman of the board of trustees, American Association of Franchisees and Dealers, 3636 Fourth Ave., Suite 310, San Diego 92103. He is author of *The Franchise Fraud: How to Protect Yourself Before and After You Invest.* John Wiley & Sons.

are involved in everything from creating new products to developing the franchise agreement.

If a problem develops at your own franchise, this group will be a powerful advocate for you in dealing with the parent company.

Unfortunately, at some companies, the franchisee association is a powerless puppet of the parent company. That's a sign to stay away.

*Self-defense:* The quickest way to tell if a franchisee association has any clout is to study the company's franchise agreement.

The best companies detail how often they will meet with the franchisees and exactly which matters they will discuss with the association. But don't just rely on the contract.

Call a sampling of the company's franchisees across the country and ask whether they are satisfied with the franchisee association.

In some chains, franchisees have found that the parent company is more responsive to franchisees that are located near headquarters than to the far-flung ones.

Most companies publish a list of their franchisees in their Uniform Franchise Offering Circular (UFOC). This is the legal and financial disclosure document that the company must send to you before you invest.

●**Be wary of franchises that operate "company stores."** If the company operates franchises and company-owned stores, at some point, the corporate stores are likely to become your competitors.

*Reason:* The parent corporation is more likely to favor the company-owned stores if their interests clash with yours.

The best way to determine whether the parent company's stores are likely to become your rivals is to speak with the company's franchisee association. The parent company should be able to direct you to a representative.

Ask the representative and other franchisees if competition with the company-owned stores has been a problem in the past...or if the franchisee association believes that these stores are likely to become a problem in the future.

Also be wary of chains that compete through mail-order, department store or discount store sales.

●**Focus on franchises that are dedicated to franchising as their primary method of distribution.** Like companies that sell their merchandise through company stores, those that sell through supermarkets or other venues may also be in competition with you. A franchiser will have a much stronger incentive to help you succeed if it depends on its franchisees for profits.

Ask the representative from the parent company how the company distributes its products and what percentage of its sales are generated through each avenue.

●**Ask the franchiser how much you can expect to earn.** About 20% of franchise companies issue a document called an "earnings claim." It provides data and/or projections to help you evaluate how much money you can expect to make if you decide to buy one of their franchises.

*Beware:* Avoid companies that tell you they are prohibited by law from providing information about potential earnings.

Current laws allow franchisers to make earnings claims as long as they provide reasonable data to back up their projections. Having reliable data to evaluate your potential profits is essential. You should not invest without sufficient data to make an informed decision.

*Trap:* Some companies will try to divert your questions about an earnings claim by advising you to ask their franchisees how much they earn. That information will not help you make an informed decision. Franchisees are not required to tell you how much they earn.

Although it is important to get feedback from existing franchisees, you can't hold your franchiser accountable for false data that franchisees might provide you.

### LEADING LOW-COST FRANCHISES

The franchises below meet most of the criteria outlined above.

And—most of these franchisers will also help you secure a loan to pay the costs that exceed the one-time franchise fee.

●**American Leak Detection**/*Palm Springs, California,* specializes in stopping leaks in people's homes and swimming pools.

***Franchise fee:*** Starts at $49,500. 800-755-6697. www.leakbusters.com.

• **Straw Hat Pizza**/*Dublin, California,* is owned entirely by a nonprofit co-op made up of individual store owners. It has shown extraordinary responsiveness to member concerns.

***Membership fee:*** $10,000. 925-829-1500. www.strawhatpizza.com.

• **Sylvan Learning Centers**/*Baltimore,* is the nation's leading provider of supplemental tutoring for families and schools.

***Franchise fee:*** $44,000–$46,000. 800-284-8214. www.educate.com.

• **Taco John's Restaurants**/*Cheyenne, Wyoming.* In 1994, the management of this Mexican restaurant chain teamed up with the franchisee association and wrote one of the fairest franchising contracts around.

***Franchise fee:*** $22,500. 800-854-0819. www.tacojohns.com.

# First Impressions

Whoever extends a hand first has an advantage in a business handshaking situation. Being first gives a person a little extra control. So—always be ready to shake hands. Keep your right hand free of food, drinks, files and papers at business functions and in other settings conducive to shaking hands.

*The First Five Minutes: How to Make a Great First Impression in Any Business Situation* by Mary Mitchell, president, Uncommon Courtesies, business-communication consultants, Philadelphia. John Wiley & Sons.

# To Overcome Fear of Cold Calling

When making cold calls, remember that rejections hurt only for an instant—and you will probably never talk to the same person again. Set goals for the number of calls you want to make each hour and each day—

and give yourself small treats for reaching your goals. Set a specific goal for each call. *Examples:* Tell yourself you will be satisfied if you just dial the number and introduce yourself… or will be pleased if you get to offer to send out a catalog. *Key:* When you feel hesitant, do not wait to start calling. Just pick up the phone and call.

David Dee, editor, *Outbound Selling,* 4660 N. Ravenswood Ave., Chicago 60640.

# New-Job Benefits

When negotiating with a prospective employer, have information that shows how much you get in bonuses, deferred compensation, vacation time, health insurance and benefits at your current job. *Try to get:* A signing bonus that matches the current-year bonus and any stock options you will be giving up…vacation time equivalent to what you have now …waivers of any waiting period before the new health insurance kicks in. *If relocating:* Ask for help in finding an appropriate position for your spouse.

Edward Hansen, associate in the benefits firm of William M. Mercer, Inc., 2 World Trade Center, 54 fl., New York 10048.

# Look Before You Sign

Employment agreements, including non-compete agreements, are reaching more employees—including middle managers and lower-level workers. *Self-defense:* Don't sign a document without reading and understanding it completely. Be sure to ask what your financial penalty will be if you leave before the agreement ends…if the agreement lets you be fired at will or only for cause…what the conditions of termination are…what happens if the company merges or is taken over.

Michael Karpeles, head of the employment law group, Goldberg, Kohn, Bell, Black, Rosenbloom & Moritz, Ltd., Chicago.

# The Hiring Interview Works Both Ways Today

Janet Reswick Long, president, Integrity Search, Inc., executive search and consulting firm, Springfield, PA, quoted in *Management Review,* 1601 Broadway, New York 10019.

In today's competitive employment market, a skilled applicant at a job interview is likely to be evaluating the company as much as the company is evaluating the applicant.

To attract the *best* job candidates, who have more than one job opportunity open to them, the company today must strive to make a good impression on job applicants just as applicants try to make a good impression on the company. From our survey of 897 professionals, the top problems that applicants report with hiring interviews...

- Interviewer not prepared/focused . . . . . .39%
- Lack of feedback on status . . . . . . . . . .38%
- Inadequate description of the job . . . . . .37%
- Kept waiting an unreasonable
  length of time . . . . . . . . . . . . . . . . . . .24%
- Next step in process unclear . . . . . . . .23%
- Process was too long and complicated . . .17%
- Interviewed by two or more people
  at the same time . . . . . . . . . . . . . . . . .14%

*Helpful:* Examine the company's own interview process and cure it of these faults to boost the company's chances of hiring the best people.

# How to Screen Out Violence Before You Hire

Lynne Falkin McClure, PhD, president, McClure Associates Management Consultants, specialists in workplace relationships, Box 40637, Mesa, AZ 85274. She is author of *Risky Business: Managing Employee Violence in the Workplace.* The Haworth Press.

The best way to avoid workplace violence is to avoid hiring high-risk employees in the first place. Unfortu-

nately, there's no fail-safe way to spot potential troublemakers. But there are a number of techniques to greatly reduce the chances of hiring someone with violent tendencies...

- **Psychological testing.** Widely used tests, such as Myers–Briggs Type Inventory, are inexpensive, and no in-depth training is required to administer them. But such tests basically assess the applicant's personality—not his psychological makeup. Psychological tests, such as the Minnesota Multiphasic Personality Inventory (MMPI), must be administered and interpreted by a trained psychologist, and can cost more than $500 per person to complete. There are also legal risks involved in using such tests.

- **Create a profile of on-the-job behavior that could result in violence.** Through experience, it can be established that certain types of behavior—such as excessive irritability...aggressive language...theft, etc.—are signs of potential violence. With that, you can ask questions about new candidates' behavior at past jobs...and about how the applicant might react in a work situation.

- **Background checks.** I strongly recommend that employers check the background of employees before they are hired. That doesn't mean digging into the applicant's personal life. But check to see if the applicant has a criminal record or has ever been in prison. Such information is public record.

*Note:* Run all prehire screening practices past your attorney to make sure everything you do complies with the laws of your state. In some states, you can refuse to hire an applicant because of a criminal record. In other states, you can't.

# Boss-Management Basics

- *Perfectionist boss:* Assure him/her that the completed task looks great...that there is little risk in moving ahead...and that *inaction* is riskier.

- *The procrastinator:* Tell him that if you don't hear otherwise, you'll start working on the project you've been discussing on a certain date.

•**The timid boss:** Build up his ego whenever possible.

•**Wishy-washy boss:** If you have a wishy-washy boss who goes off on tangents, confront him with the most important issues first.

Julius Eitington, president, Innovative Training Concepts, Rockville, MD, and author of *The Winning Manager: Leadership Skills for Greater Innovation, Quality and Employee Commitment.* Gulf Publishing.

# How to Give Bad News

When you have bad news to give, do not delay. Choose a setting where the other person can hear the news in dignity and the two of you can handle it responsibly. Give the news in a forthright way—but with a sympathetic, supportive manner. Do not make bad news sound negotiable if it is not. *Example:* If someone is being fired, the decision is not reversible. Acknowledge and respond to the other person's feelings. Whatever he/she says, help him find something hopeful in the situation. And help him figure out what to do next.

*There's Something I Have to Tell You: How to Communicate Difficult News in Tough Situations* by Charles Foster, PhD, psychotherapist in private practice, Boston. Harmony.

# How to Speed-Read People

Paul D. Tieger and Barbara Barron-Tieger, consultants in West Hartford, CT, who have helped organizations work with personality types for more than 15 years. Their most recent book is *The Art of SpeedReading People.* Little, Brown & Company.

Treating others as you would like to be treated *isn't* the most effective way to deal with them. It only works with people who are similar to you.

**Problem:** The words and gestures that would win you over might antagonize someone else.

You'll be much more successful if you can quickly "read" people's words and actions and change your approach to fit their personalities.

## MODIFY YOUR STYLE

Some people think if they adapt their behavior to suit other people, they aren't being true to themselves...or they simply don't want to bother.

But modifying your style benefits you. Whether you're dealing with a boss, coworker, customer or your child's teacher, you're more likely to get what you want if you communicate in a way that makes the other person receptive.

A good way to read people's key personality characteristics is to think in terms of four dimensions. You can learn to recognize where a person falls within these four dimensions and choose the most effective way to deal with him/her.

## INTROVERSION/EXTROVERSION

This quality has to do with how people get energized—from interacting with others...or by being by themselves.

*Clues:* Extroverts are easy to recognize. They talk a lot, think out loud and are animated when they're around other people. Introverts are calmer, speak more slowly and think before they speak.

*To reach an Extrovert:* Don't just let him talk—voice your opinions...keep the conversation moving...cover many topics—Extroverts get bored quickly.

*To reach an Introvert:* Ask for his thoughts —Introverts don't volunteer them. Listen carefully...resist the urge to finish an Introvert's sentences...discuss one thing at a time...if possible, make your points in writing...and give him time to reflect on them.

## SENSING/INTUITION

This refers to the kind of *information* we focus on. Sensing types prefer concrete facts... Intuitives are more concerned with the underlying meaning and implications of those facts.

*Clues:* Sensors are direct and to the point. They keep their sentences short, with each thought following systematically from the last one. They use a lot of facts and details when they talk. They remember the past with amazing accuracy.

Intuitives speak in longer, more complicated sentences. They are not *linear* thinkers—their thoughts jump around. They're more likely to use analogies and metaphors than facts. They talk about global issues...the big picture...the future.

**To reach a Sensor:** Present your information methodically, step by step. Come armed with facts and examples—how much will the project cost...how long will it take...who will carry out each task? Emphasize practical applications.

**To reach an Intuitive:** Talk about possibilities rather than details...use metaphors... brainstorm...emphasize the implications. What could this project mean for your company? Your industry?

### THINKING/FEELING

This quality reflects how we make decisions. Thinking types prefer logic and impersonal analysis. Feeling types are driven more by their emotions and personal values.

**Clues:** Thinkers assert themselves easily. They come across as objective and detached—even blunt. It's hard to offend them. Many Thinking types have a habit of numbering the points they make ("There are two things wrong with this idea—first...second..."). They enjoy a good argument.

Feelers have obvious emotional ups and downs. They are diplomatic, avoid conflict and are quick to compliment others. Feelers tend to reveal a lot about their personal lives—by keeping family pictures on their desks and talking about what they like to do after hours. They also use a lot of "value" words, such as *wonderful, terrible, beautiful* and *ugly.*

**To reach a Thinker:** Make sure your argument makes logical sense...appeal to his sense of fairness...stress consequences.

**Example:** If you need time off to visit a sick relative, don't talk about how important the person was to you while you were growing up. Instead, explain how your work will get done while you're away—and how much more productive you'll be once you've taken care of this situation.

**To reach a Feeler:** Start by finding points of agreement...express appreciation...discuss "people" concerns.

### JUDGING/PERCEIVING

This dimension has to do with how people structure their daily lives.

Judging types tend to be highly organized, formal and time-conscious.

Perceivers are typically more casual, spontaneous, unconventional—and disorganized.

**Clues:** Judgers tend to be right on time for their appointments, have a take-charge attitude, complete one project before starting another, move quickly and purposefully, have tidy work and living spaces and like rules and systems.

Perceivers may procrastinate, are more playful, move at a slower pace, enjoy starting projects more than finishing them, use qualifiers when they speak ("The best I can tell...," "I could be wrong, but..."), and keep gathering information and changing their plans.

**To reach a Judger:** Be punctual...be efficient and well-prepared—don't waste time...be definitive, not tentative...stick to existing plans.

**To reach a Perceiver:** Expect lots of questions, and welcome them...encourage the person to explore options...be willing to change plans.

---

# Employees Can be Much Better Than They Are

Nathaniel Branden, PhD, a practicing psychotherapist in Los Angeles and an international corporate consultant who specializes in issues of accountablilty and self-esteem. He is author of 19 books, including *Self-Esteem at Work: How Confident People Make Powerful Companies* and *A Woman's Self-Esteem: Struggles* and *Triumphs in the Search for Identity,* both published by Jossey–Bass.

Employee self-esteem has traditionally been a subject for the analyst's couch. However, in today's business environment it doesn't make sense to leave it there.

**Key:** How an employee feels about him/herself directly affects job performance and, ultimately, business success. Employees who are constantly second-guessed, micromanaged and punished for every shortcoming end up resisting change, avoiding risk-taking behaviors and passively following the pack.

A company staffed with this type of employee won't last long.

### WINNING ATTITUDE

On the other hand, employees who are empowered to do their jobs and are respected for their ingenuity—even though their ideas occasionally fail—are energized by change...eager to conceive and try new things...and are genuinely interested in working with and helping others.

This type of employee helps organizations prosper and grow.

Successful business owners know that they must be confident enough to hire and nurture intelligent, self-assured employees.

*Reason:* If you feel insecure or undeserving of success, you won't be able to applaud employee ideas and successes and inspire them to greater achievements.

So—the first step to building confident employees is to work on yourself. *Recognize that...*

•**Hiring smart people will help you and your organization be more successful.** Smart, creative people will challenge and inspire you to be smarter and more creative yourself and will give you new perspective on your business.

•**Competence beats incompetence.** You'll have more time to do long-range planning if you hire employees who can work independently...and avoid those who need your input and approval minute by minute to do their jobs.

•**Doing more means accomplishing less.** If you play the Lone Ranger and insist on meeting every customer and managing every project yourself, employees will feel second-guessed and cut off from both you and the business.

•**Other people's ideas, initiatives and accomplishments in no way detract from yours.** Some of the most creative products and services are developed by teams of people whose ideas "piggyback" on each other.

### ENCOURAGING CONFIDENCE

Employees' self-esteem at work is bolstered—or undermined—by the company's culture and by the personal relationships you and other managers have with employees. *To build confident employees...*

•**Create a culture in which it is understood that everyone—at every level—is expected to treat everyone else with courtesy and respect.** Let people know they'll be evaluated on their treatment of others and their ability to be a team player in regular performance reviews.

•**Make sure each person knows specifically what he is responsible for.** People who are clear about what is expected of them are more likely to be confident about meeting those expectations.

*Beware of task confusion.* Several years ago, the CEO of a medium-sized business asked me to help him find out why there wasn't a higher level of accountability in his firm. I asked each senior manager to write a memo stating what, precisely, he understood himself to be responsible for and also what he'd like to be responsible for.

What surfaced was tremendous confusion. In some cases, two or more executives held themselves exclusively responsible for the same part of the business. In other instances, no one claimed responsibility. We did the same exercise at each level of the organization and found the same confusion. No wonder people didn't feel confident and empowered.

•**Give people assignments that stretch their known capabilities.** Challenging people helps them grow and helps build self-esteem.

*Caution:* Be careful not to overwhelm people with new and different responsibilities. An office assistant might rise to the challenge of booking a conference center and making hotel reservations for clients who will be attending a conference.

If asked to plan the conference in its entirety, however—to determine a theme, set an agenda, find a lunchtime keynote speaker and arrange for experts to lead concurrent sessions—he is likely to feel overwhelmed.

•**Acknowledge accomplishments and excellent performance.** Recognition of outstanding work should be public and enthusiastic. But—to preserve people's dignity, correct mistakes quietly and in private.

When an employee takes intelligent risks, solves a problem or accomplishes something extraordinary, broadcast the employee's story throughout the organization. Other employees will see what kinds of behaviors are desired and rewarded. They'll also feel good to know that you recognize and appreciate their colleagues' efforts.

●**Create an environment in which people feel comfortable expressing disagreements—and airing grievances.** Convey respect for differences of opinion and don't punish dissent.

*Example:* Make eye contact with employees...listen actively to what's being said...don't permit yourself to adopt a condescending, superior, sarcastic or disapproving tone...and work with employees to understand situations and/or solve problems.

*Effective:* Ask, "What is the situation/problem/disagreement?"..."What does the work require?"..."What do you think needs to be changed or done about the situation?"

Avoid ego-focused questions, such as, "Whose wishes will prevail, yours or mine?"

●**Share information freely.** The objective is to enable every employee to understand how his work relates to the broader goals of the organization.

●**Make sure people have the authority and resources they need to do their jobs.** Find out what employees need to do their jobs to the best of their ability—and then provide it. When people feel they have little or no control over their work, they become unmotivated and feel negative about you and the company.

*Question to ask:* "What do you need to feel more in control of your work?"

# Eight Major Money Mistakes Made By Company Managers

Malcolm P. Moses, president, Malcolm P. Moses & Associates, financial consultants and crisis managers, 3428 Hewlett Ave., Merrick, NY 11566.

As a financial consultant to small and midsized companies, most of them privately owned, I see many money mistakes made by owners and managers. Here are eight, and my advice on avoiding them...

●**Imprudent use of company cash.** This can include everything from excessive executive salaries and/or perks, to large officer loans and advances, the purchase of equipment that doesn't produce an increase in cash flow and speculative investment of the company's cash.

*Best:* I much prefer to see employees rewarded by a reasonable base salary and incentive compensation for their own or the company's performance.

As for loans and advances to company officers, that cash could much more profitably be applied to the prompt payment of the company's payables, permitting discounts that will improve the bottom line.

In the purchase of equipment, my rule is to look for a three-year payback of investment. Any piece of new equipment should increase cash flow by doing the job better, faster or more productively. But if it won't pay for itself in three years, forget it.

Never speculate with excess company cash. Instead, invest it only in the safest kind of instruments—Treasury bills, or CDs from strong banks.

●**Not having a formal business plan or cash flow and profit-and-loss projections.**

*Essential:* Every company needs a formal business plan, including projections, to help it get the best return on its investment. A plan tells you where, when and for what purpose funding will be needed. Cash flow and profit-and-loss projections are equally important disciplines for management. Without these projections, the company probably won't deploy its cash properly and won't have the advance warning needed to line up adequate financing in a timely manner.

### ● Senior management not monitoring actual disbursements versus budgeted amounts.

*Warning:* By not tracking these actual expenditures, the company could easily run into unexpected cash flow problems. And that could happen at the most damaging time.

It's not only important to know when expenses are running ahead of projections, but also to find out why and take corrective action.

### ● Not keeping track of accounts receivable turnover.

*Monitor:* When a company's accounts receivable turnover goes from, say, an average of 32 days to 41 days, it's a clear warning of possible credit deterioration. It's also an indication that the credit manager may not be doing his/her job properly.

### ● Not jumping on delinquent accounts receivable.

*My advice:* Delinquent accounts tie up the company's cash. I recommend looking at any account that ages 10 days past due, and keeping collection pressure on from that time until the account debtor pays. Many delinquencies over 60 days old may indicate that the company is not doing adequate credit checking prior to making sales. Or that serious problems exist within the accounts receivable department.

### ● Not communicating adequately with key suppliers and bankers.

*Critical:* Keep key suppliers and bankers informed of the company's progress as well as its problems. When there are problems, you need to explain what the company is doing to make things improve, such as employing new sales management, adding capital or cutting expenses.

It's an old adage in the banking community that bankers don't like surprises. That could result in lower availability of cash just when the company needs it most to promptly meet its obligations, or to take advantage of bargains that may become available in the marketplace. Make it a habit to not only keep in touch with the company's account officer at the bank, but also, if possible, with other senior officers. Bank turnover these days is so great that every contact counts.

### ● Making acquisitions without proper investigation.

*Important:* Entrepreneurs are by nature enthusiastic, but they must resist rushing into deals without doing a thorough investigation of the condition of the target company. Even if its product is a good one, every acquisition or new venture carries potential problems, sometimes severe enough to swamp a healthy company. A pretransactional thorough financial and operational review should discover potential pitfalls.

### ● Not getting adequate tax advice.

*My advice:* The importance of getting good tax advice on all your business plans and operations can hardly be overstated. By sitting down with the company's accountant, it's possible to take maximum advantage of available deductions and tax credits…and to avoid many costly tax headaches later. Be certain to ask questions so that you are satisfied that you are receiving the maximum tax benefits.

# Hidden Profits… All Businesses Have Them

Barry Schimel, CPA, founder and president of The Profit Advisors, Inc., 932-32B Hungerford Dr., Rockville, MD 20850. He is author of *The Profit Game: How to Play, How to Win.* Capital Books.

With today's tricky economy making it very difficult for companies to simply grow their way to bigger profits, there's much to be gained from learning how to be more profitable *without* getting bigger. Profit enhancement is what we help clients achieve—no matter what business they're in and regardless of their size.

### A PROFIT AUDIT

It's amazing how many companies have *marketing plans,* and perhaps *business plans,* that they can show to their bankers. But very few have taken the extra step of developing *profit plans* that could explain to the banker what their *real* profit potential is down the road.

***Important:*** Traditional profit projections, based on a previous quarter's or the previous year's performance, are very limiting. When the company or a salesperson reaches those budgeted goals or exceeds them slightly, there's an inclination to sit back and do no more.

***Much better:*** A profit plan that builds in a continuous incentive to improve. Think of it as reaching for the stars—you may never get there, but you'll get a lot farther than if you failed to try.

To come up with new profit ideas for clients, we examine each of the five areas of the business—sales and marketing...personnel...financial matters...operations...and issues of organization. It is not unusual to find hidden profit potential in all areas. But most companies are strong in some areas and weak in others. Our job is to build up the weak areas so that instead of dragging down profits, they can contribute and even become profit centers.

***Example 1:*** A brick and block manufacturer complained of flat sales. In reviewing its operations, we noted that the drivers who were routinely delivering building materials to customers on construction sites were never given a key role to play. Since they were out there every day, seeing what was going on in the construction business, we proposed making them new-business scouts.

Each driver now goes out with a lead-opportunity pad on which he/she can record signs going up for new construction sites, new holes being dug, etc. If the company's salespeople end up getting new business from these leads, a percentage commission goes to the driver who came up with them.

There's no way to budget for these additional sales, but they definitely represent new profit potential for the company...and these profits will continue year after year.

***Example 2:*** A specialty liquid gas distributor found that by paying drivers a commission based on the number of used tanks they picked up from customers, it could save $340,000 being spent on buying new tanks. Previously, the drivers would take used tanks if customers insisted, but there was no policy to encourage drivers to pick up the old tanks.

***Example 3:*** A trash hauler planning to increase its business by 10% expected to pay 10% more in landfill fees. That was before we found that its drivers and helpers never got out of the truck while it was being weighed. By lightening the load this little bit every trip, the company actually saved $100,000 year after year instead of having to pay extra fees.

### PEOPLE POTENTIAL

An obvious way businesses have to save money and improve profits is to lay off employees. We find, however, that layoffs aren't always necessary. With most companies, the problem is not too many people, but too much work...often *unnecessary* work. *One of my favorite rules of thumb:* There's nothing more unprofitable than doing unnecessary work more efficiently.

***Example:*** We worked with one bank where there were 25 people compiling data they thought were required by the internal bank auditor. These employees had been doing this work for many, many years.

When we gathered everyone in the same room to discuss the work process, the auditors spoke up to say they never looked at these data and didn't need them—at all. This was the first time anybody had ever asked them!

Now, those 25 people have been reassigned to productive work that will help the bank boost deposits and thereby become more profitable.

### PRICING OPPORTUNITIES

In today's low-inflation economy, many companies are complaining of their inability to boost profits by raising prices. But often there are ways to do this when a company knows which products or services its customers value most.

Hire a third party to do in-depth research. In our experience, these surveys result in adding or dropping products or services...as well as repricing them.

***Example:*** We were able to help a wine and spirits distributor pinpoint an inventory of a special California wine. The wine was in strong demand, and it could easily justify a much higher markup than the standard markup the distributor applied to its entire inventory. *Result:* An added $350,000 of recurring profits.

### "BARBARA WALTERS" QUESTIONS

One of our most effective techniques for discovering hidden profit opportunities is to ask a series of what I call "Barbara Walters" questions. They are questions that are tough to dodge and force you to be honest with yourself. Any company can do this itself. *Ask questions such as...*

•**What does the company do best?** If no one knows, there's an obvious problem. Working toward a good answer, though, usually results in strategies that boost the company's core operations and increase profits.

•**What products or services should we eliminate?** Everyone in management has an answer to this, but usually no one asks for it. When the tough answers come out, unprofitable activities are eliminated and profits jump.

•**Exactly who are our customers?** Often money is wasted on efforts to reach the wrong people in the customer's company...or the wrong prospect altogether. Analyzing customers in terms of profitability is a powerful way to cut marketing waste and...again... increase profits.

# Tricky Overtime Traps for Businesses

Peter M. Panken, Esq., Epstein, Beeher & Gleen, 250 Park Ave., New York 10177.

Federal wage and hour laws governing overtime pay are a major trap for unwary businesspeople. Many businesses—large and small—often find out by complete surprise that they have unwittingly committed violations.

*Extent of the risk:* Liability for overtime that should have been paid, but wasn't, can extend as far back as three years and can amount to big, big bucks if many employees are involved. Typically, the issue of overtime arises when an employee is dismissed and consults an attorney to discuss filing a wrongful discharge lawsuit. If there are no grounds for such a suit, an aggressive plaintiff's attorney may decide to file suit for overtime violations instead.

*Here's how to steer clear of the most common pitfalls...*

•**Know the law.** The federal Fair Labor Standards Act (FLSA) requires employers to pay most workers at least minimum wage for the first 40 hours worked in a week, and an overtime rate of time-and-a-half their regular rate for any hours worked beyond that. But certain white-collar employees—such as executives, certain administrators and professionals—are exempt from the overtime rule.

To be exempt as an executive, an employee's "primary duty" must be managing—as opposed to doing manual or other nonexecutive tasks. This means that the person must spend more than 50% of his/her time on managerial duties. The person must also regularly direct the work of at least two other full-time employees or their equivalent. In other words, the person could supervise four people working 20-hour weeks. He must also have the authority to hire or fire other employees and regularly exercise discretionary decision making.

In addition, the employee must be paid a salary of no less than $250 a week.

The biggest problem occurs with supervisory workers whom employers consider to be exempt because they think these employees are managers. But often their duties are split. One week, one of these workers may function as a manager. But the following week, the person might do manual labor or routine office work.

*Strategy 1:* Make sure you have a job description for every exempt worker that accurately describes the employee's duties. This will provide some protection if the person later sues for overtime on the grounds he was not an exempt managerial employee.

*Strategy 2:* Make sure that all employees— even supervisors—sign a time sheet. If employees are required to sign in and out every time they report for and leave work, it will help to reduce the company's liability in future overtime disputes.

*Key:* Having a clear record of how many hours exempt employees worked should help to prevent future differences of opinion.

•**Avoid deducting less than a full day's pay for illness for exempt employees who have exhausted their allotment of sick days.** Under the federal law, employees who are exempt from overtime must be paid a predetermined amount each week, whether they work six days or one day that week. Only certain limited pay deductions—such as those for tax withholding, Social Security, retirement contributions and union dues—are allowed. If you make other deductions, you may sacrifice the exemption from overtime. That means that deductions for partial sick days are specifically prohibited.

*Example:* A company has an exempt employee who has used up his sick leave and takes off an additional four hours to visit his doctor. To preserve his exemption from overtime, you can either "dock" this worker a full day's pay or allow him to take the additional time off with no deduction at all.

• **Avoid using disciplinary suspensions without pay on workers you think are exempt.** Some employers follow a policy of "progressive discipline"—to ensure that everyone who requires disciplining gets the same treatment.

*Example:* After one or two warnings, they may suspend a worker without pay for a day or two to punish certain infractions.

*Trap:* With exempt employees, this is another prohibited deduction. If you impose such disciplinary suspensions without pay for exempt employees, you have negated their exemption from overtime status.

• **Do not assume that placing someone on high salary exempts that person from overtime requirements.** Employees still need to meet the requirements of the FLSA to be exempt from overtime pay. Common mistakes involve newspaper reporters, personnel recruiters and film or sound producers. These professionals typically earn high salaries, but may meet none of the other FLSA criteria of nonexempt employment.

• **Be discriminating in determining who must be "on call" via telephone or pager.** Employees who are "standing by" and required to report to work if they are called should be paid for their waiting time, even if they are not actually called. Similarly, employees who are required to carry pagers and report to work when paged should be paid for their on-call time.

*Bottom line: All* of the time that employees spend on call is considered compensable time, and if an employee's total compensable hours exceed 40 in a workweek, you must pay over-time. However, you do *not* have to pay employees who can be called but are not required to be reachable or can refuse to report.

• **To reduce overtime costs for possible exempt employees, use a fluctuating workweek.** To do this, management and employees agree on a predetermined amount of pay that covers all hours the employees work in any workweek—no matter how many hours they work. To determine their regular rate of pay—which will serve as the base for figuring the overtime rate each week—you divide their weekly salary by the number of hours they have worked each week. The number of hours worked, and the regular rate of pay, will constantly fluctuate.

*Key:* Overtime is still paid, but at 50% of the employee's regular rate of pay for the week, because you have already paid the employee the base rate for all hours he has worked.

*Example:* The company has a fluctuating workweek agreement with an employee who gets a salary of $400 a week, whether he works 30 hours a week, 40 hours a week or 50 hours a week. Assume that without such an agreement, this employee would get $400 for a 40-hour week, for a base wage of $10 an hour. If the person worked 50 hours, his overtime would be $15 an hour multiplied by 10 extra hours, or an additional $150 for that week.

But since the person is on a fluctuating workweek, his base pay for a 50-hour week would be $8 an hour ($400 weekly wage divided by 50 hours). Since the fluctuating workweek agreement means that he has already been paid his base rate for all 50 hours he worked that week, his overtime would be only an additional 50% of that base rate, or $4 an hour. So his overtime pay would be only $40 (10 hours of overtime multiplied by $4).

Thus, the fluctuating workweek means the company saves $110 in overtime pay for that week ($150 normal overtime minus the $40 that was actually paid).

# The Best Benefit Plans for Small Business

Avery E. Neumark, Esq., CPA, director of employee benefits and executive compensation at the accounting firm of Rosen Seymour Shapss Martin & Company, 757 Third Ave., New York 10017, and adjunct professor of tax at Brooklyn Law School and Fordham University School of Business.

Employee benefit plans can help you attract and retain capable employees. *Bonus:* They provide substantial tax advantages to your company as well as to key managers—including you, as owner–executive.

### RECIPE FOR A
### RICH RETIREMENT

There are different types of company sponsored retirement plans, so you must choose the one that works best for your company. Smaller businesses seem to prefer SIMPLEs and SEPs (described below) because they require less active administration. However, these plans are less flexible with respect to contributions and benefits.

●**Savings Incentive Match Plans for Employees (SIMPLEs).** Created in 1996, these plans may be used by firms with 100 or fewer employees. They can be structured as IRAs (everyone invests his/her own way)…or 401(k)s (participants pick from a menu of investment choices).

As the name suggests, SIMPLEs require little paperwork. There's no nondiscrimination testing so you can maximize contributions to your own account regardless of whether any employees elect to participate.

Contributions under a SIMPLE–IRA to your own account cannot exceed $12,000 per year, including a 100% company match. Other retirement plans permit greater contributions. In some cases, SIMPLEs can be expensive because of mandatory contributions on behalf of your employees.

*Bottom line:* SIMPLEs work if you're content with a relatively small retirement plan contribution to your account.

●**Simplified Employee Pension (SEP) plans.** SEP plans have been around longer than SIMPLEs…and they still are available.

Again, paperwork is minimal—there are no IRS reports to file. Contributions may be as much as $24,000 in 1999, twice as much as SIMPLEs allow.

Even at $24,000 per year, allowable contributions aren't as great as they are with some other plans. All the contributions come from the company and there is no skewing permitted on behalf of key employees.

*Bottom line:* SEP plans work if you want an inexpensive, no-hassle plan and you can accept the $24,000 limit on your own contribution.

### PAPERWORK PAYOFF

Other types of retirement plans require more administration. Nevertheless, the benefits may be greater.

●**401(k) plans.** Originally used by major corporations, many small companies now offer 401(k)s. Economical packaged plans are available from banks, insurers, brokers and mutual fund families.

Employees fund most—or even all—of their own retirement by deferring current income. Contributions from employer and employee may be as much as $30,000 per year. In 1999, employee deferrals can't exceed $10,000 per year.

Because of complex nondiscrimination rules, highly paid executives may not be able to come close to the $30,000 limit.

*Bottom line:* 401(k) plans are suitable if you want to provide a retirement plan, yet have your employees pick up the tab. If you and other key executives run into restrictions, you can increase contributions with a companion profit-sharing plan (see below) or nonqualified plan.

●**Profit-sharing plans.** These may be the most popular retirement plans among small companies.

The business owner has flexibility as to how much or how little your business contributes each year. By pairing a profit-sharing plan with a money-purchase plan,* a modest annual commitment is made—but you gain the ability to receive contributions up to $30,000 per year.

*A money purchase plan is a defined contribution plan in which the company's contributions are mandatory and are usually based solely on compensation.

"Vanilla" profit-sharing plans may require substantial expenditures on behalf of rank-and-file employees.

***Bottom line:*** These plans may be good for companies with a few low-paid employees, but most small companies will prefer to skew benefits to the key executives (see below).

●**Stepped profit-sharing plans.** By integrating plan benefits with Social Security benefits…and/or contributing more on behalf of older employees who have fewer years to build a nest egg (age based) or through cross-testing, many small companies can tilt contributions toward key personnel.

With a sophisticated plan, in 1999 top executives may receive $30,000 annual contributions while most employees get small contributions, perhaps as little as 3% of pay. In some cases, over 90% of the company's contributions can go into the accounts of the owner–executives.

These plans are expensive. Expect to spend several thousand dollars in upfront costs—plus a few thousand dollars each year for administration. The extra benefits accruing to the company's owners may be worth the added cost.

***Bottom line:*** If you work with a benefits professional, you may find a skewed profit-sharing plan is the best choice for the owner of a closely held company.

●**Defined benefit plans.** These are real pension plans. They promise to pay certain amounts in retirement.

With a defined benefit plan, your company may contribute (and deduct) amounts much larger than $30,000 per year to your account.

Defined benefit plans are expensive to administer, they lock your company into fixed contributions even in bad years, and they may require high contributions for certain employees.

***Bigger problem:*** The stock market has done so well lately that these plans may be fully funded and no additional deductible contributions can be made.

***Bottom line:*** If you're in your 50s or 60s with a much younger crew of low-paid employees, a defined benefit plan may be worth the cost.

●**Nonqualified plans.** These plans promise future compensation, at which time the company will get a deduction and the recipient will owe income tax. They're often offered in addition to other plans, such as those described above.

These plans can be targeted at a select group of employees, usually key personnel. They avoid most federal regulations governing retirement plans.

Nonqualified plans don't qualify for upfront tax deductions or tax-free accumulation.

***Exceptions:*** Money may be set aside in permanent life insurance policies, to provide tax-free buildup and access to the cash value, but this strategy requires careful implementation.

***Bottom line:*** Nonqualified plans can help motivate essential managers, especially if other retirement plan contributions are capped at $30,000 per year.

---

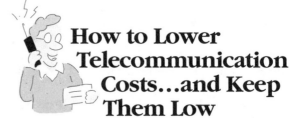

# How to Lower Telecommunication Costs…and Keep Them Low

Bruce Thatcher, president, TelCon Associates, a firm that provides consulting and cost reduction of telephone and utility services for companies of all sizes. Overland Park, KS.

---

Controlling telecommunication costs has become a stressful challenge for most businesses—thanks to a staggering number of new services and new technologies coming on the market almost daily.

Competitive offers multiply, each a little different from the last. Phone companies, resellers and cable companies all try to sell more sophisticated services and more complex technologies…promising big savings in return.

Yet—billing errors abound, costing businesses hundreds of millions of dollars each year. In fact, our experience in auditing corporate telecom bills for more than 25 years shows that *most* companies are paying far more for telecommunication services than they need.

Here are some strategies to help your business cut its telecom costs by thousands of dollars a year…

•**Be aggressive in seeking better rates.** With many other more pressing matters to claim their attention, business owners tend to forget about cutting their telephone costs. And if you're not a major customer, it's easy to slip through the cracks once a telephone company has made the original sale. So don't be shy about asking for the cheapest deal.

*Example:* You might call your current service provider and say that you've had an offer from a rival firm. Ask if your service provider can match it. Or you might note that your provider is advertising a special rate for new subscribers and ask if you can get the same rate. You may be able to save 10% or more on monthly charges just by asking.

•**Share a phone line and a fax line.** This saves money because you're using a single line for two different services.

*Example:* Your business has four regular telephone lines and a dedicated fax line. But only three of the phone lines are usually busy, and the fax line is busy only a few minutes each hour. By eliminating the fax line, and using the fourth phone line for faxes as well as for outgoing calls, you could save as much as $50 a month in some areas.

•**Make sure you really need all the services you're paying for.** Many companies add phone lines as they expand, but forget to eliminate other services they needed only when they were smaller.

*Example:* A business begins with one phone line that has both call-forwarding and call-waiting service. Then it grows and adds four new phone lines. Call-waiting and call-forwarding are no longer needed—since there are now more people—but the cost of these services is imbedded in the monthly phone bill, which is not itemized. By eliminating these two features, the company saves almost $160 a year.

*Helpful:* Ask the phone company for a copy of your company's customer service record. This record—which is typically furnished to you only when you first start telephone service—provides the key to understanding your monthly telephone bill. As your calling patterns vary, and phone service changes, the customer service record summarizes the important elements of your account.

The telephone company may balk, and tell you that you won't be able to read and understand your service record. But by obtaining this document, you will be able to figure out what all the funny letters and codes on your phone bill mean. And by understanding the bill, you'll be able to intelligently decide which services to keep…and which to drop.

•**Consider asking for a "seasonal disconnect."** If yours is a seasonal business, this allows you to disconnect some phone services during the months when you are not using them, and to reconnect—with the same telephone number—during your busy periods.

This can reduce your phone bills by 50% or more, and can be ideal for businesses that have just a few peak months a year, such as tax preparation firms and Christmas decorating firms. It could also be useful if you operate an apartment complex and have several phones in the sales office plus an additional phone out by the pool that is used only in summer. You could use the seasonal disconnect for the pool phone only.

•**Defend against "slamming."** This term—which refers to rival long-distance phone companies signing up new accounts without the customer's express approval—is a notorious business rip-off.

One of my clients—an automobile dealer—was slammed four times in three months. He didn't notice until he started getting bills from a strange service for much more than he had been accustomed to paying.

To prevent this from happening to you, ask your provider for a Primary Interexchange Carrier (PIC) Freeze. You will then receive a document that says your telephone service cannot be changed unless you make such a request in writing.

•**Be alert to billing fraud.** In California, for example, some unscrupulous companies deliberately inflate certain charges—say, imposing a $9.95 charge for a minimum collect call that normally costs about $1. They count on business owners being too busy to scrutinize their monthly phone bills.

Because it's a scam, these third-party billing agents will erase the inflated charge as soon as you question it. But it's important to review all your phone charges—especially if they are showing up month after month.

**•Dispense with "wire maintenance" charges.** This covers the cost of maintaining the connection from the pole outside your building to the office telephone jack.

Even though the cost is modest—usually just $1.25 per line per month—you don't need this coverage unless you are in a very hazardous area, perhaps one that is prone to earthquakes or flooding.

If you decide to opt for this coverage, make sure you're being charged for the right number of phone lines. It's not unusual to be charged for an extra line or two by mistake.

Nothing, though, can beat the experience of a client who was being billed for *120 phone lines* with wire maintenance charges. It turns out the phone company made a typing error and added an extra "0" to the 12 lines our client actually had. We recovered $40,000 in past overcharges due to the mistake.

**•Make sure you have the right cellular phone plan.** After you buy a cell phone, it usually takes two or three months for your usage to settle into what will be its normal pattern. Sometimes you'll be better off with the plan that seems more expensive.

*Example:* You sign up for a plan that charges $24.95 a month, gives you 30 free minutes and charges 25 cents or 34 cents a minute for each additional minute, depending upon the time of day.

After several months, your normal usage averages 670 minutes and you end up paying almost $170 per month. You'd be better off with a plan that charges $99.95 a month but gives you 1,000 free minutes, since there would not be any additional charges.

**•Ask for group discounts for cellular and digital phones and pagers.** While cell phone and pager services are often promotionally priced, you can usually do better than what's advertised if you are buying in bulk.

*Example:* Service for a single pager might run $15.95 per month, but you might be able to get the tab down to $10.95 per month if you are buying one for each of your five repairmen on the road.

**•Sign up for special cost-saving calling plans.** Don't assume that the plan you started out with is still the best for your company today. Businesses grow and contract, and calling patterns change.

The plan that is best for your business right now depends upon your calling patterns.

If your business makes most of its calls to local phone numbers, then a plan that allows unlimited local calls is most economical. If it makes most of its calls to distant areas, then a measured-rate plan may be cheapest.

Choosing the right plan for your company's phone usage could save hundreds of dollars a month.

# Phone Card Security

Give employees prepaid calling cards rather than company-owned telephone credit cards. The company will *save money* by eliminating per-call charges and getting lower rates. And prepaid cards are *safer* because the risk of loss is limited to the value of the card. *Result:* If a card is lost, there's no risk of the company becoming vulnerable to phone fraud as it might if a credit card falls into the wrong hands.

Harry Newton, founder and former publisher, *Teleconnect,* 12 W. 21 St., New York 10010.

# Computer Crime Self-Defense

M.E. Kabay, PhD, CISSP, director of education, International Computer Security Association, 1200 Walnut Bottom Rd., Suite 3, Carlisle, PA 17013.

Most of the damage that is caused to business computing systems is the work of employees with access to those systems who are dishonest...angry ...careless...or untrained. *Self-defense...*

**•Thoroughly check references and backgrounds** before hiring information technology employees. Provide ongoing training and security-awareness programs for these employees.

•**Enforce a formal policy** that bars employees from giving out *any* unauthorized information about the company's computer systems. And—name one person to be responsible for all outside contacts regarding the company's computing systems. As part of this policy, require the manager to verify all outside requests for information before answering any questions.

*Aim:* To foil computer hackers who break into computer systems using information obtained from the company's own employees. They often get the information they need by simply calling and asking questions about the system, posing as service personnel who need the information to make "remote" repairs.

•**Continuously update the company's network software.** Using outdated network software creates another window of opportunity for outside hackers to invade your company's computing systems.

*Helpful:* Subscribe to the Computer Emergency Response Team-Coordination Center (CERT-CC) advisories about computer hacker activity, and install software patches whenever the reports indicate a need.

CERT-CC (available on-line at www.cert.org) studies Internet security vulnerabilities, provides incident response services to sites that have been the victims of attack and publishes security advisories to help businesses improve computer security.

# Protect Your Phone System Against Fraud And Abuse

Neil Sachnoff, president, TeleCom Clinic, a telephone research and consulting company, 4402 Stonehedge Rd., Edison, NJ 08820.

New technology continuously provides skilled high-tech hackers with new tools to infiltrate company phone and computer systems with relative ease.

Unfortunately, most companies are unaware of their vulnerability to abuse. Here are some steps all companies should take to protect their phone and computer systems from attack…

•**Call the police if you detect fraud.** Many business owners and telecommunications managers simply don't consider phone fraud a prosecutable offense. Or—they fear that if they involve law enforcement, their company will be exposed as vulnerable to high-tech infiltration. But—telecommunications fraud that goes unreported gives perpetrators confidence to continue their work.

•**Change phone system passwords** as soon as a disgruntled employee with access to the phone system and computer network leaves. In a recent case, an unhappy employee quit, subsequently dialed into his former employer's computer network and caused file servers to crash.

•**Review your bills every month.** Be wary of international calls and 800 calls that exceed 20 minutes. Many 800 numbers are masked 900 sex-line numbers, and unless you analyze your bill, you'll never catch the abuse.

•**Never use default passwords** for voice mail or other telecommunications products. Hackers know these default codes and are amazingly good at finding companies that don't change them…thereby gaining easy access.

•**Physically secure your phone system.** In many companies, telephone switching equipment is located in unlocked closets or utility rooms. To find the best way to secure this equipment—24 hours a day—consult a locksmith or security expert.

# How to Know Who Visits Your Web Site

Collect information about visitors to the company's Web site by asking them to fill out a questionnaire…

•Provide a reward for filling out the questionnaire—such as a subscription to a special electronic newsletter.

- Clearly state that the information collected will be kept private and not sold to others.

- Have plans for integrating the information collected directly into databases used for internal marketing and other purposes, to earn a real benefit from it.

- Use the questionnaire to create a relationship with customers. Ask for information that will enable you to contact them in the future regarding matters of interest to them. Don't settle for just compiling a list of visitors.

- Stick to what you really want to know and can use, because every question asked will lower the response rate.

*Seth Godin, president, Yoyodyne, an Internet marketing database company, 1 Bridge St., Irvington, NY 10533.*

## Insure Against Web Site Liabilities

*John Kennedy, partner and intellectual property specialist, Morrison & Foerster LLP, 1290 Avenue of the Americas, New York 10104.*

Businesses that establish Web sites encounter a whole new range of legal risks. That's because many aspects of electronic publishing and communication are not clearly governed by existing laws.

Small businesses—especially those that obtain their first broad exposure on the Internet—may encounter legal traps they have never had to consider before. *Examples...*

- Lawsuits over domain names similar to trademarks used by other businesses.

- Copyright disputes over the use of text, graphics, images and photographs.

- Slander and libel suits, especially over comments posted in chat rooms.

- Suits over loss of confidential information, such as if hackers steal a list of customers' credit card numbers.

General liability insurance often *won't* cover a company's "new" activity of Web publishing.

*Self-defense:* New insurance products are being designed to *specifically* protect against liabilities related to Web sites.

When establishing your Web site, consult an attorney to identify the potential legal risks associated with your Web file. Then—ask an insurance adviser what kind of liability protection is available to cover those higher risks.

## Legal Traps In Contests On the Web

*Ira P. Rothken, attorney, Rothken Law Firm, 21 Tamal Vista Blvd., Suite 202, Corte Madera, CA 94925.*

Companies increasingly are using promotional contests to attract visitors to their Web sites. Even a small business can attract nationwide attention to its Web site with a popular contest, without the marketing costs of traditional advertising.

*Trap:* A promotional contest must be carefully designed to avoid being deemed an *illegal lottery* under local law. And a contest run on the Internet must meet the rules in *all 50 states.*

*General rule:* A contest is considered an illegal lottery if it awards a prize, requires contestants to pay something of value to enter and the outcome is based on chance.

All promotional contests offer prizes, so firms that sponsor them must beware the "entry fee" and "game of chance" conditions by making entries free and/or making contests games of skill. *Traps...*

- Not charging a cash entry fee does not make a contest "free." Anything of value required of contestants may be deemed an entry fee.

*Example:* If contestants are required to fill out a long questionnaire, the information on it may be deemed to be an "entry fee," and the contest an illegal lottery.

- Any element of chance in selecting a winner may make a contest a "game of chance" even if some skill is involved.

*Example:* One company held a contest in which it asked contestants to write an advertising jingle for it. A court held that the work that went into writing the jingle amounted to an entry fee…and that because the company didn't specify objective criteria upon which the winner would be selected, the selection was arbitrary—and thus a matter of chance. The jingle-writing contest was held to be an illegal lottery.

*Safety:* Promotional contests on the Internet have to pass legal muster in all 50 states, so consult with a lawyer who is expert in the field when designing it.

•**Expecting the buyer to run the business as you would.** Don't sell a business unless you are willing to accept whatever the new owner will do to it, or to its employees.

•**Neglecting management.** Don't focus so much on trying to sell a business that the job of running it is neglected. If the business declines, you'll lose the chance to sell it as well.

# Selling Your Business… Important Checklist

Steven Elek, partner, Pricewaterhouse Coopers, Philadelphia, quoted in *Nation's Business,* 1615 H St. NW, Washington, DC 20062.

A privately owned business is likely to represent almost all—or at least most—of its owner's wealth.

To get the best price when selling a business, avoid these traps…

•**Being unprepared.** It's impossible to know when a "surprise" potential buyer may appear. Always have documented financial statements and business plans ready that can turn an interested party's curiosity into a real desire to buy.

•**Managing the sale yourself.** The buyer probably will have much more experience at buying businesses than you have at selling them. Have an experienced financial expert or attorney on your side.

•**Marketing the business yourself.** If employees see you "shopping" the business, morale will be shaken and key employees may defect. You'll also weaken your negotiating position with potential buyers who know you want to sell.

*Better:* Use an investment banker or business broker who can find you the right buyer discreetly.

•**Counting on deferred payments.** You can never know about the firm's future profits, especially after you sell—so don't count on being paid out that way.

# Big Tax Breaks for Small Businesses *Only*

Barbara Weltman, Esq., practices in Millwood, NY and is author of several books, including *J.K. Lasser's Tax Deductions for Your Small Business,* Fourth Edition (Macmillan), and *The Complete Idiot's Guide to Starting a Home-Based Business* (Alpha Books).

H aving a small business rather than a large one isn't such a bad deal tax-wise. It's the small businesses that pull in the biggest tax breaks.

*Key question:* How is "small" defined for the purpose of qualifying for these breaks?

There's no single definition. "Small" means something different for each tax benefit—gross receipts, number of employees, level of equipment purchases, capitalization, etc.

### EXEMPTION FROM THE AMT

C corporations, like individuals, must calculate their *Alternative Minimum Tax* (AMT) and their regular income tax and pay the greater amount.

*New law:* Small C corporations are exempt from AMT starting this year. This exemption not only saves tax, but also eliminates the considerable bookkeeping required for the various AMT computations.

***Definition of "small" for AMT exemption purposes:*** Small corporations are those with average annual gross receipts of $5 million or less in tax years beginning after December 31, 1993, and ending before the tax year for which the AMT exemption is claimed. (The $5 million limit does not include the current year.)

New corporations are exempt from AMT for the first year of their existence.

Once a corporation meets the $5-million-or-less definition of a small corporation, the exemption remains available to the corporation until its average annual gross receipts exceed $7.5 million for more than three years.

Even after the exemption is lost because the company gets too big, the previously exempt company starts anew for AMT purposes.

**Impact:** AMT liability is then based on adjustments and preferences from transactions and investments entered into after loss of small corporation status.

**Planning opportunity:** Small corporations can now consider using key-person insurance and life insurance to fund buy–sell agreements.

In the past, proceeds of such policies were subject to AMT. A company that's now exempt from the AMT can buy these policies and receive the proceeds tax free.

**AMT credit:** Small corporations that are exempt from AMT are still eligible for the AMT credit, but it is reduced.

**Limit:** The allowable AMT credit for small corporations is limited to the amount by which regular tax liability (reduced by other credits) exceeds 25% of the excess (if any) of regular tax (reduced by other credits) over $25,000.

**Example:** A small corporation's regular tax liability is $45,000. Its minimum tax credit is limited to $40,000, that is, $45,000 minus (25% of $45,000-$25,000).

### SMALL-BUSINESS STOCK

Owners who sell stock in their small businesses can take advantage of *two tax breaks* to avoid—or defer—tax on their gain…

• Up to 50% of gain up to $10 million can be excluded on eligible stock held more than five years.

• Gain can be postponed by buying stock in another qualified small business within 60 days.

**Caution:** The original stock must be held for more than six months to qualify for this deferral.

**Definition of qualified small-business stock:** It means stock issued after August 10, 1993, which is acquired at original issue from a domestic C corporation. The corporation's assets cannot be more than $50 million and the company must conduct an active trade or business.

### EQUIPMENT EXPENSING

Businesses can choose to *expense*—write off in the year put in service, rather than depreciate—up to $19,000 of equipment purchases in 1999 ($20,000 starting in 2000).

**Definition of "small" for equipment expensing purposes:** This benefit is limited to smaller companies since the dollar limit is phased out dollar for dollar for equipment purchases over $200,000. In 1999, no expensing is permitted if the company places equipment in service costing more than $219,000. Equipment must then be depreciated.

### SIMPLES

Small businesses now can offer retirement plans to their employees at a modest cost and with minimum paperwork. The new kind of plan is a *Savings Incentive Match Plan for Employees*—or SIMPLE. SIMPLEs are primarily funded through employees' salary reduction contributions. The plans can be set up either as SIMPLE IRAs or SIMPLE 401(k)s.

Employers automatically meet nondiscrimination requirements as long as they make certain employer contributions—explained below.

**Definition of small businesses for SIMPLE purposes:** Refers to employers with 100 or fewer employees who received at least $5,000 in compensation from the employer in the preceding year.

Employers who maintain a SIMPLE for one year but thereafter have more than 100 employees can continue the SIMPLE for two years following the last year of being eligible.

Employers who qualify are required to make either of the following types of contributions…

• **Matching contributions** which are dollar for dollar up to 3% of compensation—reduced to as low as 1% of compensation under certain conditions.

Compensation for purposes of SIMPLE IRAs under this contribution formula means total compensation—the $160,000 annual compensation limit (for 1999) does not apply here.

• **Nonelective contributions** which are 2% of compensation without regard to employee contributions. Given these formulas, in 1999, the maximum required contribution for any employee is $6,000. That only applies to someone earning $200,000 a year and contributing the maximum $6,000 to the SIMPLE IRA.

### MEDICAL SAVINGS ACCOUNTS

Companies are always looking for ways to reduce the cost of health insurance for employees. Small employers have a unique alternative.

They can maintain a high-deductible health insurance plan and then contribute to their employees' Medical Savings Accounts (MSAs) or let their employees make such contributions.

***Definition of small employers for purposes of making MSA contributions:*** Companies with 50 or fewer employees on average during the two preceding calendar years (for new employers, it is the expected average during the current year).

Companies continue to be treated as small employers until the year following the first year in which they have more than 200 employees.

And even after the companies lose their small-employer status, employees can continue to make contributions to their own MSAs as long as they are still employed by the same employer (employer contributions are no longer allowed and new employees cannot start contributions to MSAs).

"Small employer" also includes self-employed individuals who can contribute to their own MSAs on a tax-deductible basis as long as they have a high-deductible health insurance plan.

Contributions to MSAs made by employees of small employers, and self-employeds, are deductible above the line. Contributions by small employers to their employees' MSAs are excludable from the employees' income and deductible by the employers.

# Business Tax Strategies From Ed Mendlowitz

Edward Mendlowitz, CPA, partner, Mendlowitz Weitsen, LLP, CPAs, Two Pennsylvania Plaza, Suite 1500, New York 10121. He is author of eight books on taxes, including *A Practical Guide to Transferring Your Business to the Next Generation*. Practical Programs, Inc.

## Best Ways to Take Money Out of Your Company

When you take money out of your company, Uncle Sam always wants a large share of it. But if you're careful, very little need be lost to taxes. *For starters, be sure to make full use of the following tax-saving loopholes...*

**•*Loophole:* Enter into a payback agreement with the company.** Under such an agreement, if the IRS deems a salary payment to be unreasonable compensation, the money is considered a loan to you—the shareholder—to be repaid to the corporation. You get a personal tax deduction in the year the money is actually repaid.

***Example:*** Suppose the IRS disallows $100,000 of the salary you reported as income and the company deducted in 1998. By agreement you treat the money as a loan from the company, and repay it in 2000. You can deduct the full $100,000 on your individual income tax return for 2000.

***Reason:*** There are limits on how much your company can pay you as salary because the IRS wants to minimize salary write-offs for company bigwigs. If your salary is out of line with what owners of similar businesses pay themselves, the IRS will call it "unreasonable" and deny much of the company's deduction.

The excess is considered to be a dividend payment, nondeductible by the company, and taxable to the recipient.

***Self-defense:*** Avoid unreasonable compensation issues with the IRS by documenting in corporate minutes the reasons the company is paying such a high salary.

The IRS examines salary patterns carefully. A salary that varies from year to year depending on the company's profitability is more suspect than one that increases gradually over the years.

**S corporations:** Tax planning for salary payments is difficult if you operate your business as an S corporation.

S-corporation income is taxed on your personal return, not the company's. (Also, you owe Social Security and Medicare taxes on money paid to you as salary.) So you will want to take as little salary as possible from an S corporation, rather than as much as possible.

•*Loophole:* **Take out a disability insurance policy in your own name.** At the end of the year, when you know that you will not collect any money on the policy, ask your company to reimburse you for the amount of the premiums.

*Reason:* If your company pays the premiums on a disability insurance policy, the premiums are deductible. But, if you subsequently collect the disability insurance, you will owe tax on the amounts you receive. But, if you pay the premiums yourself, the money you collect under the policy is not taxable.

*Caution:* This plan is subject to nondiscrimination rules similar to those in health insurance plans.

•*Loophole:* **Premium payments used to fund a medical insurance plan** are deductible by the corporation and are not considered income to the owner/employee.

*Caution:* Because all eligible employees must be covered by the plan, this strategy works only in companies with few or no employees. This is not applicable for S corporations.

•*Loophole:* **Have your company buy millions of dollars of group term life insurance.** The premiums will be fully deductible as long as the group term life coverage is not discriminatory. The strategy will create a big tax savings.

*How it works:* You ask your company to pay for a $1 million life insurance policy. You must pay tax on your personal return on the amounts deemed income by the IRS, that is, premiums on coverage in excess of $50,000, based on IRS tables. But new tables effective July 1, 1999, substantially lower your deemed income.

*Your net cost:* The amount of tax owed, which is substantially less than the policy premium you would have to pay if you bought the policy yourself.

•*Loophole:* **Use company cash to pay the premiums on split-dollar life insurance.** The corporation will own the policy to the extent of premiums paid, and you will own the death benefit in excess of the premiums paid.

•*Loophole:* **Life insurance trust.** Instead of holding the policy in your own name, put it in an insurance trust to keep the proceeds out of your estate.

•*Loophole:* **Put your children to work in your business.** Pay them at least $2,000, deduct their salaries and have them put $2,000 into Roth IRAs. The children can't deduct the Roth contributions, but the deductions would be worth little anyway because of their low tax brackets.

*Benefit:* The money in a Roth IRA will grow without being taxed and contributions can be withdrawn at any time. Earnings can be withdrawn tax free when the children turn 59½.

*Catch:* You will owe Social Security taxes and unemployment tax on the salaries paid to your children.

*Note:* If you are *self-employed,* you don't have to pay Social Security and Medicare taxes on wages paid to children under 18.

More loopholes from Ed Mendlowitz...

## Answers to the Questions My Business Clients Most Frequently Ask

Some tax questions are invariably asked by my business clients, regardless of the kind of business they're in. Here are a few of the tax loopholes I've learned to give out with my answers to their questions...

•**How can I put more money away in my company retirement plan for myself than I put away for my employees?**

*Loophole:* When business owners are more than 20 years older than other company employees, they can set up a defined benefit pension plan instead of a defined contribution plan. This will accomplish your goal.

Owners can put away more money for themselves than for other employees in such a plan because they are funding a specific benefit (not putting away a percentage of salary), and they have fewer years to do so.

*Loophole:* In general, defined contribution plan contributions must be in proportion to employee salaries. However, 5.7% more can be contributed on behalf of people who earn more than the Social Security wage limit ($72,600 in 1999).

### •I missed the deadline for setting up my company retirement plan. What can I do?

*Loophole:* Most qualified pension and profit-sharing plans must be set up by the end of the company's fiscal year. But a SEP (Simplified Employee Pension) plan can be started as late as the due date of the company's tax return, *including any extensions.*

### •I don't have the money to fund a retirement plan, but I will by early next year. What can I do?

*Loophole:* Set up the plan by signing the trust documents before the end of the business's fiscal year. Once a Keogh or qualified pension or profit-sharing plan is set up, it need not be funded until as late as the due date of the company's tax return, including extensions.

### •How can I pay for my child's education with the company's money?

*Loophole:* Businesses can set up plans that pay up to $5,250 in tuition per employee annually. *Limit:* Generally, people who own more than 5% of a business and their dependents cannot use tuition plans.

*Loophole:* A business owner's child who works for the company is eligible if he/she is over 21, owns no company stock and cannot be claimed as a dependent on his parents' tax return.

### •How can I keep more of the proceeds when I sell the business?

*Loophole:* Owners of closely held C corporations who plan to sell their businesses should consider switching to S corporations. Proceeds from the eventual sale will be taxed only once then—not first at the corporate level and again as shareholder dividends.

*Trap:* Any "built-in gains" will be taxed twice if the company is sold within 10 years of making the conversion to an S corporation.

*Solution:* Determine the company's fair market value on the date of the election. The double tax will apply only to built-in gains as of that date.

### •My company has retained earnings that I don't really need to put back into the business. What should I do with the money?

*Loophole:* Buy a split-dollar life insurance policy. Use excess corporate funds to buy personal insurance coverage at very little tax cost.

*Here's how:* The corporation will own the cash value of the policy or the amount attributable to the premiums paid, whichever is less—and an irrevocable life insurance trust set up on behalf of the business owner will own the policy's death benefit.

### •How do we cut the taxes on the company's investments?

*Loophole:* Consider switching from interest-producing investments such as bonds, to preferred stock. Corporations that receive dividend income from domestic corporations do not have to pay taxes on 70% of that income.

### •My corporate capital loss carryforward is expiring soon. What should I do?

*Loophole:* Corporate capital losses can be carried forward only five years and must be offset against capital gains. You can buy shares in a mutual fund that typically pays high capital gains dividends to soak up the losses.

### •What should I do with my excess inventory?

*Loophole:* Companies that donate inventory or depreciable business property to charity can deduct their cost plus 50% of the unrealized appreciation in the goods or equipment.

*Caution:* This is available only to C corporations, not S corporations.

### •How can I give my children shares in the business without owing gift taxes?

*Loophole:* To reduce the value of the business in your estate, give a minority interest in the business to your children so that you can maximize the $10,000 annual gift-tax exclusion ($20,000 if the spouse joins in the gift).

*Here's how:* Create two classes of stock, voting and nonvoting shares in the company. Give the nonvoting shares to the children. Because the shares lack voting privileges, the IRS lets you value them at discounts ranging from 25% to 50% of the voting shares.

*Loophole:* Consider putting business real estate in trust for family members. The income produced by the properties may be taxed at the children's lower rates, and the value of the property is removed from the eventual estate of the business owner. The property's appreciation will also be out of the estate.

### • What's the best way to put my kids on the company payroll?

*Loophole:* If you employ your children in the business during holidays and vacations, you can pay them up to $4,300 in salary that is free from federal income tax in 1999.

*Strategy:* The children will have $3,971.05 left after Social Security and Medicare taxes are paid. Have them put $2,000 of that money into a Roth IRA, where it will compound tax free over time. If they keep the Roth IRA until they are at least 59½, they will never have to pay out any tax on that money and its earnings.

---

**And Finally from Ed Mendlowitz...**

# Small-Business Loopholes

Careful planning with a tax professional will lead the owner of a small business to many ways to cut his/her tax bill. *Biggest opportunities...*

#### MEDICAL EXPENSES

Medical insurance premiums and other medical costs are generally personal expenses deductible only to the extent that, in total, they exceed 7.5% of AGI.

*Loophole:* When you're a C corporation, it's possible to deduct all of the medical costs you incur for yourself, your spouse and dependents. *Key:* Have the company set up a corporate medical reimbursement plan.

*Caution:* Such a plan must cover all eligible company employees or it won't pass IRS muster.

*Loophole:* S corporation owners, partners and other self-employeds can deduct 45% of their medical insurance premiums as an above-the-line write-off on page one of their personal income tax returns.

#### TAX SAVINGS

All income earned by C corporations is taxed at graduated rates that begin at 15%.

*Loophole:* Dividends earned by the business that are paid to it by domestic US corporations generally are 70% tax free.

*Strategy:* Invest any free cash the company has in preferred or other dividend-paying stock of US corporations. If you put the cash in a money market account, the interest you earn will be 100% taxable.

*Loophole:* Because the first $50,000 of income is taxed at only 15%, a corporate format could be valuable for a business that wants to accumulate earnings—or one that has high nondeductible costs like expensive cars, high travel and entertainment costs, steep life insurance premiums, etc.

#### PAYROLL TAXES

All payroll taxes incurred by businesses must be collected and paid over to the tax authorities.

*Loophole:* Sole proprietors who have their own children—younger than 18 years old—on the business payroll do not have to pay the 7.65% Social Security tax on their wages, nor do the children have to pay their share.

*Loophole:* If you have a child on the payroll, consider putting up to $2,000 a year of the child's business earnings into a nondeductible Roth IRA. The money accumulates tax free in a Roth IRA, and withdrawals, many years later, are also tax free.

*Loophole:* Earnings retained in a C corporation are not subject to payroll taxes. Earnings of an S corporation are taxed on the individual shareholder's return and no payroll taxes are owed.

#### SPOUSE ON THE PAYROLL

Salaries paid to spouses who work for the business are deductible if they are ordinary and necessary business expenses.

*Loophole:* When spouses are on the payroll, even for small amounts of salary, the costs of business trips that include the spouse can be fully deducted.

*Trap:* Putting a spouse on the payroll could double the amount of Social Security tax the family pays. Each spouse will have to pay 6.2% of up to $72,600 of salary in 1999.

## RETIREMENT PLANS

Businesses with qualified pension or profit-sharing plans can deduct amounts contributed to the plan. And employees pay no tax on those contributions until withdrawn.

*Loophole:* When you set up a SEP or a SIMPLE plan, the paperwork is greatly reduced and no tax filings are required for the plan.

*Problem:* The amounts that can be contributed are lower for these plans than for other plans.

## EQUIPMENT WRITE-OFFS

In general, the cost of equipment used in a business must be depreciated over its useful life as determined by IRS tables.

*Loophole:* Small businesses can deduct up to $19,000 paid for equipment placed in service in 1999 ($20,000 in 2000) under Section 179 of the Tax Code.

*Loophole:* Sports vehicles and vans that weigh more than 6,000 pounds are not subject to the luxury car limits and can be depreciated in full over five years.

## BUSINESS LOSSES

IRS rules require that business losses be deducted in full in the year in which they were incurred.

*Loophole:* Unused losses—business income was too low—can be carried back two years or forward 20 years.

*Opportunity:* If you don't want to carry back business losses, you can instead elect to carry them forward.

*Reasons:* You don't want to open past years' returns for audit, or you'd rather use the losses in years in which you earn more income.

## BUSINESS MEALS

As a general rule, only 50% of the cost of business meals is deductible.

*Loophole:* A business that supplies meals to its employees on its premises for its own benefit can deduct 100% of the cost of the food. Employees do not have to recognize the cost of the meals as income.

*Example:* Rather than lose the working hours, an accounting firm orders in lunch for its employees during the busy tax season.

## ALTERNATIVE MINIMUM TAX

C corporations, like individual taxpayers, have to pay the Alternative Minimum Tax (AMT) if the tax calculated under the AMT rules is greater than the tax calculated using regular income tax rules.

*Loophole:* Companies with sales of less than $5 million a year for the three prior years are exempt from AMT this year. New corporations automatically qualify for the exemption.

## ACCOUNTING CHANGES

When the IRS discovers during an audit that a business is using an incorrect accounting method, the adjustment to income must be made on the business's books in the year in which the change is picked up.

*Loophole:* A business that voluntarily changes its accounting method before the IRS discovers it can spread the income resulting from the switch over four years, starting with the year of the change. This will help ease the tax bite caused by the switch.

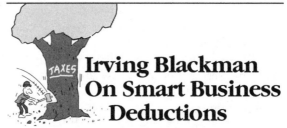

# Irving Blackman On Smart Business Deductions

Irving L. Blackman, CPA, founding partner, Blackman Kallick Bartelstein, LLP, 300 S. Riverside Plaza, Chicago 60606.

# Business Lunch Deduction Dangers

If you eat lunch with the same business associates on a regular basis, you won't be entitled to a business expense deduction for the lunches even if you do discuss business during them.

*Why:* The Tax Court says you have to eat lunch anyhow, so you have incurred no extra expense.*

*Example:* The employees of a small law firm all ate lunch together each day, during which they discussed work. The firm's partners paid for the lunches and deducted them. But the Tax Court denied the deduction, saying that because the firm's employees saw each other all the time, they had no particular business justification for the lunches. They were simply trying to convert the personal expense of lunch into a business expense.

*Anne R. Dugan, TC Memo 1998-373.

*Saver:* You can deduct daily business lunches if you take them with different persons each day and have a specific business reason for each meeting.

The Court suggested that repeated meals with coworkers would be deductible if taken no more often than once a month with each individual.*

---

**More from Irving Blackman...**

# How to Deduct Entertaining Spouses

You can claim a business deduction for the cost of entertaining your own spouse and the spouses of business associates—even if the spouses aren't involved in your business.

Use the "associated entertainment" rule. This allows you to deduct entertainment that is associated with your trade or business, and which directly proceeds or follows a substantial, bona fide business discussion.

*Example:* The night before a business meeting, several out-of-town customers and their spouses come to town. You and your spouse entertain them and their spouses. The next day, you have a business meeting with the customers. The previous night's entertainment is deductible.

Anyone with whom you can reasonably expect to have business dealings can qualify as a business associate—including customers, clients, suppliers, employees, partners, agents and advisers.

*Limit:* Only 50% of the total cost of meals and entertainment is deductible.

---

# Sales and Use Taxes

Kent Johnson, national partner in charge, sales and transactions tax services, KPMG LLP, 3100 Two Union Square, 601 Union St., Seattle 98101.

Sales and use taxes are the hottest area of state taxation today—and a top target of state tax auditors.

*John D. Moss, CA-7, 85-1 USTC ¶9285.

Many businesses pay more in sales and use taxes than income tax, but few plan for them. In fact, many business owners have no idea how much they pay in sales and use taxes, leaving them to the company bookkeeper.

*Danger:* A business may be needlessly overpaying some taxes while underpaying others—piling up a huge back tax bill.

*Opportunity:* Smart planning may enable you to claim a tax refund, escape back tax liabilities, and reduce your future tax bills.

Business owners and top managers should take charge of planning for sales and use taxes just as they do for income taxes. Here's what they need to know...

### UNDERPAYING TRAPS

Businesses can incur sales and use tax liabilities as both buyers and sellers of goods and services.

Most states that collect sales tax on sales made within the state also impose use tax on purchases from out-of-state vendors that are brought into the state for use.

•**Buyer's trap.** Purchasers must self-assess use tax when out-of-state vendors don't collect it. But buyers often think that purchases from out-of-state sellers are "tax free"—and bookkeepers who simply pay what appears on invoices won't pay uninvoiced use taxes.

*Problem:* Unpaid use taxes accumulate annually, creating, with penalties and interest, a major back tax liability. And as businesses make more purchases from out-of-state suppliers by mail order, over the Internet and so on, this problem is growing.

In many states unreported use taxes are the number-one target of state tax auditors.

•**Seller's trap.** Businesses also can owe use taxes on sales they make when they sell across state lines.

Although the purchaser technically owes use tax, states impose collection responsibility on sellers whenever they legally can. So if your business makes interstate sales, it may be incurring use tax liabilities in another state—or in several states—without realizing it.

*Danger:* If you aren't aware you owe use taxes to a state and don't file sales or use tax returns in that state, the statute of limitations does not apply. The state can go back any number of years to collect back taxes. A company may easily incur such liabilities in several states at once.

*Self-defense:* The Supreme Court has ruled that a state cannot impose collection responsibility or use taxes on an out-of-state business that has no physical presence in the state—such as a firm that sells exclusively through the mail or by phone. A company can avoid use-tax liability by limiting its presence in a state.

However, even a slight extra contact with a state may result in liability to collect tax.

*Example:* Having a service representative in the state…attending trade shows in the state.

Each state has its own rules, so consult a sales and use tax expert.

### OVERPAYING TRAPS

At the same time that a business is underpaying some taxes, it may be overpaying others. *How…*

●**The "combined bill" trap.** If a single charge on an invoice includes both taxable and nontaxable items, you may needlessly wind up paying tax on an amount that could have been tax free.

*Example:* You purchase business equipment that's taxable, and the supplier includes training for no charge. If training is not subject to sales tax in your jurisdiction, you'd do better to have the seller give you an itemized charge for the training and reduce the cost of the equipment correspondingly.

●**Taxable status.** Whether or not an item is taxable often depends on how it is used. For instance, some states don't tax equipment used in manufacturing. So if you buy a desktop computer it will be taxable, while if you buy one to run production equipment it may not be. Also, taxable status often depends on precise definitions used in local law.

*Example:* Often prepackaged software is taxable while custom software is not. But what if you customize a commercial software package? You have to check local law.

●**Exemptions.** States and localities have created literally thousands of exemptions for sales and use taxes—such as for items used in research and development and telecommunications equipment. Also, unique special exemptions often exist to serve local community and business interests.

A company that doesn't research the exemptions available to it is very likely to overpay taxes.

●**Varying tax rates.** Tax rates vary by county, town and sometimes street address. If a company operates at several locations, it may have a centralized billing address where the tax rate is higher than where goods are delivered.

*Invoice paying trap:* Sellers won't know how your business plans to use items it purchases, what exemptions may be available to you or whether you are entitled to a lower tax rate than is indicated by your billing address. So they typically will add the "standard" sales or use tax rate to all sales.

If company bookkeepers routinely pay all taxes as they are invoiced, without breaking out tax-free charges and using available exemptions, they may significantly overpay sales and use taxes.

### MANAGING TAXES

●**Use all exemptions.** Ask a local sales tax expert to find all the exemptions and "usage" rules that exempt your business's purchases from tax. You may be entitled to refunds for taxes needlessly paid in the past. Such exemptions will also reduce future taxes.

●**Train the business's bill payers.** Don't handle sales and use taxes by simply "paying the invoice." Give training to those who pay the company's bills so they understand sales and use tax rules, use all the exemptions the business is entitled to and are alert to tax-saving opportunities that arise.

●**Reorganize billing practices.** As both buyer and seller, take care to break out taxable and tax-free charges—such as for equipment and training. As a buyer, this will reduce the tax you pay—and as a seller, it will reduce the tax you have to charge, collect and remit.

●**Restructure operations.** Small changes in the way a business operates, such as eliminating a slight presence in a state, can save big use-tax liabilities.

●**Negotiate back tax exposure.** If you have incurred a big potential exposure to back taxes, hire a tax professional to anonymously negotiate a settlement of them in which you voluntarily agree to pay all future taxes in exchange for a compromise of the back tax liability.

# New IRS Law Brings Enriching Gifts to Business

Phil Brand, partner and director of tax controversy services, KPMG LLP, 2001 M St. NW, Washington, DC 20036. Mr. Brand is former chief compliance officer of the IRS, responsible for managing all IRS administrative and criminal enforcement activities worldwide.

The IRS Restructuring and Reform Act of 1998 gives businesses new rights in their dealings with the IRS and changes several provisions of the tax law to make them apply more fairly to business…

## FAIRNESS FOR BUSINESS

●**Interest relief.** Under the new law, when a business taxpayer and the IRS owe money to each other, the amounts are netted and no interest accrues on amounts that offset.

This change is important to many businesses because the IRS charges a higher rate of interest than it pays—up to 4.5 points more for large corporations.

It is common for businesses and the IRS to owe each other money, sometimes continuously. In such cases under the old law, a company could owe heavy interest charges even when it owed no net tax bill. The new rule ends this inequity.

●**Deposit-penalty relief.** When a business owes a series of tax deposits, such as for employment taxes, a mistake made with a single deposit can set off a cascade of penalties. When the first payment is missed, the IRS applies the second payment to it, leaving the second payment unpaid with a penalty. Then the third payment is applied to the second, and so on.

The new tax law codifies a recent IRS administrative action that provides relief from this problem by letting taxpayers designate the period for which each payment is made. This way, taxpayers avoid cascading penalties

and owe only a single penalty for an initial erroneous payment.

***Caution:*** IRS computers will continue to calculate cascading penalties and send out penalty notices for them—because the IRS will not be able to reprogram its computers to comply with the new law before the year 2000. For relief, the company must make the required designation for a payment during the 90-day period after the IRS's issuance of a penalty notice. In some instances, it may be in your best interest to have the deposit credited in the other manner. The law gives you the choice.

Monitor periodic tax deposits carefully to be able to claim relief in time if a problem arises. Have the company's tax adviser review IRS Notice 98-14 for additional details.

●**Suspension of unassessed interest and penalties.** Under the new law, if the IRS does not send a notice of tax liability within 18 months (after 2003, it's one year) after the date a tax return is due or is filed—whichever is later—interest and penalties on the tax liability are *suspended* until a tax assessment is sent. This provision applies to tax years ending after enactment.

***Advantage:*** When a complex audit runs for years before tax is assessed, this new rule can save the taxpayer large amounts in interest and penalties that would have accrued under the old law. But—there are limitations. The new rule applies only to income reported on personal tax returns—such as business income earned through S corporations, partnerships, proprietorships and limited-liability companies. It does not apply to regular C corporations.

●**Tax adviser confidentiality.** Under the old law, the IRS could examine the "confidential" work papers of a company's own tax adviser because no rule protected the company's dealings with a tax adviser in the way that attorney–client privilege protects dealings with a lawyer.

The new law extends the well-established protections of attorney–client privilege to tax professionals who are authorized to practice before the IRS—including CPAs, enrolled agents, actuaries, etc.

***Caution:*** Don't rely on the new privilege before its full extent is known. It does *not* apply to state tax matters…criminal tax matters…or certain dealings with tax shelter promoters.

Also, just as attorney–client privilege does not protect all dealings with a lawyer, tax adviser–client privilege will not protect all dealings with a tax professional. Details of how the new privilege will apply are yet to be determined.

●**Dispute resolution.** The new law extends to all corporations two dispute resolution programs heretofore generally available only to very large corporations being examined under the IRS's Coordinated Examination Program (CEP)…

●Early referral of issues to IRS Appeals, before an audit is concluded.

●Mediation in tax disputes involving more than $10 million.

The new law makes these options available in non-CEP audits and eliminates the $10 million threshold for mediation, so that it is now available in tax disputes of all sizes.

Also, the law instructs the IRS to develop a test program for arbitration in tax disputes of all sizes.

If the company currently is facing an audit dispute with the IRS, explore these new options.

●**Small claims in Tax Court.** The jurisdiction of the Small Case Division of Tax Court is expanded so it can now hear cases involving as much as $50,000—up from $10,000 under prior law.

Procedures are greatly simplified in the Small Case Division and no attorney is required. This change can be a big help to businesses that fear legal fees may eat up any amount they might win in a court dispute with the IRS.

●**Burden of proof.** The new law shifts the burden of proof from the taxpayer to the IRS when a tax dispute reaches court. Unfortunately, while this provision of the law has received much publicity, it will help relatively few business taxpayers. *Reasons…*

●The shift of the burden of proof applies only in the small number of tax disputes that go to court or at least to pretrial negotiations. The old rules that place the burden of proof on the taxpayer remain in effect when filing tax returns or undergoing an audit.

●The new rule is not available to corporations worth more than $7 million or that have more than 500 employees.

●To get the benefit of the new rule in court, a company must first show that it substantiated the disputed item, maintained records, cooperated with reasonable IRS requests during the audit process and exhausted all administrative remedies before going to court.

These conditions greatly reduce the potential impact of the new rule.

●**Audit protection.** The new law creates new audit rights and protections…

●Agents cannot conduct "economic reality audits" that examine a person's personal lifestyle—such as to determine whether a business owner has reported all income from the business. The only exception is when the IRS has reasonable cause to suspect tax evasion.

●In civil proceedings, the IRS cannot contact third parties—such as bankers, customers or business associates—about a company's tax affairs without first informing the company and giving it a chance to object.

●When the company takes the results of a tax audit to IRS Appeals, the revenue auditors who conducted the audit are no longer permitted to contact the appeals officers to "lobby" them about the outcome of the appeal.

●The IRS cannot coerce restaurants to sign agreements taking responsibility for employee tip reporting by threatening them with audits if they refuse.

●**Collecting fees and damages from the IRS.** The new law makes it easier to collect damages and legal fees from the IRS if it acts illegally or unreasonably.

Under this new rule, taxpayers can sue the IRS for up to $100,000 of damages caused by an IRS employee who negligently disregards provisions of the Tax Code or regulations in connection with collecting taxes. In addition, parties other than the taxpayer can sue the IRS for damages resulting from erroneous collection actions.

*Example:* The IRS issues an illegal lien against your business partner, which damages you. You can sue the IRS.

Finally, a greater amount of legal expenses can be recovered from the IRS by a taxpayer who is a "prevailing party," when the IRS's position in a dispute is found not "substantially justified."

# Andrew Biebl on Business Tax Topics

Andrew R. Biebl, CPA, partner, Biebl, Ranweiler, Christiansen, Meyer, Thompson & Co. Chtd., Box 696, New Ulm, MN 56073. Mr. Biebl is a frequent seminar speaker and writer on small-business topics for CPA professionals.

## Hot Tax-Audit Dangers For Small Business: How to Prepare for Them

Minimize the danger of an IRS audit before the auditor calls. Now is the time to examine your business's audit exposure on the hottest of IRS audit issues.

### HOTTEST RISKS

●**Independent contractors.** Businesses everywhere are making ever greater use of contract workers because of the flexibility.

But the IRS suspects that many firms use these arrangements to avoid paying employment taxes—and that the contract workers really are employees.

As a result, the IRS has put a major effort into examining independent contractor arrangements—creating one of the sharpest areas of dispute between the IRS and business in recent years.

*Danger:* When the IRS decides that contract workers really act as employees, it can recategorize them and assess a major tax bill for back employment taxes.

*Self-defense:* There's a "safe harbor" that a business can use to avoid such a tax bill. It needs to show it follows established industry practice in treating workers as it does.

Businesses should not become overconfident because of the safe harbor. It is not enough to show that the business is in an industry that makes regular use of contract workers. *You must also show that…*

●The details of the firm's practices—such as contract terms—correspond with others in the industry.

●1099s are properly filed for all contract workers each year.

●The firm treats workers consistently on a year-to-year basis.

●The firm treats workers with similar responsibilities consistently.

This is an area where preparation can avert a great deal of trouble later on. Review the company's practices with a professional adviser who is an expert on contracting practices in its industry.

●**Loans from the business.** Company owners often meet personal cash needs by borrowing from the business—and it's perfectly legitimate to do so.

However, owners of private businesses often are careless with paperwork. *Snag:* Failing to fully document a tax-free loan can lead the IRS to treat it as a taxable distribution.

Having the IRS recharacterize a loan as taxable compensation is bad enough—but if it is taken from a corporation, the IRS may treat it as a dividend that is taxable to the recipient at your top tax rates and not deductible by the business.

*Self-defense:* If you've taken loans from your business, limit audit risk by fully documenting each transaction. Have a note that sets a repayment schedule and a reasonable rate of interest. Designate security for each loan, and authorize the loan in the company's minutes and other records.

*Important:* Follow the terms of the loan. If you fail to do so, the IRS may determine the loan to be a sham and rule it to be a taxable distribution anyhow.

●**Accounting methods.** The IRS is likely to scrutinize a business's records to identify improper accounting methods.

Often, the IRS seeks to push firms that use cash-basis accounting onto the accrual-basis method of accounting, which gives the firm much less opportunity to reduce taxes by timing the receipt of income and cash expenditures. So cash-basis businesses should beware of carrying inventories and using accrual-basis accounting.

*Example:* A person reports self-employment income on Schedule C using cash accounting, but also claims a substantial deduction for "cost of sales." This deduction is associated with inventories that require accrual accounting—so IRS computers can be expected to flag the return.

Accrual-basis businesses also can have their accounting methods examined by the IRS.

*Example:* Manufacturing firms are scrutinized by the IRS to make sure they are not deducting overhead costs that should be allocated to inventory.

Again, correcting accounting errors now can head off big audit problems later. Rules vary by industry. Consult an expert on the appropriate methods for your industry.

•**Year-end reporting compliance.** Every year the IRS increases the 1099 information reporting it imposes on businesses.

*Example:* Businesses are required to report the payment of legal fees of $600 or more to any law firm—including incorporated law firms. In the past, payments to incorporated firms did not have to be reported.

Take the time to review all of your firm's information reporting requirements with a tax professional. By doing so you may avert paying a penalty for each form you fail to file.

*Helpful:* Information filings that are "squeaky clean" can help limit the scope of a future audit. They can lead the auditor to think that all your records will be in equally good order—so there will be little point in going through them.

*Trap:* The reverse is likely to occur if the auditor sees that even "simple" information reporting isn't done right. He's likely to conclude that the more complicated areas of your return will be in even worse shape—and so deserve a full examination.

•**Travel and entertainment (T&E).** This is the area of the return where good record-keeping habits are most important. And it is the part of the return where auditors know they can almost always find deductions to disallow.

It is not enough to have a credit card receipt proving you incurred the cost of a T&E expense. For a deduction to be allowed, the law requires you have a record of the time, place and business purpose of the expense. If it involved entertaining, you must also have a record of who was entertained and of your business relationship with that person.

*Best:* Get in the habit of keeping a business diary that records all the information needed to support T&E deductions. If you have employees, require that they do the same.

### GET IRS AUDIT GUIDES

A valuable new resource is available to businesses that wish to head off audit risk. These *Audit Technique Guides* cover particular industries and the IRS issues copies to auditors in the field to direct their audit efforts. The IRS is now releasing these guides to the public.

The *Audit Technique Guides* are written by IRS specialists who examine particular industries. They highlight the areas of most concern to the IRS, and give auditors specific advice about how to deal with them.

Now these same guides are being released to the public and so this information is available to taxpayers. You can know in advance what an auditor who examines your firm will be concerned about, what he/she probably will want to look at, and what his position will be on key issues. Obviously, such advance knowledge can be a great help in minimizing audit risk.

So far, the IRS has released at least 34 audit guides on industries ranging from air charters to trucking...and more are being prepared for release. The guides can be obtained free from the IRS Web site at http://www.irs.ustreas.gov/plain/bus_info/mssp. Your tax professional also can obtain them from the commercial tax reporting services.

*Best:* Find out if an audit guide has been released for your industry. If so, obtain it. If not, have your tax adviser stay alert for one that may be released in the future.

**More from Andrew Biebl...**

## Tax-Free Loans from Your Business

Interest-free loans were a favorite tax-planning device until Congress enacted rules requiring that they be taxed as if a market rate interest were being paid on them.

*Loophole:* The restrictions created by Congress do not apply to "de minimus" loans—those that do not exceed $10,000—provided that the principal purpose of the loan is not to avoid taxes.

Thus, as either a shareholder or an employee, you can borrow up to $10,000 from your business, pay no interest on the loan and incur no adverse tax consequences.

Of course, the loan principal will be tax free to you as well. So an interest-free loan of up to $10,000 can serve as a tax-favored perquisite to an employee, or a favorable way of obtaining cash from the business for an owner. However, to preserve the loan status, there should be a reasonable term for repayment of the debt due to the business.

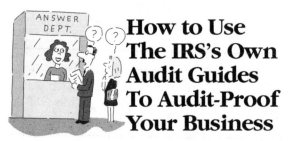

# How to Use The IRS's Own Audit Guides To Audit-Proof Your Business

Seymour Goldberg, Esq., CPA, senior partner, Goldberg & Goldberg, PC, 666 Old Country Rd., Suite 600, Garden City, NY 11530. Mr. Goldberg is author of *How to Handle an IRS Audit* and *Pension Distributions: Planning Strategies, Cases and Rulings,* both published by the *CPA Journal.*

IRS business audits are changing, posing both a trap and an opportunity for business owners. *Here's what you need to know now about these new audit programs...*

### EXPERT KNOWLEDGE

In order to increase the audit skills of its tax examiners, the IRS now has formed teams of specialists who have become experts on specific businesses under its *Market Segment Specialization Program* (MSSP).

These specialists study a particular business and then write up audit technique guides. They tell in detail how these businesses operate—and where previously undiscovered tax liabilities are most likely to be found by a tax examiner.

The audit guides then are distributed to IRS auditors in the field to direct the manner in which they conduct business audits.

*Result:* If your business is called for an audit, you are no longer likely to be dealing with an auditor who is a generalist who knows little or nothing about the workings of your business.

Instead, you'll probably be dealing with an auditor who has been given expert knowledge about the ins and outs of how your business operates. That includes the kinds of bank accounts the business has, the manner in which it collects and makes payments, levels of expenses and revenue that should be associated with a particular level of business volume, typical compensation levels and so on.

The IRS auditor will know much more about your business than did auditors you may have dealt with in the past.

### FINANCIAL STATUS AUDIT

If the auditor has a *reasonable indication* that your business has not reported all its income, he/she may conduct a *financial status audit* of you, the business owner.\*

Often called an "economic reality audit," it consists of an examination of your *style of living* to see if the personal living costs you incur correspond to the amount of income that your business reports in earnings, and that you report receiving from your business.

During a financial status audit, the IRS may ask questions about such items as your home and vacation home, the cars you own, the vacation trips you take—and how you manage to afford them on the income that your business reports, and that you report. The auditor

---

\*The *IRS Restructuring and Reform Act of 1998* prohibits the IRS from using financial status or economic reality audit techniques (asking lifestyle questions) to determine the existence of unreported income of any taxpayer—unless the IRS has a "reasonable indication" that there is a likelihood of unreported income.

may issue a summons to financial institutions to obtain your personal bank and investment records, and other records of your personal financial transactions.

The MSSP audit guides tell the auditor how other businesses like yours have been found to underreport income…and how owners of other such businesses have taken unreported income out of their firms. So an auditor who has good reason to believe that income has gone unreported will know where to look for it.

### THE GOOD NEWS

The MSSP audit guides are a potent new weapon for the IRS in its crackdown on business tax evasion. *Important:* They also present a valuable opportunity for business owners.

This is because audit guides are available *to the public*—so you can obtain the guide for your business and learn *in advance* what issues the IRS will examine during an audit.

Of course, your audit guide can be of invaluable assistance to you in preparing for an audit.

### THE GUIDE FOR YOU

IRS audit guides generally cover businesses that have significant cash dealings—and that may be tempted to keep income off the books.

The IRS also has an audit guide for passive losses, which will be important for many tax-shelter investors.

The guides are full of practical information that auditors can use to estimate whether the real income of a business corresponds to the amount of income reported on its tax return.

*Example:* The guide for pizzerias tells the auditor how to examine the quantities of pizza ingredients that were bought (and deducted as an expense) during the year, to compute how many pizzas they would have made and how much revenue the pizzeria would have received from selling them.

If the amount of revenue computed by the agent doesn't come close to matching the revenue reported on the tax return, the business owner can expect to receive close scrutiny from the auditor.

### GETTING A GUIDE

So far the IRS has released more than 40 audit technique guides, and more are being prepared.

Your professional tax adviser can find out if an audit guide exists for your business, and obtain it if it does.

The audit guides are available from several sources, including:

● **The leading tax reporting service companies,** such as…

● Tax Analysts, 800-955-3444.

● Commerce Clearing House, 800-248-3248.

● **The IRS itself,** by contacting the IRS *Freedom of Information* Reading Room, Box 795, Ben Franklin Station, Washington, DC 20044, 202-622-5164.

● **Over the Internet.** Many of the guides can be downloaded from the official IRS Web site, http://www.irs.ustreas.gov/prod/bus_info/mssp.

In addition, some IRS district offices and private tax advisory firms make audit guides available through their own Web sites. Details change frequently, so use a Web search engine to find out what's currently available.

### USING A GUIDE

If your business has been selected for an audit, examining the audit guide will give you a good idea of the degree of potential trouble, if any, you face. You can then take the appropriate steps to prepare for the audit.

*Important:* Learn the rights you have during the audit process. Obtain a free copy of IRS Publication #1, *Your Rights as a Taxpayer,* by calling the IRS at 800-TAX-FORM or downloading it from the IRS Web site, if one doesn't arrive with the audit notice.

One *key* right that you have is to be represented by a tax professional at the audit—in fact, you don't have to attend an audit in person at all unless the IRS has a specific reason for requesting to meet with you.

The audit notice will detail the items the IRS examiner will look at.

Whether or not you wish to have a tax professional attend the audit with you—or in your place—will depend on the items being examined, your understanding obtained from reading the audit guide of how serious they are and your potential exposure to additional tax. If the IRS simply wants to check the receipts for a few expenses reported on the return, and your records are in good order, you might want to handle the matter yourself.

**Caution:** Be wary of providing any information not requested in the audit notice. If asked for more information that you do not have, ask for additional time to check your records. If the audit turns hostile, use your right to be represented by a professional.

If an audit involves anything more complex than simple verification of records, you'll probably do best by being represented by a professional, and by not attending the audit yourself.

•The professional will better understand the tax issues at hand.

•You won't be there to discuss issues that are not relevant.

Remember, the auditor cannot ask personal lifestyle questions under the new law unless the agent suspects fraud. Still, if you attend the audit, the auditor might ask such questions as a matter of routine. If you don't attend, he'll have to formally ask you to appear to ask such questions—and will not do so unless he has a specific reason.

# Better Accounting Software

The quality and variety of software for small business is advancing rapidly. Typical programs not only keep books up to date, but also let you focus on ways to make more money. Research software carefully. Use manufacturers' Web sites—some even let you download trial versions for free. *Worth considering:* For time and billing, *QuickBooks Pro,* $220 (www.quickbooks.com). For a simple, basic program, *One-Write Plus,* $69.95 (www.onewrite.com). For a built-in contact manager and word processor, *Proven Edge, Professional Edition,* $599 (www.provenedge.com).

Kim Feinberg, CPA, financial analyst, New York, quoted in *Home Office Computing,* 156 W. 56 St., New York 10019.

# Saving Money on Computers

Personal computers (PCs) costing less than $800 are fine for most business uses. They have all the power—or more—of the most expensive top-of-the-line PCs of only a year or two ago and handle standard business tasks with no problem—spreadsheets, word processing and other common business applications, Internet connections, E-mail, etc. *Limits:* Low-cost PCs lack the great speed of today's most expensive PCs—but that speed is wasted on most standard business uses. And they may lack upgrade potential, but that's no problem if they do what they are bought for.

Matt Sargent, industry analyst, ZD InfoBeads, research firm, LaJolla, CA, quoted in *Your Company,* 1271 Avenue of the Americas, New York 10020.

# 8

# Doctors, Hospitals and You

## Are You Getting Less than the Best From Your Doctor?

Patients are generally all too aware of the most obvious of their doctors' shortcomings —running late for appointments, not listening carefully to their concerns and so on.

But few patients are adept at recognizing the more significant ways that doctors fail them...

•**Failing to prescribe the best medications.** Some doctors have trouble keeping up with the ever-growing list of medications. Others do keep up yet continue to prescribe outdated drugs again and again.

Still other doctors are discouraged from prescribing certain medications by restrictive rules set up by health insurers.

*Result:* Patients often wind up taking one drug even when another works more reliably, with fewer side effects and/or with some other key advantage.

*Example:* Some doctors continue to recommend only calcium-containing antacids or another source of calcium for osteoporosis patients. Yet the combination of a calcium supplement and the new drug *alendronate* (Fosamax) is better at preventing bone loss.

*Self-defense:* If a doctor prescribes a particular drug, be sure to ask what it's for...whether it could cause any side effects...whether it could interact with other drugs or certain foods...and how long it takes for the medication to work.

If you foresee any problems with using the recommended medication, ask if there are any alternatives.

•**Neglecting to order crucial diagnostic tests.** In the days before managed care, some

Alan N. Schwartz, MD, assistant clinical professor of radiology at the University of Washington School of Medicine in Seattle, and director of the MRI clinic at Stevens Hospital in Edmonds, WA. He is coauthor of *Getting the Best from Your Doctor: An Insider's Guide to the Health Care You Deserve.* Chronimed.

135

doctors had a financial incentive to order diagnostic tests.

Now there's often a financial incentive for doctors *not* to order tests. In some cases, this incentive keeps doctors from ordering tests that are clearly needed.

**Example:** Someone with chronic stomach pain should be tested for the ulcer-causing bacterium *H. pylori*. But some doctors simply prescribe *omeprazole* (Prilosec) or another acid-blocker. Acid-blockers do *not* eradicate H. pylori, so the underlying infection never gets treated. The ulcer recurs.

**Self-defense:** Ask your doctor if there is a test that would make him/her more confident in his diagnosis…or would change the course of treatment. Ask about side effects, the potential for pain and risks, too.

If your doctor seems unable to diagnose your ailment—or if a course of treatment is not yielding results—ask if there's a diagnostic test that might provide useful information.

●**Not referring patients to a specialist.** If a patient fails to respond to a treatment regimen, it's the doctor's responsibility to refer the patient to a specialist.

This doesn't always happen. In some cases, the doctor simply wants a bit more time to sort out the problem. In others, he may be unaware that his approach is failing…or he may have a financial incentive not to refer patients to specialists.

**Self-defense:** When your doctor recommends a treatment, ask how long it will take to get results. If the treatment fails to produce results by the deadline you both agreed on, he should make the referral.

●**Performing surgery despite a lack of experience with a given procedure.** Study after study has shown that the more often a doctor performs a surgical procedure, the more likely his patients are to have a good outcome.

A doctor who has scant experience with a particular procedure should admit this to his patients. Yet some doctors are too embarrassed to reveal their lack of experience.

Others keep their lack of experience secret because they want the experience or the income…or because they're pressured to do so by a health-maintenance organization (HMO).

**Self-defense:** If a doctor offers to do surgery, ask him to name the doctor *he* would go to if he needed the procedure (excluding himself). Then ask both doctors how many times they have performed this procedure.

What constitutes a good minimum? For common operations such as appendectomy, 50 times is enough. For less common procedures, even the most experienced surgeon may have done no more than a handful.

If you need help evaluating the skills of a surgeon, seek others' opinions of him.

●**Divulging confidential information.** Unless they have a patient's permission to do so, doctors are personally honor-bound not to reveal confidential medical information.

**Self-defense:** Ask your doctor about his policy regarding confidentiality. Can your records be accessed from outside his office? If so, why?

Insist that your doctor let you personally review any requests for information regarding your medical records. Ask to have those sections that you wish to remain private labeled "Not to be released without my signature."

To learn more about privacy issues, contact the Electronic Privacy Information Center at 202-544-9240…or on the Web at www.epic.org.

●**Neglecting to disclose risks associated with treatment.** Doctors are required to inform patients of risks associated with every course of treatment before administering that treatment.

Doctors are good at describing common risks, but they sometimes neglect to mention uncommon ones.

**Self-defense:** Ask the doctor to explain all the risks—and the risks of forgoing treatment. Then ask him to put these risks in their proper perspective.

---

# Doctor–Patient E-Mail Caution

You've got mail…from your doctor? More and more physicians are now communicating with patients electronically. With E-mail, patients can get easier direct access to doctors ...and some patients are more comfortable asking questions on-line than face-to-face.

***Dangerous downside:*** E-mail privacy is never guaranteed.

If your doctor takes E-mail questions, do not communicate with him/her via your company's computer system—firms have wide access to employee E-mail. Only certain types of medical information are appropriate—and safe—to discuss via E-mail, such as blood-sugar levels or other simple tests.

John Featherman, editor, *Privacy Newsletter*, Box 8206, Philadelphia 19101.

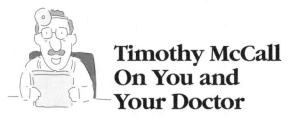

# Timothy McCall On You and Your Doctor

Timothy McCall, MD, a New York City internist and author of *Examining Your Doctor: A Patient's Guide to Avoiding Harmful Medical Care*. Citadel Press.

## How to Get the Most Out of Your Annual Physical

In recent years, experts have begun to question the value of the routine annual check-up. Since most health plans allow a free or low-cost physical each year, you may wonder if it's worthwhile to get one. I believe it is—although perhaps not for the reasons you might suspect.

Many elements of the typical exam—blood counts, EKGs and other routine tests—provide little useful information in people who are in apparent good health. The same applies to listening to the heart, checking the reflexes and most other parts of the traditional exam.

What is of value is a detailed discussion of diet, exercise and other aspects of preventive medicine. Ideally, doctors would discuss these matters with their patients during routine office visits. Yet with the recent speedup in medical visits, many doctors now find that

they lack the time. So an annual exam may afford you and your doctor the only opportunity to review the overall state of your health. Here's how to get the most out of it...

●**Discuss each of your major medical problems.** Ask your doctor whether there have been any significant advances in treatment during the past year. Is there anything more you could be doing to boost your health? Any new specialists you could be seeing? New drugs you should be taking?

●**Review your medications.** Bring all your medications to the doctor's office, along with a typewritten list of these drugs. Include over-the-counter drugs and dietary supplements as well as prescription medications. That way, you can be sure that your doctor knows *exactly* what you're taking.

Since every drug carries risks, it's a good idea to ask if you really need to be taking every one. Are there safer alternatives to any of the drugs? Are there potentially dangerous interactions between any of the pills?

●**Get the few screening tests proven to work.** Like most doctors, I urge my patients to have their blood pressure checked at least once every other year. I also recommend checking total cholesterol and HDL cholesterol levels every few years. Tests for colon cancer should include yearly checks for hidden blood in the stool and sigmoidoscopy every three to five years after age 50. I also side with the experts who say that women should have a Pap smear every one to three years, as well as an annual breast exam and, starting at age 50, mammograms.

Mammograms *before* age 50 are of uncertain value. So is the PSA test for prostate cancer. Some experts believe in these tests. Others suspect that they do more harm than good—for instance, by leading to unnecessary surgery. Carefully review the pros and cons of each test with your doctor.

●**Review your immunizations.** Parents tend to be good about remembering to have their kids vaccinated—but forget about themselves. Doctors, too, often neglect this vital issue. Studies show that most people at risk for hepatitis B, influenza and pneumonia have not had the protective vaccines. The result? More than 60,000 American adults die of vaccine-preventable diseases each year—compared with fewer than 1,000 children.

Your doctor needs to devote enough time to the exam to do it right. How long is long enough? That depends on your age and over-all health. Expect 20 to 30 minutes if you're young and healthy—twice that if you're not.

The longer time usually allotted for annual exams should allow you and your doctor to get to know each other a bit better. And that could be the most valuable part of all.

---

**More from Timothy McCall...**

# Just How Competent Is Your Doctor?

Doctors have long been among the most trusted members of society. It's natural to assume that if someone was smart enough to get through medical school, he/she must be smart enough to provide good medical care. I think it's important—even therapeutic—to trust your doctor. But blind faith can be dangerous.

Fact is, the quality of doctors varies enormously. Some are great. Others are so-so. A few are very, very bad. That's why I commend to you the old Russian proverb—trust, but verify.

Luckily, more information on doctors is becoming available. If you have Internet access—either at home or at a local library—you might want to check out the list of doctors at the American Medical Association's Physician Select site (www.ama-assn.org). Using it, I discovered that my mother's doctor had graduated not from the University of Florida—as claimed—but from a second-rate school in the Caribbean.

You can find out whether a doctor is board certified by calling the American Board of Medical Specialties (800-776-2378). Board certification means the doctor completed an accredited training program after medical school—and passed a rigorous exam.

The best information on disciplinary actions taken against doctors comes from the con-

sumer group Public Citizen, 1600 20 St. NW, Washington, DC 20009. Regional editions of the group's book *Questionable Doctors* are available for $23.50.

Some health insurers publish patient satisfaction ratings of doctors. If you examine these records, keep in mind that doctors' ratings often have less to do with their competence than with how nice they are—and how long their patients have to wait in the office. As you might expect, some not-so-great doctors wind up with mostly satisfied customers.

As important as a doctor's credentials are, I believe they're sometimes overrated. Even excellent doctors in high-risk specialties like obstetrics and neurosurgery often end up getting sued a few times in their careers. But a pattern of lawsuits should raise a red flag.

Disciplinary actions are another matter. Since states and hospitals are often lax in punishing bad doctors, even a single fine, license suspension or revocation of hospital privileges may be significant.

Ultimately, what matters most is how well your doctor practices medicine. The best way to monitor that is to learn as much as you can about each condition you're diagnosed with—and every drug you're prescribed. Go to the library, get on-line or call the National Health Information Center at 800-336-4797. The more you know, the better you'll be able to participate in medical decisions—and know whether your doctor is up to speed.

Ask your doctor how much experience he has in taking care of your specific medical problem. It's well documented that the more often a doctor deals with a problem, the better the care.

Finally, good doctors are willing to spend time with their patients—time enough for you to describe your symptoms, understand your treatment options and learn how to take your medicines. They take this time even if it means they won't be able to squeeze as many patients into each day and even if it annoys the HMO. There's no hard and fast rule about how much time is enough. But if your visit feels like a pit stop in the Indy 500, that's a very bad sign.

# What to Do When Your Doctors Disagree

Medical experts say it's always prudent to get a second opinion before elective surgery. I agree. But I also recommend getting a second opinion if your doctor seems unable to diagnose your problem, if you fail to get better, as anticipated, or if you've just been diagnosed with cancer or another life-threatening ailment.

What do you do when the doctors' opinions differ? Just because doctors disagree does not necessarily mean one of them is wrong. There are reasonable differences of opinion, and often more than one approach will work. Sometimes we simply don't have enough scientific data to say which treatment is best.

Here's what I suggest to help you resolve conflicting advice...

•**Do your own research.** Learn as much as you can about your diagnosis and the recommended treatments. The more you know, the smarter your questions to the doctors will be—and the better your ability to evaluate what each doctor says.

•**Think things through.** Don't feel pressured to make your decision right away. Except in true emergency situations, a couple of weeks' delay in making a decision is unlikely to cause any problems. Some people go along with treatments or tests they really don't want because they sense that their physician favors it.

I think it's good to get out of the doctor's office, read about your problem, talk over the options with your loved ones—and then make your decision.

•**Ask for explanations.** Find out each doctor's reasons for recommending a particular test or treatment. If you can understand the rationale for each doctor's recommendation—and not just the recommendation itself—you'll be in a better position to evaluate it.

Are there scientific data behind the advice? Is the advice based on personal experience? What would happen to you if you declined to do what is recommended? Would a delay be harmful?

•**Ask each doctor to evaluate the other's advice.** One doctor may spot weaknesses in another doctor's reasoning that might not have occurred to you—or to the other doctor. If possible, get each doctor's advice in writing and show it to the other.

•**Follow the money.** In sorting out a doctor's recommendations, it pays to know where the financial incentives lie. It stands to reason—and studies confirm—that doctors are more likely to recommend treatments or tests when they stand to profit by doing so. That's the case with most traditional fee-for-service health insurance. Under managed care, doctors are less likely to recommend costly interventions—even if they might benefit you.

•**Get *another* opinion.** If you think it's necessary, don't hesitate to get a third or even a fourth opinion. In obtaining these additional opinions, it's usually a good idea to consult doctors who are unaffiliated with either of the other doctors. Given the financial incentives in HMOs against providing expensive services, it's often a good idea to get an opinion from a doctor outside of the plan—even if you have to pay extra.

•**Go with your gut.** Ultimately, many medical questions have no right answers. Since you're the one who will have to deal with the consequences of any medical decision, it ought to be your values—and not those of your doctors—that determine which path you'll follow.

# Your Responsibilities for Your Health

I frequently write about what doctors should—and shouldn't—be doing. But to ensure first-rate medical care, patients need to do their part, too.

•**Know your medical history.** One patient I was seeing for the first time, a high-powered civil engineer, was able to identify the blood pressure medication he'd been taking for several years only as "a little pink pill." That made my job tougher.

I suggest that you keep a record of all major diagnoses. Be sure to include medical terminology *and* what it means in plain English. The record should also include the dates and descriptions of all operations you've had, results of diagnostic tests, any allergies and all medications you take.

●**Prepare for your visits.** Before your appointment, prepare a list of questions you have about your condition—and problems you'd like the doctor to address. The doctor's time is limited, so try to focus on the matters of greatest concern.

●**Don't let embarrassment get in the way.** If you are drinking 12 cups of coffee a day, having sex problems or bowel trouble or seeing an alternative healer, tell your doctor. Don't let embarrassment stop you.

If you'd like certain information to be kept out of your medical record, ask if the doctor will agree not to write it down.

●**Be honest.** If you haven't been taking a medication the doctor has prescribed, 'fess up. Maybe the doctor didn't realize your concern about the cost of the drug or its side effects. Similarly, tell the doctor if you have no intention of filling a prescription, giving up cigarettes or showing up for a scheduled test. If your doctor knows precisely what you are—and are not—willing to do, you may be able to reach a mutually satisfactory solution.

●**Get to the point.** Try not to have a hidden agenda for your visit. It's best to reveal your major concerns as early as possible during the visit. Many patients waste precious minutes on trivial matters, only to spring their real concern at the last minute. This makes it virtually impossible for the doctor to address the problem fully.

●**Describe your symptoms.** Doctors are more interested in hearing a description of your symptoms than your theory about what might be causing them. If you've been having abdominal pain, for example, you might say to the doctor, "I've been having gnawing abdominal pain." Do not say, "My ulcer's been acting up." After all, not all abdominal pain is caused by ulcers.

The more detailed your description of your condition, the easier it will be for your doctor to sort things out.

●**Put yourself in your doctor's shoes.** If you're unable to make it to a scheduled appointment, call your doctor to cancel as soon as possible.

Don't call your doctor in the middle of the night for a problem you've had for weeks, unless it has suddenly become much worse. If a doctor's fee is reasonable, pay it. If you can't afford to pay right away, ask the doctor if you can make arrangements to pay in installments. Always try to be polite and respectful—even if you need to assert yourself.

Especially in this age of managed care, it's important to keep your doctor on your side. And you'll be a lot more likely to get your needs met if you consider your doctor's needs, too.

# Planning for A Medical Emergency

Post your medical information in a prominent place in your home. EMS workers waste precious time searching patients' homes for medicine bottles and other clues about health status. *What to do:* Write a brief medical history of each family member on an index card. Tape the cards to the refrigerator door. Include name, doctor's name and phone number, medical conditions, prior or current treatment regimens and dates, major operations and dates, allergies you have, names and dosages of all drugs you take, name of insurance carrier, plus your group and personal identification numbers. *Also:* Photocopy the cards and keep them in your wallet in case you become ill or sustain an injury away from home.

Peter Canning, EMT-P (emergency medical technician-paramedic) in Hartford, CT, and author of *Paramedic: On the Front Lines of Medicine.* Fawcett Columbine.

# Better Doctors' Visits For Kids

Visits to the pediatrician go more smoothly if the doctor blows soap bubbles to soothe and distract the child.

Bubbles can even keep children from crying after an injection. They work best for children four months to 10 years of age.

*Arthur Lavin, MD, a pediatrician in private practice in Beachwood, OH.*

# How to Make Your Hospital Stay Briefer, Safer and Less Expensive

*Sheldon Blau, MD, clinical professor of medicine at the State University of New York at Stony Brook, and a physician in private practice in New York. He is author of* How to Get Out of the Hospital Alive. *Macmillan.*

Spending time in a hospital can be hazardous to your health. About 200,000 Americans *die* each year of hospital-related errors. One out of every 10 patients receiving treatment in a hospital acquires a hospital-transmitted infection.

**Problem:** Hospitals are run by people who may be overworked and stressed out.

*To make a hospital stay briefer—and safer...*

●**Ask the nurse when checking in if any other patients on your floor have a similar last name.** If so, ask to be moved. It's not uncommon for hospital personnel to confuse you with another patient.

*If this is impossible:* Write your name and allergies clearly on a piece of paper. Post the paper prominently above your bed. A list of your allergies will at least prevent confusion over medication or treatment.

●**Avoid sharing a room with a patient who has a draining infection or a persistent cough.** Most infections are spread through the air, so you want your room as germ-free as

possible. Pay out of your own pocket for a private room if necessary.

●**Be wary of combining medications with the wrong foods.** Certain drugs become ineffective, less effective or downright dangerous when mixed with the wrong foods—or when taken at the wrong time.

*Examples:* Certain penicillins aren't effective when taken right after eating specific foods...some antidepressants can trigger dangerously high blood pressure when taken with yogurt, chocolate, bananas or some cheeses.

*Helpful:* Asking your doctor or nurse to review your medications and your menu. Also ask for a list of foods that should never be taken with your medication.

●**Keep a chart by your bed of what medication you're supposed to receive—*and when.*** Nurses often get called away on emergencies and forget to bring you your pills. Or they can give you the same medicine twice. Keep careful track of the drugs yourself to prevent dangerous errors.

●**Know who is qualified to help you.** The woman in the white uniform who brings you medication might not be a nurse, and the guy with the stethoscope examining your chart might not be a physician.

Before you complain about pain or let someone examine you, ask who he/she is, and make sure he has the credentials to assess your condition or the authority to perform the procedure.

Hospitals have rules about who can do what, but the rules are not always followed.

●**Prevent falls.** This seems like a no-brainer, but hundreds of perfectly coordinated people who never hurt themselves at home wind up with broken bones because they forget they are sick and in an unusual environment. *Helpful...*

●Crank the bed down before trying to get out.

●Don't climb over the side rails of a hospital bed.

●**Follow doctors' orders—but not blindly.** If your doctor tells you not to eat after midnight in preparation for a test or procedure, refuse breakfast if a tray arrives in the morning. Somebody at the hospital probably forgot to discontinue your meals.

However, if someone comes in to perform a procedure that you weren't told about, don't submit to it without seeing the orders and understanding why they were given. Take charge. It's your health, and you have a responsibility to protect it.

### IF YOU'RE HAVING SURGERY

• **Mark with a pen the part of your body where your surgeon is supposed to cut.** Although this step might seem silly, it can help avoid a disastrous mistake.

• **Make sure that any surgeon operating on you has been vaccinated against hepatitis B.** Most patients worry about HIV infection, but hepatitis B is more common and more easily transmitted.

An estimated 1,900 surgeons are infected with it, so don't be shy about your surgeon's feelings. All surgeons should be vaccinated.

# Picking a Hospital Can Be Very Tricky

Gary E. Rosenthal, MD, associate professor of medicine, Case Western Reserve University School of Medicine, Cleveland. His review of nearly 90,000 patients treated in 30 Ohio hospitals was published in *The Journal of the American Medical Association*, 515 N. State St., Chicago 60610.

Hospital patients tend to get better care in teaching hospitals than in nonteaching hospitals.

*Recent study:* The patients treated in teaching hospitals had a 19% lower risk of death—and went home an average of one day sooner—than similar patients treated in nonteaching hospitals.

This finding presumably reflects the fact that teaching hospitals tend to have more specialist physicians and better access to state-of-the-art medical technology.

*Caution:* A teaching hospital may not be the best bet for all patients. When choosing a hospital, ask yourself...

• **Do I really need the special services a teaching hospital can offer?** If you're scheduled for a technically demanding surgical procedure, a teaching hospital may be the better bet. If not, a nonteaching hospital may be more appropriate.

• **Do I mind that much of my care will come from doctors-in-training?** At teaching hospitals, there's often little day-to-day contact with "name" doctors.

• **Do I mind that I may be asked to be evaluated and examined by medical students?** If so, a teaching hospital may not be for you.

# Keep Your Medical Records Private

To make sure that your medical records are kept private, confirm with your physician that he/she will not send anything about you out of the office without first showing it to you and getting your approval. *Especially important:* Information on mental health...and substance abuse. If you see anything ambiguous in your record that could cause legal problems for you later, discuss it with your doctor and find replacement terminology that is mutually acceptable.

Harold J. Bursztajn, MD, associate clinical professor of psychiatry, Harvard Medical School, Boston, and psychoanalyst in private practice, Cambridge, MA.

# How to Get First-Rate Hospital Care in an Era of Shrinking Hospital Staffs

Lynn Rew, EdD, RN, associate professor of family health nursing at the University of Texas School of Nursing in Austin. She is the author of *Awareness in Healing*. Delmar/ITP.

If you or a loved one is facing hospitalization, continuing reports that hospitals have cut back on staffing and services may have you feeling a bit apprehensive. Under constant pressure to contain their rising costs, many hospitals *have* made significant changes—and not always in the best interests of patients.

***Example 1:*** Registered nurses (RNs) are being replaced with licensed practical nurses (LPNs) and other personnel with less training—and lower salaries.

In some cases, unpaid volunteers are performing tasks that used to be performed by RNs.

***Example 2:*** Patients are being discharged earlier and earlier. Surgical procedures that once involved three-day hospital stays are now routinely done with stays of just a day or two.

Here's how to ensure that you or your loved one gets first-rate hospital care despite these sorts of changes…

●**Bring along an advocate.** Even if you're not very ill or heavily sedated, you may be unable to watch out for yourself—to prevent medication errors, rude treatment, etc.

For this reason, it's good to have your spouse, a sibling, a grown child or a close friend on hand to speak up for you. If you need help around the clock, line up a few advocates to work in shifts.

***Good news:*** Your advocate may be able to sleep right in your room. Many hospitals now provide bedding and even meals at nominal cost.

●**Make sure your caregivers have the proper credentials.** Only a registered nurse or physician should perform invasive procedures—giving injections, drawing blood, changing intravenous bags, etc.

If an unqualified person attempts to perform an invasive procedure, you or your advocate should not permit it. Speak with your doctor or the nursing supervisor right away.

●**Be *very* courteous.** Nurses are supposed to administer the same level of care to all patients. But they're human. Treat them discourteously, and they are apt to reciprocate.

Being courteous won't necessarily help you get better faster, but it should make your hospital stay more pleasant.

What about gifts? Nurses are discouraged from accepting money or other valuables from patients. But many do appreciate it when patients offer them cookies or other tasty foods.

If visitors bring more than you can eat, it's good politics to share with the nurses.

●**Don't tolerate inconsiderate behavior.** If a nurse or any other hospital worker treats you with disrespect, you or your advocate should alert your doctor or the nursing supervisor.

***Typical indignities:*** Being called "Pops" or another overly familiar name instead of by your real name…having to wait more than 15 minutes for a nurse to come after you ring for assistance…being handled roughly.

If you're being bothered by a noisy or disruptive roommate, you or your advocate should ask a nurse to have you moved to another room. Hospitals can usually accommodate such requests.

It's not selfish to make such a request. Emotional stress slows the healing process.

●**Don't let yourself be discharged prematurely.** If the hospital wants to send you home before you feel ready, you or your advocate should ask your doctor to finesse an extra day or two.

While doctors are required to follow discharge guidelines put forth by insurers, they have some latitude.

Usually all your doctor must do is note on your chart that you're not yet walking securely…that you're having trouble keeping food down…or that you're having some other problem that would make discharge unwise.

# Hospital Danger

Hospital patients have less resistance to disease than people who are well—and many bacteria in hospitals are resistant to antibiotics. *Danger:* Picking up *more* infections during your stay. *Self-defense:* When you're about to be examined, ask doctors and nurses politely if they have washed their hands. Many are remiss about this vital precaution. Also—don't touch your dressings yourself. This can infect your wounds.

Frank Lowy, MD, professor of medicine at Albert Einstein College of Medicine in New York.

# Medical Mistakes Can Be Very, Very Costly

Edward L. Bradley III, MD, vice chairman of the department of surgery at the State University of New York at Buffalo and chief of surgery at Buffalo General Hospital. Dr. Bradley is author of *A Patient's Guide to Surgery.* Consumer Reports Books.

Mistakes happen in some of the best hospitals. How can you minimize your risk? *By taking an active role...*

● **When you're given a new medication, ask what it is—and why you are getting it.** Have the nurse check your chart to make sure that the doctor ordered it.

● **Know which tests and procedures you'll be getting...and ask about their purpose, risks and discomfort.** If you expect you'll be in no condition to monitor your hospital care after surgery, arrange to have a friend or relative act on your behalf.

### MOST COMMON MISTAKES

*Mistake:* **Failure to investigate nonsurgical alternatives.** All surgery is inherently dangerous, so safer, *nonsurgical* treatments should always be considered before you schedule time in the operating room.

If your primary-care doctor recommends surgery, don't take his/her word for it. Ask the *surgeon* about other options.

*Reason:* A surgeon who specializes in gallbladder surgery, for example, probably knows more about gallbladder disease—including *nonsurgical* treatment options—than a general internist.

*Mistake:* **Failure to get a second opinion.** Insurance industry surveys indicate that despite what many people think, very little unnecessary surgery is being performed in this country. For this reason, many insurance companies no longer require their customers to get second opinions before scheduling surgery. However, any time a recommendation for surgery seems to come right out of the blue, a second opinion is always worth the effort.

*Mistake:* **Having unrealistic expectations.** Before surgery, find out precisely what the surgeon plans to do, the reason for it and what the outcome is likely to be.

*Example:* If you assume that surgery intended only to *reduce* back pain will *eliminate* your back pain, you'll be disappointed even if the operation is an unqualified success.

Medical science has come to appreciate the biological connections between mind and body. People who approach surgery with an informed, positive attitude generally do better during the operation. They also heal faster.

*Mistake:* **Failure to ask about laparoscopy.** Many operations can now be performed with a *laparoscope,* a telescope-like instrument. Laparoscopic surgery requires smaller incisions than conventional "open" surgery. As a result, less tissue is destroyed... and recovery time is dramatically shortened.

Laparoscopy is now the method of choice for gallbladder removal and repair of esophageal hernias. It's an option for other procedures, including fibroid removal and inguinal hernia repair. Ask your surgeon to explain the pros and cons.

*Mistake:* **Failure to ask about the surgeon's credentials.** If you're having a hernia repaired or another simple operation, almost any decent surgeon can do it safely. But for complex orthopedic, abdominal or brain surgery—or if you have additional health problems that might cause complications—look for a surgeon who belongs to the...

● **American College of Surgeons.** Election to this group by colleagues attests to a surgeon's professional and ethical reputation.

● **American Surgical Association or a surgical specialty society** (such as the American Academy of Neurological Surgery and the American Board of Thoracic Surgery). This identifies a surgeon with special expertise and experience.

*Mistake:* **Failure to use a competent anesthesiologist.** Although the skill of the surgeon determines how successful the operation will be, the anesthesiologist literally holds your life in his hands.

That's why it's vital to scrutinize your anesthesiologist as well as your surgeon. When I had an operation recently, I chose the anesthesiologist first—then I picked the surgeon.

***Strategy:*** Ask your surgeon for the name of the best board-certified anesthesiologist on the hospital staff. Have him arrange for that person to administer your anesthetics.

***Mistake:*** **Picking the wrong kind of anesthetic.** In many cases, the patient has at least some choice regarding anesthetics. If you do, discuss with the anesthesiologist the pros and cons of each option.

If you have a choice between a general anesthetic (which knocks you out) and a regional or local anesthetic, it's safer to choose one of the latter.

***Reason:*** Being awake during surgery may be unpleasant, but you'll be less likely to suffer potentially fatal respiratory problems...and you should recover faster.

***Mistake:*** **Failure to check the hospital's track record.** Especially when complicated operations are involved, hospitals tend to specialize. You don't want a heart valve fixed in a hospital that specializes in eye surgery. *Ask the hospital representative...*

•How often is this procedure performed at this hospital?

•What is the hospital's track record with this procedure? In some states, figures are readily available. For example, you can find out how many patients died and how many had complications after cardiac surgery simply by contacting the state department of health. *But you have to ask.*

***Mistake:*** **Eating, drinking or taking aspirin before surgery.** If you're scheduled for morning surgery, nothing—no solid food, no water—should pass your lips after midnight.

***Also:*** Refrain from taking aspirin for at least four days before surgery. Aspirin can interfere with blood clotting...and that can have disastrous consequences for surgical patients.

***Mistake:*** **Scheduling surgery for a weekend.** Never schedule elective surgery for Saturday or Sunday. On those days, many hospitals run on reduced staff...and equipment and consultations are hard to obtain.

***Mistake:*** **Failure to inquire in advance about postoperative pain relief.** Today, more

and more hospitals are offering their patients *patient-controlled analgesia* (PCA). This system lets you push a button on your IV to give yourself as much or as little painkilling medication as you'd like—within safe limits.

Patients who use PCA are generally much more comfortable than those who must wait for a nurse to administer the next dose.

Ask your surgeon and the anesthesiologist about PCA...and be sure to make your preference known immediately upon entering the hospital.

---

# Protect Yourself and Your Family from Medication Mishaps

Michael Cohen, RPh, president of the Institute for Safe Medication Practices, 300 W. Street Rd., Warminster, PA 18974. He is also adjunct associate professor of pharmacy at Temple University School of Pharmacy in Philadelphia.

Prescription medications are supposed to make us well. But each year, according to a recent University of Toronto study, about 100,000 Americans die from adverse reactions to drugs prescribed by doctors. Another two million are injured.

And these are unfortunate patients who got the correct drug at the correct dosage.

Thousands more deaths and injuries occur each year from medication errors, in which the wrong dose was administered...or the patient was given the wrong drug altogether.

The key to avoiding these problems is *information*. Patient, doctor and pharmacist should all be fully informed about dosages, side effects, allergy risks, etc.

All should be fully aware of the patient's medical history, too, including any other medications being taken.

### AT THE DOCTOR'S OFFICE

When a doctor prescribes a drug, ask him/her exactly why it's being prescribed. Find out the exact dose being prescribed and when and how the drug should be taken.

Ask about side effects, too. Although you should already have filled out a form listing other drugs you take, it's best to double-check this list with your doctor at the time he writes the prescription.

Ask the doctor for a list of pertinent medical facts that your pharmacist should know—including the results of any kidney function tests you've had.

Adverse drug reactions are often associated with kidney problems.

### THE PRESCRIPTION FORM

The written prescription should include your height and weight...the drug's generic and brand names...the dosage being prescribed...and the reason for taking the drug (unless confidentiality is an issue).

For children and cancer patients, the prescription should also include the dose relative to body weight (milligrams per kilogram) used to calculate the total dose.

*Handwriting trap:* Half of all medication errors occur when pharmacists misread doctors' scribbled prescriptions. If you have trouble reading what your doctor has written, ask him to rewrite it neatly.

The doctor should write out the word "unit" at all times, instead of using a capital "U"—which can be misread as a zero.

If the dose being prescribed is less than one unit, the doctor should place a zero before the decimal point.

*Example:* For a dose of three-tenths of one milligram, the doctor should write "0.3 mg" instead of ".3 mg."

Doctors often use a set of abbreviations that can be misinterpreted by pharmacists...

- pc...after meals
- po...take orally
- qd...every day
- qid...four times a day
- tid...three times a day
- tiw...three times a week.

To avoid confusion, ask your doctor to eschew these abbreviations and use plain English instead. If you or your pharmacist have any questions about any aspect of your prescription, contact your doctor immediately.

### AT THE DRUGSTORE

Have all your prescriptions filled at one drugstore—ideally one with a computerized screening system.

These systems automatically warn of interactions with other drugs...as well as the risk of allergies and side effects.

If your doctor offers you free samples of the drug he is prescribing, take these to the drugstore to have the pharmacist check them using his system.

Do not rely on your doctor to remember all pertinent information about drugs. With thousands of prescription drugs now on the market, it's impossible for even the smartest person to know all drug–drug and food–drug interactions, side effects, etc.

Double-check the name of the drug, and what the pills look like. Some spellings are easily confused when handwritten.

*Example:* The antihypertensive *amlodipine* (Norvasc) is often confused with the antipsychotic *thiothixene* (Navane).

Review the dosage and means of administration with the pharmacist. Be sure the pharmacist knows about any other drugs you take, as well as whether you're pregnant...have high blood pressure or diabetes...or suffer from kidney disease or impaired liver function.

Ask the pharmacist for a plain-language information sheet on the drug. These sheets—developed by the US Pharmacopeia—are easier to understand than package inserts provided by drug manufacturers.

For more detailed information, consult a consumer drug reference. A good example is *Consumer Reports Complete Drug Reference*, Consumer Reports Books/$39.95.

### AT THE HOSPITAL

Each time a nurse arrives to administer a drug, ask him to double-check the name of the drug and the exact dosage.

If the doctor has ordered a change in your medication, ask that the hospital pharmacist screen the drug for interactions.

The day before your discharge, ask a friend or relative to bring in all the drugs you'll be using at home. Go over each with the doctor who prescribed it.

**AFTER TAKING THE MEDICATION**

If you experience any unexplained symptoms after taking a drug, contact your doctor immediately.

Do not stop taking any prescription drug without your doctor's knowledge. Discontinuing certain drugs abruptly can be dangerous.

# Do You Really Need that Diagnostic Test?

Lynne McTaggart, editor of the newsletter *What Doctors Don't Tell You,* 4 Wallace Rd., London N1 2PG. She is author of *What Doctors Don't Tell You.* Avon.

In the "good old days" of medicine, diagnoses were made with little more than a stethoscope and good judgment. Now doctors have an array of high-tech tools that can scan and probe every inch of your interior.

Used properly, this equipment saves lives. Too often, however, diagnostic tests are performed needlessly. That wastes patients' time and money …and can subject them to needless danger.

*Examples:* An X ray involves exposure to cancer-causing radiation…and a misread angiogram can lead to unnecessary heart surgery.

Next time a doctor recommends diagnostic testing for you, ask these questions…

●**Do I really need this test?** Most doctors will automatically answer "yes." Follow up by asking whether there's a less risky alternative that can yield the same information.

*Example:* Magnetic resonance imaging (MRI) and computed tomography (CT) yield similar information. A CT scan involves radiation. An MRI scan does not—though it involves other risks.

*Helpful:* Ask what doctors did before the diagnostic test was developed. In many cases, older doctors know how to provide excellent care without being overly reliant on the latest gadgetry.

●**What will you advise me to do if the test result is abnormal?** Consider the likely chain of events as far as possible. Try to find a way to cut the number of procedures you'll have to undergo.

*Example 1:* If an abnormal reading on one test means that another test will be needed, why not have that second test right away?

*Example 2:* If an abnormal test result suggests a treatment that you find unacceptable, why have the test in the first place?

Many pregnant women undergo testing for *alpha-fetoprotein* (AFP), which can indicate Down's syndrome or spina bifida. If you're unwilling to consider an abortion, getting tested may be pointless.

●**How reliable is this test?** Diagnostic tests sometimes indicate that you have a disease when you really don't (false positive)…or that you don't have a disease when you really do (false negative).

A test with a false positive/false negative rate in excess of 25% is so unreliable as to be of questionable value.

*Example:* The test for *prostate-specific antigen* (PSA)—an indicator of prostate cancer—has a false negative rate of 40% and a false positive rate of up to 75%.

Three out of every four men who have an abnormal PSA reading are subsequently shown via biopsy *not* to have prostate cancer.

●**What risks are involved with this test?** Ask how often people who undergo the test experience side effects. Decide whether the risks associated with being tested outweigh the risks of not being tested.

*Example:* One of every 1,000 cardiac angiography procedures—used to diagnose heart disease—results in stroke or heart attack. Ask your doctor what risks you face if you decline to get tested.

●**Is the equipment operator fully qualified?** If your doctor doesn't know, ask the manager of the testing facility—or the test operator.

Look for certificates detailing the operator's training. You want someone who has administered the test at least 50 times.

*Especially important:* The operator's track record for accuracy. His/her record should match the equipment's standard for accuracy (the rate of false positives/false negatives).

If the operator acknowledges having more or fewer inaccuracies than the standard, try to find out why.

A high number of inaccuracies may mean he isn't fully qualified. A low number suggests that his skill level is unusually high…or that he is being dishonest.

**Helpful:** When scheduling a test, ask to be one of the first three appointments on the operator's shift. This will help eliminate errors associated with end-of-shift exhaustion.

●**When was the equipment last calibrated?** There are different standards for each machine, but most equipment should be checked for safety and accuracy at least once a year.

If the most recent calibration occurred more than 12 months ago, discuss the calibration guidelines with the operator.

**If you must have an X ray:** Make sure you'll be getting the smallest possible dose of radiation.

Find out the typical radiation dose for your particular X ray, then compare it with the dose you'll receive from the equipment to be used to test you.

Doses in excess of the standard mean that the machine is needlessly inefficient. Find another X-ray facility.

**Important:** Use lead shielding on body parts that aren't being X-rayed.

●**Is it possible to make use of previous test results?** Whenever possible, have your doctor rely on results from a previous test. That saves you time and money…and keeps you from being exposed to additional risk.

●**If a family member of yours were in my shoes, would you urge him to have this test?** This question forces the doctor to think on a different level. You shift from being just another case to being compared with a family member.

Watch for signs of ambivalence. If the doctor pauses or frowns when you pose this question, follow up with questions about what the concerns might be.

Don't be needlessly confrontational when probing for information. Calmly let your doctor know that you want to be fully informed about your options before making your decision regarding the diagnostic test.

# Secrets of Successful Surgery

Peggy Huddleston, MTS (master of theological studies), a researcher and psychotherapist in private practice in Cambridge, MA. She is author of *Prepare for Surgery, Heal Faster.* Angel River Press.

Even minor surgery can be very stressful. And no wonder, given the anxiety elicited by the idea of being "put under"… the risk of complications…and the fear of postoperative pain.

Stress does more than just make things unpleasant. It boosts the risk for infection and slows the healing of incisions.

**To the rescue:** Whether you are facing bunion removal or coronary bypass, the surgery itself and your recovery will go more smoothly if you follow this program…

### DEEP RELAXATION

Stress causes your body to produce *cortisol.* Chronic high levels of this stress hormone can torpedo your immune system just when you need it most.

**To lower cortisol levels:** Starting two weeks before surgery, do the following exercise for at least 20 minutes, once or twice a day.

●Sit comfortably or lie down. Close your eyes.

●Focus on the muscles in your neck. If they're tense, let them relax.

●Now focus on other muscle groups—shoulders, arms, chest, abdomen, back, pelvis, right leg and left leg. Feel the tension, then allow the muscle to relax.

●Think of a loved one. Recall a time when you most strongly felt love for him/her. Imagine receiving love in return.

Master all this, and you'll be able to have deep, healing relaxation all day—while driving, preparing meals, etc.

### POSITIVE VISUALIZATION

During periods of deep relaxation, your mind is highly "suggestible." It treats *wishes* almost as if they were *reality.*

Use this time to "seed" your mind with images of fast-healing incisions, pain-free recovery and other desired outcomes pertaining to surgery.

Recent research conducted at the University of Texas at Austin showed that surgical patients who visualized a fast-healing incision healed faster than patients who did not do visualizations.

*What to do:* Twice a day for five minutes, imagine chatting happily with your best friend just after surgery. "I feel fine," you might say. "Things went well."

Next, see yourself leaving the hospital. You might say, "My _____ [whatever body part was operated on] feels great. I'm healing just as fast as I'd hoped."

Now imagine yourself fully healed and doing something you love. If you're facing hip replacement surgery, you might see yourself dancing at an upcoming wedding reception.

### SUPPORT FROM OTHERS

In the days leading up to surgery, friends and/or family members may ask, "How can I help?" That's terrific. Recent studies indicate that the emotional support of loved ones promotes fast, smooth recovery from surgery.

Tell those who want to help that you need their *love.* Ask them to think of you for the 30 minutes leading up to your surgery…and to "send" you their best wishes for comfort.

How does one send these wishes? Tell the person, "Think back to a time when you felt great love for me. When you feel truly connected to me—as if I were right next to you—imagine wrapping me in a blanket of love."

Specify the color of this imaginary blanket—whatever hue seems most reassuring to you.

This strategy is not as farfetched as it might sound. A growing body of scientific research confirms the power of such "distance healing."

For more direct support, ask that your spouse or a close friend stay with you just before you head to the operating room. Skin-to-skin contact with a loved one—and his/her soothing words—are remarkably effective at helping control stress.

### HEALING STATEMENTS

As you go under anesthesia—and throughout the operation—you're powerfully influenced by what you hear.

In a recent study conducted at the Royal Infirmary in Glasgow, Scotland, 30 women undergoing hysterectomy listened to a taped message during surgery that said, "You'll feel warm and comfortable. Any pain you feel after surgery will not concern you."

*Result:* After surgery, these women needed 23% less morphine than a control group who heard no comforting words.

To put healing statements to work for you, jot the following statements on a note card and ask your anesthesiologist to recite each five times…

*As you go under:* "Following this operation, you will feel comfortable. You will heal well."

*As the procedure ends:* "The operation went well. You will wake up hungry for _____ [your favorite food]. You'll be thirsty and able to urinate easily."

Some patients are too embarrassed to ask for these recitations. Don't be. These days, most anesthesiologists are happy to cooperate, admitting that they talk to their patients during surgery anyway. In fact, much of the research on suggestibility during surgery was done by anesthesiologists.

*Important:* Talk to the anesthesiologist no later than the night before surgery—and preferably several days before surgery. If you cannot arrange a face-to-face meeting, talk by phone.

Ask about the anesthetic he'll use…and about the painkillers you'll use after surgery.

Just talking helps to establish a supportive doctor–patient relationship. A Harvard study of 218 surgical patients found that a five-minute talk with the anesthesiologist before surgery was more calming than an injection of the sedative pentobarbital.

# Surgery Self-Defense

For many patients, particularly those already at risk for heart disease, the stress of surgery can trigger a heart attack.

**Recent study:** Surgical patients given the prescription beta-blocker *atenolol* (Tenormin) were 67% less likely to die of heart disease during the two years following surgery, compared with patients given a placebo.

If you're scheduled for surgery, ask your doctor if you should take atenolol.

*Dennis T. Mangano, MD, PhD, director, surgical intensive care unit, and professor of anesthesiology, University of California, School of Medicine, San Francisco. His study of 200 surgical patients was published in* The New England Journal of Medicine, *10 Shattuck St., Boston 02115.*

# Eye Surgery Is Not Always Safe

Highly touted surgery to correct nearsightedness is remarkable when it works—but it is not at all risk free.

The LASIK procedure, which uses lasers to flatten the cornea, generally corrects nearsightedness. But the laser dose may not be quite right, creating a problem that can be very difficult to correct...and healing is sometimes imperfect, affecting vision.

**Another problem:** Because eyes change with age, people who elect LASIK surgery to correct nearsightedness in their 30s may wind up needing glasses to read in their 40s or 50s. If the decision is made to undergo the procedure, an experienced surgeon with a good track record offers the best chance for patient satisfaction.

*Kenneth Barasch, MD, associate clinical professor of ophthalmology at New York University Medical School and a specialist in corneal diseases and transplants.*

# Artery Surgery Trap

Artery-clearing surgery makes sense *only* if arterial blockages are severe.

**Trap:** In people whose carotid (neck) arteries are only mildly blocked, *carotid endarterectomy* is more likely to cause a stroke than to prevent one. The surgery can loosen a tiny piece of the fatty plaque making up the blockage...and send it to the brain, where it blocks circulation.

**Bottom line:** If your carotid arteries are blocked by 70% or more, endarterectomy can dramatically reduce your risk of stroke. But if your arteries are less severely blocked, it may be safer to live with the blockages.

*Henry J. Barnett, MD, principal investigator, North American Symptomatic Carotid Endarterectomy Trial, Robarts Research Institute, London, Ontario. His 11-year study of 2,885 people who had had a stroke or a transient ischemic attack was presented at a recent meeting of the American Heart Association.*

# Smoking and Surgery

Smokers should be sure to quit before elective surgery...and to avoid smoking for at least three weeks afterward.

Doing so helps clear the body of nicotine, which constricts blood vessels and slows the healing process.

*David Netscher, MD, associate professor of plastic surgery, Baylor College of Medicine, Houston.*

# 9

# Simple Solutions to Common Health Problems

## The Common Cold Need Not Be So Common

The average person gets two colds a year, and the average cold lasts seven days. Below, Dr. Bennett Lorber, a leading expert on the common cold, gives some practical advice on how to beat these averages…

### WHAT CAUSES COLDS?

A cold is not a single disease. It's a set of related symptoms caused by a viral infection of the upper respiratory tract. Colds can be caused by any of more than 150 different viruses.

A cold begins when a virus particle binds to chemical receptors found on cells in the upper part of the nose.

Each time you touch someone who has virus particles on his/her skin and then transfer the virus to your nose or eyes, you're likely to catch the cold.

**Trap:** Cold viruses can survive for three to four hours on the skin surface. Thus, you can shake someone's hand in the morning, then rub your eyes at lunch…and still become infected.

Viruses can also be transferred from drinking glasses, door handles, pens and other inanimate objects for about three hours after being handled by an infected person.

Occasionally, colds are caught by inhaling virus particles put into the air after a cold sufferer has sneezed or coughed.

Studies show that the common cold is almost never transmitted by kissing. High temperatures inside the mouth seem to inhibit the reproduction of the viruses that cause colds, keeping the virus population down.

### WHO GETS COLDS?

Anyone can catch a cold—especially someone who spends lots of time around children.

Because they haven't yet developed immunity to many cold viruses, children under age 12 typically get five to seven colds per year—

Bennett Lorber, MD, DSc, professor of medicine and microbiology and chief of the section of infectious diseases at Temple University School of Medicine, Philadelphia.

151

twice that number if they're in day care. When these kids get sick, they tend to pass the illness along to their families.

Another factor that can raise the risk of catching a cold is psychological and/or physical stress, such as that associated with the loss of a loved one...or running a marathon or another form of extremely vigorous exercise.

### MINIMIZING YOUR RISK

There's no foolproof way to avoid colds. But adopting these strategies—especially during cold season—should help...

●**Avoid shaking hands with someone who obviously has a cold.** If someone is sneezing or sniffling, offer a smile—but *not* your hand.

A cold sufferer is most infectious two to three days after the onset of symptoms. Five days or so after symptoms appear, the person is no longer infectious.

●**Wash your hands often.** Any soap is capable of killing cold viruses. Don't worry about using antibacterial soap.

Until you wash your hands, keep your hands away from your nose and eyes.

●**Keep your home clean.** The cleaner your household, the less likely countertops, telephones, cooking utensils, etc. are to spread cold viruses.

Make liberal use of household disinfectant. To make your own disinfectant, mix one part bleach with nine parts water.

### GETTING RELIEF FROM SYMPTOMS

Despite its reputation as a cold fighter, vitamin C is of no value for the prevention or treatment of colds. That's been demonstrated by several good studies.

Nor is there any solid evidence that echinacea, goldenseal or any herbal remedy is of value against colds. The same is true for homeopathic remedies.

Antibiotics are effective only against bacterial infections—not against viral infections like the common cold.

What about zinc? In recent years, this purported cold remedy has become so popular that drugstores have had trouble keeping their shelves stocked with it.

Several studies have shown that sucking on lozenges of zinc gluconate does reduce the severity and duration of cold symptoms. But other studies have found just the opposite.

Since zinc lozenges are of unproven effectiveness—and since zinc gluconate can cause nausea—it's best to stick to cold remedies of proven effectiveness. *These include...*

●**Over-the-counter antihistamines.** *Clemastine fumarate* (Tavist) and *brompheniramine maleate* (Dimetapp) can reduce nasal discharge by up to 25%, sneezing by up to 50% and coughing by up to 40%.

●*Pseudoephedrine.* This drying agent, found in Sudafed and other cold remedies, is effective against a range of symptoms, including congestion and runny nose.

In a recent study, 60 mg given four times a day for four days improved overall symptoms by nearly 50%.

●*Naproxen.* This nonsteroidal anti-inflammatory drug—the main ingredient in Aleve and other over-the-counter painkillers—is effective against headache, body aches, malaise and cough.

*Caution:* Aspirin and acetaminophen have been shown to prolong "shedding" of cold viruses, thereby making colds last longer.

●**Nasal spray.** Medicated sprays or drops such as *oxymetazoline* (Afrin) provide temporary relief of congestion. Afrin is off limits to people with high blood pressure.

*Caution:* Such sprays should be used for no more than three days. Used longer than that, the sprays can cause "rebound" congestion, in which stuffiness becomes worse than it was before treatment.

Recent studies suggest that the asthma drug *ipratropium bromate* (Atrovent) may be effective against colds. In one study, use of an ipratropium inhaler reduced nasal discharge by 25%.

If nothing else works for your cold, ask your doctor about trying ipratropium.

### HEAT VS. COLDS

One study published recently in the *British Medical Journal* found that breathing humid air heated to 109.4° Fahrenheit for 20 minutes at the first sign of a cold decreased symptoms by 40%. But other studies found no such benefit.

Given the conflicting findings, what is a cold sufferer to do? Consider breathing steam from a boiling kettle several times a day. It won't hurt—and could help.

# Simple Ways to Lower Cholesterol

There are several nondrug ways to lower your cholesterol level. Worth discussing with your physician...

*Garlic:* One clove of fresh garlic daily—or a 900-mg capsule of garlic—can lower cholesterol by 9% and triglycerides by 17%.

*Psyllium*: This bulking agent can reduce cholesterol by 6% to 10%.

*Oat bran:* A bowl daily can lower cholesterol by 6%...the fat substitute—Oat Trim—can lower LDL (bad cholesterol) by 6% to 16%.

*Niacin:* 500 mg three times a day can reduce cholesterol by 15% to 30% and triglycerides by up to 15%. A new brand, Niaspan, is effective if taken once a day. Have your doctor do liver function tests before taking niacin. Don't take it if you have arthritis, diabetes or gout or have had stomach ulcers in the past year.

*Diet* combined *with exercise:* This is the best approach. A 20%-fat, low-calorie diet—1,200 calories/day for women and 1,500/day for men—combined with a daily 30-minute walk can reduce cholesterol by 20% and triglycerides by 30%.

Mary McGowan, MD, director, Cholesterol Management Center, New England Heart Institute, Manchester, NH, and author of *Heart Fitness for Life: The Essential Guide for Preventing and Reversing Heart Disease.* Oxford University Press.

# Better Blood Pressure Reduction

Ask your doctor if you can try weight loss and sodium reduction to reduce blood pressure instead of hypertension drugs. A study of 975 people between 60 and 80 years old found that a third of them could stop taking blood pressure medication after losing less than eight pounds and reducing their sodium intake by 25%. And among those people who only lost weight *or* reduced their sodium consumption, a third were able to stop taking medication.

Paul Whelton, MD, dean of the School of Public Health & Tropical Medicine at Tulane University in New Orleans.

# The Very Simple Secret Of Stopping Side Effects From Medications

Jay Sylvan Cohen, MD, associate professor of psychiatry at the University of California, San Diego, School of Medicine. He is author of *Make Your Medicine Safe: How to Prevent Side Effects from the Drugs You Take.* Avon.

Each year, medication side effects account for an estimated 115 million doctor visits and 8.5 million hospitalizations.

Each year, 100,000 Americans die as a direct result of the drugs they take. That's more than are killed in automobile accidents and all other accidents combined.

Less dramatic, but often just as serious, many people are so bothered by side effects that they stop taking the medicines needed to fight their illnesses.

### TOO MUCH MEDICATION

More than 80% of all side effects are *dose-related.* The higher the dosage, the greater the risk for side effects.

Research has shown that low dosages often work just as well. But few doctors—perhaps one in 10—make a serious effort to find dosages that maximize the benefits to patients while minimizing side effects.

Most physicians do just what they learned in medical school, prescribing the dosages listed in the *Physicians' Desk Reference (PDR).* The dosages listed in this giant reference book are supplied by drug manufacturers.

How do drug manufacturers calculate the dosages listed in the *PDR*? In most cases they test just a few dosages, then settle on one that is effective for about 75% of patients.

***Trap:*** People differ in how they react to drugs. One person might do well on 10 mg. Another might need several times that much.

In general, older people are more sensitive to the effects of a drug than are young people. And women often do well on a lower dosage than men.

### SMALLER BUT STILL EFFECTIVE

The dosages listed in the *PDR* are only part of the story. Once a new drug begins to be widely prescribed, it often becomes clear that many patients fare well on smaller dosages—with a smaller risk for side effects...

•**Antidepressants.** The recommended initial dosage of *fluoxetine* (Prozac) is 20 mg per day. But a study published recently in *The New England Journal of Medicine* demonstrated that 5 mg per day is often effective—and less likely to cause headaches, anxiety and other side effects. Other studies show that 2.5 mg is often enough.

Similar success has been reported with lower-than-usual dosages of other antidepressant drugs.

•**Ulcer drugs.** Acid-blocking drugs like *omeprazole* (Prilosec) and *lansoprazole* (Prevacid) can cause headaches, joint pain, nausea and constipation or diarrhea.

The usual dosage of omeprazole is 20 mg per day. But studies have shown that 10 mg works well for many people. Some elderly people do fine on 5 mg.

•**Cholesterol-lowering drugs.** Preliminary testing of *simvastatin* (Zocor) and other "statins" suggested that these drugs had few side effects. Now it's clear that statins can cause severe muscle pain and gastrointestinal problems.

The starting dosage usually prescribed for simvastatin is 10 mg per day. But many people achieve significant cholesterol reduction with 5 mg or even 2.5 mg.

•**Blood pressure drugs.** ACE inhibitors like *enalapril* (Vasotec) are less likely than other blood pressure drugs to cause side effects. But these drugs can cause a constant cough or lightheadedness.

The *PDR* recommends a starting dosage of 5 mg per day for enalapril. But a recent report issued by the Joint National Committee on Prevention, Detection, Evaluation and Treatment of High Blood Pressure suggests starting at 2.5 mg per day. Unfortunately, few doctors have read this report.

•**Pain medications.** *Ibuprofen* (Motrin) and other nonsteroidal anti-inflammatory drugs (NSAIDs) are highly effective at controlling pain and inflammation caused by conditions like arthritis or tendinitis.

But these drugs can cause severe stomach irritation, ulcers and bleeding.

Over-the-counter NSAIDs are typically half the strength of prescription-strength NSAIDs. They're often just as effective...and much easier on the stomach.

### USING DRUGS PROPERLY

Doctors have no desire to prescribe more of a drug than is needed. It's just that they're unaware that lower, safer doses are often found to be effective after a medication has been approved. That's where the patient comes in...

•**Alert the doctor to side effects you've experienced in the past.** If a drug you once took caused fatigue, odds are you'll be sensitive to a new drug for which fatigue is a common side effect. The doctor may be able to suggest an alternative.

•**Encourage the "start low, go slow" approach.** Unless your ailment is severe, it's often prudent to begin at a low dosage and—if that doesn't work—boost the dosage gradually.

This strategy lets the doctor find the smallest effective dosage. It also gives your body a better chance to adjust to a new medication.

•**Try intermediate dosages.** Most drugs come in just a few strengths. But often the lowest effective dosage falls between two different strengths.

Finding a way to get this intermediate dosage can require a little creativity—taking a fraction of a pill, for instance, or dissolving the contents of a capsule in juice and then dividing the dose.

*Example:* Fluoxetine is available in 10-mg and 20-mg pills. It's usually prescribed at 20 mg per day—then, if necessary, 40, 60 or 80 mg. But a patient might not respond to 40 mg...and 60 mg might cause serious side effects.

For this patient, taking 50 mg (two 20-mg pills and one 10-mg pill) might work perfectly.

• **Bring the dosage down.** Especially for blood pressure drugs and other medications that must be taken on an indefinite basis, it's important to find the lowest effective dosage. No one wants to endure troublesome side effects for a lifetime.

*Good news:* While a high dosage may be needed at first to bring a condition under control, it's often possible to notch down to a "maintenance dose" later on.

• **Divide the dose.** Most people find it most convenient to take medication once a day. But a single large dose can cause a high concentration of the drug in the bloodstream.

Ask your doctor about dividing one large dose into two or three smaller doses.

*Caution:* Never start or stop taking any prescription medication—or alter the dosage—without first checking with your doctor.

# Faster Pain Relief

For quicker pain relief, use a liquid pain reliever, such as Alka-Seltzer (which is liquid aspirin), liquid Tylenol *(acetaminophen)* or liquid Advil *(ibuprofen)* for the first dose. Liquid pain relievers are absorbed by the body much faster than tablets and capsules. Switch to an anti-inflammatory medicine such as Advil or Aleve several hours later.

Warren Scott, MD, director of sports medicine at Kaiser Permanente Medical Center, Santa Clara, CA.

# Caffeine and Ibuprofen

Caffeine boosts the headache-fighting power of *ibuprofen*. When volunteers took the pain reliever along with the caffeine equivalent of two cups of coffee, 71% experienced total pain relief. Only 58% of those who took ibuprofen alone experienced total relief. The combination should also relieve other types of pain, including backache and muscle soreness. *If you suffer from pain:* Ask your doctor about taking 400 mg of ibuprofen along with two eight-ounce cups of coffee.

Seymour Diamond, MD, director, Diamond Headache Clinic, Chicago. His study of 400 headache sufferers was published in *Clinical Pharmacology and Therapeutics,* Cornell University Medical College, 1300 York Ave., New York 10021.

# Sciatica Solution

Sciatica—pain that radiates along the sciatic nerve in the buttocks and leg—is typically caused by a spinal disk abnormality, poor posture, muscle strains, pregnancy...or sitting on a thick wallet.

If you're diagnosed with sciatica, soaking or swimming in warm water often provides fast, temporary relief.

*Also:* Take 500 mg of powdered ginger once or twice daily with food...or 400 mg to 600 mg of curcumin three times a day.

*Long-term relief:* Learn yoga (Yoga International, 800-253-6243)...or see a physical therapist specializing in the Feldenkrais Method (800-775-2118 for a referral) or the Alexander Technique (800-473-0620).

Andrew Weil, MD, director of the Foundation for Integrative Medicine, University of Arizona and founder of the Center for Integrative Medicine, Tucson. He is author of *Spontaneous Healing* and *8 Weeks to Optimum Health,* both published by Fawcett.

# Gallstone Prevention

Exercise prevents gallstones. Men who exercised for 30 minutes five times a week were 34% less likely than sedentary men to develop stones. *Under study:* Whether exercise prevents gallstones in women. *Another risk reducer:* Weight loss.

Michael F. Leitzmann, MD, MPH, epidemiologist, department of nutrition, Harvard School of Public Health, Boston. His eight-year study of 45,813 men 40 to 75 years of age was published in the *Annals of Internal Medicine,* Sixth St. at Race, Philadelphia 19106.

# Minimize Sleep Interference

Turning on the lights during the night can interfere with your ability to get back to sleep. *Problem:* Even brief exposure to light causes the body to stop producing the sleep-inducing hormone *melatonin.* To minimize sleep disturbance when you get out of bed during the night, keep a flashlight at your bedside…and/or install a night-light in your bathroom.

David C. Klein, PhD, laboratory of developmental neurobiology, National Institute of Child Health and Human Development, Bethesda, MD.

# Memory-Boosting Marvel

Dharma Singh Khalsa, MD, medical director of the Alzheimer's Prevention Foundation, Tucson. He is author of *Brain Longevity: The Breakthrough Medical Program That Improves Mood and Memory.* Warner Books.

If you've begun to experience problems with your memory, ask your doctor about taking *phosphatidylserine.*

This compound occurs naturally in the outer membranes of brain cells…and in certain plants as well.

In recent studies sponsored by the National Institutes of Health, phosphatidylserine improved memory and concentration in people suffering from age-related memory loss and even early stage Alzheimer's disease.

Phosphatidylserine seems to work just as well as *tacrine* (Cognex) and *donepezil* (Aricept), the only approved prescription medica-tions for Alzheimer's. Tacrine can cause liver damage. Phosphatidylserine is free of harmful side effects.

For otherwise healthy individuals who simply want to hone their mental skills, I often recommend one 100-mg capsule of phosphatidylserine per day.

For mild to severe memory impairment, two or three capsules a day often work better. There is no additional benefit to taking more than 300 mg a day.

Phosphatidylserine can also be taken in conjunction with *ginkgo biloba,* the memory-enhancing herb. It's usually best to take 40 mg of ginkgo for every 100 mg of phosphatidylserine.

Phosphatidylserine and ginkgo biloba are sold in health food stores.

***Caution:*** Consult your doctor before taking ginkgo if you're taking aspirin, *warfarin* (Coumadin) or another blood-thinning drug. Pregnant women should avoid both phosphatidylserine and ginkgo.

# How to Stop Sinus Misery And Keep It from Coming Back

M. Lee Williams, MD, associate professor of otolaryngology and head and neck surgery at Johns Hopkins University School of Medicine in Baltimore. He is author of *The Sinusitis Help Book: A Comprehensive Guide to a Common Problem.* John Wiley & Sons.

More than 50 million Americans a year experience sinus trouble. Common as it is, sinusitis is very poorly understood. Even many physicians are in the dark about causes and effective treatments.

### WHY SINUSES HURT

There are more than 40 different sinuses (hollow spaces) located in the head. The eight sinuses located next to and above the nose tend to cause the most trouble.

When these *paranasal* sinuses are healthy, mucus continually drains from them into the nose. The mucus helps protect delicate nasal membranes from irritation and infection.

Sinus trouble arises when the tiny drainage holes through which this mucus flows become blocked.

*Result:* Mucus backs up into the sinuses. Bacteria flourish in this accumulating mucus. Sinus membranes become inflamed and/or infected, causing pain and a sensation of pressure.

Sinusitis typically occurs in the aftermath of a cold or flu. These respiratory illnesses cause nasal membranes to swell, blocking sinus openings.

Nasal congestion caused by allergies to pollen, dust, animal dander, etc., can also set the stage for sinus infection. The same goes for exposure to airborne irritants such as soot, paint fumes and car exhaust.

Most cases of sinusitis last only a week or two. But severe, prolonged or recurrent sinus infections can cause scar tissue to form within the sinuses or their drainage openings.

The scar tissue can block sinuses permanently. Permanent blockage can also be caused by a cyst or polyp in the sinus…or by a malformation of the cartilage or bone within the nose.

Whatever the cause, obstruction that is allowed to persist inevitably leads to sinusitis.

### SINUS SYMPTOMS

Sinusitis is often accompanied by a milky or greenish-yellow nasal discharge, postnasal drip, bad breath, sore throat and dull head pain.

The pain usually occurs around or between the eyes…in the forehead…at the base of the nose…or in the cheeks. Occasionally, it's felt along the top, sides or back of the head. Sinusitis pain usually disappears at night, only to return the following day.

### PREVENTION—THE BEST CURE

Especially if you're prone to sinusitis, take steps to prevent the sinus blockage that leads to infection and scarring…

•**Reduce your chances of catching colds and flu.** Avoid close contact with anyone who is obviously infected. Wash your hands frequently during the cold/flu season.

Each fall, ask your doctor about getting a flu shot.

•**Minimize exposure to air that is too dry or humid.** Dry air thickens mucus and inhibits its flow.

Excessive humidity can cause nasal and sinus membranes to swell, leading to sinus blockage.

There's little you can do about being exposed to humidity extremes while outside. But try to keep the humidity inside your home at 45% to 65%. Use a humidifier or dehumidifier if necessary.

Don't sit or sleep near a drafty window, radiator or heating or air-conditioning vent.

Steer clear of saunas and steam baths if you're prone to sinus trouble.

•**Avoid exposure to allergens and irritants.** Take steps to avoid contact with pollen, dust, dust mites, animal dander and any other allergens that have bothered you in the past.

Don't smoke. Limit contact with secondhand smoke, too.

Avoid swimming pools in winter. Chlorine can irritate already-dry sinus membranes, making them vulnerable to infection.

Limit your consumption of alcohol to one drink per day. Drinking can cause sinus and nasal membranes to swell.

### SELF-CARE FOR SINUSITIS

If you have sinus symptoms, you can usually ease the discomfort on your own…

•**Take an over-the-counter decongestant that contains *pseudoephedrine,*** such as Sudafed. This will open sinus passages and allow mucus to flow.

Decongestant pills work a bit better than sprays, which frequently don't penetrate deeply enough. And unlike sprays, pills do not cause "rebound" congestion, in which the nasal swelling goes away briefly only to come back worse than before.

*Caution:* Avoid decongestant pills if you have high blood pressure or urinary problems. If you take any prescription drug, ask your doctor or pharmacist if it could interact with pseudoephedrine.

•**Apply hot compresses** to the painful area for five minutes every few hours—especially after being out in cold weather.

In addition to relieving pain, compresses will improve circulation in the region, helping the body fight sinus infection.

•**Sleep with your head and shoulders elevated.** This promotes drainage of mucus from your sinuses. Try sleeping on three pillows or—better yet—on a foam sleeping "wedge" with a pillow on top of that.

*If you sleep on your side:* Keep your head turned so that the more painful side faces up.

•**Avoid air travel.** Pressure changes that occur during descent can force infected matter deeper into the sinuses. That makes the infection harder to treat.

If you *must* fly with a cold or sinus infection, take a decongestant just before departure. Ask your doctor if you should be taking an oral antibiotic as well.

#### WHEN TO SEE THE DOCTOR

If sinusitis persists for 10 days or longer—or if symptoms are severe and/or getting worse—you may need antibiotic therapy.

Treated promptly, even severe sinusitis generally clears up with a couple of weeks of antibiotic therapy. If you ignore the symptoms for weeks or months before seeking treatment, however, several *months* of antibiotic therapy may be necessary.

#### DO YOU NEED AN OPERATION?

Sinus surgery may be necessary if the pain and congestion persist despite prolonged treatment with decongestants and/or antibiotics. It may also be necessary if…

…the sinuses are filled with pus and cannot drain.

…the infection has extended to the eyes or surrounding bones.

…the sinuses are blocked by a polyp, cyst, scar tissue or some anatomical defect.

The simplest form of surgery is *puncture and irrigation.* In this procedure, the surgeon flushes out the infected sinus by injecting a salt-containing solution through the nose.

This outpatient procedure is performed under local anesthesia. Complications are rare. Recovery is usually immediate.

Another commonly used surgical technique is *functional endoscopic sinus surgery.* Here, the surgeon uses a small, lighted "telescope" inserted through the nose to remove diseased tissue, open clogged drainage openings and restore sinus function.

Endoscopic surgery typically involves several weeks of healing. The most common complications include swelling and infection.

# Cold Sore Remedy

Cold sores heal faster and cause less pain when treated topically with Pepto-Bismol or another bismuth-containing antacid. *What to do:* Once every four hours, use a cotton ball to dab the liquid onto the sore. Other potentially effective remedies for cold sores include the over-the-counter amino acid supplement *lysine* and the prescription ointment *acyclovir* (Zovirax).

Matthew Lozano, MD, a family physician in private practice in Fresno, CA.

# Dandruff Magic

Dandruff can often be controlled simply by shampooing in cool water.

***Reason:*** Hot water strips the skin of natural oils that help control flaking. So do alcohol-based styling products like mousse or gel.

Individuals with severe dandruff often benefit from rotating dandruff shampoos with different active ingredients—tar, selenium, zinc and salicylic acid.

Dee Anna Glaser, MD, vice-chairman of dermatology, St. Louis University School of Medicine.

# Allergy Pills for Motion Sickness

The active ingredient in Benadryl blocks signals from the inner ear to the stomach, helping reduce motion sickness. The Food and Drug Administration actually approved using

Benadryl for this purpose 10 years ago, but the label still does not reflect this use. Take the medicine 30 minutes before starting your trip. But beware, this medicine can cause drowsiness—don't drive after taking it. *Also worth considering:* The prescription allergy medicine Allegra—which does not cause drowsiness. Some doctors prescribe it for seasickness. *Other helpful steps:* Eat healthful foods...watch the horizon as much as possible while moving.

Edwin Monsell, MD, PhD, director of ear surgery, Henry Ford Hospital, Detroit.

## Bad Breath Remedy

Bad breath doesn't always come from teeth, but can also come from bacteria at the back of the mouth. So brushing teeth does not cure it. Bad breath can be worsened by gum disease, and also by alcohol-laden mouthwash. Some mouthwashes may mask odor temporarily but also can dry out the mouth, which helps bacteria grow. *Remedy:* The best way to eliminate bad breath may be by abrasion. Buy an inexpensive tongue scraper at a drugstore and use it to scrape dead tissue and loose particles from the back of your tongue. Then use a toothbrush to brush the roof of your mouth, gums and all other soft tissue in your mouth. If these simple approaches don't do the trick, see your dentist. *Also useful:* Specialty mouthwashes formulated to kill bacteria are available by prescription.

Sheldon Nadler, DMD, a dentist in private practice in New York City.

## Breathing Problems Are Not Always Asthma Related

Breathing problems thought to be caused by asthma are sometimes caused by exer-cise-induced *vocal cord dysfunction* (VCD). Many of the symptoms of the two disorders are similar—difficulty speaking and breathing, chest tightness and panic. *Self-defense:* If you suffer asthma attacks only when exercising, ask your doctor about undergoing *spirometry* (breathing into a breath-measuring device) and other tests to distinguish VCD from asthma. VCD patients often benefit from a few weeks of speech therapy.

Susan M. Brugman, MD, pediatric pulmonologist, National Jewish Medical and Research Center, Denver.

## Best Way to Clear Red Eyes

To clear red, irritated eyes, use cool compresses or artificial tears, such as *Viva* drops or *HypoTears*. If redness persists or is around the iris, see your doctor. Avoid daily use of eyedrops. They can mask potential eye problems. *Also:* Be cautious of eye decongestants. Regular use of this type of product regularly can create a rebound effect leading to swollen eyelids and conjunctivitis.

Melvin Schrier, OD, retired optometrist, Rancho Palos Verdes, CA.

## Vitamins Fight Cataracts

In a recent study, regular users of multivitamin supplements were one-third less likely than nonusers to develop *nuclear* cataracts—the most common type. Those who took daily vitamin E supplements cut their risk in half.

M. Cristina Leske, MD, MPH, chair, department of preventive medicine, University Medical Center, Stony Brook, NY. Her four-year study of 764 men and women was published in *Ophthalmology*, 655 Beach St., San Francisco 94109.

# Cataract Surgery Can Do More

Cataract surgery can be even more effective. A new implantable lens lets surgeons correct nearsightedness and farsightedness at the same time that they remove cataracts. The multifocal intraocular lens consists of five concentric rings, like a bull's-eye. Three rings correct for distance vision, two for close-up vision. *Bonus:* The lens can be folded during surgery. That means a smaller incision—and a faster recovery.

Sam Fanous, MD, assistant professor of ophthalmology, University of Montreal.

# Liver Spot Magic

The reddish or brownish spots can usually be lightened with an over-the-counter 2% *hydroquinone* lotion, such as Porcelana.

Hydroquinone works by blocking synthesis of the pigment melanin. If hydroquinone fails to lighten spots within three months, ask a doctor about prescription-strength hydroquinone (4%) or another skin-lightening option.

Liver spots (*lentigo senilis*) are caused by long-term exposure to the sun.

Pearl E. Grimes, MD, director, Vitiligo and Pigmentation Institute of Southern California, Los Angeles.

# Faster-Healing Paper Cuts

Paper cuts and severe dry skin on the fingertips heal faster when they're coated with *cyanoacrylate* glue (Krazy Glue). It seals the outer layer of skin, allowing inner layers to heal quickly. *What to do:* Clean the cut with warm water, then dry it thoroughly. Using a toothpick, dab on a thin, smooth coating of glue and let it dry. The glue will gradually come off over the next few days. *Caution:* Some people are allergic to cyanoacrylate. Stop using it if it causes skin to redden or become inflamed.

Sheryl D. Clark, MD, assistant professor of medicine and dermatology, Weill Medical College of Cornell University, New York City.

# Dry Germs Away

Even after a thorough washing, hands that aren't dried can transfer disease-causing bacteria.

***Recent study:*** When people with washed but still-wet hands touched skin and food, they transferred 68,000 and 31,000 microorganisms, respectively.

Drying their hands for 10 seconds with a clean towel—followed by air-drying for 20 seconds—cut these numbers by 99.8% and 94%, respectively.

Tom Miller, PhD, DSc, senior research fellow, department of medicine, University of Auckland, New Zealand.

# Foot Ulcer Help

Diabetic foot ulcers heal faster when treated with *becaplermin* (Regranex).

A recently approved prescription gel, becaplermin promotes growth of healthy tissue faster than the usual treatments—antibiotics and repeated removal of dead tissue (debridement).

Painful, slow-healing ulcers are caused by poor blood flow and nerve damage to the extremities—two common results of diabetes.

Gerald Bernstein, MD, associate clinical professor of medicine, Albert Einstein College of Medicine, New York City.

# 10

# The Winning Edge

## Nathaniel Branden Tells How to Be Assertive Without Being Aggressive...Impolite... Or Boorish

Is it possible to be assertive without being obnoxious? Are there ways to become effectively assertive without turning off the very people you are trying to win over?

Nathaniel Branden, PhD, one of the country's leading authorities on assertiveness and self-esteem, answers these questions and more...

### What is assertiveness?

Assertiveness isn't about being pushy or negatively aggressive. To be assertive means behaving in a direct and honest way and not faking what you think or feel in order to be liked.

### Why is assertiveness so important?

It is an essential part of self-respect. Whenever you keep quiet about your thoughts, feelings and desires because you are afraid people will disapprove of you, you're putting yourself second. This is humiliating.

You can't live according to your values without being assertive. Without assertiveness, you're not likely to get what you need in life—nor are you likely to make much of a contribution.

As a corporate consultant, I've seen people keep quiet even when their ideas might contribute to the resolution of a problem—because they're afraid to rock the boat. The company suffers, and so does the person's self-esteem.

### Is it possible to be *too* assertive?

Many people confuse assertiveness with having to get their own way all the time. Being assertive doesn't mean demanding to be the

Nathaniel Branden, PhD, a practicing psychotherapist in Los Angeles and an international corporate consultant who specializes in issues of accountability and self-esteem. He is author of 19 books, including *Self-Esteem at Work: How Confident People Make Powerful Companies* and *A Woman's Self-Esteem: Struggles and Triumphs in the Search for Identity*, both published by Jossey–Bass.

161

center of attention...elbowing to the front of the line...or being rude to intimidate others.

Assertiveness is a matter of being authentic—not obnoxious. It's about having the courage to stand up for your beliefs in appropriate ways.

When we have viewed assertiveness negatively, that so-called assertive person usually invaded our space. Such behavior is *beyond* assertive. That can be confrontational, aggressive, impolite.

We can't expect to have our rights respected if we don't respect others' rights.

### Where is the line between inappropriate and appropriate levels of assertiveness?

*Inappropriate* assertiveness includes shouting down another person...interrupting so that you're the only one who gets a chance to speak...insulting someone...and other behaviors that treat people as though they exist only to make the offensive person's life much more convenient.

*Appropriate* assertiveness is saying what you think—even if you don't know if your listeners agree. It could mean telling someone that his/her behavior is unacceptable—without name-calling. Paying a genuine compliment is assertive—positively assertive. Even silence can be assertive—such as when you refuse to laugh at an offensive joke.

Appropriate assertiveness advances your cause through courage—but not at the expense of others.

### What's a good way to deal with an inappropriately assertive person?

Stay calm, describe the behavior to which you object, and state what you want and/or intend to do. By refusing to meet the other person's aggression with hostility, you retain dignity and control—and your words will be much more effective.

Examples of what to say to an inappropriately assertive person...

• "If you're unwilling to lower your voice and speak in a normal manner, I'm unwilling to continue this conversation now."

• "I don't find hostility productive for getting problems solved—so I'm going to wait until you're willing to have a nonhostile discussion with me."

Asking the other person a question about the way he's acting is also effective. It invites him to stop and think—and possibly change what he is doing. *Examples...*

• "Do you think that shouting louder will make you more convincing?"

• "Do you feel a need to go on talking or arguing even though I've made it absolutely clear that I'm not going to do what you want?"

• "Is it your intention to be insulting right now?"

That doesn't mean you should never get angry. Some people won't pay attention unless you have an edge to your voice or use strong language. But I've never seen any good come from losing control, being insulting or saying anything you might regret later.

### How can we learn to assert ourselves more often?

One of the best ways is to spend a few minutes a day doing sentence-completion exercises.

This process is extremely simple and takes no more than 10 minutes a day. But it produces powerful change. *How to do it...*

Every morning, soon after you wake up, write the following sentence stem...

• "If I were 5% more self-assertive today..."

Then write six to 10 endings for that sentence, without stopping to think. Don't worry about whether your endings are "right" or "wrong."

Next, write six to 10 endings each for a few more sentence stems...

• "If I had the courage to treat my needs as important..."

• "If I don't stand up for my thoughts and feelings..."

• "If I am willing to ask for what I want..."

Do this every morning for a week. On the weekend, reread the week's sentences. Then write six to 10 endings for this sentence...

• "If any of what I have been writing is true, it might be helpful if I..."

Some examples of sentence endings are ..."I'd tell people what I think"..."I'd be more honest about what I feel"..."I'd let people know what I need."

As you do these exercises, you will become more aware of the situations in which you censor yourself...and less willing to remain silent when it's appropriate to be assertive.

# Tish Baldrige Makes Super-Successful Socializing Very Simple

Letitia Baldrige, who served as Jacqueline Kennedy's White House chief of staff. She is author of 16 books on manners, including *In the Kennedy Style*. Doubleday.

Feeling comfortable while socializing takes time and practice. My secrets for becoming the social magnet of any party...

### BEING POSITIVE PAYS

If you go in thinking you're going to have a terrible time, you will. Before you walk into a roomful of strangers, look in a mirror and smile. Take some deep breaths. Tell yourself you are as good and as smart as anybody in there.

Go over to the most agreeable-looking group of people. Wait until there's a break in the conversation and say, "My name is Joe Smith. I don't know anybody here. You all look like you're having such a good time, I thought you wouldn't mind if I joined you." They will take care of you. It always works.

### MAKE EYE CONTACT

Don't think about what you're going to say next. When you think, you look down and away. Listen instead. Making eye contact will be a natural reaction. If you look in people's eyes when they are talking, they will be much more responsive and enthusiastic. Making eye contact will also keep you from thinking while they're talking, and will make your eye contact natural and unforced.

### LEARN TO DISCUSS ANYTHING

Instead of spending so much time on your exercise equipment, exercise your brain. If you read the newspaper, you will pick up all kinds of things—somber, glamorous and funny. It will make you a good conversationalist.

If people ask about your work and you don't want to discuss it, don't dismiss the question. Answer briefly and politely. Learn to talk about your company in a short, complimentary manner. Then change the subject. Say, "I'd really like to know what you think about..."

### DON'T DRAG OUT STORIES

Don't use clichés in conversation. Don't use technical jargon. If people's eyes glaze over, you've become a bore. Instead, draw information out of people by asking questions.

### DETONATING BORES

If you must socialize with boring people, invite an interesting close friend—or friends—along. Explain the situation in advance. Ask for their help. If you're trapped by a bore at a party, glance at your watch, then say that you must make a phone call right away and excuse yourself. To make it credible, get out some change for the pay phone. Excuse yourself, and go make a call to anybody.

### ENTERTAINING WHEN YOU'RE BUSY

Throw small dinners. I invite eight or 10 people. I give up one hour a night for three nights before the party and prepare the bar, food and decor. Use the same menu often so you can do it without thinking—pasta and a great salad, peppermint ice cream and chocolate sauce. Or buy prepared food.

To keep up with hard-to-reach people, ask to take them out to dinner on a *Sunday* night. Or invite them for Sunday lunch...but don't let them take up your whole day. I always say, "I'm working all weekend. Come at 12:30, and I hope you'll leave by 2:30"—and I laugh. Nobody minds. They know I'm serious. At 2:30, if no one has made a move to leave, stand up and say, "Hasn't this been great?" Don't forget to laugh again.

# Zig Ziglar Tells How to Release the Awesome Power Within You

Zig Ziglar, chairman, Ziglar Training Systems, a training and development company, 3330 Earhart Dr., Suite 204, Carrollton, TX 75006. He is author of 13 books, including *Success for Dummies*. IDG Books Worldwide.

Nearly 75% of world-class leaders studied were raised in poverty, had been abused as children or had some serious physical disability.

How did these people overcome these problems and get to the top? And how did they stay there?

The key is motivation. Motivation gives you the *want to* and provides the spark. It enables you to utilize your training and experience while finding the strength, character and commitment to keep you going when the going gets tough.

### MOTIVATIONAL STRATEGIES

•**Self-talk.** You must be in your own corner. To start, take a 3" x 5" card and write such positive affirmations as, *I am an honest, intelligent, responsible, organized, goal-setting, committed individual whose priorities are firmly in place.*

On another card, write, *I am a focused, disciplined, enthusiastic, positive-thinking, decisive extra-miler who is a competent, energized, self-starting team player determined to develop and use all of these leadership qualities in my personal, family and business life. These are the qualities of the winner I was born to be.*

Read these positive affirmations to yourself several times a day.

•**Goal setting.** Be specific. Create a *Wild Idea Sheet* of everything you want to be, do or have.

Wait a day or two and then write the reason why you want to reach each goal. Ask yourself if each goal will make you happier or healthier, improve family relations, make you more secure or give you hope. Most important, will reaching each goal contribute to a balanced, successful life? Divide remaining goals into short-range (one month or less)...intermediate (one month to one year)...and long-range (one year or more).

•**Positive thinking/positive training.** When I was on the seventh-grade boxing team, I stepped into the ring with a much smaller opponent. I was a confident, excited positive thinker.

All of those things disappeared in the flash of an eye—or maybe a fist. My opponent might have been smaller, but he had been on the boxing team since he was in fifth grade and understood the defensive aspects of boxing. He also knew that a straight punch was

the shortest distance to my nose. Luckily, a compassionate coach took me aside and gave me some good instruction—fast.

*Lesson:* In addition to having a positive attitude and enthusiasm for what you're doing, you need to learn the skills of your trade. Education and training are essential. Enthusiasm by itself is like running fast in the dark.

•**Professional counseling.** If you broke your leg, you would not hesitate to seek professional medical help. But there are still many people who believe we should be able to take care of our emotions or our mind-sets and heal ourselves.

You get information out of books, magazines and newspapers. You get knowledge out of encyclopedias and educational institutions. Yet until you add the spiritual dimension, you're going to miss the insights, wisdom and common sense that are critical to any healing process.

Get counseling from a person who has *wisdom* as well as knowledge. Someone with knowledge has only a command of the facts. But someone with wisdom has good judgment and insights into what you're facing.

Go right to the top—the best person you can identify—to get the help that you need to solve your problems.

•**Control your environment.** You might not be able to change the world, but you can change *your* world. A sound exercise program and sensible eating habits are as important as feeding your mind good, clean, powerful positive inputs.

Even the kind of music you listen to will affect your feelings and energy level. Soothing melodies are best when you need to relax and wind down. Positive messages in songs are useful when you need to get up in the morning and get started for the day.

•**Use words that paint the right picture.** The sales manager who says to the salesperson going out to make a call, *This is our number-one client...be careful...don't foul up the deal,* paints the wrong picture and shakes the salesperson's confidence. Such comments do more harm than good.

*The right picture: This is our number-one client. That's the reason I'm sending you out to make the call. I know you will handle it professionally and effectively.*

Use a notepad. When you catch yourself saying something that paints a negative picture, write down what you just said and then later rephrase it to paint a positive picture.

*Example:* Don't say, *I hope I don't forget my keys.* It's far better to say, *I'm going to remember that I placed my keys in my top drawer.*

The most influential person you talk to all day long is *you*, and what you tell yourself has a direct bearing on your performance.

•**Last deposit.** Leave every encounter on a positive note. If one person gives you a negative feeling, change your mood by going to an upbeat friend or acquaintance to get a quick fix.

---

# Paul Ekman Tells How Not to Be Fooled by Liars

Paul Ekman, PhD, professor of psychology at the University of California Medical School, San Francisco. He is author of *Telling Lies.* W.W. Norton.

---

Few people do better than chance when judging whether someone is lying or telling the truth. That includes the professionals in mental health, criminal justice and journalism who have opportunities to practice their lie-detection skills every day.

The odds are worse when you deal with a person over the phone, have limited personal contact, listen to a presentation or watch a political candidate deliver a speech or participate in a debate.

Liars, or people who conceal information, often succeed because the target of their lies makes it so easy for them.

*Examples:* A manager who doesn't admit making a major hiring or firing mistake...parents who don't want to acknowledge that their teenager might be taking drugs...a wife who doesn't want to entertain suspicions that her spouse is being unfaithful.

Unless you are prepared to deal with the truth, you are very likely to overlook the subtle signs in a person's words and voice, face and body movements that signal deception. Even after you train yourself to recognize these clues, don't be overconfident.

## INEFFECTIVE LIE DETECTION

The most typical barriers to making the right judgment call...

•**Not enough time spent with the suspected liar.** First meetings or rushed encounters are especially vulnerable to errors. Some people are on their best behavior. They speak carefully and suppress giveaway body activities. Others are anxious, fidgety and tongue-tied, suggesting that they are being evasive when they are not.

•**Charm.** People who you like instinctively and want to get closer to immediately, even before you know anything about them, are much more likely to get away with lies than those with dour, cranky personalities. Charmers are not necessarily more inclined to lie. You'll just have far more trouble detecting when they do.

•**Relying on hunches or intuition about how liars act.**

*Most common mistake:* Assuming that people who don't look you in the eye are probably lying. Other faulty stereotypes include people who fidget a lot...who are hesitant in how they speak...or who give roundabout answers to straight questions.

## LIE-DETECTION STRATEGY

There is no universal sign of deceit—no gesture, facial expression or muscle movement that in and of itself means the person is lying. People would lie less if they thought there was such a sign.

When you suspect a person of lying, give yourself time to observe that individual face-to-face. Create situations that enable you to shift the conversation from noncritical topics about which you would not expect lies to the critical topic about which the person may be tempted to lie.

*Goal:* Establish a baseline in your mind of how the person talks and gestures while discussing noncritical topics. Then try to identify differences when the subject gets hot.

You are most likely to focus on the person's words and face. But these observations are not likely to provide the most powerful clues.

•**Words.** Liars are most careful about their choice of words. They know that they will be held more accountable for what they say than for the tone of their voice, their facial expressions or their body movements. If they have time, they fine-tune their messages. But they can be careless.

***Giveaways:*** Significant word slips…emotional tirades—outpourings of words caused by overwhelming anger, fear or distress—that reveal more information than the liar anticipated.

• **Faces.** A person's face is the primary site for displaying emotions. But liars can still exert considerable control over their facial expressions—especially easy-to-identify expressions such as smiles.

Most people like to believe they can easily detect false expressions, but research shows they rarely can.

Lie-detection researchers have discovered that fleeting expressions, which flash on and off in less than one-quarter of a second, are often good clues to deceit—but they can usually be observed only by playing a videotape over and over again at a slow speed. In day-to-day life, use these chief clues to detect a false expression…

• **It's more evident on one side of the face than the other.** This is very subtle, but it can be detected once you train yourself to observe closely.

• **It lasts longer than five seconds.** Genuine expressions of delight, surprise, etc. are very short-lived.

• **It's not exactly synchronized with the related verbal statement.** *Example:* An angry facial expression follows a vigorous verbal denial.

### RELIABLE CLUES

Pay close attention to detect some fairly reliable clues to deception in how a person speaks…

• **Pauses that are too long and too frequent**—especially in response to a question.

• **Many nonwords,** such as "ah…uhh."

• **Partial words,** such as "I re-really worked on that a-all afternoon."

• **Higher pitch to the voice**—though this is really evidence of fear or anger and not necessarily a clue to deception.

***Beware:*** Good liars often deliberately keep their voice tones flat to disguise emotion. This unflappable style deceives many people who think it is evidence of truth telling.

Pay much closer attention to body movements than you're likely to do instinctively in most personal encounters. A liar's body leaks a great deal of information about deception because most people ignore small gestures. *Key signs are…*

• **Disguised gesture.**

***Examples:*** A person's voice or face may not reveal anger, and he/she may even deny being angry—while keeping a tightly clenched fist in a lap. The meaning of a two-shoulder shrug or turning the palms upward is generally clear—*I can't help it…*or *What does it matter?* But when a person makes such a gesture only partway—a quick, almost imperceptible lift of one shoulder—it can suggest fear that the lie doesn't seem to be effective.

• **Less use of illustrative gestures than is usual.** Illustrative gestures give emphasis to a word or phrase or describe a picture in space (a spiral staircase, for instance). Once you develop a good sense of how much use a person usually makes of such gestures, it's a tip-off that he is bored…or uninterested…or sad…or uninvolved in what is being said…or is only feigning concern or enthusiasm when there is a sudden decrease in such activity.

Squirming and fidgeting are far less accurate indicators of lying than most people think. These actions are fairly easy to bring under control. And since liars know that people connect such behavior with lying, they make themselves get it under control.

# Balancing The Brain

Ann McCombs, DO, an osteopath in private practice in Kirkland, WA, and a trustee of the American Holistic Medical Association.

Each of us can be said to be either primarily left-brained or right-brained. The terms refer to which side of the brain (hemisphere) dominates your approach to the world.

**The left brain is logical.** It analyzes and catalogs information, keeps track of time and creates and responds to language. Engineers, accountants and scientists tend to be predominantly left-brained.

**The right brain is creative, intuitive and emotional.** Artists, social workers, entrepreneurs and teachers tend to be predominantly right-brained.

*Trap:* Relying too heavily on one side of the brain (a condition called *hemisphericity*) can cause physical problems.

Left-brain overreliance can cause excessive worry. You may make poor use of your time, get lost in the details and communicate poorly with others.

Right-brain overreliance can cause excessive emotionalism. You may be unable to focus on the task at hand and quick to anger when criticized by others.

*Self-defense:* Consider your problem-solving style...what kind of work you do...and how you spend your leisure time.

If you seem to rely mostly upon one hemisphere, set aside time each day to do something that nurtures the other hemisphere.

If your left hemisphere is overtaxed, do things that involve creativity and sensory stimulation. Listen to music, dance, act in local theater, take a painting class, walk in the woods, etc.

If your right hemisphere is overtaxed, take on tasks that require strategy and order. Play chess, learn new software, plan a budget, organize a closet, do crossword puzzles, etc.

# How to Make Your Relationship Much, Much Better

Ellen Wachtel, JD, PhD, a psychologist and marital therapist in private practice in New York City. She is author of *We Love Each Other But....* Golden Books.

A strong, loving marriage brings more than happiness. It brings good health, too. Consider these recent findings...

•Marital strife raises the risk for depression.

•People who are separated or divorced suffer more illness—and face a greater risk of car accidents—than happily married individuals.

•When couples attack each other maliciously during an argument, they show steep declines in immune function.

Though often neglected, the techniques for preserving intimacy and warmth in marriage are quite simple. They're based on one basic principle—*We love people who make us feel good about ourselves.*

Remember how you felt during the early days of your relationship? You appreciated each other's intelligence, sense of humor, etc....and took the time to say so.

Over time, most couples spend less time talking about what they admire in each other. Instead, they start to focus on what bothers them.

### POSITIVE REINFORCEMENT

To make your partner feel good about himself/herself, make him feel appreciated...

•**Praise him for traits you appreciate or admire.** The more often you express your appreciation, the more responsive your partner will be on occasions when you bring up something that bothers you.

Be as specific as possible. Specific compliments carry more weight than general ones.

*Example:* "I admire the way you drew out that shy couple at the party. I love how you bring out the best in people."

•**Save your criticism for what's really important.** Criticism erodes love. For most couples, even one critical remark a day is too much.

•**Practice kindness.** Ask yourself, "What simple action can I take to make my partner feel valued and loved?"

*Examples:* Making a fresh pot of coffee in the morning...calling from the office to say hello.

Given frequently, small gestures of affection keep your partner feeling close.

### SOLVING COMMON PROBLEMS

Many marital problems have surprisingly simple solutions...

*Problem:* **Decisions are impossible.** If differences of opinion often lead to conflict, these techniques will help you stop acting like adversaries...

•**Explain why you feel the way you do.** You may *think* your spouse knows why you prefer one choice over another. But he may not be aware of all your reasons—or may have a poor understanding of your reasons.

When you explain yourself, some aspect of your thinking may strike a chord with your partner. This will keep the two of you from being polarized.

●**Look for a third alternative.** Don't spend time arguing over which of you should give in to the other. Look for a choice that pleases *both* of you.

Imagine a couple fighting over where the family should live. The wife wants a house in the suburbs. The husband wants to keep their apartment in the city.

Their solution? Buying an attached condo near the train station. The wife gets the most important thing she wants—a safe environment for the kids. The husband avoids a long freeway commute.

●**Ask yourself, "Do I really care?"** Few decisions are worth making a fuss over. Choose your battles wisely.

*Problem:* **Fights spin out of control.** Two skills are needed to keep fights from getting ugly. First, the ability to de-escalate arguments before they get out of hand...and, second, the ability to talk about conflict in an open, honest way.

The most effective strategy for de-escalating conflicts is to have a standing rule that either of you can call a cease-fire at any time. *Also helpful...*

●**Recognize the signs that an argument is getting out of control.** These might include a sinking feeling...a discussion that's going in circles...saying deliberately hurtful things.

●**Set a date to revisit the issue.** In the meantime, agree honestly to consider your partner's point of view.

To be more open and honest...

●**Don't bring up difficult subjects when you're angry.** If you feel you must speak up while you're angry, say, "I'm upset and I want to talk about this—but I think we should wait until I'm not so mad."

●**Start with the positive.** It's hard for people to listen when they feel criticized. So be sure to acknowledge what your partner is doing right.

*Example:* "I know your intentions are good, and I don't want you to think I'm dismissing your efforts, but..."

●**Keep it short.** Make your point in a sentence or two, then let your partner respond.

Limit discussions to 20 minutes. That way, you'll avoid rehashing the problem all day. If the issue still isn't resolved, agree to return to it at another time.

●**Listen for areas of agreement.** In the midst of conflict, we tend to focus on what we disagree with. Ask yourself, "What element of what my partner is saying is right?" Taking that simple step can dramatically improve the tone of a conversation.

*Problem:* **The marriage is in a rut.** To keep your relationship lively...

●**Don't take your spouse for granted.** You wouldn't read at the dinner table if a guest were over for dinner...or dress like a slob if you were going out with a friend. Extend the same courtesies to your spouse.

●**Don't pigeonhole yourself or your partner.** Instead of saying, "This is what I like (or don't like)," develop the attitude, "I'm game. I'll try it!" Support your spouse when he acts in new or unexpected ways.

Be open to new experiences, too—classes, hobbies, foods, movies, etc. You'll bring energy and enthusiasm to the marriage.

Include new activities to do as a couple—so you grow together as well as individually.

---

# Dr. Bernie Siegel's Very Simple Secrets Of Happiness

Bernie S. Siegel, MD, one of the country's leading experts on the connection between a positive mind and a healthy body. He is founder of Exceptional Cancer Patients, 53 School Ground Rd., Unit 3, Branford, CT 06405, which provides support to people with life-threatening illnesses. He is author of several books, including *Prescriptions for Living: Inspirational Lessons for a Joyful, Loving Life.* HarperCollins.

---

Most people feel happy only when their material desires are satisfied. I have found, though, that happiness is a sensation that has little to do with external forces, such as what we possess and what we earn.

Instead, it is an emotional state that we can turn on and off at will. By embracing the talents and opportunities we're given instead of clinging to the pain we've suffered in the past, we can create internal joy at any time.

Steps to take that will help you feel true happiness…

**•Take responsibility for your mistakes.** We fear others will dislike us when we make mistakes, so we torture ourselves by trying to hide or deny them. In fact, what people dislike are the excuses and the blame used to cover up mistakes. Owning up to your mistakes shows you care and helps bring resolution and healing. *Helpful…*

**•Forgive yourself first,** which is perhaps the biggest hurdle. Mistakes are tough on self-esteem—if you aim to be perfect. However, no one gets through life without making a few.

**•Apologize**—and rectify the error. Others will welcome your help, and you'll feel happier with yourself for taking constructive action.

**•Think of the most recent mistake you've made.** If you haven't made amends, it's probably not too late to say, "I'm sorry."

**•Stay in charge of your thoughts and feelings.** Although you can't control events, you can manage your reactions to them. Only you can decide whether to choose harmony or turmoil.

*Example:* After some treasured family heirlooms were stolen from me several years ago, I realized that my anger had taken over my thoughts. Only by vividly picturing the thief using the robbery money to buy presents for his children was I able to reclaim my thoughts. Unrealistic? Probably…but instead of obsessing about the injustice, I was able to get beyond my resentment.

*Helpful…*

**•Use mental imagery.** Holding a positive image in your mind crowds out negativity…and positive thoughts have been shown to create happier feelings.

**•Exaggerate your troubles,** stretching complaints to such hilarious limits that you end up laughing.

**•Take a time-out.** Go for a nature walk—the outdoors is a natural tonic. Or meditate, listen to music or give yourself a pep talk.

**•Have faith that you can overcome obstacles.** Why give up in despair when nature constantly gives us the hopeful message that we can always find a way?

*Example:* Jogging on a recently repaved road, I noticed one area of the new asphalt changing over a period of weeks. It first rose up several inches, then cracked, then opened like a volcano. What emerged was foliage.

Trapped under the pavement, a skunk cabbage seed had grown into a plant so hardy it broke right through to the light and air.

Everyone faces walls and barriers. The unhappy choice is to let them stop you. Believing you can find an opening to grow and blossom is the joyous, life-affirming option. *Helpful…*

**•Be open to redirection.** When things don't go as you have planned, stop and think where this different path might be leading you. Events that at first seem to be unfortunate or undesirable may actually provide surprising advantages.

**•Judge each problem as an opportunity to grow.** Many patients I've treated and counseled over the years have said their illnesses taught them to value their lives and implement wonderful changes.

**•You don't have to "break through the pavement" in a single day.** Take troubles one step at a time. Celebrate each sign of progress before taking the next step.

**•Deal constructively with criticism.** The Sufi poet Rumi wrote, "Criticism polishes my mirror."

Regarding criticism as a threat, an insult or proof that you're worthless won't make you happy. Instead, it is better to take a more optimistic view and see criticism as a learning tool to help you improve.

I've been fortunate to have many critics among my patients. When people give you criticism, it means they feel you are willing to listen and change. *Helpful…*

**•Evaluate the source of the criticism.** Those who love finding fault with everyone will only scratch your mirror, not polish it.

**•When criticized by people you trust,** think of yourself as an athlete getting direction and support from a coach who wants to see you perform better.

**•Don't let criticism shake your confidence.** Use appraisals as a way to help you reach a higher level of performance.

# How to Get Back on Schedule When You're Always Running Behind

Stephanie Winston, time-management consultant and editor of *Stephanie Winston's The Organized Executive,* Georgetown Publishing House, 1101 30 St. NW, Washington, DC 20007.

Even the most efficient people frequently feel as if they are constantly running behind schedule.

Here's how to overcome the diversions that prevent you from accomplishing as much as you would like to each day...

●**Catch your breath and start to plan.** One of the biggest enemies of good time management is poor planning. The more rushed you feel, the less productive you'll be. The more frantic you are, the less decisive you will be.

*Helpful:* Go into the office one hour earlier than usual one day a week...or stay later. Spend the time writing down your three most important priorities. Then set deadlines for them ...and create a manageable to-do list that prioritizes the tasks.

●**Use peak time wisely.** Tackle your toughest or least pleasant projects when you feel most productive.

The best time of day for most people is early in the morning, when you are least distracted and most motivated.

Your hardest tasks should be slotted for the early hours. Once this work is out of the way, you can make better use of the remaining hours.

●**Know when to run and hide.** Sometimes you need absolute silence to concentrate on what needs to get done. Sitting in your office—with the door open or closed—isn't always the best solution.

*Better:* Commandeer an empty conference room or head out to a coffee shop. Distraction-free time—even if it's just 15 minutes to a half-hour—is powerful when used to refocus on what needs to be done.

●**Just say *no*—very politely.** Interruptions by people who need your help can throw you off track. While you can't stop these requests, they can be controlled.

*Helpful:* Learn to deflect assignments when you're too busy. Say, "I'm just snowed under right now."

If you really can't say no, take on only part of the assignment—and not the whole thing.

●**Delegate down—and down.** Some of my clients would be less overwhelmed if they identified and delegated the less important areas of their jobs.

The key is to start thinking of the people who work with you—and this can include your boss—as your helpers. They are there to help you get things done so that you can be more efficient and productive.

Don't be so obsessed with setting things right that you can't let go of an assignment. Never feel guilty in the least about backing off and using resources to reach your goals at work.

●**Keep track of interruptions.** Some people are overwhelmed at work because subordinates ask them for more guidance than they should.

Others spend too much time talking to friends or family members. Some may pay too much attention to the stock market.

*Helpful:* Keep a running list of interruptions, the topic and how long you were distracted. Review this list every day to see where you can limit your availability and willingness to give up precious time.

●**Cut down on business travel.** Most business travel is a waste of time. While it is important to travel to make a presentation or close a deal, many of your trips away from the office and home aren't as critical as you think.

Before you agree to attend a conference or to go out of town to meet with people, ask yourself what you could accomplish if you remained at the office.

Unnecessary business travel and "networking" actually make you less efficient and distract you from what's truly important—your staff's needs and your company's goals.

# Simplifying Your Life Doesn't Have to Be Complicated

Elaine St. James, a writer and consultant in Santa Barbara, CA. She is author of several books, including the best-sellers *Simplify Your Life* and *Inner Simplicity*, both published by Hyperion.

The kind of simplifying I'm going to guide you through is about clearing out the clutter in your living space—and your mind—so that you will have more time to do the things that are truly important to you.

### REMOVE DISTRACTIONS

To simplify your life, you must eliminate the kind of clutter I call *distractions*—belongings you never use, space you don't need, uncontrolled buying, etc.—things that keep you from spending your time the way you want to.

First, get rid of all the material things you don't need…

•**Hall closet.** Find a new home for overcoats you no longer wear to the office…coats, boots, hats, mittens or sports equipment belonging to grown children…other outerwear you no longer need.

*Helpful rule:* If you haven't used a piece of clothing or equipment in a year, dispose of it.

•**Kitchen.** Start with the very top shelves in the cabinets. Throw out anything coated with a layer of grease or grime. The grime means that it hasn't been used in a long time and may never be used again.

Pull out all the so-called "convenience items" —breadmakers, plate warmers, rice cookers, pasta machines, etc.—that you've only used once or twice in the past five years. Pass them on to someone who might like to have them.

*Even simpler:* One woman simplified her kitchen so that she has only two items more than she normally uses of each plate, cup, knife, fork and spoon. This paring down gives her more space and forces her to keep up with the cleaning, since she no longer has the leeway to let the dishes pile up.

•**Wardrobe.** If you're not going to an office anymore, get rid of the business outfits you no

longer need. When you buy clothes, make sure they fit your new simplified lifestyle.

*Helpful:* Dispose of one old garment or accessory for each new one you buy.

### EXPAND THE PROCESS

Extend this simplifying program to the rest of your house. Make it a rule to get rid of one old household item each time you buy a new one.

*Examples:* If you buy a new toaster oven, donate your existing toaster to a local charity. If you buy a new set of flannel sheets, give an older set of sheets to your kids.

•**Clean out your files.** Sort through old files and ruthlessly throw things out. Do you really need to keep phone bills from 1975? Of course not—so throw them away.

If you have trouble with this, ask one of your grown children, a friend or a professional organizer for help. *For professional help:* Call the National Association of Professional Organizers, 512-206-0151.

### MAKE SIMPLIFYING A PRIORITY

Once you've eliminated the clutter, keep it from building up again by changing your buying habits.

The early and middle years of your life were spent buying products, food and clothing at a rate needed to support a growing family. Now, with the kids grown and your career not as important, you can replace high-consumption habits with simpler ones. *Strategies…*

•**Question each addition to your life.** Before you add anything new to your life—a service, an object, a responsibility or an activity—ask yourself, *Will this simplify my life?* You might discover that a change you thought would make life simpler will actually do the opposite.

*Example:* We were doing some minor renovations to our home and had drawn up a list of the changes we wanted to make. As we worked our way down the list asking ourselves the question, *Is this going to simplify our lives?* we found that some changes were good (replacing our old, unreliable washer and dryer might actually prevent a fire), but some were life-complicating.

Redoing our kitchen countertops seemed like a good idea at first, but we soon realized it would disrupt our lives and our household for a long time and would add an unnecessary expense to our newly simplified budget. We decided to skip it.

●**Put a hold on purchases.** Create a 30-day list for potential purchases. Before you rush out to buy anything, put it on a list—with the item name, price and current date. Set the list aside for 30 days.

If, at the end of the 30-day period, you still want to buy the item, do so. Chances are, though, you'll look at the list in 30 days and realize that you can get along just as well (and perhaps even better) without buying anything.

*Helpful:* Keep the 30-day list posted on the refrigerator or, even better, wrapped around your credit card or checkbook and attached with a rubber band.

●**Adopt a gift *receiving* policy.** Don't allow gifts from others to complicate and clutter your life.

Crayoned pictures, camp and school projects —and even expensive trinkets from children, grandchildren and friends—can thwart your efforts to simplify your life and living space.

*Helpful:* Encourage your family to give you a box of homemade fudge, a basket of holiday cookies or other consumable item that's within the range of the grandkids' talents and their parents' patience.

●**Move to a smaller space.** Less living space will hold less clutter and will force you to evaluate everything you bring into it.

### FIRST THINGS FIRST

As you work toward simplifying your living space, concentrate on other things as well...

●**Simplify your meals.** Unless you enjoy cooking elaborate meals, prepare simple foods like steamed vegetables, fresh salads, broiled or grilled chicken, soups and muffins.

●**Simplify exercise.** Nothing is as simple as a daily walk, and walking regularly does wonders for your body and mind.

●**Simplify your thinking.** Weather permitting, spend some time every day sitting under a beautiful shade tree, or in some other special place, meditating and generally exploring who you are and what you want to do with your life. Get to know yourself. This is your time— make the most of it!

# The Sound Judgment Improvement System

John S. Hammond, DBA, management consultant, John S. Hammond & Associates, 46 Winter St., Lincoln, MA 01773, and former professor at Harvard Business School. He is coauthor, with Ralph L. Keeney and Howard Raiffa, of *Smart Choices: A Practical Guide to Making Better Decisions.* Harvard Business School Press.

The ability to make wise decisions *consistently* is the key to success. By systematically applying tested principles, you can improve your decisions, experience less wheel-spinning and be better able to explain the soundness of your decisions to others.

### THE FIVE STEPS

While some decisions are too trivial to bother spending much time and energy on, those that have lasting consequences should involve these five steps...

●**Define the problem.** How you evaluate a problem and take it apart determines whether you identify the problem's central issues.

Your whole decision-making process will be undermined if you work on the wrong issues.

*Example:* You think your problem is how to find more time to get your daily tasks done. So you decide to work late into the evening. But perhaps you should have concentrated on how to do the tasks more efficiently or focused on which tasks to eliminate.

Flexibility is very important in sharpening your definition of a problem. Don't be afraid to change the definition as you better understand your decision situation or as circumstances change.

●**Clarify your objectives.** What do you want your decision to accomplish? What are your goals? Your needs? Clear, honest objectives will guide you in seeking information and evaluating alternatives.

To define your objectives, write down all the concerns you hope to address through your decision. At first, be creative rather than rigorous. Then narrow down the concerns and express each important one succinctly.

Separate the *means* from the *ends*. A common mistake is stating objectives in terms of means instead of digging for more fundamental underlying objectives.

*Example:* When my niece was house hunting, one of her objectives was to find "a house that was less than three years old." There weren't many of those to choose from. Going beneath her initial objective, however, she realized that "a house in move-in condition" was what she really wanted. In shifting from the *means* ("less than three years old") to the *end* ("move-in condition"), she vastly expanded her options.

The way to get down to fundamental objectives is by asking yourself—*why*.

*Example:* When planning a new distribution center, a company may list one objective as "to minimize construction time." If you ask why, you may find it is to get the new center operational as quickly as possible. Ask why again, and you discover it is to reduce cost and disruption of transition.

Probing your fundamental objectives may suggest additional possibilities that open the decision-making process.

●**Create attractive and imaginative alternatives.** The decision you eventually make is only as good as the best alternative you present to yourself. So there is much to be gained from creating better alternatives.

*Common mistakes:* Repeating what you did in the past...making small changes that don't really make much difference...going with the first alternative that comes to mind...choosing among options presented by others rather than coming up with some of your own.

*Helpful:* Generate new alternatives by taking a fresh look at each objective and asking *how* it can be achieved. How can you minimize costs of a new program at work? Get your child a good education? Find a vacation spot that is both relaxing and interesting?

You may fall back on the tried and true, but you may also find something new—and much, much better.

●**Envision the consequences.** If you haven't thought out the consequences—how you'll fare with each alternative—before you make a major decision, you may not be happy with what you end up with.

*Helpful:* Imagine yourself in the future, living with each alternative. Then write a free-form description of the consequences, as precisely as possible.

Some alternatives may seem clearly inferior at this point. Eliminate them. Organize descriptions of the remaining alternatives into a consequences table that enables you to compare them easily.

*Example:* You're choosing among several job offers. List them across the top of a page. Then list the important objectives—salary, location, vacation time, job satisfaction, job security, etc.—along the side. Fill in the chart with judgments and data about how each potential job measures up.

●**Analyze trade-offs.** Making a decision is difficult when one alternative best meets one objective but another is superior in other ways.

*Example:* Job A offers a higher salary, but Job B is more interesting...and Job C has more security and better benefits.

You have to trade off advantages and disadvantages to find the best overall choice. Use the "even swap" method—a kind of bartering system to play alternatives against each other.

*How it works:* If the $200-a-month salary advantage of Job A is counterbalanced by the better promotion prospects of Job B, you can eliminate "salary" and "advancement" and base your choice between Jobs A and B on other grounds, such as satisfaction and benefits.

### COMPLICATING FACTORS

Although all decisions require that you work through these five steps, some decisions are complicated by other factors, including...

●**Uncertainty.** Often you can't be sure about the consequences of your decision until after you decide. *Example:* One flight is cheaper...but if it arrives late, you'll miss a connecting flight.

*What to do:*

●Identify the uncertainties that most influence the consequences (whether the flight will be on time).

●Determine potential outcomes of the uncertainties (the flight will be on time or it won't).

●Judge how likely each outcome is. (What's the on-time record of the airline and flight in question?)

●Determine the consequences for each outcome. (How much of a difference would the missed flight make? For example, would you lose a day of vacation?)

●**Risk tolerance.** How much risk you're willing to live with is a personal matter. Investigate your feelings about risk in each situation by considering the relative desirability of various consequences.

●**Linked decisions.** The decision today influences your future choices, so think ahead. Make contingency plans.

### AVOID PSYCHOLOGICAL PITFALLS

Even savvy decision makers can be derailed by psychological traps. Pitfalls to avoid…

●**Anchoring.** You tend to give too much weight to initial impressions and information.

*Solution:* Look at the problem from different perspectives. Get input from others, and focus on what you're likely to learn rather than on what you already know.

●**Protecting past decisions.** You're tempted to make a decision today that will justify an earlier one, even if it means throwing good money or time after bad.

*Solution:* Ask yourself, "Is my decision based on trying to salvage my self-esteem?" If so, you'll need to pull your self-esteem out of the thought process if you want to come up with the best solution.

●**Seeing what you want to see.** We tend to seek or give more weight to evidence that supports an existing predilection and discount opposing information.

*Better:* Expose yourself to conflicting information by getting someone to play devil's advocate. Exposing yourself to your argument's flip side often produces solutions that you hadn't considered.

---

# How Not to Get Hurt by What You Don't Know

Martin Groder, MD, a Chapel Hill, NC, psychiatrist and business consultant. He is author of *Business Games: How to Recognize the Players and Deal with Them.* Boardroom Classics.

---

There's a lot to know in today's world— new information…expanding technology…whole areas of expertise that never existed before.

No one can know everything, and what you don't know won't necessarily hurt you—as long as you *know* that you don't know it.

*Example:* If you're aware that you can't change a tire, you won't get in trouble when you get a flat—because you'll call for assistance instead.

What poses the biggest threat to us are the things we think we know but actually don't know. In this state of denial, we become like the person with computer problems who pops it open and causes all kinds of damage trying to fix it. This type of thinking is the source of business blunders, poor management and personal strife.

The wise person is the one who knows his/her limitations and has a healthy respect for the extent of his ignorance.

### WHAT YOU DON'T KNOW AT WORK

Most people try to do a good job on the basis of what they think they know, seeking out information that they lack.

But today's world has become so complex that few people know much at all outside of their limited area of expertise. Technical tasks, analysis and business operations, require detailed know-how possessed only by those who do them.

This means that managers are faced with the task of supervising and evaluating people who are doing mysterious things for mysterious reasons.

Managers try to correct "problems" in systems whose mechanics, principles and purposes they don't understand.

Today's manager is often in the position of a person who not only can't ride a bicycle, but doesn't even know how a bicycle is supposed to ride.

*Trap:* If you think you know more than you do about the work your employees do, your direction, criticism and supervision will be worse than ineffective. Systems will be "fixed" when they aren't broken, and real problems will go uncorrected.

Technical workers will feel misunderstood. You'll become frustrated and anxious, and suffer from feelings of incompetence.

*What doesn't help:* Groups of managers who get together to decide how their employees should do their jobs better, creating synergistic ignorance.

They spend hours at meetings where they encourage one another to believe they know things they don't. They also develop plans that have nothing to do with authentic goals and the problems that get in the way.

### ESCAPE FROM IGNORANCE

Our most important step is accepting the extent and depth of our ignorance, and realizing that it is nothing to be ashamed of or defensive about.

We're all in the same position. With so much developing on so many fronts—so much new information and so many new ways to use it—what we don't know is expanding exponentially.

We wake up more ignorant every day, and we will for the rest of our lives. Better get used to it.

*The good news:* There are people around you who know more than you do. This is an age of specialists and subspecialists—people who spend time and energy mastering every area that is dark to you. Learn from them.

### LEARNING TO KNOW MORE

• **Make smart workers your teachers.** Not only will this put you in a better position to evaluate what is being done and avoid unnecessary efforts, but it will also raise workers' self-esteem and help you develop much better working relationships.

• **Assume you know absolutely nothing about the process,** mechanism or operation at hand…and don't be afraid to ask the most simpleminded questions. Get a working model of the worker's area of expertise…how does he/she know when things are functioning properly and when they have gone wrong? How does he troubleshoot?

• **Stop talking—and listen, until you get a sense of what questions to ask.** What most annoys specialists in any area are outsiders who invariably ask the same questions, assuming they know something and are unaware of how stupid they sound.

*Better:* Take the position of an absolute beginner.

• **Seek honest feedback.** Your best friend may tell you when you're misinformed, but it

is unlikely that people who work for you will. For good reason—the bearer of an unflattering truth is vulnerable to retaliation.

*Helpful:* Create a climate in which everyone feels safe giving feedback. Make it clear that you know there are things you don't know and that you need to find out what they are.

• **Play a supportive role.** A single individual is as limited and powerless as a single cell. But when a team of experts band together, they become a multicellular organism, a highly intelligent entity that can accomplish wonderful things.

As a manager, you bring expertise in coordinating efforts, resolving conflicts, acquiring the resources that your employees need. The more you know about what each member of the team actually does, the better you can help the whole operation function smoothly.

### OVERCOMING PERSONAL IGNORANCE

The same principles apply in interpersonal relationships—inside and outside the office—where conflicts and bad feelings tend to arise when people don't know the effect they have on others, but think they do.

*Example:* You think you're communicating concern and sympathy, but others experience you as intrusive. Or you're sure your spouse accepts your need to put in long hours at the office, but he actually resents your absence.

*Solution:* Don't assume you know other people's thoughts, feelings and reactions. Seek feedback. When you explain something, make sure you're understood. Be open to the honest feelings of others.

What you don't know about yourself can be far more enlightening than you imagine, too. When we feel confused or unhappy, we often have no idea why.

*Helpful:* Journaling—writing freely and at length to explore your feelings more deeply. Journaling also helps you discover parts of yourself that were hidden.

You may not find immediate answers to personal dilemmas and tough decisions. But you will learn more clearly what the problems are and what steps must be taken to resolve them.

# How to Harness the Full Power of Your Mind

John Kehoe, author, *Mind Power into the 21st Century: Techniques to Harness the Astounding Powers of Thought*. Zoetic Books. Over the years, Mr. Kehoe, a consultant to a number of Fortune 500 companies, has spoken to hundreds of thousands of people on the subject of mind power.

We spend most of our time dealing with our conscious thoughts and feelings. But we each have a second mind as well—our *subconscious* mind, which becomes richer as we age and add more experience to it.

The subconscious is powerful and complex. Scientists have shown that the subconscious records every event that *ever* happened to us, along with the emotions and thoughts evoked by those incidents.

The conscious and subconscious work together to create the reality that we experience every day.

The subconscious is like fertile soil, which accepts any seed you plant. Your habitual thoughts/beliefs are the results of these seeds.

The conscious mind is the gardener. Its job is to be aware of the seeds allowed in to your subconscious. It must choose wisely which seeds to cultivate—encouraging constructive beliefs and actions.

By imprinting positive thoughts and images in your subconscious, you'll find positive, helpful situations and relationships. It's easy to do. *Here are some simple techniques for "seeding" your subconscious...*

### VISUALIZATION

When Michael Jordan hit a last-second shot to win a key play-off game, he explained that it was instinctive: "In my mind, I've practiced hitting the winning shot hundreds of times."

Visualization is now standard training for leading athletes all over the world. Visualization techniques are also being used in some clinics to help cancer patients fight their disease, with remarkable results.

When you spend a few minutes picturing yourself achieving the results you want or getting something you desire, you are imprinting this image on your subconscious.

Do this regularly and your subconscious will begin to steer you automatically through important situations in your life.

Athletes call this "being in the flow." When Jordan went up for that final shot, he didn't have to think consciously about how high to jump or how hard to shoot the ball. His carefully prepared subconscious already knew how to do everything.

### AFFIRMATIONS

Another way to influence the conscious mind is with affirmations—simple positive statements that you repeat to yourself.

***Example:*** When you're in a situation that makes you tense, quietly repeat to yourself: "I feel calm and relaxed. I feel calm and relaxed. I feel calm and relaxed." Don't try to force yourself to feel calm and relaxed—just keep repeating the statement to yourself for a few minutes.

Remember—you don't have to believe in your affirmation for it to work. Your mind will naturally pick up the phrase as you say it again and again.

### WEED OUT NEGATIVE BELIEFS

We're all guided by a set of beliefs and assumptions, some dating from childhood. Many of us unwittingly use certain beliefs against ourselves. If you look at any of the problem areas in your life, you'll find they are rooted in limiting beliefs.

By replacing negative beliefs with positive affirmations, you'll begin to reshape the way your subconscious mind views the world. *Keys to changing...*

•**Pick an area of your life in which you are having difficulty**—finances, relationships, health, business. Then write down all your beliefs about the area. When you've finished, look for limiting beliefs such as, "I can't do it." It doesn't matter whether these beliefs are true or not—only whether they are limiting.

•**Next to each limiting belief,** write a new, supportive belief...

"It's hard to meet people."/"It's easy to meet people."

"I'll never get ahead."/"I'm bound to succeed."

"I have little time to work on this project."/"There is lots of time to work on this project."

● **Choose one or two new beliefs** from your list. Repeat each one to yourself several times a day. After awhile, these positive beliefs will join your subconscious.

Repetition is essential. Your new belief is a tender shoot—nurture it daily. Imprinting requires one to three months before its effects are fixed in your mind. *Now repeat...*

Every new belief needs time and attention to flourish...Every new belief needs time and attention to flourish...Every new belief needs time and attention to flourish.

---

# How to Keep Everyday Aggravations from Ruining Your Day

Richard Carlson, PhD, a frequent lecturer and stress consultant based in San Francisco. He is author of 12 books, including *Don't Sweat the Small Stuff...and It's All Small Stuff* and *Don't Worry, Make Money: Spiritual and Practical Ways to Create Abundance and More Fun in Your Life,* both published by Hyperion.

Most of us have within ourselves the emotional resources to endure true calamities—the death of a loved one, a natural disaster, etc.

Yet some of us come unglued when confronted with traffic jams, misplaced keys, rude colleagues and other everyday annoyances.

Sound familiar? Read on for nine ways to stop overreacting...

### SEE ANNOYING PEOPLE AS TEACHERS

Is the salesclerk dawdling despite the long line? If so, you can fume about how he/she is wasting your time—and raise your blood pressure in the process.

Or you can see the clerk as a person who is teaching you to have patience...and to appreciate individuals who perform hard work for little pay. The same method works in many other scenarios...

**Example 1:** A motorist cuts in front of you. He's teaching you how foolish it is to be in such a hurry and to take needless risks.

**Example 2:** A woman steps in front of you and takes the taxi you've just hailed. She's teaching you the importance of leaving yourself plenty of time to get to your appointments and of being considerate of others.

### DON'T LABEL THINGS AS "GOOD" OR "BAD"

Getting passed over for a promotion *seems* bad...but you never really know. Maybe you'll get a job at another company the next day—and end up earning more money and feeling more fulfilled. When one opportunity is lost, *look for another.* There are many.

### KEEP MISHAPS IN PERSPECTIVE

Although it's hard to realize this at the time, spilling soup on your suit just before an important meeting is *not* a tragedy. Even having your wallet stolen isn't particularly important in the long run. Before you "catastrophize" a particular situation, stop and picture yourself looking back at the incident a year later. Did the stain on your tie really matter? Were you able to get your credit cards reissued? In both cases, the "calamity" passed...and life went on.

### DON'T EXPECT LIFE TO BE FAIR

It may not be "fair" that you sprained your ankle just before a long-awaited golf vacation ...or that you worked your whole career for the same company only to have someone else receive credit for a great idea you had. But there's not much you can do about these common injustices. They happen to all of us. An awareness of this simple fact will help you avoid wasting precious time by whining. You'll move on enjoying the good things life offers.

### AVOID NEEDLESS STRESS

If you feel a twinge in your foot while jogging, it is prudent to stop—to avoid aggravating any possible injury. Similarly, it's a good idea to resolve not to tolerate stressful situations.

**Example:** If your mind is full of lists of things you have to do, notice your thinking as soon as possible. Stop it before it gets out of control.

Emotional stress is a warning signal that must be heeded. Either you have too much to handle...or you're letting the little things bother you too much. Either way, you need to make some sort of change in your life.

### AVOID MATERIALISM

Consider all the objects that hold sentimental value for you—an heirloom vase, a beautiful necklace, your child's first drawing, etc.

We know that these things can be easily broken, destroyed or lost. And when something valuable to us is lost, we become deeply upset. Keep this from happening by periodically imagining that the treasured items are *already* gone.

Aren't there still beautiful sunsets? And you can still enjoy the *memory* of lost objects.

Now if someone breaks that vase or spills coffee on that drawing, you won't go to pieces.

### SCHEDULE TIME FOR RELAXATION

Our society encourages us to *defer* relaxation. Relaxation is something we'll have time for on our next vacation or in retirement.

Such thinking is terribly misguided. The average person gets only a few weeks of vacation each year...and most of us must work until our 60s to receive full retirement benefits.

In the meantime, we spend so much time rushing around and thinking about what needs to get done next that we're unable to derive much pleasure from our lives.

**Better way:** No matter how busy you are, schedule relaxation breaks into your day. They can be nothing more than taking a few minutes to breathe deeply...going for a brief walk...or writing a note to someone who needs cheering up.

Fight your tendency to put off relaxation until tomorrow. Spend at least a few minutes relaxing today—*every day.*

### DON'T EXPECT EVERYONE TO LIKE YOU

It's a fact of life—some people you meet during your life will like you...and others won't. Trying too hard to make people like you generates a great deal of emotional stress. Always do your best...but don't get mad or upset if someone does not seem to like you.

If someone criticizes you, minimize the annoyance you feel simply by *acknowledging* the criticism...and moving on.

### ALWAYS BE FLEXIBLE

It's fine to be organized and plan ahead. Just don't be surprised or upset if your schedule changes. Count on it—airline flights will be delayed...promises will be broken...and the weather won't always cooperate. When these things happen, don't get angry. Shrug them off and get on with your life.

---

# Write Anger Away

Write out your anger instead of acting out. Keep a log of your anger at work.

Reread it regularly to look for patterns. Write down what thoughts about people set you off—and remember that you cannot change people, but you can change how you react to them.

Write down how you feel after having angry thoughts, and describe how you show the anger—slamming doors, swearing, spreading rumors.

Study your anger pattern so you can intercept your feelings before they blow up into aggression.

Paul Pearsall, PhD, clinical and educational psychologist, Henry Ford Community College, Dearborn, MI, and author of *Write Your Own Pleasure Prescription: 60 Ways to Create Balance & Joy in Your Life.* Hunter House.

---

# 11

# Investment Wisdom

## From America's Shrewdest Investors: What We Do... How We Do It

To determine what makes brilliant investors so special, Steven Mintz interviewed several of these experts about their uniquely successful investment styles...

### FOSTER FRIESS
### BRANDYWINE FUND

Foster Friess is always aggressively searching for stocks with very strong growth prospects. And he then acts to catch them before they rise dramatically in price.

Whenever Friess finds a stock with great earnings prospects likely to exceed Wall Street's expectations, he sells a less attractive stock—regardless of tax consequences. Stocks with earnings increases of 50% a year are not uncommon in his portfolio.

The time frame is short. An average stock in the Brandywine Fund lasts about six months. Many stocks are sold while they still have upside potential. Nonetheless, the fund's long-term performance has been outstanding—a 683.6% total return over the past 13 years.

*Friess is guided by two rules...*

• Once you own a stock, never look where it has been, only where it is going.

• If a stock you own is not going up in price faster than an alternative over the next three to 12 months, sell that stock and buy the alternative.

### JOHN NEFF
### FORMER MANAGER OF THE WINDSOR FUND

Over the 30 years that John Neff managed Vanguard's Windsor Fund, it outperformed the S&P 500 Index with an annualized gain of 13.8%, versus 10.7% for the S&P.

Neff is a large-cap value investor. He looks for big companies that have fallen from favor.

Steven L. Mintz, New York bureau chief, *CFO Magazine.* He is coauthor of *Beyond Wall Street: The Art of Investing.* John Wiley & Sons.

His biggest moneymakers have been Atlantic Richfield, Chrysler, Citicorp, IBM and Tandy as their fortunes fell and then rose again, sometimes several times.

*What Neff looks for before buying a company's stock...*

• A price-to-earnings ratio (P/E) that is below the market's average P/E. Typically, stocks in his fund were purchased for nine to 11 times earnings—less than half the market's P/E.

• A high dividend yield, which provides investors with a good income cushion until the price improves. Even when they're in trouble, quality companies do not like to reduce their dividends.

• Fundamental earnings growth of 7% a year or better.

• A great product customers need.

Neff is a patient investor. The average stock in his portfolio was held for two years. But sometimes it took as long as eight or nine years for the investment to pay off.

### WILLIAM F. SHARPE, PHD
### STANFORD UNIVERSITY

Professor Bill Sharpe shared the 1990 Nobel Prize in Economic Science for his contributions to theories of risk and reward in investing.

His ideas led directly to the development of the investment strategy called *indexing*. It was designed to match or closely replicate the overall market's performance.

Investing in an index fund is cheaper for individuals because fees, expenses and taxes are lower than those of actively managed funds. Active management requires lots of research, analysis and profit-taking.

Sharpe's ideas were resisted on Wall Street, where there is still a very strong dedication to stock picking. But in the mid-1970s, indexing won the support of Vanguard's John C. Bogle. Bogle's flagship Vanguard Index Trust 500 Portfolio has grown to be the second-largest fund behind Fidelity's Magellan.

*Sharpe's investment advice...*

• Decide on a mix of stocks and bonds that suits your tolerance for risk. Invest the stock portion in index funds that specialize in US and foreign stocks.

• Take a hard look at annual expense ratios, which range from around one-third of 1% to more than 1%. Spending too much on commissions and transaction fees can really eat into your nest egg.

### MARK MOBIUS, PHD
### TEMPLETON EMERGING MARKETS FUND

Like his mentor, legendary investor Sir John Templeton, Mark Mobius is an optimist.

With better communications, improved travel, more international commerce and generally better relations between nations, the opportunities for emerging-market investors are better than they have ever been.

Mobius looks for markets that are down, where bargains abound. When we hear about recessions, disasters and revolutions, he says, we know there will be opportunities.

*Mobius's advice to investors...*

• Invest with a five-year time horizon. As events in Southeast Asia have shown, it's not always possible to get out when these thinly traded emerging markets have a downswing.

• Invest when markets are doing poorly.

### WILLIAM GROSS
### PACIFIC INVESTMENT MANAGEMENT CO.

William Gross manages close to $140 billion. When he started out in 1971, bonds were seldom traded. Investors bought and held them in the vault, clipping and redeeming the coupons until maturity.

Now, however, all that has changed. Active bond trading is standard practice. Trying to figure out which way inflation is headed is what we're all about, says Gross.

**Reason:** When inflation causes interest rates to rise, bond prices go down. When slowing inflation drives interest rates down, bond prices go up.

*Gross's advice to investors...*

• At least some bonds belong in every investment portfolio.

**Rule of thumb for conservative investors:** Subtract your age from 100, call the difference a percentage, then put that amount in stocks and the rest in bonds.

**Exception:** 90% in bonds may be suitable for someone of retirement age or older who relies on a fixed-income cash flow.

• When properly managed, bonds are ordinarily less risky than stocks. But they seldom reap more than 8% returns, versus an average of more than 10% for stocks.

● Don't get greedy and invest too much of your bond assets in high-yield securities. They are very risky.

● When inflation appears to be on the rise, invest in bonds of short to medium maturities—three to seven years.

Once your short-term bonds mature, determine whether rates have peaked and it's time to invest in long-term bonds—10 to 30 years.

Long-term bonds are ideal investments when interest rates are high and starting to decline.

***Reason:*** You'll be able to lock in a high interest rate—and earn a profit if you have to sell before the bonds reach maturity.

---

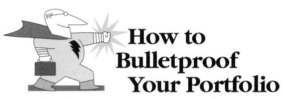

# How to Bulletproof Your Portfolio

Margaret Miller Welch, president, Armstrong, Welch & MacIntyre, Inc., a Washington, DC, financial-planning and investment advisory firm. *Worth* magazine recently named her one of the 300 best financial advisers in the country.

**M**any investors have been shaken by sharp movements in the stock market. But, as history has repeatedly proven, the answer is not to dump all your stocks as the market drops.

***Example:*** A study shows that if you had kept your money in the 500 stocks that made up the S&P Index for the decade beginning with the crash of 1987 and ending December 31, 1997, and reinvested all dividends, you would have earned an annualized total return of 18.1%.

But if you had missed the market's 10 best days, your return would have dropped to 14.3%.

If you had missed the market's 30 best days, your return would have slumped to 9.1%—roughly half the profit earned by investors who bought their shares on January 1, 1988, and held them for 10 years.

***Key:*** It is the time you spend in the market—not market timing—that builds wealth.

Fortunately, there are shrewd ways to be defensive without abandoning stocks. *Here's how…*

● **Allocate your money more conservatively.** This means selling some stocks and shifting the proceeds to less risky bonds.

***Recommendation to our clients:*** Consider moving your portfolio toward 60% stocks and 40% bonds when stocks are bearish.

When stocks are bullish we suggest investors have 80% in stocks and 20% in bonds.

● **Stay diversified.** *Best:* Divide your stock holdings. Put 75% in domestic issues or stock funds and 25% in foreign stocks or funds. You might split domestic stock holdings this way…

● 55% in large-company shares.

● 25% in midsize-company shares.

● 20% in small-company shares.

Very aggressive investors could put half of their small-company allocation, or 7.5% of their stock portfolios, into a high-technology fund.

My favorite no-load stock funds…

● **Large-cap.**

***Janus.*** 800-525-3713.

***Oakmark.*** 800-625-6275.

● **Mid-cap.**

***Oak Value.*** 800-680-4199.

***Sound Shore Fund.*** 800-551-1980.

● **Small-cap.**

***Baron Growth & Income.*** 800-992-2766.

***SSgA Small Cap Fund.*** 800-647-7327.

For the overseas portion of your stock portfolio, invest in a diversified international fund. Aggressive investors, however, could put a tiny part of that allocation—no more than 2% to 5% of the international portion—in an emerging-markets fund. My favorite no-load funds in these categories…

● **International.**

***Janus Worldwide.*** 800-525-3713.

● **Emerging markets.**

***SSgA Emerging Markets.*** 800-647-7327.

• **Take advantage of the great rates on intermediate-term municipal bonds.** These municipal issues have an unusual rate advantage over Treasuries with the same maturities.

Both yield about 5%, but since municipal bond interest is free of federal taxes, the effective rate for investors in the 28% bracket is 6.4%—and even more for investors in higher tax brackets.

This unusual situation won't last long. Typically, when Treasuries yield 5%, tax-free munis yield 3.5%.

*Smart move:* When you sell stocks to reduce your portfolio's equity portions, reinvest the proceeds in 10- to 15-year munis—or intermediate-term muni bond funds.

*Warning:* Investors whose tax advisers warn that they may be subject to the Alternative Minimum Tax (AMT) because of large deductions for state income taxes, should avoid funds that invest in munis, which produce AMT income.

My favorite muni fund for investors without an AMT problem…

*Vanguard Intermediate-Term Tax-Exempt Fund.* 800-523-7731.

For investors who do have to worry about the AMT, I like…

*Tax-Exempt Bond Fund of America.* 800-421-0180. This fund can be purchased through a discount broker.

• **Boost cash reserves** if you depend on your investments for income. In a bull market, we recommend that clients keep only three to six months' worth of expenses in a money market fund.

In a volatile market, most retirees or parents of college students should boost their cash holdings to one or two years of expenses.

*Strategy:* By building up your cash reserves, you can keep your portfolio's equities growing as long as possible and sell shares only by choice, when the market or a particular stock or fund is doing especially well. Above all, avoid forced sales—dumping shares at low prices when money is desperately needed.

With one or two years of expenses socked away in a money market fund, you should be in excellent shape to survive any downturns.

Remember that even during the bear market of the early 1970s, when market conditions were the worst in recent memory, stocks had only two really bad years—1973 and 1974.

*Strategy:* Keep half your cash in a money market fund and half in a higher yielding intermediate-term bond fund.

My favorite intermediate-term bond fund, which can be purchased only through a discount broker or a financial adviser…

*Intermediate Bond Fund of America.* 800-421-0180.

Then, instruct the money market fund to send a set amount to your bank each month for living expenses.

Meanwhile, put your stock dividends and profits from stock sales in the bond fund, and let the money grow there until you need to switch cash to the money fund.

• **Dollar cost average into beaten-down sectors.** Use dollar cost averaging when there are depressed prices. This strategy calls for systematically investing a set amount of money in a stock or a stock fund at regular intervals, usually monthly or quarterly.

You must stick to your buying schedule, no matter what happens in the market. This can be tough during down markets since you wind up buying just when everyone else seems to be selling.

On the other hand, your investments will buy more shares than when prices are high.

---

# Portfolio Checkup Time: How to Do It Right

John J. Costello, CPA, president, Fairfield Financial Planning Inc., a fee-only investment advisory firm, 2 Greenwich Plaza, Suite 100, Greenwich, CT 06830.

Given the recent volatility in stock prices, it's smart to take a close look now at the structure and health of your mutual fund portfolio. Then you can take steps to limit your risk.

Be wary of a portfolio that is overweighted or underweighted in a particular area. To find out if you are overweighted, take a sheet of paper and create four columns across the top with these headings: US large-cap…US small-cap…international stocks…bonds.

Under each heading, list the funds you own and the amount you have in each fund. Many funds will fall into more than one category.

***Examples:*** A balanced fund, which includes stocks and bonds, usually falls half under "US large-cap" and half under "bonds." A global stock fund falls into both US and international categories. Find fund allocations in the *Morningstar Mutual Funds* directory, available in libraries or at www.morningstar.com.

Add up the numbers in each column and calculate each total as a percentage of the whole portfolio. Then compare these allocation percentages with the ones you originally set up for yourself.

If your original allocations aren't close to the new ones, you'll see where you should make corrections.

Here are the big fund portfolio warning signs—and how to rebalance your portfolio efficiently…

***Red flag:*** **A portfolio heavy with large-cap stocks.** Most investors think having too much in large-caps is a blessing, since much of the high returns of the past few years has come from these stocks.

But owning too many large-cap stocks is not good if they have distorted your asset-allocation plan. If you have too much in stocks, you are accepting more risk than you originally wanted…and too little risk if you have too much in bonds. Unless your risk tolerance has changed, this is a problem.

***Red flag:*** **Too much invested in one market sector.** *Morningstar* lists how much each stock fund has invested in 10 sectors: Utilities, energy, financials, cyclicals, durables, staples, services, retail, health and technology.

***Helpful:*** List the 10 sectors across the top of another page, and fill in your own sector weightings.

Then compare your own numbers with the weightings for the Wilshire 5000, or any broadly based index. Your weightings should approximate those of the Wilshire 5000.

***Example:*** Say your portfolio includes $10,000 in Fund A, half of which is invested in technology stocks and half in financials. And let's say you also have $20,000 in Fund B, which is 25% invested in technology stocks and 75% in financial issues.

On your work sheet, you'll have $10,000, or one-third of your portfolio, allocated to technology stocks. You'll have $20,000, or two-thirds, in financials.

The question is whether you are comfortable with this mix.

***Important:*** Pay close attention to technology, health or financial stocks, as they can be especially volatile.

***Red flag:*** **Management of a fund you own changes.** Ask your fund whether the lead portfolio manager has left within the past year.

If he/she has, you are paying for the services of a manager you may know nothing about. If he manages a fund now, look at its track record. If he has no record, or if you're unsure about the record, consider selling.

***Note:*** Selling stock may have tax consequences. If you'd have to pay a lot, consider "gifting it" to charity.

***Red flag:*** **Your fund expenses are going up.** Check these in the *Morningstar* directory, too.

***Rule of thumb:*** In US large-cap funds, don't pay more in annual fees than an average of 0.75% of your assets…for US small-cap and international funds, not more than 1.4%…for a bond fund, not more than an average of 0.5%.

***Red flag:*** **Your stock fund generates a lot of taxable income.** The manager should be reacting to the 1997 tax law changes by selling assets that qualify for the lower, long-term capital-gains rate…and that have the highest cost basis.

The new tax rates are 20% on capital gains for assets held 12 or more months…and up to 39.6% on assets held less than a year. *Note:* This isn't applicable to funds you hold in your IRA.

### REBALANCING ACT

•**Make portfolio and allocation changes to your IRA and other tax-deferred accounts first.** You won't incur taxable income.

•**Use new money** to beef up the underweighted areas of your portfolio.

●**Consider donating appreciated stocks** in overweighted areas to charity to avoid taxes.

●**If you must sell some assets to realign your portfolio,** sell shares that you have owned for more than 12 months to get the lowest capital gains tax rate, 20%.

●**Look to sell stock funds that have declined in value** so you can take tax losses now, rather than at year-end. Losses can offset gains from other investments.

### ALLOCATIONS

The following funds create a diversified portfolio that is both tax-efficient and cost-effective…

#### US large-cap:

●**Vanguard 500 Index Fund,** 800-523-1154.

●**Vanguard Total Stock Market Index Fund.**

#### US small-cap:

●**Vanguard Small-Cap Index Fund.**

●**Vanguard Extended Market Index Fund.**

#### International stock:

●**Hotchkiss & Wiley International Fund,** 800-236-4479.

#### Bonds:

●**Vanguard GNMA Fund.**

●**Vanguard Intermediate-Term Municipal Bond Fund.**

*Allocation percentages:* There's no rule of thumb…investors have different risk tolerances. *Use this as a guide…*

*Retired or close to retiring:* 40% to US large-cap, 10% to US small-cap, 10% to international stocks and 40% to bonds.

*Between five and 20 years to go before retirement:* 45% to US large-caps, 10% to US small-caps, 15% to international stocks and 30% to bonds.

*At least 20 years to go before retirement:* 50% to US large-caps, 15% to US small-caps, 15% to international stocks and 20% to US bonds.

# America's #1 Stock Market Timer Tells How He Does It

Gerald Appel, president, Signalert Corp. He is publisher of *Systems and Forecasts,* which, according to *Hulbert Financial Digest,* is one of the top market-timing newsletters around. 150 Great Neck Rd., Suite 301, Great Neck, NY 11021.

Attempting to boost investment returns by timing the market has long been discouraged by financial advisers. Yet market timing has been getting a great deal of positive attention in the media lately.

### WHAT EXACTLY IS MARKET TIMING?

Market timing is attempting to buy stocks when you believe their prices are at a relatively low point and are about to rise…and selling when you think they've peaked.

This strategy's purpose is to achieve higher returns than you would using a buy-and-hold strategy. You also reduce portfolio volatility by holding cash positions during uncertain market periods. The thinking here is that you'll do better by liquidating holdings during periods of anticipated market decline rather than by riding out the entire market cycle.

To be successful, returns must outpace the capital gains taxes you'll owe—and the commissions on your trades.

### WHY DOES MARKET TIMING HAVE SUCH A BAD REPUTATION?

Many people who try to time the market underperform a market index, such as the S&P 500 or the Dow, because they are not disciplined. They also trade without a clear plan or method.

They either buy before the stock's price reaches bottom…or they become too optimistic at the stock's top, thinking its price can go higher…or both.

There also is a built-in bias against market timing among people in the financial field who favor investors who buy and hold for long periods of time.

Most investors who buy and hold do so with the hope that broad gains in the stock market will eventually carry their investments onward and upward.

But many people in the financial field who claim they are opposed to market timing are actually market timers themselves.

***Example:*** The annual turnover of assets in the average stock fund is 100%. Managers are constantly rotating in and out of stocks. They call it asset reallocation, but it is still market timing.

### WHEN DOES MARKET TIMING MAKE SENSE?

Whenever there is a sharp run-up in the stock market, investors look for ways they could have gotten in ahead of the run-up.

Similarly, whenever there is a downturn in the market, people look for ways they could have gotten out ahead of the fall.

People who bought and held assets through the summer and fall of 1998 saw their portfolios hit hard. Investors who sold and stayed out, fearing the worst, missed out on the comeback.

### WHAT INDICATORS DO MARKET TIMERS WATCH TO DETERMINE MARKET HIGHS AND LOWS?

Some market timers watch the performance of the whole market—or industry sectors— while others watch individual stocks and funds.

Some market timers use technical analysis to anticipate an asset's high and low prices. Others use fundamental analysis, looking at price and earnings histories. As you can see, there are lots of ways to be a market timer.

### MY STRATEGY

I trade in funds that track market sectors that I want to be invested in.

I feel it is easier to gauge the totality of the market rather than a small part of it, which is what one does if market timing individual stocks.

I watch the S&P 500 and look for several indicators that signal the market is being oversold or overbought.

***Example:*** Expect at least some pause in market advances when the S&P 500 rises to a level that is greater than 4% above its 21-day moving average.

### HOW CAN THE AVERAGE INVESTOR TIME THE MARKET?

The best way for individuals to market time is to use index funds, such as those offered by Vanguard (800-523-7731). Purchases and redemptions of shares can be made quickly at no or low cost.

Watch the number of stocks in the index that hit new highs and lows. The data is published daily in *The Wall Street Journal* and weekly in *Barron's*. Investors also can look at the "Advances" and "Declines" lines in the "Market Laboratory" section in *Barron's*.

It is a bullish sign if more stocks advance than decline on a given day. It is bearish if declines outnumber advances. So—buy when a declining trend ends and an advancing one begins. Sell when the opposite occurs.

Another good indicator is the price direction of three- to five-year bonds, which also can be found in *Barron's* "Market Laboratory" section.

If the yields of these bonds are lower than they were six months ago, there should be no serious decline in the market, and it is a good time to buy. If the bond rates are not lower, it means advances will come at a much slower rate.

Also, it is bullish for the stock market when cumulative totals of weekly advances minus weekly declines remain above its 30-week average. It may be a sign of trouble if the cumulative total of advance–declines falls below its 30-week average.

# 21st-Century Investment Opportunities and Traps

Robert H. Stovall, CFA, president, Stovall/Twenty-First Advisers, Inc., 780 Third Ave., New York 10017.

Investors had a great ride the past 10 years. But the market can be extremely bumpy. Any of several world-influencing events could cause a shake-up in the normal pattern of things...

●**The launch of the Euro.** As the new unified currency takes hold across Europe, we will begin to get an idea of what it will mean for the US.

There could be considerable competition in Europe against dollar-based goods, for example.

Initially, retail prices in Europe will, I believe, fall as the Wal-Mart stores of Europe offer bargains in consumer durable goods like refrigerators. They'll buy them in Spain or Italy where they're cheaper and sell them in Austria and Belgium where they're more costly.

US companies will be involved to the extent they own manufacturing facilities in various countries.

●**More problems for "gold bugs,"** assuming there are any left. Since the coming of the Euro will mean less reserves held by individual governments, we can expect another body blow to gold prices as gold stocks are unloaded.

●**Turnover of the Panama Canal.** Aside from receiving a big bill from the Panamanians for so-called damage to their territory, I don't think this historic event scheduled for the year 2000 will have too much effect on Americans. But it will be of considerable significance to the Asians who depend on the canal to ship their exported material to the East Coasts of the US and Latin America.

### CHOOSE STOCKS CAUTIOUSLY

I believe that the less imagination investors use in picking stocks this year, the better off they'll be. Don't fool around with small companies or Internet initial public offerings (IPOs). The Internet bubble is going to burst one of these days, and you don't want it to splatter on you. Similarly, I would avoid global stocks from emerging countries like Russia or Singapore.

I would also avoid consumer staples companies such as Procter & Gamble and Coca-Cola, which are currently priced too high and are too dependent on foreign earnings. *Three growth areas I like now…*

●**Health care…**

*Healthsouth* (NYSE:HRC).

*Johnson & Johnson* (NYSE:JNJ).

*Merck* (NYSE:MRK).

*Pfizer* (NYSE:PFE).

●**Financial services…**

*Allstate* (NYSE:ALL).

*Household International* (NYSE:HI).

*SouthTrust* (NASDAQ:SOTR).

*Union Planters* (NYSE:UPC).

*Washington Mutual* (NYSE:WM).

●**Technology…**

*Cisco Systems* (NASDAQ:CSCO).

*Dell Computer* (NASDAQ:DELL).

*Gateway* (NYSE:GTW).

*IBM* (NYSE:IBM).

*Unisys* (NYSE:UIS).

---

# Investment Rules From a Winning Investment Club

Patricia Matthews, professor of finance at Mount Union College in Alliance, OH and adviser to the school's 10-member investment team.

---

●**Use stop-loss orders to protect gains.** Few individuals can monitor their investments every hour of the day. So quick responses to changing news can be difficult.

*Solution:* We place stop-loss orders on stocks. We set target prices depending on recent volatility and past behavior. A stop-loss order instructs your broker to sell shares if the stock's price falls to a specified level.

*Result:* If news of a pending merger or acquisition drives up a stock's price—but then the deal doesn't happen—we don't have to react on a moment's notice. We also aren't likely to lose all of our gains.

●**Put a stock's valuation ratios in context.** Price-to-earnings ratios (P/Es) and other measures of a stock's valuation can be useful when determining whether a stock is overpriced or a good buy.

But in today's market, you can't simply assume that a high P/E means a stock is not worth at least a look. Consider the context. Is the stock's P/E high by the historical standards of that stock? Is the P/E high compared with that of other stocks in its sector?

●**Technology no longer can be viewed as a single sector.** The rules of investing suggest it is a good idea to diversify your investments among sectors in order to reduce portfolio risk. But in today's market, it is no longer accurate to consider technology one sector. Technology is so pervasive in modern society that technology companies are very diverse.

*Example:* Our portfolio includes companies ranging from computer hardware manufacturer Dell to chip maker Intel to software giant Microsoft to on-line service provider America Online to telecom technology firm Lucent Technologies.

# How to Make Money in a Down Market

John Rothchild, former financial columnist for *Time* and *Fortune* and coauthor of three of Peter Lynch's investing books. He is author of *The Bear Book: Survive and Profit in Ferocious Markets.* John Wiley & Sons.

A bear market occurs when the market falls at least 20% from its latest high. Some bear markets last just a few months...others last years.

*Example:* In the 1973–1974 bear market, stocks lost 45% of their value.

There have been eight bear markets since 1948, one almost every six years. The last one was in 1990, so we are overdue.

### DEFENSIVE STEPS TO TAKE

If you believe that stocks are overvalued and that we are historically overdue for a bear market, consider these self-defense measures...

•**Allocate portfolio assets.** No one should be 100% in stocks, or anywhere near that in this market. The best asset mix depends on your age...and how much time you have before you need to start liquidating assets.

For the cautious investor, I think 50% in stocks, 30% in bonds and 20% in cash are reasonable amounts. Funds that will provide you with an allocation of stocks, bonds and cash...

**Balanced funds** allocate assets among stocks, bonds and cash in fixed amounts that rarely change. Balanced funds with high Morningstar ratings...

☐ *Carillon Capital.* 888-259-7565.

☐ *UAM FPA Crescent Fund.* 800-638-7983.

**Asset-allocation funds** own stocks, bonds and cash. The mix changes depending on the manager's perspective or his/her computer program. Funds that held up well in three recent bear markets...

☐ *IAA Trust Asset Allocation.* 800-245-2100.

☐ *Stagecoach Asset Allocation.* 800-222-8222.

•**Move out of aggressive investments.** Cut back on growth stocks with high price-to-earnings ratios and invest in areas that do better than others in tough times. *Helpful...*

**Bear-resistant industries.** The most resilient industries in past market declines were makers of consumer-goods containers (metal and glass)...electric utilities...household products...and foods.

While these industries declined between 11% and 15%—overall the drop was much less than the market's. Other bear-resistant industries included banking, drugs, oil and supermarkets.

Funds run by seasoned managers Shelby Davis and Marty Zweig have weathered past bear markets well...

☐ *Davis New York Venture.* 800-279-0279.

☐ *Zweig Strategy Fund.* 800-272-2700.

**Value funds.** These own stocks in companies with low price-to-earnings ratios that sell at relatively low prices based on their book values. These stocks tend to fall in price less in a bear market. No-load funds that are high on Morningstar's list...

☐ *American Century Value.* 800-345-2021.

☐ *Royce Total Return.* 800-221-4268.

**Utility funds.** You can get double protection against bear-market losses by investing in low-risk categories, such as utilities. Top-performing utility fund...

☐ *MFS Utilities Fund.* 800-637-2929.

•**Invest in stocks that pay high dividends.** Dividends often account for one-third of a stock's gains over the years. Invest in dividend-paying stocks—or funds that invest in stocks with high dividends.

A reliable dividend acts as a brake on stock prices in a bear market, and the income is a comfort while waiting for stocks to regain ground. Top-performing no-load examples…

□ *American Century Equity Income.* 800-345-2021.

□ *Heartland Value Plus Fund.* 800-432-7856.

**Growth-and-income funds.** In 1973–1974, when pure growth funds lost almost 50% on average, stodgier growth-and-income funds that invested in high-performance growth companies that paid dividends lost only 29.9%. Top-performing no-load examples…

□ *T. Rowe Price Capital Appreciation Fund.* Keeps about 50% stake in value stocks, the rest in bonds and cash. 800-638-5660.

□ *T. Rowe Price Dividend Growth Fund* has kept up with the gains in the S&P 500 without taking much risk. 800-638-5660.

# The Bigger They Are The Harder They Fall

The biggest companies in a particular industry are often worse investments than smaller ones. GM, IBM and other stumbling giants learned this the hard way. A study of 3,000 companies in 240 industries found that the companies with the highest market shares earned the highest returns *less than 30%* of the time.

**Reason:** Higher market share improves the bottom line only if extra customers make their costs lower than competitors'. If marginal customers lower profits, companies are better off without them.

**Lesson for investors:** Choose companies with higher returns, not higher market shares.

Donald V. Potter, president, Windermere Associates, a management consulting firm in Moraga, CA, specializing in corporate strategy.

# Bad News for Them… Good News for You

Bad news about a company can often mean a golden opportunity—if you invest at the right moment. Look for financially strong companies whose stock prices have declined due to short-term or nonrecurring impact on their earnings, such as the weather…a strike…plant shutdown. Wait until the stock has had two or three days of upward movement, then invest. *Important:* Avoid a company that has lost 50% or more of its price quickly.

Kevin J. Bannon, chief investment officer at Bank of New York, 1 Wall St., New York 10286.

# Investing Savvy from John Markese

John Markese, president, American Association of Individual Investors, 625 Michigan Ave., Suite 1900, Chicago 60611.

## On-Line Trading Self-Defense

If you think a trade was not executed in a timely way or at the best price, call the broker and ask for the "time stamps" showing when your order was received and executed …plus the time-and-sales data around your trade. The National Association of Securities Dealers (NASD) requires that all brokers have this information.

If you don't get a satisfactory response, visit the NASD Web site at www.nasdr.com or call 301-590-6500. Complaints are investigated and responded to in writing.

**More from John Markese…**

## Dollar Cost Average Investing

The best day of the month to invest when dollar cost averaging is the third-to-last trading day of the month.

***Reason:*** Statistically, the market performs best in the last two trading days of the month and the first five days of the next month. So systematic buying on the third-to-last trading day generates the lowest average cost over the long term.

# How to Play The Junk Bond Market... And Win

John Rekenthaler, research director, Morningstar Inc., an independent fund rating service and publisher, 225 W. Wacker Dr., Chicago 60606.

When junk bonds have low prices and high yields, here's what you need to know to invest wisely...

•**Invest in junk bonds only after you have invested in the basics.** Junk bonds are a second-tier investment. They are for investors who have already invested at least two-thirds of their portfolios in large-cap stocks, Treasury bonds and investment-grade bonds, which have credit ratings of BBB or higher.

•**Invest in a no-load junk bond fund rather than in individual issues.** Funds hold a diversified portfolio of high-yield bonds.

•**Before choosing a fund, compare its record and manager.** Consider only those funds that have performed in the top half of all junk bond funds over the past three and five years. This information is available free at www.morningstar.net. Then make sure the current manager was responsible for that record.

•**In a bull market, be wary of choosing top-performing funds.** Their yields almost always fall hardest in a bear market.

### MY FAVORITE NO-LOAD FUNDS

•***Fidelity High-Income Fund.*** 800-544-8888.

•***Northeast Investors Trust.*** 800-225-6704.

•***Vanguard High-Yield Corporate Fund.*** 800-523-7731.

# How Manager of Top Internet Stock Fund Finds His Best Buys

Paul Cook, lead manager of the Munder NetNet Fund, which invests only in Internet–related stocks, 480 Pierce St., Birmingham, MI 48304. The fund had an annualized return of 79.45% since inception on August 19, 1996, through June 30, 1999, compared with 29% for the S&P 500. The fund returned 98.48% in 1998.

There is tremendous long-term opportunity in Internet stocks—if you know where to look and can handle the dramatic ups and downs.

### THE INTERNET'S POWER

Even now, few people appreciate the Internet's growth potential over the next 10 years. That potential is enormous for three reasons...

•**Internet technology is already proven.** Unlike biotechnology, the Internet's biggest hurdles have already been overcome. The biggest obstacle to the Internet's growth is rewiring homes for high-capacity data transmission. But existing phone lines do an adequate job of linking people to the Internet. All that is required is time and money—not technological breakthroughs.

•**The Internet's acceptance is growing rapidly.** It has taken just four years for the Internet audience to reach 50 million people. No product in history—not even television— matches that rate of adoption. Further, the rate of adoption is accelerating today, not slowing.

•**There are few limits to Internet applications.** There is hardly an industry—from bookselling to stockbrokerage—that hasn't already been touched by the Internet or that won't be soon.

And those are just the consumer applications. The use of the Internet by businesses already tops the consumer market by three-to-one. That ratio will rise to 10-to-one within five years.

### THE INTERNET'S FUTURE

So far, nearly all our interaction with the Internet is through the personal computer. But with the Internet's unique ability to get devices talking to one another, big changes are on the horizon.

*Example:* Internet links will soon exist to your home-security system, your heating and cooling systems, your telephone and even the navigation system in your car.

### HOW TO PICK HOT STOCKS

The potential of the Internet is so great that even conservative investors can invest up to 5% of their portfolios in Internet stocks. More aggressive investors can have a 10% stake in Internet stocks.

Don't buy Internet stocks for quick profit. Plan to hold Internet stocks for at least five years.

*Reason:* Conventional yardsticks for determining the value of stocks—such as price-to-earnings and price-to-book ratios—don't apply to most Internet stocks. Most Internet stocks don't earn money today—and may not for several years.

Here are the yardsticks I use when assessing Internet stocks...

●**Go for growth.** Since few Internet stocks are profitable now, I look at the growth in gross profits—which is revenues less cost of goods sold. You can find that figure in company quarterly and annual reports or through your broker.

The gross profits of successful Internet companies should have an annual growth rate of 80%.

●**Understand the business.** Every Internet company has a plan. Invest in those companies that have realistic plans. Can this particular Internet company displace an existing business, and what can it gain if it succeeds?

●**Measure the expertise of management.** Since most Internet companies have little or no track record, the skill of management is key to Internet investing.

Are key management posts filled with industry professionals? What is the background of the chief financial officer? How creative has he/she been in the past in raising the money it takes to finance the superheated growth of an Internet company?

What is the background of the chief technology officer?

### WHERE TO INVEST

The Internet touches so many industries that the range of Internet stocks is enormous. Here are my favorite Internet categories and stocks within those categories...

●**Major players.** Some well-known industry names already have major positions in the Internet's development. Favorites now...

☐ *Cisco Systems, Inc.* is the leader when it comes to routing data from one place to another. NASDAQ:CSCO.

☐ *Oracle Corp.* provides the database software for the top on-line commerce sites. NASDAQ:ORCL.

●**Infrastructure stocks.** These companies make cable modems and other equipment for the cable industry to bring high-speed Internet connections into homes. Stocks I like...

☐ *Com21, Inc.* NASDAQ:CMTO.

☐ *Terayon Communication Systems.* NASDAQ:TERN.

●**On-line discount brokers.** This has been an area of dramatic growth on the Internet. Prime examples right now...

☐*AmeriTrade Holding Corp.* NASDAQ: AMTD.

☐ *Charles Schwab & Co.* NYSE:SCH.

☐ *E*Trade Securities, Inc.* NASDAQ: EGRP.

●**Search engines.** Yahoo! is the premier player in helping people navigate from one site to another. But the stock is very expensive now. A good stock at a lower price...

☐ *Lycos, Inc.* has been active in partnering and acquiring on-line sites. NASDAQ:LCOS.

●**Content providers.** These are companies with Web sites that offer unique advantages and unusual potential. My choices now...

☐*Amazon.com, Inc.* is still the premier business-to-consumer on-line commerce site. NASDAQ:AMZN.

☐ *CNET, Inc.* is a leading on-line technology news and information company. NASDAQ: CNET.

☐ *Intuit Inc.* makes Quicken financial software and can convert its loyal software consumers to Internet users. NASDAQ:INTU.

●**On-line service.** These companies deliver the Internet to computer users. Stock I like...

☐ *America Online, Inc.* is still a good value, even at its current stock prices. NYSE:AOL.

●**Business-to-business commerce.** This is where the real growth in on-line commerce exists. Leading example...

☐ ***Sterling Commerce, Inc.*** makes software that allows companies to do business over the Internet. You find their software being used by employees at more than 400 of the *Fortune* 500 companies. NYSE:SE.

# Low-Stress Investing Advice from Vanguard's Pioneering John Bogle

John Bogle, senior chairman and founder of The Vanguard Group, Valley Forge, PA, which manages 102 US funds with $490 billion in assets. He is author of *Common Sense on Mutual Funds: New Imperatives for the Intelligent Investor.* John Wiley & Sons.

Investment expert John Bogle, who 25 years ago founded The Vanguard Group and in 1975 invented the index mutual fund, answers questions on how to save for the future without complicating your life or worrying about the markets.

●**You warn against investing in actively managed funds. Why?**

I don't know of a single actively managed fund that has beaten the Standard & Poor's 500 index by a significant amount over a period of 50 years.

Beating the index over time is—from all that is known now—impossible. Managers of managed funds are subject to the same psychological frailties as the rest of us—maybe even more so. Their training convinces them that they know more than they really do.

What we do know is that an index fund returns 98% to 99% of the index it tracks. While an index's return varies from year to year, all indexes have risen steadily over long periods of time.

Many of the best fund managers have earned annual returns equal to only 80% to 85% of the indexes against which their funds are compared.

What's more, actively managed funds charge you fees that are often 10 times as high as those of index funds. They also cost you more in taxes.

Fund managers are constantly buying and selling shares in an attempt to produce higher returns. The capital gains taxes that those funds generate are passed along to you. The average investor really should think twice before picking anything other than index funds.

●**Are there special risks with index funds?**

Most important—index funds do expose you to overall risk of the market, which could go down or up at any time. Because of stock market risk, conservative investors should balance stock index funds with low-cost bond funds and bond index funds. Remember, too, that an S&P 500 index fund invests only in large-cap stocks. Full-market diversification is available in a total stock market index fund, which also includes small- and mid-cap stocks, a strategy I happen to prefer.

●**What about investors who want to invest in actively managed funds?**

Here are characteristics to look for…

☐ No load, with an annual expense ratio of 0.75% per year or less.

☐ Annual portfolio turnover of less than 40%.

☐ Clear investment style—and a manager who sticks with the fund's original style.

●**How many index funds are adequate to diversify a portfolio with minimum risk?**

You can do it with one fund—a balanced index fund. This type invests about 60% of its assets in stocks making up the total stock market…and 40% in bonds making up the total bond market.

Such a single balanced index fund is a particularly intelligent choice for retirement accounts, which are tax deferred. You don't have to worry about taxes each year on the dividends and gains the fund generates. For a taxable account, create a more tax-efficient portfolio by holding one balanced fund with 50% of assets in a growth-stock index portfolio and 50% in a tax-exempt municipal bond portfolio.

●**Is there a place for foreign funds in a diversified portfolio?**

I don't believe it's essential to own foreign funds. Remember that 25% of the revenue and profits of S&P 500 US corporations already come from abroad. I don't think the average individual investor should have any more foreign exposure than that. Investing abroad is just too risky, and I don't believe in taking more portfolio risk than necessary.

●**How do you compare owning index funds with a diversified portfolio of common stocks?**

Index funds are for everyone, no matter how sophisticated you are. However, there is a case to be made for common stocks if you can afford them. You could buy 25 or 30 of the largest growth stocks and hold them for 25 years. You would probably do as well as the S&P 500 index—maybe a bit better. As you can see, I don't believe in trading stocks. People never get the timing right.

●**What's the most important thing investors need to remember?**

Over time, the market delivers an average annual return to investors based on dividend yield and earnings growth. However, in individual years, the return may be much higher than that norm. In other years, the return will be much lower than the norm.

If you take the average of above-normal years and below-normal years, you get the market's long term *mean*.

Wherever the market is now, it ultimately will rise or fall until it reverts to the mean return based on earnings and dividends. The way to deal with market fluctuations is to have realistic goals and stick to them over time.

*Time* is your friend.

*Impulse* is your enemy.

Because the market has always reverted to the fundamental mean, there is no point in taking chances on whether growth or value is going to do better this year. There's also no point trying to time the market. If you accept this as fundamental investment truth, then you might as well buy the entire market through an index fund and just hold on to it for as long as possible.

---

## Know Your Funds' Assets

Don't rely on the name or category of a fund to describe its assets accurately when planning the allocation of different types of funds in your portfolio. To boost their funds' growth, fund managers are increasingly going outside of their specific funds to buy stocks and bonds from different asset classes. Some US stock funds, for example, have significant positions in foreign stocks. *Strategy:* Maintain control of your portfolio's percentages of stocks, bonds and cash by getting a list of your funds' assets. Call your funds for an up-to-date breakdown.

*Kurt Brouwer, president, Brouwer & Janachowski, Inc., an investment advisory firm, 1831 Tiburon Blvd., Tiburon, CA 94920.*

# Better Fund Selection

Brokers and financial advisers commonly use lists of preferred mutual funds—called *short* lists—to recommend investments. Each list is based on the firm's particular investment criteria—which you should understand before investing.

Before selecting a fund from the short list, find out why that particular fund is on the list instead of similar funds from other companies.

***Also:*** Make sure the broker/adviser will help evaluate funds of interest to you that are not on the short list.

*Stephen Savage, executive director, Value Line Mutual Fund Survey, 220 E. 42 St., New York 10017.*

---

# When to Get Out of a Mutual Fund

*Doug Fabian, president, Fabian Investment Resources, a mutual fund advisory service in Huntington Beach, CA. Fabian's Lemon List of expensive, underperforming mutual funds is available free on-line at www.fabian.com.*

---

To check your fund holdings for "lemons," look at the quarterly Lipper Analytical Services mutual fund data.

These are reported in many newspapers and financial publications. *Guidelines to use...*

●**Make proper comparisons.** Measure your fund's performance against funds with a similar investment objective.

*Example:* Don't compare against the Standard & Poor's 500 Index unless yours is an index fund with the same objective.

●**Use meaningful time periods.** Check your fund's relative performance against its peer average for one year, three years and five years.

*Reason:* Any fund manager can have a bad quarter, and that's not necessarily a reason to dump the fund.

*First cut:* Funds that have been underperforming for all three periods.

*Second cut:* Funds that are marginal performers—or worse—and charge more in annual fees than the average in their peer group. *Benchmark:* The average fee for a domestic stock fund is 80 basis points (0.80%).

*Third cut:* If you are fairly heavily invested in growth, capital appreciation or index funds where you have substantial profits but are concerned about a market correction, lower your risk by moving some of those assets into balanced funds and/or growth-and-income funds.

*Caution:* Consider the tax consequences of any sale carefully.

# Prudent Way Out

Investors who aren't happy with a mutual fund's performance may, for tax reasons, not want to sell it. What they can do though is stop reinvesting the fund's distributions. Most of the larger funds now allow you to redirect distributions from one fund to another in the same family. If you don't have a new pick, just park the distributions in the fund family's money market fund until you decide where you want to redeploy them.

Sheldon Jacobs, editor, *The No-Load Fund Investor,* Box 318, Irvington-on-Hudson, NY 10533.

# Better CD Buying

CDs bought through stockbrokers can pay up to one-half point more than CDs sold directly by local banks. There is usually no commission payable to the broker. Most brokers will resell CDs before maturity for their customers, and there are no early withdrawal penalties. However, the price may be lower than what was paid—especially if interest rates have risen. A few brokers offer super-high-rate CDs known as *Multi-Step CDs* that may be called by the issuers—but pay higher and higher interest if not called. As long as you have an established account, you can buy CDs from brokers by phone without filling out any additional paperwork. Brokered CDs up to $100,000 each per purchaser are fully insured if the issuing bank is a member of the FDIC.

Malcolm P. Moses, president, Malcolm P. Moses & Associates, financial consultants and crisis managers, 3428 Hewlett Ave., Merrick, NY 11566.

# Deceptive CD Advertising

Some ads for CDs play up teaser rates as high as 20%. But the rates expire within weeks. Other ads offer high teaser rates, then switch to variable rates that are impossible to predict—the opposite of the certainty you should get in a CD. Some institutions play up high rates that are available only with large deposits. Yields on shorter-term CDs are quoted in annualized figures. Do not assume that you will be getting that return unless you roll over your investment for a full 12 months at the same rate.

*Important:* Be sure everything is FDIC-insured before you buy. If it is not, you are essentially buying the bank's IOU, and there is no guarantee that you will get your principal back.

Sara Campbell, senior vice president, Bank Rate Monitor, a company that tracks rates at more than 2,500 banks nationwide, Box 088888, North Palm Beach, FL 33408.

## Buy Treasury Bills To Defer Income

Instead of paying cash interest, US Treasury bills are sold at a discount and redeemed at face value on maturity.

The difference between their higher redemption value and what you pay for them is your interest.

*Opportunity:* Because you receive no income from Treasury bills until they mature, you can use them to *defer income.* Six-month Treasury bills acquired after midyear 1999 defer income into 2000.

You may want to defer income and the related income taxes into 2000 to retain the use of your tax dollars for another year.

Or, you may want to do it for a more specific reason, such as to qualify to convert a regular IRA to a Roth IRA, by keeping income under $100,000.

*William G. Brennan, CPA/PFS, CFP, Columbia Financial Advisors, LLP, 1730 Rhode Island Ave. NW, Suite 800, Washington, DC 20036.*

# Some of the Very Best Investment Sites Are Free

*John Edwards, a computer industry analyst and writer on high-tech, in Mount Laurel, NJ.*

Any computer user can become an informed and effective investor by using free on-line information…

### MARKET NEWS

• **CNNfn (www.cnnfn.com).** Breaking business news…20-minute-delayed stock quotes …corporate profiles and mutual fund performance data from Lipper Analytical Services.

### MARKET QUOTES

• **Fox Market Wire (www.foxmarketwire. com).** Up to 50 free real-time stock quotes per day…searchable news of stocks or funds… stock market news alerts. Register to receive five free stock research reports per month.

### MUTUAL FUND INVESTING

• **Find a Fund (www.findafund.com).** Provides information on funds…simplifies complicated financial concepts, such as analyzing fund loads and calculating capital gains. Free monthly performance update on your funds sent by E-mail.

### ANALYSTS' ADVICE

• **The Financial Center (www.tfc.com).** Buy, sell and hold recommendations from more than 30 of Wall Street's top analysts.

### LEGAL/REGULATORY INSIGHT

• **SEC LAW.com (www.seclaw.com).** From the Securities Exchange Commission, information on securities law and compliance…the SEC and regulations of the National Association of Securities Dealers…bankruptcy…arbitration…what to do if you have a complaint.

### WOMEN INVESTORS

• **Women's Wire (www.womenswire. com/money).** Advice on stocks…mutual funds…retirement strategies…credit…taxes. Particularly applicable to single women.

# 12

# Retirement Planning Strategies

## How to Retire Rich... Starting with Only $5.50/Day

The big excuse I hear from people who are not saving for retirement is that they need every penny they have to pay their bills now—but they'll start saving once the bills are paid off before you begin.

Saving for retirement is much easier than most people think, and you *don't* need to have paid off all your bills before you begin.

### BUDGETS AND BILLS

People who think that saving for retirement should come only after their bills are paid off generally think they need to budget to get their expenses in line. But I've never met a person who actually lives within a budget. Budgets are too difficult to set up—and life changes so fast that they are nearly impossible to stick to.

As for your debts, the reality is that you'll probably never pay them *all* off.

Once you acknowledge these realities, setting up a budget and paying off all of your bills will no longer be valid excuses for not saving.

### FINDING THE MONEY

The money you need to save to become rich is in your pocket right now...

• **Anyone can save $5.50 a day.** That $5.50 a day totals about $2,000 at the end of a year—the maximum you can contribute to an Individual Retirement Account (IRA).

• **Anyone can become a disciplined saver by having this amount**—about $165 a month—automatically withdrawn each month from your checking account and put into your IRA.

---

James O'Shaughnessy, manager of two no-load mutual funds based on his investment strategies—O'Shaughnessy Cornerstone Growth Fund and O'Shaughnessy Cornerstone Value Fund, 35 Mason St., Greenwich, CT 06830. He is author of three books on investing. His latest is *How to Retire Rich*. Broadway Books.

●**Invest your IRA assets in stock funds or individual stocks.** Only the stock market can produce the kind of returns over time that are necessary for you to retire rich. If you invest $2,000 a year for 30 years and it compounds at 15% annually, you'll have $1 million.

### INVESTING BY STRATEGY

Following the right strategy keeps you from making the mistakes that most investors make. They are tempted to buy stocks they think are hot because they think they have a special gift for determining which stocks are going to make them rich quick. *Result:* They often invest in the wrong ones.

*Helpful:* Recognize that you are not the world's greatest investor. Recognize that if you tried to do it on your own, you probably would not do a great job.

Here are my investment strategies…

●**Cornerstone Growth Fund strategy.** This strategy has beaten the S&P 500 for every 10-year period over the past 45 years. Because the stocks that fit this strategy tend to be more volatile, they are appropriate for people who can stay invested for 10 years or more. I look for smaller stocks that are on the mend but that are still cheap. *I want stocks that…*

●Have market capitalizations greater than $150 million.

●Sell at price-to-sales ratios of 1.5 or lower. The S&P Industrial sells at a 1.7 ratio.

●Report earnings that are higher than the year before.

●Have the best one-year price appreciation among stocks that fit this profile.

You can find stocks by studying the past year's biggest market gainers. Ask your broker for help in finding these stocks. Stocks that meet these criteria—you need to invest in all of them to take advantage of this strategy…

☐*Abercrombie & Fitch.* NYSE:ANF.

☐*Bally Total Fitness.* NYSE:BFT.

☐*Best Buy Co.*, consumer electronics retailer. NYSE:BBY.

☐*Bon-Ton Stores, Inc.*, a department store chain. NASDAQ:BONT.

☐*First American Financial Corp.*, a leading provider of real estate-related financial services. NYSE:FAF.

☐*Hanover Direct, Inc.*, a catalog mail-order company. AMEX:HNV.

☐*Musicland Stores Corp.*, a retailer of music-related products. NYSE:MLG.

☐*Texas Industries*, a steelmaker. NYSE:TXI.

●**Cornerstone Value Fund strategy.** This compounded at an average 15.4% over the past 46 years. Over those 46 years, this strategy never had a five-year period in which it lost money. That makes it suitable for someone who doesn't have a long time horizon—who wants to be in the market but wants a less volatile portfolio. Here I want big, well-known companies that pay high dividend yields. *Specifically, I want stocks that…*

●Have market capitalizations greater than the average stock in their categories.

●Have sales 50% higher than the average stock in this universe.

●Exceed the average in both number of shares outstanding and cash flow.

●Offer the highest yields in the group I'm considering.

Stocks that meet these criteria—you have to invest in all of them to take advantage of this strategy…

☐*Atlantic Richfield Co.*, a large oil company. NYSE:ARC.

☐*Bankers Trust New York Corp.*, a New York City banking giant. NYSE:BT.

☐*British Airways Plc.* NYSE:BAB.

☐*Dow Chemical Co.* NYSE:DOW.

☐*Ford Motor Co.* NYSE:F.

☐*GTE Corp.* NYSE:GTE.

☐*J.C. Penney Co., Inc.* NYSE:JCP.

☐*Mobil Corp.* NYSE:MOB.

☐*Shell Transport & Trading Co., Plc,* the global oil company. NYSE:SC.

### APPLYING THE STRATEGY

Shift from growth toward value as the time when you'll need the money gets closer.

*Example:* A 38-year-old might be 70% in the growth strategy and 30% in the value strategy. At age 62, that might shift to 40% growth and 60% value.

Both strategies must be updated. Once a year, review your IRA portfolio and sell stocks that no longer meet the standards I've outlined. Replace them with stocks that do. There won't be any taxes to pay on the gains until the money is withdrawn. However, commissions can add up, so don't buy and sell your holdings more than once a year.

# Wealth-Building Smarts For Catch-Up Retirement Savers

Jonathan Pond, president of Financial Planning Information, Inc., 9 Galen St., Watertown, MA 02472. He is host of *Your Financial Future*, a series on public television, and author of *4 Easy Steps to Successful Investing*. Avon.

The best way to retire rich is to start saving when you are young. Then keep saving until at least the day you stop working. Get in the habit—and you can continue saving after you stop working.

But few people stick to that strategy. There are too many other "unavoidable" expenses that seem to emerge.

*Result:* Most people reach their 50s with little saved.

It's never too late to start saving. But if you are starting late, you must save more than if you started when you were young.

### HOW TO BE A CATCH-UP SAVER

• **Go into retirement lifestyle mode sooner.** If you start saving for retirement in your 40s, you must save at least 20% of your gross annual income to live comfortably in retirement. If you start in your 50s, you must save even more—or put retirement on indefinite hold.

*Spending less:* Unless some huge source of income comes along, the only way to save more is to spend less. Aggressive ways to avoid reckless spending…

• *Hang on to your car as long as you can.* Buying a new car can really eat into savings. Consider a used car. Leasing is too expensive in the long run. If you are around age 50, plan on buying only one more car before retirement.

• *Downsize your home.* You needed a large home when the kids were growing. But do you still need all that room today? With the new tax rules, you can take all or most of the appreciation out of your home, federally tax free. Then you can buy or rent something smaller and add the gain to your retirement savings.

If you don't want to sell now, keep paying down the mortgage and start planning to move to a smaller, less expensive home when you do retire. There are some wonderful parts of the country where great condominiums or homes are quite inexpensive.

*Example:* A friend who is retiring will teach part-time at a college in North Carolina. He rented a beautiful three-bedroom apartment near the college for $375 a month. Try doing that where you live now.

• **Put saving for retirement ahead of paying the college bills.** Most families do not start saving aggressively for retirement until their last child has graduated from college.

That's a mistake. Putting money away for retirement is far more important than paying 100% of your child's college tuition. Every financial institution in the country makes college loans. Not one of them will lend you money to pay for your retirement.

*What really matters:* Of course, you would prefer not to burden your kids with thousands of dollars of college loans. But don't think children must be launched into the world debt free. In fact, saddling college graduates with some loans makes the youngsters more vigorous in seeking out work.

• **Max out your retirement savings plans.** Even though 401(k) and 403(b) plans are the best ways to save for retirement, many people continue to ignore their importance.

• *Put every penny you can into such plans.* They offer big tax advantages, and because contributions are made with pretax dollars, your income tax at year-end is reduced. If you are considering a job change, look for employment at companies that offer to match your contributions.

• *Don't permit yourself to make any excuse* for not contributing to an Individual Retirement Account (IRA).

*Reason:* Your IRA is important, especially if you didn't start saving for retirement until late.

Even if you are maxing out on your 401(k) plan, the IRA will make a big difference.

*Example:* A 50-year-old individual makes a $2,000 IRA contribution for the first time. By contributing $2,000 annually until he/she retires at age 65, his late start at making IRA contributions will nevertheless enable him to add $4,000 to his annual retirement income. If a couple both follow that plan, they will add $8,000 to their annual retirement income from the IRAs alone.

●**Look into moonlighting.** To have a nest egg within 10 to 15 years, you may need to boost present income by doing extra work on the side. *Reasons...*

●You gain current income now and prepare yourself for income-producing work after you retire.

●You can write off most of the expenses you run up while you are moonlighting—meaning you gain tax advantages plus the added income.

●You gain access to still another tax-advantaged retirement savings plan—a Keogh or Simplified Employee Pension (SEP) for the self-employed.

●**Invest like someone who is richer than you.** Clients say, "I can't afford to take risks because this is all the money I have." I respond, "You must take risks because it is all the money you have." There's no way you can save enough for retirement if you put everything into ultrasafe accounts or securities.

*Example:* If you had $1 million, you could afford to put $500,000 into bonds as a safe haven. But you don't have $1 million, so you have to invest for growth.

That doesn't mean you take imprudent risks, but you must emphasize growth.

*Strategy:* I recommend that clients in their 40s or 50s who are trying to play catch-up put 80% of savings into stocks, and 20% into bonds. *My allocation...*

●**Growth stock funds** (20%). No-load examples...

☐ *Janus Fund.* 800-525-8983.

☐ *T. Rowe Price Capital Appreciation.* 800-638-5660.

●**Growth and income funds** (20%). No-load examples...

☐ *Babson Value.* 800-422-2766.

☐ *Vanguard Index Trust—500 Portfolio.* 800-523-7731.

●**Small-cap funds** (20%). No-load examples...

☐ *Baron Asset Fund.* 800-992-2766.

☐ *T. Rowe Price Small Cap Stock.* 800-638-5660.

●**International funds** (20%). No-load examples...

☐ *Janus Worldwide Fund.* 800-525-8983.

☐ *T. Rowe Price International Stock.* 800-638-5660.

●**Bond funds** (20%). No-load examples...

☐ *Fidelity Capital & Income Fund.* 800-544-8888.

☐ *Vanguard Fixed Income Securities Fund—Intermediate-Term US Treasury Portfolio.* 800-523-7731.

# Lewis Altfest on Retirement Matters

Lewis J. Altfest, CFP, president, LJ Altfest & Co., a financial planning firm, 116 John St., Suite 1120, New York 10038.

## Financial Rewards of Aging

●**Age 55:** Penalty-free withdrawals from company retirement plans upon separation from service.

●**Age 59½:** No penalty on any withdrawals from IRAs and retirement plans/accounts.

●**Age 62:** Earliest age that Social Security retirement benefits can be collected. (Widows and widowers can receive these benefits as early as age 60.)

●**Ages 65 to 67:** Full Social Security benefits. The exact age depends on the year in which you were born.

●**Age 70:** Earned income no longer reduces Social Security benefits—if you are under age 65, $1 is cut from your benefits for every $2 earned above $9,600 in 1999. From ages 65 to 69, $1 is cut for every $3 earned above $15,500 in 1999.

●**Age 70½:** Minimum distributions must be withdrawn from most retirement accounts. But—you can continue to invest tax-deferred in a Roth IRA.

More from Lewis Altfest...

## Retirement Savings Options When Moving to a New Job

•*Transfer funds* to the new company's retirement plan *if* it offers good investment choices.

•*Leave funds behind* at the old company *if* the firm allows you to and the choices are better there.

•*Cash out some of your savings* *if* you will need money for college expenses or medical bills or to start a new business.

*Caution:* First you should find out about the tax consequences.

•*Move the funds to an IRA.* Have them transferred *directly* to the IRA to avoid possible IRS problems.

# SIMPLE Retirement Plans Aren't So Simple At All

Stephen J. Krass, Esq., managing partner, Krass & Lund, PC, 419 Park Ave. S., New York 10016. He is author of *The Pension Answer Book.* Aspen Law & Business/ Panel Publishers.

Savings Incentive Match Plans—*SIMPLE* plans—are a relatively new retirement plan option for small businesses.

SIMPLE plans can be set up as either SIMPLE IRAs or SIMPLE 401(k)s.

*How they work:* Employees contribute a part of their salaries to the plan. To satisfy government nondiscrimination requirements, employers make required contributions, too.

All this is supposed to make things simple, but it really doesn't.

SIMPLE plans have been available for several years now. They're still very confusing to most small-business owners and, probably because of that, have yet to catch on.

Despite this, SIMPLE plans may be the best alternative for certain business owners. It's worth the time it takes to understand the rules.

### WHO'S ELIGIBLE

•SIMPLE plans are available to *small* companies—that is, companies that employ 100 or fewer eligible employees who received at least $5,000 of compensation during the preceding calendar year.

•An employer with a qualified retirement plan cannot also maintain a SIMPLE IRA plan.

•An employer with a qualified retirement plan can have a SIMPLE 401(k) plan to cover employees not covered in its other plan.

•An employee who participates in a qualified retirement plan with one employer can also participate in a SIMPLE plan of another employer—assuming he/she meets the income requirement for participation (see below).

•An employee is eligible to participate in a SIMPLE IRA plan if he earned at least $5,000 in compensation from the employer during any two preceding calendar years—they don't have to be consecutive—and if he reasonably expects to earn at least $5,000 in the current year.

•Employers can adopt *less* restrictive participation requirements.

*Example:* No prior-year compensation requirement.

•SIMPLE 401(k) plans can have minimum age or service requirements (not to exceed completion of one year of service).

### CONTRIBUTION LIMITS

•**Employees.** They can contribute up to $6,000 per year—indexed for inflation—to a...

•**SIMPLE IRA.** There's no percentage limit on contributions to a SIMPLE IRA so someone earning $6,000 can contribute every dollar earned to the plan.

•**SIMPLE 401(k).** Contributions are limited to 25% of annual compensation, with a $6,000 per year cap.

•**Tax impact.** SIMPLE plan contributions are excludable from income and not subject to federal income tax withholding. However, they are still subject to FICA and FUTA taxes and must be reported annually on the employee's Form W-2.

•**Self-employed individuals.** They can base contributions on net earnings from self-employment without regard to any SIMPLE plan contributions on their own behalf.

•**Employers.** A plan is treated as nondiscriminatory if employers make required contributions. *They have a choice...*

***Option 1:* Matching contributions.** Match employee contributions, dollar for dollar, up to 3% of compensation.

•There's no limit on the amount of compensation taken into account for matching contributions to a SIMPLE IRA. However, the tax law's $160,000-of-compensation limit applies to a SIMPLE 401(k) plan.

•In a SIMPLE IRA plan—but not in a SIMPLE 401(k) plan—the percentage may be reduced to 1% for any two years in a five-year period as long as proper notice is given to employees.

***Option 2:* Nonelective contributions.** Contribute 2% of compensation without regard to whether employees contribute to the plan.

•"Compensation" means compensation up to $160,000 per year (indexed for inflation) for both SIMPLE IRAs and SIMPLE 401(k)s.

### EXAMPLES OF CONTRIBUTIONS

Let's assume that a small employer with a SIMPLE IRA plan pays an employee a salary of $30,000 in 1999. How contributions by the employer and employee play out under the optional contribution formulas...

| If employee contributes | 3% matching contribution | 2% nonelective contribution |
|---|---|---|
| $6,000 | $900 | $600 |
| 500 | 500 | 600 |
| 0 | 0 | 600 |

As you can see, where employees are expected to participate to the fullest (i.e., contribute $6,000), the employer's contributions are minimized with the nonelective method (they would only have to put in $600). Where employees do not participate, or fund only a fraction of what they are entitled, then the 3% matching formula produces the smaller employer contributions.

### SIMPLES VS. KEOGHS

How does the contribution under a SIMPLE compare with a combination profit-sharing/money-purchase Keogh? Assume an individual nets $20,000 from a sideline business. Here are the maximum contributions that can be made to SIMPLE IRA plans versus Keogh plans (ignore the adjustment for one-half of self-employment tax for this illustration—profit sharing contribution is 13.0435% and money purchase contribution is 20%)...

| SIMPLE IRA | Profit-sharing Keogh | Money-purchase Keogh |
|---|---|---|
| $6,600* | $2,609 | $4,000 |

### ADMINISTRATION

Employees are fully vested in all contributions made to the plan. However, withdrawals before age 59½ are subject to the 10% early distribution penalty unless an exception (such as disability) applies. Further, withdrawals within the first two years of plan participation result in a 25% penalty (unless one of the exceptions to the early distribution penalty rules applies).

Amounts in SIMPLE IRAs can be rolled over to other SIMPLE IRAs or to a regular IRA. However, a rollover from a SIMPLE IRA to a regular IRA within the first two years is treated as a taxable distribution and may be subject to the penalty tax.

Employers must give employees 60 days notice that they can make salary reduction contributions to the plan. The notice period begins no later than the date the plan starts and ends no earlier than the day before the plan starts.

***Example:*** If the plan starts July 1, 1999, the 60-day notice period must begin no later than July 1, 1999, and cannot end before June 30, 1999. Employers can provide longer notice periods (for example, 90 days) if they want.

Employees must be permitted to terminate their agreed contributions at any time. The plan can, but isn't required to, allow employees to resume participation when desired or at the beginning of a new quarter. Alternatively, a plan can require these employees to wait until the following year to resume making salary reduction contributions.

There's no annual reporting requirements for SIMPLE IRAs.

SIMPLE 401(k)s are subject to the same annual reporting requirements as any other qualified retirement plan and must file an annual information return in the 5500 series.

*$6,000 salary reduction contribution, plus $600 company matching contribution.

# Retirement Wisdom from Attorney Sidney Kess

Sidney Kess, attorney and CPA, 10 Rockefeller Plaza, Suite 909, New York 10022. Over the years he has taught tax law to more than 600,000 tax professionals. Mr. Kess is consulting editor of *Financial and Estate Planning* and coauthor of *1040 Preparation, 2000 Edition,* both published by CCH Inc.

## Early Retirement May Be Much Better for Your Financial Future Than Continuing to Work

When offered an early retirement package—if you are given a choice—consider it carefully. Accepting early retirement may be a better deal for you financially than continuing to work.

### INCENTIVES

What will your financial position be if you accept early retirement? Compare your *net* income in retirement with your *net* income if you continue working.

Even though you might receive less income when you are retired than when working, you'll have more *net income* during retirement because of early retirement incentives and reduced expenses.

Early retirement plans typically offer incentives such as…

•**Cash bonus.** Often based on years of service, a well-invested bonus may increase your future income.

•**Bigger pension.** If the regular pension provides a benefit of 25% of your average salary in your three highest paid years, the enhanced early retirement pension might offer 30%—a lasting benefit that also increases your income.

•**Continuing fringe benefits,** such as medical coverage and life insurance for a period of time, perhaps until you reach age 65. While these are "noncash" benefits, include their value in your retirement income estimates.

### OTHER FACTORS

•**If you retire early** and are not earning anything but your spouse is still working, you can still, together, put $4,000 per year into a Roth IRA.

•**FICA taxes.** No FICA taxes are due on retirement benefits, while they would be due on salary.

•**Social Security.** If you take Social Security at age 62, it will be at least partially tax free, while salary would be fully taxed.

•**Out-of-pocket employee expenses.** You'll no longer have to pay for commuting, lunches, work clothes, etc.

•**Lower income tax bracket.** Because your gross income will be lower, income tax as a percentage of total income will also fall. The higher your combined federal and local tax rate is now, the greater this effect will be.

*Bonus:* Some states offer *complete* tax exemption to certain types of retirement income—such as income from federal pensions or regular retirement income up to a specified dollar amount.

•**Downsizing.** You may have the option of relocating to a state that has no income tax at all, such as Florida…or to an area that has a low cost of living.

•**Some spending money.** Retiring from your current employer does not mean you have to stop earning money. Even while collecting an "enhanced" pension, you may be able to use your experience to generate income by working part-time or full-time as a consultant—or by starting a new business of your own.

If you have a serious hobby that you enjoy—such as photography or collecting antiques, rare coins, etc.—early retirement may provide you with both the funds and the time you need to convert it into a real business. And that can generate extra income, valuable business tax deductions and personal satisfaction.

Combine all these factors and you may actually come out ahead by taking early retirement.

### THE HUMAN FACTOR

Consider things other than money when you make your early retirement decision. What really matters is your future *quality* of life. *Key considerations…*

●**Self-esteem.** Do you get personal satisfaction from your current job that you won't be able to replace in retirement?

●**Relationships.** Will you be comfortable suddenly spending much more time in close contact with your spouse and other family members?

●**Social life.** If you move to a lower cost, lower tax location, will you be happy there—away from your current friends and family?

Money is only one contributing element to happiness. Remember your real bottom line.

---

**More from Sidney Kess...**

## Best Thing to Do with a Retirement Account Inherited from a Spouse

You may some day face critical decisions about what to do with your deceased spouse's retirement accounts.

*Problem:* A surviving spouse who makes the wrong decisions may permanently jeopardize his/her financial security.

Wrong decisions are most likely to be made when a person first confronts complex choices at a time of great stress.

*Safety:* Nobody likes to think about death—but it's important for spouses to prepare each other to make the right financial decisions when the time comes.

They should examine the options in advance and be sure each clearly understands them. How to handle inherited retirement accounts should be a key part of this planning. *What spouses need to know...*

### MINIMIZING TAXES

Money in retirement accounts may well be a couple's largest asset. So keeping taxes on this money to a minimum is critical.

There are several different ways to handle an inherited 401(k) account or other employer-provided retirement account. Each way of treating the money has different tax consequences. *Options...*

●**Take a taxable lump-sum cash distribution.** This is simplest, but results in the most tax unless you qualify for income averaging (explained on the next page). The full amount of the plan payout is simply added to the surviving spouse's taxable income, where it is likely to pile up into higher tax brackets. This big tax bill will reduce the amount available to meet the survivor's future financial needs.

●**Roll over the distribution into an IRA.** Funds can be transferred from the deceased's retirement account into an IRA, avoiding current income tax. The money should be transferred *directly* from the trustee of the company's retirement plan to the IRA trustee.

*Trap:* If the surviving spouse takes a distribution into his hands, it will be subject to 20% income tax withholding.

If the spouse then makes a rollover deposit of the funds into an IRA, the withheld 20% will have to be made up out of pocket to deposit the full amount of the distribution in the IRA, and preserve the rollover's full tax-free status.

●**Make an IRA rollover—*then convert to a Roth IRA*.** Funds taken from a company retirement plan can't be rolled over directly into a Roth IRA.

However, they can be first rolled over into a conventional IRA, which is then converted into a Roth IRA. *Advantages of putting the money in a Roth IRA...*

●Funds held in a Roth IRA for at least five years that are qualified distributions are *tax free* when withdrawn, while withdrawals from other retirement accounts are taxable.

●Roth IRAs are not subject to the tax law's minimum annual distribution rules, so funds can be held in them *longer* to earn tax-free investment returns. And they can serve as a flexible device to fund tax-favored bequests to children and meet other estate-planning goals.

*Disadvantage:* Conversion of a regular IRA into a Roth IRA results in the value of the regular IRA being included in taxable income. In general, a person must be able to afford to pay the resulting tax from separate funds—without taking money from the IRA—for the conversion to be worthwhile.

*Caution:* To be eligible to make a conversion, Adjusted Gross Income must not exceed $100,000.

*General rule:* Putting the money in a Roth IRA makes most sense for a person who is young enough to expect to earn many years of compound investment returns in the IRA... who can afford to leave the money in the IRA, rather than need to spend it...and who can pay the tax on the conversion from non-IRA money.

●**Use income averaging.** Depending upon the age of the deceased spouse, the surviving spouse may be able to take a lump-sum distribution of the retirement plan balance and reduce the tax due on it through the use of income averaging.

This lets the tax be computed as if the distribution were received in separate equal payments spread over several years. The tax is reduced because each "payment" gets the benefit of the lowest tax bracket rates. *If the deceased spouse was...*

●At least age 59½ at death, five-year income averaging is available.

●At least age 50 on January 1, 1986, there is a choice of using five-year income averaging and current tax rates, or 10-year income averaging using pre-1986 tax rates.

***Rule of thumb:*** For amounts less than $320,000 in 1999, 10-year averaging is best. For larger amounts, five-year averaging means less tax.

Income averaging lets the surviving spouse take the inherited retirement plan balance in cash, while paying a relatively low tax bill.

But there is still a tax payment due—and this reduces the amount that can be invested to fund future retirement needs. So again there is a trade-off.

In general, if the amount of a distribution subject to five-year income averaging is...

●***Less than $100,000:*** It's best to take the distribution and pay the tax.

***Example:*** On a distribution of $50,000, the tax would be only $6,900.

●***More than $200,000:*** It's best to roll over the funds into an IRA and invest the tax savings.

●***Between $100,000 and $200,000:*** You have to work through the figures with the details of your specific situation to decide what's best.

●**Keep the money in the company plan.** Some employers will continue to maintain the retirement plan account of a deceased employee for the benefit of a surviving spouse.

This avoids any tax on a lump-sum distribution, and the need to make an IRA rollover.

However, this option is not always available. And if it is available, be sure that the terms and conditions of the plan meet the surviving spouse's long-term needs.

# Penalty-Free Withdrawals From Your IRA

You can take early IRA withdrawals penalty free *if* you take them in the form of an annuity. Withdrawals before age 59½ are not penalized if they consist of a series of "substantially equal" annual payments of a size calculated to last over your life expectancy. *New:* The IRS has recently ruled that an annual inflation adjustment can be built into the annuity payment schedule. You can use this so that the payments grow each year. If early year payments are smaller, more money will remain in the IRA to earn tax-deferred investment returns.

*IRS Letter Ruling* 9816028.

# When Not to Roll Over To an IRA

A rollover to an IRA is not always advisable for company stock held in a company pension plan. It may be better to pay current tax on distributions of stock than roll them over.

***Why:*** Current tax is figured on the value of the stock when it was contributed to the plan. All subsequent appreciation is tax deferred until the stock is sold, at which time it would be taxed at favorable capital gain rates.

Rolling over the stock to an IRA would postpone tax, but all withdrawals would be ordinary income.

***Key factor in opting for not making a rollover:*** Appreciation in the stock since its contribution to the plan (the higher the appreciation, the less favorable a rollover).

**Other factors:** When IRA withdrawals are anticipated…and taxpayer's tax bracket.

Joel Philhours, professor of accounting, Western Kentucky University, Bowling Green, KY 42101.

# Roth IRA Rollover Trap

If you are taking required distributions from a regular IRA that you wish to convert to a Roth IRA, there's a hidden trap.

To convert a regular IRA into a Roth IRA, your Adjusted Gross Income (AGI) cannot exceed $100,000.

The trap is that under current IRS rules, your minimum required distribution from your regular IRA is included in your AGI even if you never take it because you converted the regular IRA into a Roth IRA. This amount may push you over the $100,000 limit, making your Roth IRA conversion invalid and causing you to incur penalties.

The IRS says that if you have a regular IRA for a year, the Tax Code requires that the minimum distribution from it be included in your income—and that the Roth IRA legislation did not change this.

Starting in 2005 required minimum distributions will no longer be taken into account in figuring AGI.

Ed Slott, CPA, E. Slott & Co., CPAs, 100 Merrick Rd., Rockville Centre, NY 11570. Mr. Slott is publisher of *Ed Slott's IRA Advisor.*

# More on Roth IRA Conversions

Year-end mutual fund distributions could push your Adjusted Gross Income over the $100,000 limit for converting a traditional IRA to a Roth IRA. *Self-defense:* If you have already made the conversion, convert the Roth

IRA *back* to an ordinary one. Generally you have until the due date of your return to act.

Norman Fosback, editor-in-chief, *Mutual Funds Magazine,* 2200 SW 10 St., Deerfield Beach, FL 33442.

# Canadian Retirement Plan Can't Be Rolled Over To an IRA

When an American who had worked in Canada wanted to roll his Canadian retirement savings plan into an IRA, the IRS said no.

**Warning:** An even worse trap faces US residents with foreign retirement accounts. Unless such accounts are "qualified" under US rules, they may be *fully taxable* even if they are tax deferred or tax exempt under foreign rules.

Specific US tax rules for foreign retirement accounts often are established in tax treaties that the US has with foreign countries. There's no way to know these rules without looking them up. If you have a foreign retirement account, consult a tax professional.

*Letter Ruling* 9833020.

# Ted Benna On 401(k) Traps and Opportunities

Ted Benna, inventor of the 401(k) savings plan and president of the 401(k) Association, an employee benefits consultancy, 15 Lingwood Ct., Bellefonte, PA 16823. He is author of *Escaping the Coming Retirement Crisis: How to Secure Your Financial Future.* Piñon Press.

## New 401(k) Strategies

When there is a wild run-up in stocks, it tends to leave many 401(k) plan investors complacent about their asset allocations…and confident that their portfolios will keep on growing.

***Reality:*** Just because the total value of your retirement account is way up does not mean that you should relax and forget about managing it.

Here's what I'm advising clients do to protect gains from a bear market…

●**Review your asset allocations.** The greatest impact on your fund performance is how you divide your money among stocks and bonds—not what particular funds you have chosen.

The tremendous rise of the Dow over the past few years means that your allocations probably are now somewhat lopsided compared with what you had originally intended.

***Example:*** If you started out 10 years ago with an allocation of 70% stocks and 30% bonds, the stock assets now may represent 90% of your portfolio while the bond assets may represent only 10%.

One way to bring your holdings into line with your comfort level might be to direct all new plan contributions to invest in bond funds.

In fast-rising markets, that strategy may not restore your original allocation fast enough. If that's the case, a quicker approach is to move some of your holdings from stock funds to bond funds to bring the allocations back to what you had wanted in the first place.

●**Choose an allocation you can live with for decades,** not one based on current market performance. I don't like allocations that are based solely on age.

Age is only one of many factors to be considered. *Two other major factors…*

●**Major savings objectives.** Are you saving for a down payment to buy a first house in a few years? Are you saving for your five-year-old's college education? Saving for retirement in 25 years?

If the time horizon before you expect to tap your plan investments is short—say, two or three years—you need to be more conservative about where you put your money than if your time horizon extends for decades.

●**Tolerance for risk.** Do you have the ability to hang in there through the market's ups and downs—or would you panic if the Dow started to fall slowly and steadily over several months? If you become unsettled by such events, you'll probably be more comfortable with a conservative allocation that stresses bonds over stocks.

●**Consider other sources of retirement income.** If you will be receiving a traditional pension that will pay you a set amount per month once you retire, you can be more adventurous with your investments than if your 401(k) plan were the only source of your retirement income.

Here are the allocations that I advise different types of clients to consider…

●***Conservative:*** 60% bonds/20% stocks/20% cash.

●***Moderate:*** 60% stocks/40% bonds.

●***Aggressive:*** 100% stocks.

●**Be conservative if you work in a tricky industry or your job is uncertain.** Despite strong economic growth and low unemployment, mergers and acquisitions are continuing to consolidate the financial industry—particularly banking. If you work in this field—or in any other that is tightening—your job may be less certain than if you work in other fields.

The reality is that if you are affected by your industry's consolidation, you may be forced to tap the assets in your 401(k) plan for a short period of time until you find a job that you like. So—your primary concern now should be that your fund investments hold their present value.

●**Don't overreact to bad—or good—news.** Remember, your 401(k) plan is intended for long-term investing, and you must expect some market bumps along the way.

***Example:*** When Asian markets were hammered there was no reason to bail out of *foreign* funds. In fact, your foreign funds may not even be invested predominantly in Asia but in Europe, where markets may perform differently.

And there's no reason to dump a particular fund just because it has had a bad quarter or two—provided the reason you invested in the fund remains sound.

●**Beware of volatile funds.** Most diligent investors who research funds' five- and 10-year performances could automatically conclude that the fund with the highest average annual return for the period is the best one.

But that's not necessarily so. You often accumulate less money with a top-performing mutual fund that has dramatic ups and downs than with a less stellar performer whose returns vary less year to year.

*Example:* Let's say a fund had a 13.2% average return over 10 years. It had some terrific years, including a return of 50.3% one year, but it also had three down years, including one drop of 8.7%. It would seem a better choice than another fund with an average return of 12.6%—38.7% in its best year and a minus 2.5% in its worst year.

But if you invested $1,000 a year for 10 years, you would wind up with only $15,759 in the first fund—and $17,278 in the other.

*Reason:* The second fund fluctuated less and held its value better than the first fund in down markets.

•**Check your fund's fees.** Fees charged by the managers of mutual fund portfolios don't jump out at you, especially in 401(k) plans. And in hot markets, fees tend to be forgotten as high returns roll in. But these innocuous fees can make a huge difference in how much winds up in your pocket over the long term.

Fees can range from as little as 0.3% of assets with index funds to as much as 1.5% of assets with international funds.

If your funds are not being sold directly to your 401(k) plan but are being handled through an intermediary such as a bank or an insurance company, there can be more fees on top of that.

The rule of thumb is that for every additional 1% in fees you pay, you'll accumulate 20% less over a period of 30 years.

*Example:* If you invest $885 each year and you're paying 1% more in fees than the norm, you'll wind up with only $100,000 in your retirement nest egg instead of the $120,000 that you otherwise would have had. If the fees for your plan are too high, push your employer to change funds.

---

**More from Ted Benna...**

## Retirement Fund Trap

A 401(k)-to-IRA switch may require that all investments in the 401(k) be sold—and new ones bought for the IRA.

Employers may let former employees leave money in the company plan. But if the ex-

employee decides to move the money to a rollover IRA, many plans require the investments to be sold. If the rollover is handled properly, no tax should be due.

*However:* Brokerage fees may be involved...and there may be a surrender charge when cashing out in some plans.

*Bottom line:* Be sure you understand a 401(k)-to-IRA switch before you make it.

---

# Correct Your Social Security Records

Barbara Weltman, Esq., practices in Millwood, NY and is author of several books, including *The Complete Idiot's Guide to Starting a Home-Based Business* and *The Complete Idiot's Guide to Making Money After You Retire*, both published by Alpha Books.

---

Check the amount of annual earnings recorded under your name and number in the Social Security Administration's files every three years. It's harder to correct mistakes after this.

Why? You may have thrown out your own earnings records once the three-year limitation period on IRS audits has expired.

*How to check your records:* Send Form SSA-7004, *Request for Earnings and Benefit Estimate Statement,* to Social Security requesting a copy of your personal earnings and benefits estimate statement. (Get Form SSA-7004 by calling 800-772-1213. Or download the form from its Web site at http://www.ssa.gov.)

*If you find a mistake:* Suppose the statement says you earned $5,000 in 1998 when, in fact, you earned $50,000—call the number at the bottom of the statement. If the problem cannot be corrected over the telephone, you may be instructed to write to the Social Security Administration.

•**Ask the SSA to update your statement immediately.**

•**Ask them to send you a new statement** so you can confirm that the correction has been made.

# Pension Plan Pitfall

About half of all pension plans calculate the likely amount of Social Security that retired workers will receive—and include that number as part of the total pension.

***Example:*** A company might say you will receive a pension of $4,000/month—but that means $1,500 from Social Security and $2,500 from the company.

***Self-defense:*** Have your benefits department show you how your pension is calculated —and analyze the numbers with your financial adviser so you can better plan for retirement.

Brian Graff, executive director, American Society of Pension Actuaries, Arlington, VA.

# Don't Rush to Relocate

If planning retirement relocation, do not look for a new town until five years before you are ready to move. Some fast-growing areas may be undesirable in 10 or 15 years. *Helpful:* Vacation in an area where you might want to live. Be sure to spend time there in the off-season, too. After retiring, rent a house for one year before buying, to get a better sense of where to live.

Alan Fox, editor,*Where to Retire,* 1502 Augusta, Suite 415, Houston 77057.

# Wonderful...Offbeat Retirement Havens

Lee Rosenberg, CFP, partner, ARS Financial Services, Valley Stream, NY. He is editor of *50 Fabulous Places to Retire in America*. The Career Press.

Not everyone can afford to retire to Palm Beach or Scottsdale or San Francisco. Not everyone wants to, either. Here are some very attractive, not-so-obvious alternatives you may not have considered...

●**Fayetteville, Arkansas.** The University of Arkansas (14,384 students) provides this town with unending cultural and educational opportunities—amidst national parks, forests, mountains and crystal-clear lakes. Named one of the best places to live by *Money, Inc., USA Today* and *Places Rated. Population:* 52,976.

Fayetteville Chamber of Commerce, 800-766-4626.

●**Fort Collins, Colorado.** Gets only about 50 inches of snowfall annually—but within easy reach of the mountains for those who like to ski. *Population:* 109,000.

Fort Collins Chamber of Commerce, 970-482-3746.

●**Daytona Beach, Florida.** Located far north of Florida's crowds (except for auto race weeks in February and October), Daytona Beach has some of the widest, most beautiful beaches in the country. You can buy a two-bedroom apartment on the water for under $150,000. *Population:* 68,000.

Daytona Beach and Halifax Area Chamber of Commerce, 904-255-0981.

●**Winter Haven, Florida.** A small, quiet town that recalls the pre-Disney World Florida, Winter Haven has 14 natural lakes for recreation as well as active arts and theater groups. *Population:* 25,000.

Winter Haven Area Chamber of Commerce, 941-293-2138.

●**Clayton, Georgia.** At the southern tip of the Blue Ridge Mountains, Clayton is home to Sky Valley, the southernmost ski resort in the country, so you can ski and golf on the same day. A true mountain climate, complete with New England-style foliage. *Population:* 2,000.

Rabun County Chamber of Commerce, 706-782-4812.

●**Coeur d'Alene, Idaho.** Located on one of the world's most beautiful lakes, surrounded by towering mountains. And while it's a famous resort community, the cost of living for residents of Coeur d'Alene remains surprisingly affordable. Three-bedroom homes sell in the $100,000 to $125,000 range. *Population:* 31,000.

Coeur d'Alene Chamber of Commerce, 208-664-3194.

●**Carson City, Nevada.** Carson City retains much of the flavor of the Old West, while also providing great golfing, hiking, water sports and skiing. Located near the dazzle of Reno, the beauty of Lake Tahoe and the inspiring Nevada desert. *Population:* 50,300.

Carson City Tourist Bureau, 800-638-2321.

●**Brevard, North Carolina.** In the Appalachians in the far western part of the state, Brevard is the South with four full seasons—it even snows occasionally. Brevard College (700 students) and the famous Brevard Music Center provide a large amount of cultural stimulation for such a small town. *Population:* 6,200.

Brevard Chamber of Commerce, 800-648-4523.

●**Lincoln City, Oregon.** On the Pacific Coast, with a wide, sweeping beach that recalls Malibu, California—but without the high prices, celebrities or crowds. Lincoln City's weather is cooler, too. Often windy, it's called the "Kite Capital of the World." *Population:* 6,800.

Lincoln City Area Chamber of Commerce, 541-994-3070.

●**Kerrville, Texas.** A friendly, progressive town in the Texas Hill Country, Kerrville has a small but active arts community. Only an hour from San Antonio and two hours from Austin. *Population:* 20,000.

Kerrville Area Chamber of Commerce, 830-896-1155.

●**St. George, Utah.** The epicenter of some of the world's most picturesque landscapes—gold-streaked cliffs and canyons, brilliant red mountains, turquoise lakes and lush green forests. Close to Zion National Park. *Population:* 45,000.

St. George Area Chamber of Commerce, 435-628-1658.

●**Sequim, Washington.** A short 40-minute ferry ride from Seattle, Sequim (pronounced "skwim") sits under the lip of the Olympic Mountains, so it gets an average of only 17 inches of rain annually, compared with Seattle's 39 inches. Often called the Northwest's answer to San Diego. The weather, though, is much cooler. *Population:* 19,300.

Sequim–Dungeness Chamber of Commerce, 360-683-619.

# Ruler Substitutes for On-the-Spot Measurement

- dollar bill ...... 6⅛ x 2⅝ inches
- quarter ...... approximately 1 inch diameter
- penny ...... approximately ¾ inch diameter
- business letterhead ...... 8½ x 11 inches
- credit card ...... generally 3⅜ x 2⅛ inches
- business card ...... generally 3½ x 2 inches
- floor tile ...... generally 9 x 9 or 12 x 12 inches
- belt
- necktie
- shoelace
- shoe
- arm span
- hand span

...... multiply length by number of times covering measured area

# 13

# The Smart Consumer

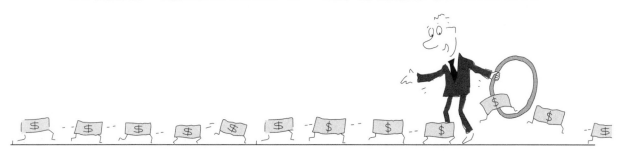

## How to Save Much More… While Living Very Well

You don't have to turn into a cheapskate to save a lot of money on everyday expenses. And you don't have to sacrifice the quality of your life to substantially reduce your living costs. Here are proven strategies to save more while still enjoying your life…

● **Manage your funds strategically.** Make the first bill you pay each month a check to your savings account or investment fund.

*Point:* It's harder to waste money when it isn't readily accessible in your checking account.

● **Avoid taking on most kinds of debt.** And go even further. Use a credit card only when nothing else is convenient. Instead, use cash, a check or a debit card linked to your checking account.

● **Shop on the Internet.** You can save a tremendous amount of money on travel, elec-

tronic equipment, books, CDs and almost everything else on the Web—even without a computer. For about $99 you can get hooked up via a WebTV device (WebTV Network, Inc., 800-469-3288). You'll still need to pay a monthly access fee of $19.95, but it will be worth it.

*Example:* I bought a Polywell computer (300 megahertz Pentium, 4.3 gigabytes hard disk storage and 64 megabytes of RAM) for $1,000 from the Polywell Web site (http://www.polywell.com).

You can buy just about anything via the Internet and save money.

*How to proceed:* Call up a search engine, type in words describing what you're looking for, such as "storm window."

You can also find great travel deals at many sites. *My favorite sites…*

● http://www.bestfares.com.
● http://www.previewtravel.com.

---

Mark W. Miller, a writer and lecturer based in Atlanta and a former stockbroker and financial planner. He is author of *The Sensible Saver: A Common Sense Guide to Saving More While Still Living Well.* Macmillan.

For last-minute ticket availability, use the sites sponsored by individual airlines.

**•Save on entertainment.** Instead of spending a fortune going out to dinner and a movie, save by renting a video and having friends over for dinner. Involve a group and have hosts alternate each time. Dinner can be potluck.

**•Sell your car on your own.** You can save $1,500 by eliminating the middleman.

*Helpful:* Either call your local banker and ask for the National Automobile Dealers trade-in value and retail value of your car...or search on the Web for "used car prices." On the Web, you will find out the average wholesale and retail price for the car. Expect to receive a price right in between the wholesale and retail prices.

Then spruce up your car, waxing the finish and cleaning the engine...and the interior. (A service will do this for $100.) Fix any minor defects. Then advertise in the most popular local paper and in a car shopper. Your asking price should be $300 to $500 more than you really want. Invite all interested buyers over to see the car at the same time. A crowd will add perceived value to your car.

**•Buy a home thermostat.** You can get one for about $35 at Home Depot and save 25% on heating and cooling bills by setting the thermostat a few degrees hotter or cooler at different times during the day. A thermostat is easy to install.

*Note:* If your house has had the same thermostat for decades, you'll probably save by buying a new one. Today's technology is far superior.

**•Do major grocery shopping every two weeks.** The less often you shop, the fewer impulse items you'll buy. Drop in to buy perishables as needed. Buy meat, poultry and fish in bulk when they're on sale and get the full economic benefit of your freezer.

**•Buy floor models.** You can save as much as 50%—often more—by buying electronics, appliances and furniture that have been on display. Sometimes the item will have a nick or two, but many of the new things we buy are imperfect anyway and almost all will be that way eventually—usually sooner rather than later.

Make sure that you receive the manufacturer's warranty on a floor model.

**•When clothes shopping, beware of small sizes.** Many of us would like to be thinner, but this desire can have a costly impact when we shop. If you buy pants that just barely fit in the waist and can't be let out, odds are you'll soon have a pair of unwearable pants. Someday you'll just have to bite the bullet and give them to Goodwill.

*Better:* Buy clothes that have a little extra room. If you lose weight, you can always have them taken in. If you gain weight, however, you'll still have clothes you can use.

**•Start a book exchange with friends.** Relying on the library is wonderful, but sometimes you can't get the book you want when you want it.

*Saving strategy:* Organize a book-buying group with friends. If six people buy two new books a year, each of them can read 12 new books for the price of two.

**•Get term life insurance.** Don't rely on an insurance policy for investing. Instead, buy cheap term insurance. *Best rates now:* Quotesmith (800-556-9393) or SelectQuote (800-343-1985).

*Saving strategy:* Ultimately, however, your goal should be to become self-insured. Once your home is paid off and you have $300,000 to $500,000 in savings, you may not need life insurance any longer.

**•Avoid insurance with terrible odds.** Never pay for accidental death or dismemberment insurance, credit life insurance or mortgage life insurance. The odds are dramatically in the insurers' favor and the payout, should it ever come, is often minimal.

**•Buy gifts on sale throughout the year.** Keep a gift list—complete with sizes—with you. When you see the right item on sale, buy it—even if your relative's birthday is six months away. Not only will you save money, but you'll avoid the last-minute rush to find a gift.

**•Stop playing the lottery.** If you really enjoy it, okay. Spending $100 to $200 a year on genuine recreation is reasonable enough. But if you think you have a real chance to win—*forget it*. You're kidding yourself. The odds of picking the right six numbers are about the same as being hit by lightning seven times.

# Save Money On Almost Everything

Linda Bowman, author of the *More for Your Money* series of guides, including *Free Food & More* and *Freebies (and More) for Folks Over 50*, both published by COM-OP Publishing.

A few dollars saved here and there can add up very quickly. Here are some resources that will help you cut costs without sacrificing...

## UTILITIES/ENERGY

• **For free evaluation of your energy usage, call your local utilities company.** Many utilities also *give away* energy-saving devices, such as low-flow shower heads, water heater blankets and fluorescent bulbs.

• **Repair major appliances yourself.** *How:* Call manufacturers' customer service hot lines for instructions.

  • **General Electric,** 800-626-2000.
  • **Whirlpool,** 800-253-1301.
  • **White-Westinghouse,** 800-245-0600.

• **Gather free firewood** from any of our 155 national forests. Contact your regional office of the US Forest Service for a permit, which allows you up to six cords of downed or dead wood. At the going rate of about $150 a cord, this will save almost $1,000.

• **Install a water restrictor for your shower.** It saves thousands of gallons of water a year. Check with your utility for a free restrictor.

## HOME AND HEALTH CARE PRODUCTS

• **Take advantage of refund/rebate offers.** Take the time to save UPC symbols, labels and receipts. The savings can easily reach hundreds of dollars a year. *Good source of offers:* Supermarket and drugstore bulletin boards.

• **Ask for free samples at department store cosmetics counters.** Say you need to try products before you buy, and you'll receive handfuls of high-priced makeup, skin care products and fragrances.

*Watch for:* Fine print in magazine ads offering free samples of perfumes or moisturizers if you write or call an 800 number.

• **Have your hair cut, colored, permed or styled at a cosmetology school.** Students are closely supervised by expert instructors.

*Savings:* About 60% less than a salon. The average American woman spends $238 a year at hair salons, so expect to save $143.

• **Get routine dental care at a dental school.** Services at the country's 57 dental school clinics, including orthodontics, are high-quality and 60% less expensive than normal dentists' fees.

• **Ask your doctor for free samples of medications whenever you get a prescription.** Most doctors have plenty to give away.

## HOME ENTERTAINMENT

• **Take advantage of free magazine offers.** Don't throw away subscription invitations from periodicals. Most publications will send you a free issue, then begin your subscription unless you cancel.

*Key:* Write "cancel" on the invoice, and mail it back. The postage is almost always paid, and you owe nothing.

• **Use your public library** to borrow books, records, audiotapes, videotapes, even artwork.

• **Order free publications from your favorite manufacturers.** Almost every food company offers a free cookbook, including Quaker Oats, Dannon, Kikkoman and Nestlé...as does almost every trade organization, including the American Mushroom Institute in Washington, DC, and the Idaho Potato Commission in Boise.

*Examples:* Eastman Kodak of Rochester, New York, offers three free booklets on photography...and United Van Lines of Fenton, Missouri, offers a free booklet called *How to Hold a Garage Sale*, as well as other brochures related to planning a move.

Check package labels for the location of company headquarters. Then contact the company's customer service department.

# How to Save Thousands On Personal Finance, Clothing and Cars

James Steamer, a Pennsylvania-based financial planner and author of *Wealth on Minimal Wage.* Berkley Books.

Trisha King, who cowrites a weekly bargain column for the *Los Angeles Daily News* and is coauthor of *Buying Retail Is Stupid!,* now available in US, Southern California and Chicago editions. Contemporary Books.

Remar Sutton, consumer advocate and auto expert, and president and cofounder, with Ralph Nader, of the National Consumer Task Force for Automotive Issues. He is author of *Don't Get Taken Every Time.* Penguin.

R ecent months have shown that the stock market does not always produce big profits for investors. *Safer bet:* Build assets by spending less.

*How to save big, big bucks…*

### SLASH PERSONAL FINANCE FEES
### James Steamer

The average American couple pays $1,000 a year for banks, insurance companies and investment companies to handle their money. How to cut that in half—*and* earn more for your money…

●**Checking account.** Bank long-distance by phone, computer or mail. Many long-distance banks offer no-fee, high-interest-rate checking accounts. *Example:*

●Security First Network Bank, perhaps the best on-line bank, www.sfnb.com.

Or, join a credit union. Credit unions usually have the lowest fees and highest interest rates.

*Examples:* Average monthly fee for an interest-bearing checking account with a bank, $7.34…with a credit union, $1.78.

If you don't qualify to join a credit union, small banks and savings and loans are usually the next best options.

*Downside:* Smaller banks or credit unions have fewer affiliated ATMs. That means you're more likely to pay a fee at nonaffiliated ATMs.

●**Check-printing charges.** Banks charge as much as $20 for 200 checks.

*Better:* Independent check printers, which charge under $6.00 for the same number of checks. *Examples:* Current, 800-426-0822… Image Check, 800-562-8768.

●**Check-bouncing charges.** Call your bank and ask it to link overdraft protection to a credit card issued by that bank.

●**Savings accounts.** Bank savings accounts rarely pay more than 2% or 3% interest a year.

*Better:* Stash emergency cash in a good money market fund. You will gain about $25 a year for every $1,000 invested.

*Caution:* Some money market funds limit the number of checks you can write each month for free…and set a minimum on the amount you can write them for.

*Some of my favorite money market funds…*

●**Strong Investors Money Market Fund.** 800-368-3863.

●**Vanguard Prime Money Market Fund.** 800-662-7447.

●**American Century's Benham Prime Money Market Fund.** 800-345-2021.

●**Credit cards.** If you don't carry a balance on your credit card, ask the issuer to waive the annual fee. If the issuer refuses, find another card.

There's always a company offering a teaser rate of perhaps 5.9% for the first six months. Switching from card to card every six months takes effort, but if you have a $5,000 balance, paying 6% instead of 19% will save you about $650 a year.

*Caution:* If you do carry a balance and card hop do so only two or three times, or it can have a negative reflection on your credit report.

Watch out for cards that charge transfer fees…always shop for the next teaser rate at least a month before your current one expires.

Close each account as you stop using it…or the fact that you have got outstanding available credit could hurt your credit rating.

●**Use your credit card instead of your checkbook to pay for your purchases.** This lets you take advantage of the "float," the month-long, interest-free grace period most credit card users get to pay their bills when they don't carry a balance.

Even if that money is invested in a money market fund paying only 5%, the float means a $100 profit each month on $2,000 in monthly credit card spending.

*Caution:* This strategy will work only if you pay your bill in full. If you run a balance, you will forfeit the float...and additional charges will lead to additional interest payments, not savings.

●**Keep your credit card issuer's phone number in your wallet, in your car and at home.** If your wallet is stolen, you're probably responsible for up to $50 in charges. But if you can cancel the card immediately before the thief uses it, you can avoid all charges.

## SAVE BIG ON CLOTHING
### Trisha King

●**Outlet shopping can save you more than 50%.** Outlets that consistently offer excellent discounts...

●**Bugle Boy,** mostly for boys' and men's clothes. You can get great deals on sale items...savings of 20% to 70%. 172 outlets nationwide. 800-421-1240.

●**Carter's,** for baby and children's wear. Savings of 20% to 70%. There are 150 outlets nationwide. 888-782-9548.

●**Nine West,** for women's shoes. There are 151 outlets nationwide. 800-260-2227.

●**Off 5th–Saks Fifth Avenue Outlets,** for high-end men's and women's clothes. Most items sell at about half off retail price. There are 40 outlets nationwide. 212-940-4048.

●**Shop outlets from the back of the store forward.** The best deals are typically buried deep in the store.

●**Order through discount mail-order catalogs.** *My favorites...*

●**Albarene Scottish Cashmere.** 40% to 50% off quality, two-ply, cashmere sweaters, vests and other clothing. 800-843-9078.

●**Holabird Sports.** 20% off current sneakers and racquet sports equipment. 410-687-6400.

●**Sierra Trading Post.** 35% to 70% off men's and women's travel-related clothing. 800-713-4534.

●**Check out high-end resale stores.** You can typically expect to pay one-third of the retail price or less. I once found a $3,000 dress for $195 at Past Perfect, Studio City, California. 818-760-8872. Others...

●**Bailey's,** Pasadena, California. Men's clothing. 626-449-0201...and **Bailey's Back Street.** Women's clothing. 626-449-4101.

●**Cynthia's Consignments,** Lincoln Park, Illinois. Women's clothing only. 773-248-7714.

●**Once Upon a Child,** a national chain carrying both quality used clothing and discontinued new clothing. Also carries some maternity clothes...and slightly used and new baby furniture and children's furniture. 800-476-9249.

*Elsewhere in the US:* Check with the National Association of Resale and Thrift Shops, www.narts.org, for local listings.

## BETTER USED CARS—FOR LESS
### Remar Sutton

New cars lose 40% of their value the moment they're driven off the lot. But buying a used car can save you a bundle. *Here's how...*

●**Find the right car.** You can find a great car through many sources—classified ads, used-car lots, friends buying new cars, even the Internet. But wherever you find a car, always do two things that most people don't...

●**Talk to the previous owner.** Ask how many miles were on the odometer when he/she turned the car in, and what was wrong with the car.

*Important:* Ask *what* was wrong, not *if* anything was wrong. It's a salesperson's trick for getting the scoop.

If the dealer won't provide the previous owner's name, walk away. The only acceptable reason for the dealer not to is if the car was rented or leased. In that case, insist on seeing documents proving that the car was rented or leased.

●**Take the car to an unbiased mechanic.** You will pay up to $100—but it's worth it. Use any problems the mechanic finds as bargaining tools.

●**Negotiate *up* from the vehicle's "loan value," not *down* from the seller's asking price.** Loan value is 80% of the average wholesale price of a clean model, with mileage and options taken into account. Your bank should have this information.

*Example:* If the loan value is $8,000, it's unlikely that the seller will part with the car for less than $10,000. But it's better to start the negotiations low.

●**If you're buying from a dealer, get a good warranty.** It should extend at least 90 days from purchase and cover 100% of the drivetrain.

Short-term warranties like this help only the buyer who gets a lemon. It shouldn't cost extra. Don't mention the warranty until you've settled on a price, or the salesperson may up the asking price.

***Caution:*** So-called "50/50" warranties, which state that the seller and the buyer split repair costs, are often worthless. The 50/50 warranty usually requires the seller to do the repairs. So...an unscrupulous seller will just charge twice as much as he/she should for a repair—leaving the buyer to pay effectively 100% of the cost.

•**Finance your car purchase through a credit union.** Astronomical interest rates—as high as 29%—are not unheard of in the used-car business. But many credit unions charge only 1% to 2% above the typical new-vehicle annual percentage rate, which is currently about 8%.

***Resource:*** Call the Credit Union National Association to see whether you can join. 800-358-5710.

If you can't join a credit union, pay attention to the interest. If it's more than a percentage point or two above the new-car interest rate, don't agree to it.

***Another great option:*** Refinance your mortgage to cover the cost of the car, and pay that portion of the loan off quickly. Or use a home-equity loan or line of credit. These loans are tax-deductible.

•**Avoid used-car leases.** Salespeople are increasingly pushing these, but they're usually bad deals because you can negotiate a better purchase price—and own the car.

# Better Warehouse Buying

Before signing up for a warehouse shopping club, shop a few times with a friend who is a member or on your own trial membership. See if savings are enough to justify

membership costs. Compare prices carefully—buying big quantities does not guarantee the lowest unit price.

If you do join, store items carefully after buying. Divide big packages of meats and canned goods, and freeze them in serving-size portions ...take toiletries out of huge bottles, and pour them into more manageable containers.

***Also:*** Watch out for products near their expiration dates.

Edith Flowers Kilgo, editor, *Creative Downscaling*, Box 1884, Jonesboro, GA 30237.

# Outlets for Great Luxury Products... At Discount Prices

Randy Marks, publisher of *Outlet Bound: Guide to the Nation's Best Outlets.* Outlet Bound.

Many high-end manufacturers are setting up outlet stores—with prices of 25% to 70% off retail stores or catalogs. Shop by mail if you can't get to an outlet. Select items from the store's regular catalog... call the outlet to see if they are discounted. *Key:* Know the items' exact styles.

### WATCHES
•**Movado Company Store**—18 locations. Call 888-688-5382 for the outlet nearest you.

***Recent sale:*** Men's Classic Black Face wristwatch with leather band, $495, retail... $265, outlet.

•**Seiko Factory Store**—11 outlet locations. Call 888-688-5382 for the outlet nearest you.

***Recent sale:*** Ladies Kinetic Sport Watch, $425, retail...$212, outlet.

### LUGGAGE/HANDBAGS
•**The Ghurka Store,** one location, at Woodbury Common, Central Valley, New York.

***Recent sale:*** Bellows large all-leather handbag, $460, retail...$350, outlet.

•**Hartmann Luggage Outlet**—four outlet locations. Call 888-688-5382 for the outlet nearest you.

*Recent sale:* Pack-A-Derm leather travel case, $750, retail…$397, outlet.

•**Hunting World**—one location, at Woodbury Common, Central Valley, New York.

*Recent sale:* Black leather attaché case, $1,300, retail…$919, outlet.

•**Judith Leiber Company Store,** at Desert Hills in Cabazon, California, and Woodbury Common, Central Valley, New York.

*Recent sale:* Women's handbag, $2,010, retail…$1,410, outlet.

### HOME FURNISHINGS

•**West Point Stevens**—44 outlets. Call 888-688-5382 for the outlet nearest you.

*Recent sale:* Burlington goosedown quilt, $300, retail…$67.49, outlet.

•**Sheridan Australia**—one location, at Woodbury Common, Central Valley, New York.

*Recent sale:* Toscana King sheets, $55, retail…$33, outlet.

# Shrewder Shopping in Electronics Store Jungles

Jay Van Rein, a spokesperson for the California Department of Consumer Affairs, who specializes in reviewing and regulating problems with consumer electronic repair warranties.

Trying to get the best deals on high-tech products like TVs, computers, camcorders and other electronics isn't always easy. Helpful…

•**Shop as if you were purchasing a car.** Never accept the price without first making a reasonable offer. Most salespeople have some flexibility.

*Helpful:* Know the "profit margin" of your purchase—what the store is trying to earn above wholesale.

*Typical profit margins:* Video equipment/12%…audio components/14%…stereo speakers/20% to 25%…extended warranties/50% to 60%.

•**Be wary of in-house financing.** Electronics stores' credit cards with low introductory interest rates usually jump to a 20% interest rate or higher, even if you make your payments on time.

•**Learn the language.** Many consumers buy more than they need because the sales staff's technical jargon confuses them.

•**Features worth extra cost…**

•*VCRs:* Remote control with backlit buttons for easier use in dark rooms…skip search to fast forward through commercials.

•*TVs:* Block-out to limit your child's viewing choices…automatic volume control to keep volume from increasing at commercials.

•*Camcorders:* Jack to attach a better microphone…audio and video fades for smoother transitions between scenes.

•*CD players:* Memory buffer that prevents skips when unit is jolted.

•**If you can't get the price down, try negotiating for extras** like free delivery…free installation.

•**Use caution with extended warranties and service contracts.** Mechanical problems usually start when the contract runs out—and the contract often duplicates the manufacturer's warranty. Check if your credit card adds a year to the factory warranty if you charge the purchase on the card.

*Helpful:* If possible, wait for the manufacturer's warranty period to expire before buying a service contract.

*Exception:* Consider an extended warranty or service contract for expensive-to-repair items, like projection TVs.

•**If you buy a service contract…**

•**Study the "abuse" and "misuse" clauses carefully.** The contract may not cover the product if you don't maintain it as directed.

•**See how much coverage you really get.** Is the entire product covered, or just certain parts? Are there hidden fees for labor?

•**Ask to see all policies, promises and warranties in writing.** Many consumers get burned because they don't get all the information they should.

*Example:* A salesperson tells you the store has a 30-day return policy. When you try to return the purchase, you find it must be returned in its original packaging…and can only be exchanged, not refunded.

**Helpful:** Check out the free guide to service contracts at www.pueblo.gsa.gov/cic_text/misc/service-contracts/consumer.txt, the government's consumer information Web site.

# Best Way to Return Unwanted Merchandise

When returning unwanted merchandise, *return receipt* is better than registered mail. This postal service provides a mailing receipt, return receipt and record of delivery—all for less than the cost of registered mail.

Rick Doble, editor, *$avvy Discount$ Newsletter*, Box 96, Smyrna, NC 28579.

# Better Shopping Strategies from Larry Roth

*The Best of Living Cheap News* by Larry Roth, publisher, *Living Cheap News*, San Jose, CA. Contemporary Books.

## Smart Shopping Secret

Don't be self-conscious about asking whether an item will go on sale soon before you buy it. Some stores will not tell you if a sale is planned shortly—but some will and may let you buy the item immediately at the sale price…or put it on hold until the sale starts.

**More from Larry Roth…**

## Beware of Duty-Free Stores

At duty-free stores, some liquor prices are higher than what you will find at home …cologne almost always costs more than at a discount store…and local crafts are not dutiable, so they cannot offer good deals on these items. Duty-free shopping aboard airlines is no better. It is rare if not impossible to find bargains at duty-free stores—and purchases at these stores are just extra things for you to carry home.

# Great Ways to Cut Entertainment Expenses

Andy Dappan, author of *Shattering the Two-Income Myth: Daily Secrets for Living Well on One Income.* Brier Books.

• **College and university events.** Attend lectures, concerts, movies, live performances and sporting events at a fraction of the cost of professional performances. *Helpful:* Contact the student activities center or public events office and ask to be put on the mailing list. If you are enrolled in an accredited course, you'll receive a valid student ID, good for even greater discounts.

• **Movie matinees.** See an early evening show and pay half the price for twice the elbow room. *Also:* Movie theater concession stands charge $3 for 30 cents worth of popcorn, so bring your own refreshments and escape the scalping.

• **Last-minute theater tickets.** Some theaters sell half-price tickets at the box office on show day. Others unload remaining tickets through half-price brokers. *Helpful:* Contact the box office about its policy or look in the *Yellow Pages* under Ticket Brokers.

• **Continuing education classes.** You won't necessarily get credit or a student ID, but the courses provide enlightenment—and entertainment—at very low cost.

• **Hospitality exchanges.** Members are listed in a directory and exchange visits with other members. Besides inexpensive lodging, travelers learn more about the area and culture they are visiting. *Contact:* The Hospitality Exchange, www.goldray.com/hospitality or 406-538-8770…United States Servas, www .servas .org or 212-267-0252.

• **House swap.** Exchange homes with a friend who lives in another city. *Idea:* Each of you develops an itinerary of local favorites for the other to enjoy during the exchange. *Also:* Organized exchange clubs greatly increase your options. *Contact:* HomeLink, www.swap-now.com or 800-638-3841...Trading Homes International, www .trading-homes.com or 800-877-8723...Intervac, www.intervac.org or 800-756-4663.

•**Last-minute travel.** If your schedule is flexible, you can take advantage of last-minute deals offered by airlines, cruise lines, hotels, etc. *Information:* Get a current issue of the newsletter *Best Fares,* which should be available in your local library.

Also, last-minute booking with different travel clubs can save 50% to 70% off the normal fare, but you have to be able to plan quickly. Most clubs charge an annual fee.

*Examples:* Last Minute Travel, 100 Sylvan Rd., Suite 600, Woburn, Massachusetts 01801, 800-527-8646...Vacations To Go, 1502 Augusta Dr., Suite 415, Houston 77057, 800-338-4962.

•**Do lunch.** You'll get the very same food for about half the price of dinner. *Also:* Look for restaurants that offer early bird specials—discounts of 30% to 50% available usually before 6 pm.

•**Join a book club...**or form your own. *How it works:* Each month, members read an agreed-upon book that they discuss in depth during the next meeting. *Benefits:* You'll expand your mind...read and discuss good books...spend less time on frivolous pursuits.

# Making Out on a Markdown

If a store slashes the price of an item shortly after you purchase it, go back and ask to see a manager. Many stores have price-protection policies that apply to their own sales as well as those of other stores. But even stores without formal policies will often refund the difference to keep a customer happy.

*Alternative:* If the store isn't cooperative, simply return the merchandise. Be sure to keep your sales receipt so you get back the full amount you paid. You can then repurchase the item at the lower price.

Corey Sandler, author of *Secrets of the Savvy Consumer.* Prentice Hall.

# Garage Sale Secrets

To hold a high-profit garage sale, think like a retailer. Price items the way stores do—$1.95 sounds cheaper than $2.

The more merchandise you have, the better. Go through every room of your home for items you no longer use or like.

*Top-selling items:* Baby clothes, toys, children's books and computer or video games.

Display everything neatly and tidy up occasionally during the sale. Keep valuables—like jewelry and higher-priced items—near the cash box, so you can watch them.

Cathy Pedigo, whose annual garage sales for the last 12 years have taken in $1,000 a day. Based in Colorado Springs, she is author of *How to Have Big Money Garage Sales.* Winning Edge.

# Beware of Antibacterial Products

These products are often confusingly or misleadingly labeled and advertised. *Examples:* TV ad for antibacterial window cleaner shows it being sprayed on and wiped off, for what seems to be an instant, germ-free shine. But the product's label says it kills germs only when left on for at least 10 minutes. A toothbrush is labeled *antibacterial* in large letters on the front, implying it fights germs in the user's mouth. But fine print on the back says the antibacterial ingredient inhibits bacterial growth on the toothbrush's handle. *Self-defense:* Be skeptical of claims of antibacterial action—and read all labels very carefully. The most important thing you can do is wash your hands with soap and water.

Mitchell Cohen, MD, director, division of bacterial and mycotic diseases, Centers for Disease Control and Prevention, Atlanta.

# Proven Ways to Cut Medication Costs

Val Ulene, MD, a Los Angeles-based physician and author. She and her father, Art Ulene, MD, are coauthors of *How to Cut Your Medical Bills*. Ulysses Press.

Over the last several years, prices of the top-selling prescription medications have climbed rapidly—in many cases, much faster than the rate of inflation.

Fortunately, there are practical ways to keep drug costs down…

•**Request generics.** Generics can cost up to 70% less than their brand-name counterparts. Yet doctors are often hesitant to prescribe generics.

*Reason:* Like many of their patients, they assume medications that *cost* more must be *better.*

That is simply not so. By law, generics and brand names have the same active ingredients. But some generics are *absorbed* up to 20% faster or 20% slower than their brand-name counterparts. For some conditions, such as epilepsy, switching between the generic and the brand-name medication can cause problems.

*Self-defense:* Whenever you start a new medication, ask your doctor to prescribe the generic if appropriate.

•**Opt for over-the-counter (OTC) drugs.** Some prescription drugs—Motrin, for example—are available in lower doses as OTC medications.

In some cases, you will save at least 20% by purchasing the OTC version. The difference in dosage can be made up by taking several non-prescription pills instead of one prescription-strength pill. Ask your doctor if a prescribed medication is available without a prescription—and compare prices.

•**Pick a pharmacy carefully.** People often shop for drugs at the most *convenient* phar-

macy—a costly mistake. A prescription that runs $60 at your neighborhood drugstore might cost half that elsewhere. Big discount chain pharmacies are usually cheapest.

•**Check out mail-order pharmacies.** If you need antidepressants, birth control pills or other medications for chronic conditions, mail order can save you a bundle. Again, call around. Prices also vary significantly among mail-order pharmacies.

**MAIL-ORDER POSSIBILITIES**

•**American Association of Retired Persons (AARP) Pharmacy Service.** For prescription and OTC medications. 800-456-2226.

•**Cystic Fibrosis Services Pharmacy.** Specializes in antibiotics, enzyme supplements, vitamins and other medications that meet the needs of cystic fibrosis sufferers. Many drugs are offered at below wholesale cost. 800-541-4959.

•**Diversified Prescription Delivery.** For prescription and OTC medications. 800-452-1976.

•**Medi-Mail Pharmacy.** For prescription and OTC medications. 800-331-1458.

Mail-order pharmacies aren't suitable for acute infections and other conditions that can change quickly and unpredictably.

*Reason:* By the time the prescription arrives, your condition could be worse.

# More Medication Savings

A prescribed medication may be cheaper than a similar over-the-counter one if the prescribed one is in your insurer's formulary of drugs that qualify for benefits. *Examples:* Prescription treatments for yeast infections and asthma inhalers are available in slightly higher dosages than over-the-counter products, which health insurers never cover. *To reduce your co-pay further:* Ask your doctor to prescribe generic brands where appropriate. *Helpful:* Clip coupons for over-the-counter medications you use, and compare the cost to your co-pay for the prescribed version.

Frank Darras, partner, Shernoff, Bidart, Darras & Arkin, a law firm that specializes in claims against health insurers, 600 S. Indian Hill Blvd., Claremont, CA 91711.

# OTC Drug Savings

Choose over-the-counter (OTC) drugs by price, not brand. Many consumers opt for products whose names they recognize—especially those formerly available by prescription only. *But:* Generic versions contain the same active ingredients, are equally effective and usually cost much less. Compare labels to be certain the same active ingredients are present and in the same percentages. *Warnings:* Inactive ingredients may not be the same—people who are highly allergic or hypersensitive should be cautious when switching brands …ask your pharmacist what interactions an OTC drug may have.

Harold Silverman, PharmD, a pharmacist and health care consultant in Washington, DC, and author of *The Pill Book: The Illustrated Guide to the Most Prescribed Drugs in the United States*. Bantam.

# Buying a Used Boat

Buy used boats in the fall, when availability is high and sellers are anxious. A used boat should cost *at least* 10% less than a comparable new one. Buyers often don't pay extra for upgraded features installed by earlier owners—such as depth finders, automatic pilot and radar equipment. BUC International (800-327-6929) publishes a *Used Boat Price Guide* for various model years. They are used by most dealers, lenders and insurers to establish comparative market values. Buyers should consider using a professional boat surveyor to help evaluate a craft's quality, condition and seaworthiness. An experienced boater or dealership can give you referrals of surveyors in your area. *Cost:* $250 and up.

John Jirsa, yacht broker, Larsen Marine Service, Waukegan, IL.

# Smart Computer Buying

When purchasing a computer, refuse to pay restocking fees, which some retailers charge when you return an unsatisfactory machine.

*Also:* Avoid stores that allow returns only if you exchange the unit for another.

If buying by mail, deal only with a company that will pay the shipping costs if a return is necessary. Get low-price protection from retail stores—if you ask, many will agree to match lower prices you find within a set time after you buy.

Always pay by credit card—the card company can help if you have problems, and some cards double the length of the manufacturer's warranty.

Ira P. Rothken, an attorney specializing in technology and business law, Corte Madera, CA, writing in *Home Office Computing*, 156 W. 56 St., New York 10019.

# How to Buy the Right Mattress

Richard L. Jebber, president of Mattress Warehouse, a 44-store chain in the Midwest, headquartered in Akron, OH. Mattress Warehouse is the sixteenth-largest retailer of bedding in the US, according to the most recent survey by *Furniture/Today* magazine.

There are few home products you'll use as much as your mattress. That makes it very important to shop carefully when buying a new one.

But the $6-billion-a-year US mattress industry doesn't make it easy to shop. That's because most big retailers use a different name for basically the same mattress.

*Reason:* The name-brand manufacturers—Sealy, Serta, Simmons and others—make mattresses to retailers' specifications. The differences among the specifications are minor—such as the build-up materials of the mattress, which get covered anyhow.

But each dealer ends up with a distinct line of mattresses, with model names different than any other dealer's.

Further complicating the picture for consumers are the factory/direct sellers, who make their own mattresses and label them with their own brand names.

*Here's how to pick a quality mattress, regardless of its label...*

●**Coil construction.** Manufacturers use various designs to make the mattress conform to the body...give support...and provide separation from a bed partner.

*Example:* Sealy uses parallel rows of individual coils running head to toe...Serta's rows are each made of one continuous wire...and Simmons inserts each coil into a pocket.

All of these designs do their job. The differences give sales clerks something to talk about. What *does* matter is the *number* of coils in the mattress.

*Best:* If you want a premium mattress, buy one with *at least* 400 coils. The best models have between 600 and 700 coils (based on a full-sized mattress).

●**Wire gauge.** A high coil count alone doesn't guarantee that the mattress will be durable or comfortable, because the coils themselves can be flimsy.

*Best:* Coil wire thickness gauge between 13 and 15½. The *lower* the number, the better.

●**Latex.** If you have an aversion to springs, you can opt for an all-latex mattress—pure foam, no coils. Some people swear they're the most comfortable beds around.

*Downside:* Latex is expensive—around $1,400 for a queen-sized mattress, versus $699 to $999 for a good coil mattress. And it lacks rigidity, which makes it hard to carry a latex mattress.

●**Padding** covers the coils. It used to be made primarily of cotton and stiff foam.

But new high-density foams, made with a higher percentage of pure urethane, are softer and less apt to crumble, as did the old latex and high-clay-content foam. These new foams provide more cushioning from springs. Density of 1.8 is a good standard.

*Best:* You will find "zone foam" available on some better mattresses. Its waffle-like design delivers different levels of firmness for different areas of the body—firmer in the middle for the small of your back, and softer in the hip and shoulder area.

Edge guards help prevent edge breakdown caused by sitting, and they increase sleep space by allowing you to sleep closer to the edge without giving the sensation that you are going to roll off.

●**Softness.** Most mattresses come in three levels—firm, plush and pillow top—with prices increasing in that order.

The differences are based on the amount of padding, as well as the softness of the foam and other materials in the padding. Pillow top—for which an additional cushion is attached to the top and bottom of the mattress—is softest.

Assuming the coil construction is good, buy what feels best to you. All three will protect your back if the mattress is well-constructed, so the comfort level is up to you. Most people seem to prefer plusher models.

*Best:* For a pillow top, the extra layer should be sewn *and* glued to the mattress...so it won't shift.

●**Ticking** is the material that covers the mattress.

*Best:* Look for cotton damask or cotton chintz, as opposed to synthetic materials. Cotton is more durable and more breathable.

●**Box spring.** If you put a new mattress on an old box spring, it is likely to break down sooner. Also, the coil systems in mattresses are designed to work with those of a matching box spring.

*Best:* Pick the mattress you want—and add the box spring that goes with it.

●**Frame.** Look for one made with heavier-gauged steel and wider rollers (approximately 2" to 3") to make cleaning under the bed easier ...and a center support beam that rests on the floor, if you're buying a queen size or larger.

●**Warranty.** Any good mattress will offer a warranty that lasts from 10 to 15 years. But your warranty may be void if you use an old box spring...or if you don't use a mattress pad on top of the mattress to protect it from stains.

*More shopping points...*

●**Buy by the pound if you're overwhelmed by choices.** With mattresses, bigger —and heavier—is usually better. The more springs and padding a mattress has, the more comfortable and durable it is likely to be. To test for weight, pick up a corner.

•**There's no substitute for a leisurely test-snooze.** Ordering by phone is convenient, but only for a spare bed that won't be used much.

Otherwise, try the bed out yourself. If you sleep on your side, lie that way. Use a pillow. And have your partner lie on the bed at the same time, and roll around.

Return policies vary greatly, but since few retailers allow you to return a mattress once you've brought it home, this in-store test-drive is critical—so take your time. Don't worry about dozing off. If you do, buy that mattress.

# Shrewder Shopping for Moisturizers

Paula Begoun, former makeup artist. She is author of *Don't Go to the Cosmetics Counter Without Me, Fourth Edition* and *The Beauty Bible,* both published by Beginning Press.

Despite what many cosmetics companies claim, all any moisturizer can do is add moisture to your skin and help it feel smoother. Most moisturizers—even low-cost ones—do that job very well.

•**Not everyone needs a moisturizer.** Only people with dry or combination oily/dry skin need one—applied only to dry patches. People with oily complexions don't.

•**Typically, a $50 moisturizer is not better than a $10 one.** The ingredients are usually similar.

•**Beware of specialty moisturizers—for eyes, throat, etc.** They are usually similar to most face moisturizers—but usually cost more and you get less.

•**Beware of moisturizers that claim they "firm," "lift" or "energize" skin.** While the products may be good moisturizers, the phrases are usually nothing more than marketing gimmicks.

•**How to apply moisturizers.** Use a mild cleanser like Cetaphil Gentle Skin Cleanser...

blot skin...apply moisturizer to dry spots on slightly damp skin.

### EXTRA-DRY SKIN

Use products that are nongreasy...contain water-binding agents to seal in moisture... have antioxidants to fight environmental damage. *My favorites...*

•**Eucerin Light Moisture Restorative Lotion.** $7.17/8 ounces.

•**L'Oreal Plenitude Overnight Defense.** $10.99/1.7 ounces.

•**Lubriderm Seriously Sensitive Lotion.** $6.75/8 ounces.

### NORMAL-TO-DRY SKIN

Apply lightweight moisturizers that hydrate skin without leaving behind too much oil... contain water-binding agents...no heavy waxes. *My favorites...*

•**Avon Maximum Moisture Super Hydrating Gel.** $10.50/2.5 ounces. *To order:* 800-500-2866.

•**Basis All-Night Face Cream.** $6.95/2 ounces.

•**Neutrogena Healthy Skin Antiwrinkle Cream.** $10.95/1.4 ounces.

### NORMAL-TO-OILY SKIN

Lightweight moisturizing toner that won't clog pores. *My favorites...*

•**Avon Moisturizing Alcohol-Free Toner.** $7.50/6.7 ounces.

•**Nivea Visage Alcohol-Free Moisturizing Toner.** $5.49/6 ounces.

•**Physicians Formula Gentle Refreshing Toner.** $6.95/8 ounces.

# Best Pool-Testing Kits

The least expensive pool-testing kits do everything pool owners need—for about $5. Higher-priced kits—up to $20—tend to be harder to use and include unnecessary extras. *Helpful for pool owners:* Do not use chemicals left over from last year's kit. Do not use a kit after its expiration date. If buying a liquid kit, avoid *round* sample holders—they make it harder to read the test.

Sandy Kuzmich, PhD, director, chemistry department, Good Housekeeping Institute, quoted in *Good Housekeeping*, 959 Eighth Ave., New York 10019.

# Best Ways to Earn Frequent-Flier Miles... On the Ground

Randy Petersen, publisher, *InsideFlyer*, 4715-C Town Center Dr., Colorado Springs 80916. He is also editor of *The Official Frequent Flyer Guidebook*. Randy Petersen Publishing.

You know you can use a credit card with a tie-in to an airline to earn miles, or you can get them through car rentals and hotel stays. But there are many other programs to consider...

•**Long-distance phone service.** Today, every major airline has a tie-in with a long-distance phone service provider. Generally, these programs award five miles per dollar spent.

*Key:* To be eligible for a long-distance awards program, you must register for the long-distance program offered by your frequent-flier program.

•**Flowers.** You can earn 300 miles with United Airlines for each order of $30 or more purchased through 800-FLOWERS (800-356-9377).

FTD Direct (800-736-3383) has a similar deal with United Airlines, but you also will receive an extra 100 miles for every $10 you spend over $29.95.

The Flower Club (800-800-7363) gets you miles with Continental, Northwest, US Airways, TWA and others.

•**Home mortgages.** American Airlines' AAdvantage Program for Mortgages (800-852-9744) offers 1,000 miles for every $10,000 borrowed —if you get the loan through a participating lender.

TWA offers the opportunity to earn up to 125,000 Aviator Miles by selling or buying a home through Better Homes and Gardens Real Estate—which has offices in 34 states. Call 800-654-5409 *before* you list your property for sale.

Delta Airlines HouseMiles Program allows members to earn 1,000 miles for every $10,000 borrowed from the North American Mortgage Company for a home purchase or refinancing. There is no limit on miles. 800-759-0306.

United MileagePlus allows members to earn miles when refinancing their homes in almost all states. Members can earn 1,000 miles for every $10,000 borrowed—up to 109,000 miles—through real estate transactions via a participating broker. 800-421-4655.

•**Dining programs.** All major airlines give you miles when you dine at selected restaurants. But you have to sign up for the dining program to receive miles. Call the frequent-flier program of the airline in which you are interested to learn more about its dining program.

# Health Care Credit Card Trap

Don't sign up for health care credit cards—or any other credit cards—without checking the interest rate very, very carefully. Some companies are offering these cards expressly for paying health care expenses not covered by insurance—and are charging sky-high interest rates.

*Better alternative:* Try to arrange an affordable payment plan directly with your health care provider. If that isn't possible, most providers today accept payment via regular credit cards, which have much lower interest rates than these "dedicated" cards that are mainly dedicated to enriching their issuers.

Gerri Detweiler, education adviser, Debt Counselors of America, a nonprofit organization, Box 8587, Gaithersburg, MD 20898. She is coauthor of *Invest in Yourself: Six Secrets to a Rich Life* (John Wiley & Sons) and *Debt Consolidation 101: Strategies for Saving Money and Paying Off Debts Faster* (Good Advice Press).

# Safety on the Internet

Not one credit card theft has been reported in the past year for cards processed using encryption technology built into Netscape Navigator and Microsoft Explorer browsers. This makes Internet commerce safer than giving a credit card to someone at a store or a restaurant.

*Caution:* You still must deal with a known and trusted merchant to ensure that your card number is stored safely in the vendor's computer.

Robert McKinley, president, CardWeb, Inc., Box 3966, 1270 Fairfield Rd., Suite 51, Gettysburg, PA 17325. He is also publisher of *CardTrak,* a newsletter listing the best credit card deals in the US.

# Simple Self-Defense Against Internet Retail Rip-Offs

Jim and Audri Lanford, publishers of the free E-newsletter *Internet ScamBusters* (www.scambusters.org). They lecture throughout the US about how to avoid Internet fraud and scams.

People frequently ask us whether Internet shopping is safe. *Our response:* As long as you use secure browser software—with encryption features such as Secure Sockets Layer (SSL) or Secure Electronic Transaction (SET)—giving out credit card information to reputable, on-line retailers is at least as safe as using your card at a restaurant or department store.

But—there are traps that can be costly. *Here are the big ones—and how to protect yourself...*

• **On-line shopping can sometimes cost you more than retail.** Generally, on-line shopping is about convenience—not the lowest prices. If you get a better price on-line than retail for a product, make sure shipping and handling fees don't wipe out your savings.

*Best bargain sites:* The best buys on the Internet are usually found at sites for travel and accommodations. *Examples...*

• **www.priceline.com** enables you to submit your lowest-fare bid to a network of airlines and travel packagers to see who will meet your price. You can get amazing fares this way—but you won't get frequent-flier miles or much choice of flight times and connections on your day of travel.

• **www.bbchannel.com** has the largest, most detailed listing of bed and breakfasts, and includes direct E-mail addresses to property owners around the world.

• **www.usairways.com** offers frequent fliers of US Airways "e-savers"—a list of weekly bargains on domestic and international flights.

• **Products you receive may not be what you expected.** Watch out for glowing product descriptions with poor photographs—or none at all. Ask for a paper catalog or brochure to get an idea of merchandise. And, don't assume that a good-looking site means the retailer sells quality goods.

*Caution:* Fees for returned merchandise run as high as 15% of the product's price on some sites. Determine the company's refund and return policies before you place your order.

*Self-defense:* Pay by credit card. If you encounter a problem and the company won't fix it, you can notify the bank that issues your credit card, and you won't have to pay the charge while your dispute is being investigated. And, if the company doesn't deliver the item or is running a scam, you are in a much better position to get your money back. Check with your credit card company for additional warranty or purchase-protection benefits.

Also visit www.bizrate.com. It critiques the service and reliability of more than 500 Internet retailers.

• **On-line auctions offer great deals for many products—but some are unreliable.** To help ensure that an auction Web site delivers its goods as promised, make sure the site you use has bulletin boards where buyers are free to rate sellers and post good and bad experiences about merchandise received.

*Examples:* www.auctionuniverse.com and www.ebay.com.

The most reliable auction sites typically sell name-brand products still under warranty, such as refurbished computers and electronic equipment.

*Example:* www.onsale.com.

Generally, be wary of collectibles and antique sites unless the seller lives in your area. Otherwise, you have no way of verifying the condition and the value of the merchandise before you buy it.

*Helpful:* If you find a site you like, but are concerned about its reliability, consider an on-line escrow service to serve as a middleman. The service holds your payment, usually charging you a fee—up to 5%—until you receive and are satisfied with your purchase.

*Example:* www.iescrow.com.

• **Customer service is spotty.** *Biggest complaints:* No response to E-mail queries about purchased products…shipping delays…products were damaged or not received at all.

*Self-defense:* Get the retailer's street address and alternate contact number—not just its E-mail address. Typically, the Web sites with the best customer service are on-line mail-order companies with established toll-free numbers.

*Examples:* www.1800flowers.com, 800-FLOWERS…www.towerrecords.com, 800-ASK-TOWER.

*Important:* Keep a hard copy of your purchase order and confirmation number. The law treats on-line purchases the same way as mail and telephone orders. Unless otherwise stated, merchandise must be delivered within 30 days, and if there are delays, the company must notify you.

*To complain:* Contact The National Fraud Information Center at www.fraud.org—you can file a complaint, read other complaints and get contact information about your state attorney general's office.

• **Many Internet retailers sell personal information they receive from you.** *To protect your privacy and avoid lots of junk E-mail…*

• **Don't fill out on-line surveys** asking for your age…income…etc.—even if it seems like it's mandatory. It's not.

• **Don't purchase from bulk E-mailers.** They are the most likely to send you junk E-mail—and to scam you.

• **Look for a company's on-line privacy policy.** It should disclose what information is being collected on the Web site and how that information is being used.

• **Check the appropriate boxes to forbid Web vendors from sharing your personal information with others.** If you don't, Web retailers assume you want to be contacted or have your information shared.

*Helpful:* Visit the Scam Check Station, at www.scambusters.org/scamcheck.html, for a list of scams to look out for and resources to help you avoid getting ripped off.

*Resource:* The free brochure, *The ABC's of Privacy,* about personal privacy on-line, published by Call for Action, a nonprofit network of consumer hotlines. www.callforaction.org or 800-647-1756.

# This Internet Scam Could Cost You Big Bucks

Unauthorized Internet charges on credit and debit card statements are on the rise.

Thieves acquire credit/debit card account numbers…then use them to charge cardholders for Internet services they didn't order—a scam that has cost consumers millions of dollars.

*Warning signs:* On your statement, unfamiliar businesses with an 800 number, followed by a charge. Special concern—charges of $19.95, identical to some on-line services' monthly fees. *Aim:* For you to confuse the bogus charges for on-line service fees.

*Self-defense:* Write to card issuers for reimbursement within 60 days of discovering the problem.

Paul Luehr, an attorney and assistant director of marketing practices for the Federal Trade Commission, Washington, DC.

# How Not to Lose the Telemarketing Wars

A quick way to cut the number of dinnertime telemarketing calls is to get on the *do not call list* that's legally required of every tele-marketer except nonprofits, political action committees and public opinion polls.

**Bonus:** If a telemarketer calls after you have asked to be put on its list, the company is subject to penalties—which *you* can collect. Steps to follow...

● **Put a notepad next to each phone.**

● **As soon as a caller begins the sales pitch, write down the date and time.** Interrupt to ask for the caller's name, the company's name and its address. Write these down, too.

● **Then ask to be added to the company's *do not call* list.** If you receive another call from the same company, send it a certified-return-receipt letter requesting payment of fines—$500 for calling again and $500 for any other violation, such as calling before 8 am or after 9 pm. Include a copy of the notes taken during their calls.

● **If you don't get a positive response to your complaint,** you have the option of filing suit in small claims court.

*Barbara Joyce, consumer advocate in Rockville, MD, who has collected more than $5,000 from telemarketers who called after she had asked to be placed on their* do not call *lists.*

# Phone Bill Checkup

Telephone cramming slips extra charges for unwanted services like voice mail and pagers onto your telephone bill. The charges usually run $5 to $30 per month—and some customers may not even notice them for months. Crammers may use sweepstakes entry forms, phone solicitation or even forgery to bill you for extra services. *Self-defense:* Check your phone bill carefully every month. Call your local phone company immediately if you notice any charges for unwanted services.

*Bob Spangler, deputy chief, enforcement division, FCC Common Carrier Bureau, 2025 M St. NW, Washington, DC 20554.*

# How to Win the Phone Card Game

Prepaid phone cards are the cheapest way of calling long distance when you're away from home. *Caution:* Different cards charge time differently.

**Self-defense:** Find out whether a minimum time is charged for each call...whether the first minute is charged at a higher rate...whether you pay for time used before the connection is made. Generally, the more minutes you buy, the lower the cost per minute—down to about 10¢ per minute.

**Cheapest of all:** Free phone cards with five minutes or so of phone time. Retailers often offer them as premiums. Check ads in Sunday newspapers.

*Marc Ostrofsky, publisher,* Telecard World, *Box 42375, Houston 77242.*

# Samuel Simon on Cutting The Cost of Phone Calls

*Samuel Simon, Esq., chairman, Telecommunications Research and Action Center, a consumer group. Box 27279, Washington, DC 20005.*

## High Directory Assistance Charges

Some telephone companies are charging more for directory assistance within your own area code than your local Baby Bell.

In most parts of the US, directory-assistance services are competing with Baby Bell (411) directory services—sometimes charging nearly seven times more.

**Example:** Los Angeles consumers who make 10 local directory-assistance calls a month through 411 pay $1.25...$9.50, if they use AT&T 00 Info directory service...$9.99, if they use MCI's 10-10-9000. *Key:* Although 00 Info and 10-10-9000 are competitively priced for long-distance directory assistance (1-area code-555-1212), 411 is usually lowest for local service.

*Caution:* Some services offering to connect your directory-assistance call for free charge their highest per minute rates if you accept this connection.

---

**More from Samuel Simon...**

## Prepaid Air Time Provides Savings

To save on cellular phone charges, pay for air time in advance. Prepaid calling plans let you buy up to $100 of air time up front. The average rate is about 65 cents per minute—and some plans charge considerably less.

*Caution:* Though costs are low, prepaid time expires quickly—usually within 30 to 60 days. So prepay only for time you are sure to use. Prepaid cards are available from service providers and at some drugstores and other retail locations.

---

**And Finally from Samuel Simon...**

## Long-Distance Telephoning Trap

Calls between 5 pm and 7 pm are no longer charged at less-expensive "evening rates." And most calls after 11 pm are no longer charged at even lower "night rates."

*Bottom line:* Major discounts may be limited to weekends. Check with your long-distance carrier for details.

---

# News from Call for Action

Call for Action, a nonprofit consumer fraud mediation organization, 5272 River Rd., Bethesda, MD 20816.

---

### Area Code Scam

Ordinary-looking area codes may connect you to foreign countries. Thieves know the codes look innocent and often set up scams on that basis. *Example:* 809 connects to most Caribbean countries. US laws don't always apply when you are a victim of an international phone scam. *Self-defense:* Call the operator or check your phone book before calling an unfamiliar area code. If you want to block international calls, contact your local and long-distance carriers.

---

**More from Call for Action...**

## 500 Numbers Are Not Toll Free

Phone numbers starting with 500 are *follow-me* numbers. They can be forwarded to several different places. The 500 looks like an area code—it comes before the number itself. *Example:* Your call may go first to a person's home, then to a business and then to a cellular phone. If you call a 500 number, you pay for the call—unlike 800 and 888 numbers, where the recipient pays.

---

# Phone Company Scam Alert

Never cash an unsolicited check from a phone company unless you want to make it your long-distance carrier.

*Trap:* By cashing the check, you agree to transfer your business to the company that sent it, and let it enroll you in an assigned billing plan. If the plan doesn't meet your needs, bigger phone bills that follow may more than offset the value of the check.

*Warning:* The big phone companies are just this side of the law with this "unsolicited check" marketing ploy. It's as near as they can legally come to "slamming"—unauthorized switching of long-distance carriers.

Remember they make money off the checks they send out. Otherwise they wouldn't do it.

Harry Newton, editor-at-large, *Teleconnect,* 12 W. 21 St., New York 10010.

---

# Beware of Funeral Scams

To avoid funeral home scams when a relative dies, bring a clergyman or relative to protect you from high-pressure sales tactics. Ask for an itemized price list showing charges for each service—the funeral director legally must give you one. Find a discount casket dealer—they can ship a casket within 24 hours for much less than funeral homes charge, and the funeral director is legally required to let you use it. Understand that embalming is never required—refrigeration is fine, and costs much less. Consider cremation, which costs about one-tenth the cost of an average funeral-parlor funeral. *For more information:* Funeral and Memorial Societies of America, *www.funerals.org/famsa.*

Lisa Carlson, director, Funeral and Memorial Societies of America, Box 10, Hinesburg, VT 05461. Ms. Carlson is author of *Caring for the Dead.* Upper Access Book Publishers.

# Is the Government Holding Your Assets?

Mark Tofal, consumer advocate specializing in unclaimed asset issues. He is author of *Unclaimed Assets: Money the Government Owes You.* 800-247-6553.

State and federal governments are holding about $300 billion in unclaimed assets. One in every four Americans is owed part of it.

The money is sitting in dormant bank and investment accounts, forgotten insurance policies, unknown inheritances, unrefunded utility deposits, uncashed Social Security checks... and literally *dozens* of other sources.

Government agencies are supposed to make a good-faith effort to track down the owners or rightful heirs. But we have to question whether they're even trying. Why should they? If they don't find you, bureaucrats get to spend the money.

To get what's yours, you'll have to uncover the cash on your own. *Where to start...*

**STATE GOVERNMENT**

●**State offices of unclaimed property.** Each state (and the District of Columbia) has one. Any state where you—or your family members—have lived, worked or done business could conceivably be holding your cash.

*Example:* If you currently reside in Florida but formerly worked in New York and attended school in Massachusetts, contact all three. If your potential benefactors held investments or insurance policies with a company headquartered in Chicago, contact the State of Illinois as well.

Most states prefer letters to phone calls. A complete list of state offices of unclaimed property and a sample letter of inquiry are available at www.unclaimedassets.com. Links to a growing number of states with searchable missing-owner databases on-line are also provided. But beware—the underlying search engines can be very sensitive, and because these listings often comprise just a fraction of what's available for claim, writing is still the best policy.

*Important:* Include in your letter any variations on your name, such as maiden name or previous married names, middle name, nicknames, even initials and common misspellings, as well as your Social Security number. Do the same for your parents and other members of your family.

*Helpful:* Check states like Massachusetts, New York and Delaware—even if no family members have ever lived there. Many financial services firms and major corporations are legally registered in these states.

**FEDERAL GOVERNMENT**

The federal government has no central repository for unclaimed funds. To see if you're owed money, you'll have to contact individual agencies directly.

Consider querying any of the following that might be holding funds owed you, either as the original owner or rightful heir. Once again, it is generally better to make search requests in writing, except when dealing with particularly large agencies that have local service centers or branch offices, like the IRS and the Social Security Administration.

●**Social Security Administration.** If you lost or missed a check, call 800-772-1213—or contact your local office. You may also want to request a Personal Earnings and Benefit Estimate Statement (PEBES), to ensure all payroll deductions have been properly credited to your account. The SSA's "suspense file" of uncredited earnings and unpaid benefits currently totals more than $250 billion.

• **Internal Revenue Service.** If your records indicate a refund check was never received or deposited, call the IRS at 800-829-1040...or write your local service center (where you mail your tax returns).

• **Federal Deposit Insurance Corporation.** If you had savings in an insured institution but never collected, start by contacting your state unclaimed property office. They take custody for an initial 10-year period.

If the closure occurred more than 10 years ago—or if the state never got the money—contact the FDIC at the Division of Compliance & Consumer Affairs, 550 17 St. NW, Washington, DC 20429, www.fdic.gov.

Assets from failed credit unions are handled by the National Credit Union Administration (NCUA), 4807 Spicewood Springs Rd., Suite 5100, Austin, Texas 78759-8490, www.ncua.gov.

• **Department of Housing & Urban Development.** HUD owes some 60,000 home owners about $1,000 each in excess mortgage insurance premium payments made on FHA-insured loans.

Request Form 27050-B from HUD Disbursements Branch, Box 44372, Washington, DC 20026-4372.

You can also call 800-697-6967 or visit www.hud.gov for a detailed explanation and basic search.

• **Pension Benefit Guaranty Corporation.** More than 50,000 private pensions are insured by this agency. So if a company goes out of business or otherwise has an underfunded pension plan, do not necessarily assume all retirement benefits are lost.

Write PBGC Search Program, 1200 K St. NW, Suite 930, Washington, DC 20005-4026...visit www.pbgc.gov...or call 800-326-5678.

# Your Rights Against a Collection Agency

To stop harassment by a collection agency, write the agency and demand it stop calls and other troublesome activities. A copy should also go to the creditor. Under federal law, the activities must stop. *Other laws affecting collection:* Collectors must keep your debts private—they may contact others to try to find you but may not indicate that they are trying to collect a debt. They must send you written notice of the debt within five days of contacting you. They can't threaten, lie or use profanity.

David Gilbert, partner, Mintz, Levin, Cohn, Ferris, Glovsky & Popeo, PC, 1 Financial Center, Boston 02111.

# When to Take Your Case to Small-Claims Court...Winners' Secrets

Ralph Warner, Esq., author of *Everybody's Guide to Small Claims Court.* Nolo Press.

The man you hired to paint your house while you were away cashed your deposit but never got his paintbrush near the house, as far as you can tell.

And the dry cleaner has refused over and over again to compensate you for the suede coat it ruined.

You have two good claims here. They probably fall into the category of "small claims," which you can take to small-claims court on your own. *Here's how to go about it...*

### THE BASICS

In small-claims court, your case is heard and decided quickly, in a matter of weeks or months from the time you fill out the complaint form.

You don't need to hire a lawyer to take a case to small-claims court—although in most states you can use one if you choose.

The cost of bringing a small-claims case is modest, usually about $10 to $25 for the court filing fee depending on your state.

***Limitation:*** You can only sue in small-claims court for up to a certain dollar amount that is set by your state's law. This limited amount is what makes the suit a "small" claim.

***Example:*** The top amount of money you can seek in small-claims court is only $1,500 in Kentucky.

This situation is quickly changing. The dollar limits on small claims have increased in recent years in many states. Today, "small" can be fairly large—it goes up to $7,500 in Alaska and Minnesota, for example. Some states are even trying to raise the limit to $20,000.

### BEFORE YOU BEGIN

Make sure it's worth your time and effort to take a case to court. *Consider...*

●**Do you have a solid case?** To win, you'll have to be able to *prove* your claim.

●**Have you acted promptly?** You must start your action within a certain time—depending on your state's law.

You can't put off going to court indefinitely, even if you preserve all your evidence. The time limit for court action depends on the type of case. You may have only a year from a personal injury to launch court action—but up to four years from the date a contract is broken to sue. Check your state's law carefully before you run to court.

●**Do you know whom to sue?** You must name the correct parties in court papers.

***Example:*** If the case involves a car, you'd better know who the *owner* of the car is and not just the name of the driver.

●**Will you be able to collect the money if you win a judgment in court?** Don't waste your time on a lawsuit just to score a paper victory. If the company that owes you money has gone into bankruptcy, you probably won't get your money back even though the court says you should. But if you're suing someone with a job, you will be able to get a small amount from his/her paychecks.

### NUTS AND BOLTS

Assuming that you have concluded that the case is worth pursuing, make sure to follow these key rules...

●**Keep your claim within the court's dollar limits.** If your state allows a small-claims suit for up to only $2,500 and your loss is $3,000, you're not out of luck. You can cut down your claim to fit the limit. Of course, doing so means you forever lose the right to seek that $500 difference.

Alternatively, you may be able to split a claim into two or more suits to fit the limit. This will not work if they're based on the same claim, but may work if there are independent claims.

●**Figure the amount of your loss.** If a coat you've owned for several years is lost or damaged, is your loss what you paid for the coat—or what the coat is worth today?

Generally, you can only recover the current value of a lost article (not what you paid for it). If the coat is damaged, you can recover what it would cost to repair it.

●**State your claim correctly.** Fill in all the information asked by the plaintiff's statement that you get from the clerk of the court.

Usually, you have to boil things down to a single simple sentence, such as, "I paid $1,000 to get new storm windows that were never delivered."

You may have to attach certain evidence—such as a bill—to your claim.

●**Prepare for court.** It is essential that you accumulate convincing evidence and present it effectively.

***Strategy:*** Start with the end of your story—what really happened. And then work backward to pull in key points.

●**Try other means to settle your dispute.** Even if you have a great case and think you'll win, there are other ways to do so without going to court.

You may be able to settle the dispute by talking things through. Negotiation can give you partial relief and, as the saying goes, a half a loaf may be better than trying for a whole one.

●**Start the ball rolling by sending a formal "demand" letter.** In it state your claim and demand payment. Be sure to send the letter by certified or registered mail to have proof that you've taken this step.

●**Consider mediation.** In a mediation procedure, a neutral party tries to arrive at some middle ground. Some states require that mediation be used before a case can even be considered by the court.

In some states, binding arbitration is permitted. That is similar to mediation except the decision of the neutral party must be accepted by both sides and can't be appealed.

Even if you start a court case, you can still agree to a settlement at any time.

Keep the channels of communication open. You have no guarantee of victory before the judge, so a settlement may be in your best interest.

## Sweepstakes: Worth It Or Not?

When evaluating sweepstakes mailings, make sure rules and instructions are easy to understand—throw out anything unclear or contradictory. Be sure no purchase is needed to win. Look for a grand prize awarded to one winner, not a shared or pooled grand prize. A shared prize can be worth only a few cents. Check your odds of winning. Look at indicia—a notice that you may have won probably means little if sent by bulk mail instead of first class. Avoid any sweepstakes requiring you to pay shipping or handling charges or claiming you must pay taxes on winnings to the sponsor. Taxes are paid only to the IRS.

*Marsha Goldberger, spokesperson, Direct Marketing Association, 1111 19 St. NW, Suite 1100, Washington, DC 20036.*

## Foreign Lottery Trap

Foreign-lottery scams claim people have won or may win money in another country, but you must send cash to get the winning tickets—and then your cash disappears.

***Self-defense:*** Never believe any claim about a foreign lottery.

***Remember:*** It is illegal to transmit lottery materials through the US mail.

*Council of Better Business Bureaus, Inc., Arlington, VA.*

# 14

# Better Estate Planning

## Newest Strategies In Estate Planning

The smartest new strategies in estate planning not only reduce the tax bite, they also give you much more flexibility and control over your assets— now and even after you die—than if you simply leave them to heirs through bequests in a will.

With careful planning, you can even give assets away, yet continue to use them—or get them back, should you need them in old age.

*Best techniques available today...*

### TUITION PLAN PLANNING

The majority of states now offer, or are considering offering, qualified state tuition savings programs.

This is an ideal way for affluent people with several grandchildren or other beneficiaries to achieve three goals at once...

• **Put away money** for their grandchildren's educations. (The money is deposited in which-

ever financial institution has been selected by the state. Each state has its own program.)

• **Reduce the income tax bite** on the earnings from the money that is contributed.

• **Get money** out of their taxable estates.

***Example:*** New York State allows contributions of as much as $100,000 per beneficiary and does not limit the program to New York residents. And federal tax law *(Internal Revenue Code Section* 529[c]*)* allows taxpayers to elect to treat tuition plan contributions as if they had been made in equal annual payments over five years for gift tax purposes.

That means a couple could give the maximum of $100,000 per grandchild free of federal gift and estate tax consequences because each individual is entitled to an annual exclusion on gifts of up to $10,000 apiece ($20,000 joint) to as many recipients as he/she likes.

Unlike gifts made through the *Uniform Transfers to Minors Act,* the donor retains con-

---

Gideon Rothschild, Esq., CPA, a frequent lecturer on estate planning and a partner in the law firm Moses & Singer LLP, 1301 Avenue of the Americas, New York 10019.

trol over the money in the tuition plan savings programs.

If a child does not need the money—say he wins an athletic scholarship or does not go to college—the beneficiary can be changed. Should the grandparent need it himself, he can withdraw the money, but he will have to pay any income taxes on the earnings and at least a 10% penalty.

If all goes as expected, however, the money will grow on a tax-deferred basis. Then when withdrawals are made for qualified education expenses, taxes on the income will be due at the student's rate, not the donor's. And the donors will have moved $100,000 per grandchild out of their taxable estates. For a couple with a number of grandchildren, that can really add up.

***Drawback:*** The donor can't control the investments. The state determines how the money is invested. (There are no performance guarantees.)

### FAMILY LIMITED PARTNERSHIPS

Although family limited partnerships are often thought of in connection with family businesses, I have been quite successful in using them for marketable securities and real estate, as well.

***How they work:*** Partnership papers are drawn up, and assets are transferred to the partnership. The general partner or partners retain a 1% ownership and control over the assets. The general partner can give away the remaining 99% of the limited partners' units to family members immediately or over time.

Because the limited partners have no control over their assets—they cannot sell or exchange them—the value of those assets is less than the value of a no-strings-attached gift of the underlying assets. Therefore, for gift tax purposes, the value of the gift is discounted.

Say a couple put $25,000 of securities into a family limited partnership. Their child's 99% share would be worth $24,750. With the discount the child's share might be valued at $20,000 or less, qualifying for the couple's annual gift tax exclusions of $10,000 each ($20,000 joint).

In practice, given the legal costs involved in setting up a partnership and the annual legal and accounting costs involved, this technique is attractive only when greater amounts are also involved. It works well if the amounts given are more than $100,000.

It can be a very advantageous way to transfer money to heirs at today's discounted values, rather than leaving securities to grow in one's own account, thus setting the stage for a large estate tax bill.

***Caution 1:*** The Clinton administration wants to bar passive investments from being discounted. So if you want to take advantage of this strategy, act now. And it is not enough simply to set up the partnership. The assets have to be transferred and the partnership interests given as well.

***Caution 2:*** Be prepared for an IRS challenge on the discount. Nevertheless, the IRS has been settling quite favorably, often allowing discounts of 20% to 40%, especially when there is a nontax reason for the partnership, such as keeping control of assets in the hands of a responsible adult.

### QUALIFIED PERSONAL RESIDENCE TRUSTS

Senior family members can transfer their principal residence or vacation home to their children at reduced tax cost by putting it in a qualified personal residence trust. The parents continue to live in the home, or to manage the vacation home, for the term of the trust. At the end of the trust's term, the children (or a continuing trust for the benefit of the children) own the property. Generally, however, the parents can rent it from their children.

If the rents are structured properly, that gets more money out of the taxable estate. If parents are worried that the rent might be too expensive, this technique might best be reserved for vacation homes.

***Caution 3:*** This is another loophole that the Clinton administration wants to close, so people who delay may lose the opportunity.

### SALES TO GRANTOR TRUSTS

Another technique involves selling, rather than giving, assets to a grantor trust. If the trust is set up properly pursuant to certain specific provisions of the Internal Revenue Code, the appreciation on the assets will not be included in your estate, even though you pay income tax on the trust's income.

Say you are involved in a start-up company with a hot new product or service. You have $2 million of stock today that you expect to be worth $100 million someday. You can sell it to the trust and hold a promissory note calling for interest payments of 5% a year, but no payment of principal for 20 years.

This strategy allows you to use leverage to get assets out of your estate, and because you have sold them, rather than having given them, you are not liable for gift tax during your life nor have you used any of your unified gift and estate tax credit. This can also be used in combination with a family limited partnership for further leverage.

# David Rhine On Minimizing Estate Taxes

David S. Rhine, CPA, partner and national director of Family Wealth Planning, BDO Seidman, LLP, 330 Madison Ave., New York 10017.

## Save Gift and Estate Taxes: Give Your House to Your Kids

For most home owners, the problem of capital gains on the sale of a residence has been eliminated because of the new $250,000/$500,000 home sale exclusion.

However, estate taxes on the family home may still be a problem if the value of all of your assets is more than the amount exempt from estate tax. In 1999, $650,000 is exempt from estate tax ($675,000 in 2000)—rising to $1 million by 2006.

If you are concerned about estate taxes eating into your children's inheritance, there may be a way for you to have your cake and eat it too.

• You can continue to live in the house for as long as you want.

• The transfer tax costs are greatly reduced. It is much less costly to transfer the house now than to leave it to your children later.

The way to achieve these objectives is with a qualified personal residence trust (QPRT).

### PARTICULARS OF QPRTs

A QPRT is an IRS-sanctioned trust in which the only asset (with limited exceptions) is a personal residence. It can be a principal residence or a vacation home.

The trust is set to run for a term of years. In order to maximize the benefit of a QPRT, the term of the trust should be long enough to reduce the value of the gift but short enough so that you are expected to outlive the term. During that term, you continue to live in the home and are treated as the owner. At the end of the term, the home becomes the property of the beneficiaries you have named, typically your children or a trust. At that point, if you want to continue living in the home, you can rent it at a fair rental amount.

You can't buy the home back from the trust beyond the end of the QPRT term or at any time when the trust is a grantor trust.

When the trust is created, you are treated as making a gift of the remainder interest in the home to your beneficiary. The value of that gift essentially is the value of the home minus the value of the interest you've kept (that is— the right to live in it for a certain number of years). The value of your retained interest is figured using special IRS tables.

*Example:* If you are 55, the home is worth $500,000 and a 5.4% interest rate is used, then the value of the gift is only $257,905 for a 10-year trust…or only $175,490 for a 15-year trust.

Gift tax on the gift can be offset by your applicable exclusion amount—the same amount your estate is entitled to at death—so there may be no out-of-pocket tax cost.

*Strategy:* Get a professional appraisal for the value of the home when creating a QPRT. It may well be that the appraisal will support a lower value than you may have arrived at on your own.

### IMPACT OF THE QPRT

If you die during the term you've retained, it's as if you had not made the trust. Your house is included in your estate as if no transfer had been made.

If you outlive the trust term, your children will own the home at a very low transfer tax cost.

***Rule of thumb:*** The longer the retained interest to the home owner, the smaller the gift to the children. But older home owners who choose long trust terms are gambling with the chance that they won't outlive the term they've retained.

### PLANNING WITH QPRTs

If a principal residence is placed in a QPRT, a parent can effectively transfer *liquid* assets to a child.

***How:*** The home is sold near the end of the trust's term to someone other than the grantor. The sale qualifies for the home sale exclusion since the parent is treated as the owner.

The trust, which now holds *cash,* becomes a Grantor Retained Annuity Trust (GRAT) under the terms of the QPRT.

The cash is invested to pay the parent an annuity for the remainder of the trust. When the trust terminates, the child receives the "liquid" assets held by the trust with no further transfer tax costs.

***Caution:*** Even though you could create a QPRT with a vacation home, the home sale exclusion applies only to a principal residence.

***New homes:*** Instead of holding the cash from the home's sale, the trust can buy another home allowing the owner to move.

***Who can benefit:*** Persons with no estate tax liability don't need a QPRT. But those with potentially taxable small and midsized estates who do not have liquid assets they can afford to give away may want to consider the QPRT.

***Bottom line:*** QPRTs are most attractive when interest rates are high. At lower rates, the value of the gift is larger—because the value of the retained interest is smaller.

On the other hand, lower interest rates help to push up home prices, so it becomes more important to find tax-efficient ways to transfer the home.

And, rising property values mean that the benefit from a QPRT is even greater because the gift tax is figured on what the home is worth at the time, not what it will be worth when the beneficiary receives it.

***Caution:*** QPRTs must meet strict requirements, so consult a knowledgeable tax adviser.

---

More from David Rhine...

## Executors: How to Avoid Big Liability for Estate Taxes

The executor of an estate can be held *personally liable* for an estate's taxes that remain unpaid after the estate's assets are distributed to heirs.

***Trap:*** The IRS has three years after an estate's tax return is filed to audit the return and impose extra taxes.

So an executor who distributes all of an estate's assets before then risks incurring personal liability for taxes the IRS may impose later. However, a delay may make heirs very unhappy.

***Solution:*** Ask the IRS for an *early discharge* of personal liability for the estate's taxes. The IRS then has just *nine months* to notify you of the amount of tax the estate owes. The IRS can still impose additional taxes later—but you won't be personally liable for them.

To obtain an early discharge, write the IRS a brief letter that identifies the estate you are representing, and which requests "a determination of estate tax due and discharge from personal liability therefrom."

***Caution:*** Using a living trust won't help—the trustee is treated as the executor and can also be personally liable.

---

# Two Trusts That Take Good Care Of Children and Grandchildren

Alfred Cavallaro, Esq., CPA, 630 Fifth Ave., Suite 2162, New York 10111. Mr. Cavallaro, a former adjunct professor of taxation at Pace University, lectures and writes on estate-planning issues.

---

Here are two little-known trusts you might consider using to help out your children and grandchildren...

## 2503(C) TRUST

Parents and grandparents often make gifts to children and grandchildren. Such gifts may be made to help a child save for college, or as part of a long-term estate plan. In either case it's important that the gift funds be used by the child as the gift-maker desires.

A Section 2503(c) trust can be a big help in achieving this goal—not only until the child becomes an adult, but for as many years as desired.

***How it works:*** Set up a trust for the child under Section 2503(c) of the Tax Code and name an independent trustee. Each year, various individuals can transfer to the trust up to $10,000 each without any of them owing any gift tax or having to file a gift tax return—$10,000 from each parent, $10,000 from each grandparent, $10,000 from Aunt Sally, etc.

The creator of the trust has flexibility in specifying how it will use its funds for the child—but the trustee's discretion must not be excessively restrictive. *A trust for...*

●**College savings**—may spend all its assets on education, but pay what's left—if anything—to the child on graduation.

●**Long-term estate planning**—may hold assets until a child reaches age 30, 40 or older, making payments of specified amounts, or to meet specified needs.

***Key:*** To avoid gift tax, when the child reaches 21, the trust must provide a window of at least 30 days within which the child can withdraw all the assets in the trust. After the 30-day period expires, assets in the trust will be governed by its terms permanently.

***Note:*** If the primary purpose of the trust is to be a "college savings" trust, its job may be done by the time the child reaches age 21.

If it is an estate-planning trust, the child will realize that other estate-planning decisions that affect him/her will depend on his respecting the wishes of the trust's creator regarding the 30-day window.

A 2503(c) trust can be a better way to hold funds for a child than an account set up under the *Uniform Gift to Minors Act* (UGMA)—or the *Uniform Transfers to Minors Act* (UTMA)—which has these drawbacks...

●Funds deposited in an UGMA account legally become the child's property. Then, on reaching the age of legal majority—18 or 21—the child obtains the legal right to take the funds and do anything he wants with them.

The funds in a 2503(c) trust aren't the child's but are legally owned by the trustee. The trustee makes distributions of the trust's assets pursuant to the terms of the trust agreement.

●UGMA funds, being the child's, may reduce eligibility for college aid. Funds in a 2503(c) trust aren't the child's and are less likely to do so.

●State law determines the terms that apply to UGMA funds. But you set the terms that govern a 2503(c) trust—and have flexibility in doing so.

●If you die while serving as custodian of an UGMA account to which you made contributions for a child, the UGMA funds will be taxed in your estate. But funds placed in a 2503(c) trust are removed from your estate if properly created.

A 2503(c) trust costs more to set up than an UGMA account, since you must hire a lawyer to draft an agreement to meet your special circumstances. Generally, setting up a 2503(c) trust will cost less than $1,000.

## SPECIAL NEEDS TRUST

A child who suffers a disability—now or in the future—may be entitled to government aid.

***Trap:*** If you bequeath or make a gift of assets to the child outright, the child may *lose eligibility* for assistance as a result of exceeding an income or asset-ownership threshold. The family's out-of-pocket costs for the child could then rise significantly.

***Strategy:*** Set up a "special needs" trust that holds assets for the benefit of a child without reducing the child's eligibility for assistance.

The terms of such a trust state that it will only make expenditures on behalf of the child that supplement government assistance received by the child—rather than replace it.

***Example:*** A child who suffers a disability becomes entitled to receive 12 hours per day of state-financed nursing care. The trust can provide for an additional 12 hours of care, providing the child with around-the-clock care—without causing the child to lose the state-paid 12 hours.

In contrast, a child who owned assets of his own sufficient to pay for 12 hours of care might not be eligible to receive any care from the state.

***Planning ahead:*** Even if a child is healthy, you can't tell what may occur in the future. If you are setting up a larger trust arrangement—such as a 2503(c) trust—include "special needs" provisions that will become effective if the child becomes disabled…

• If you are transferring assets to a minor child, you *must* set up a trust, so include special needs provisions as a matter of course.

• If you have an adult child who is receiving assistance, or is likely to need assistance in the future, create a special needs trust to protect the child's eligibility for assistance.

***Important:*** Special needs trusts must be drafted carefully to comply with local laws that vary by state, so consult with a legal expert.

# Family Home Saved From IRS… By a Trust

A couple put their home in a trust benefiting their five-year-old son, then continued living in it. Later, the IRS tried to seize the house for back taxes. It said the trust was fraudulent because the couple owed a tax debt when it was set up, and the trust was a sham because the couple still used the home as their own.

***Court:*** The trust had a genuine purpose, to assure the house would pass to the son. The tax debt that had existed when it was set up had been paid, so the trust hadn't been set up to avoid taxes. And the trust's terms restricted how the couple could use the home, so it was not a sham. Thus, the trust was valid—and the home was beyond the reach of the IRS.

*In re: Eugene T. Richards, Jr.,* Bankr ED Pa., No. 97-14798DWS.

# When to Leave Your IRA to Charity

Robert E. Harrison, attorney, CPA and cochairman, Eisner Tax Consulting Services, Richard A. Eisner & Company, LLP, 575 Madison Ave., New York 10022, one of the nation's top-20 tax and accounting firms.

If you are planning to make a bequest to charity through your will, consider leaving the charity an IRA or other qualified retirement savings account—such as a Keogh or 401(k)—instead of cash or other property.

By doing so you will cut taxes that go to the IRS, and leave more wealth for your heirs and the charity to share. *Uncle Sam pays:* The government can usually wind up paying for more than 73% of your charitable bequest.

Distributions from retirement plan accounts are *taxable income* to your heirs. Moreover, unless the retirement account is left to a surviving spouse, it will also be subject to *estate* taxes.

But a tax-exempt charity can receive distributions from your retirement accounts income tax free, and no estate tax is imposed on bequests to charity.

So when you leave a retirement account to charity, simply designate the charity as a beneficiary of your IRA or other retirement account on the account's beneficiary designation form. The designated charity could even be your family's private foundation.

***Tactic:*** If you own more than one IRA, name a charity as beneficiary of one of them and arrange for the balance therein to be approximately the amount of money you want the charity to receive.

At 70½, when you must begin taking mandatory withdrawals from a traditional IRA, take them from your other IRAs and leave your "charity" IRA intact.

***Observation:*** This technique is focused on traditional IRAs and other qualified retirement plans. It is generally not applicable to the new Roth IRAs, since funds can be withdrawn from Roth IRAs without incurring income tax liability.

# Stanley Hagendorf, Esq., On Smoother Estate Settlement

Stanley Hagendorf, estate and tax attorney in private practice with offices in New York and Florida. He is a former professor of law in the estate-planning program at the University of Miami law school and author of numerous books on various aspects of estate taxes.

## How to Keep Family from Fighting over Estates

Through the years, I've seen hundreds of arguments erupt among even the most loving siblings over the estates of their parents.

In nearly every case, such fights could have been avoided had their parents anticipated the problems.

Here is what can be done to ensure a peaceful transition of assets…

*Problem:* **One child is wealthier than the other.** I call this the rich-kid/poor-kid syndrome. The problem is how to divide the family assets when one child has more money than another.

*Challenge:* Take the case of parents with two daughters—one is a successful lawyer…the other is a struggling artist. If the parents ignore the differences in their daughters' financial situations and divide everything evenly, the artist might not have enough money to send her children to college.

But if they give the artist more than the lawyer, the lawyer or her spouse may complain the parents have cheated her out of her birthright. Typically, the lawyer's argument would be that it is not her fault that her sister chose a low-paying occupation.

*Solution 1:* Explain you would like to leave the less-fortunate child with financial assets, but ask the wealthier child if there is a family asset he/she wants. Or ask if there is any preferred method of inheritance, such as a trust to save income or estate taxes. Sometimes the wealthier child is content with inheriting that asset or a particular method of inheritance in exchange for less of an inheritance.

*Solution 2:* If the child of modest means has children, consider making gifts to the grandchildren to help fund their college educations. If the gift is a "qualified transfer" for tuition directly to an educational organization, it is excluded from gift taxes. Grandparents could also set up trusts for their grandchildren and make regular transfers from their accounts into the trusts.

*Solution 3:* Parents can take out an insurance policy with the proceeds paid to an educational trust for the children of the less-wealthy child.

*Problem:* **A house must be divided among heirs.** Nasty battles often occur on issues of ownership or sale of a house. Not only is a home an estate's largest asset, but there is often sentimental value attached.

*Solution 1:* If possible, while parents are still alive, they can raise the issue with their children of who gets the house so that they can reach an acceptable agreement. They can draw up a will in accordance with the agreement and limit the likelihood of fights among the children.

In situations in which only one child wants the family house but doesn't have enough money to buy out his siblings, you can leave the house to that child—and have the rest of the family divide the remaining assets. Of course, this depends on the fair market value of the house and the remaining assets.

Or you could put the house into a trust and require that the child who wants to live in it after your death pay rent to the trust. The other children are the beneficiaries of the trust and the rental income. The child could also buy the house from the trust, and the sale proceeds could be divided among the other children.

*Solution 2:* If reaching an agreement is impossible, the best way to resolve prolonged wrangles over family real estate is to stipulate in the will that the property must be sold within a set period of time and the proceeds divided among the children.

*Problem:* **Family vacation house.** The biggest challenge that arises in the case of a second home in a vacation area is that all the heirs usually want to use the home during peak seasons.

Sometimes, one child wants to buy out his siblings. But disputes often erupt over fair market value of the property since most children who are not interested in buying the house think it is worth more than the appraisal. This is especially so when one child or several children want to buy the house and the proceeds are paid to other siblings.

**Solution:** While alive, try to state by agreement which child will get the house during which time of year—or which child can buy the house. This would be offset by an allocation of other assets to the others.

**Problem: Many heirs want the same family heirlooms, art or jewelry.** Sometimes these items have emotional value, regardless of their financial value. Most of the time, however, the issue is money.

**Solution 1:** If children cannot agree on how to divide up these items, one technique is to allow each child to make one choice (first choice by lot) and then to rotate turns until everything at issue is distributed. Specify this process in your will, but don't list the assets by item.

Specifying valuable items in a will could cause valuation problems in the event of an audit.

**Solution 2:** If the children are unable to do this, another approach is to state that all the disputed items will be sold within four to six months after probate and the proceeds of the sale will then be equally distributed among the children.

**Problem: The wrong child is named executor.** Parents should share with heirs their decision about who will serve as their estate's executor. This will keep it from being a big— and in some cases, unwelcome—surprise. It also allows the matter to be discussed among the children to determine who is most qualified to take on the task.

**Solution:** Usually it makes sense to name the most financially astute child as executor. That's because an executor is held to legal standards of behavior.

If the other children suspect the executor of being unfair, they could seek a court hearing. If they are not "at war" with each other, you can use coexecutors.

**Important:** By law, an executor is entitled to be paid for his time for handling the affairs of the estate, though some children decline to be compensated and many parents make this a condition of the will. Fees can vary widely. They are often figured as a percentage of the estate and range between 2% and 5%.

It is not necessary to name a lawyer as executor. Doing so can dramatically increase the fees. Many lawyers charge $200 to $300 an hour to settle an estate and also may use paralegals that charge up to half of the same hourly fee.

**Problem: A wealthy parent marries a new spouse who has children.** The fear here among heirs from the first marriage is that all the assets will pass to the parent's new spouse —or to the new spouse's children.

**Solution:** If you are remarried and want to protect your children from your first marriage, establish a living trust. You can fund it during your lifetime or at your death using a "pour over" from your will. After your death, the trust pays the income to your spouse during your spouse's life. Upon his death, the trust can either pass the assets to the children of your first marriage—or divide them among the children of both marriages. As an added benefit, this type of trust can be eligible for a marital deduction, which would reduce or eliminate federal estate tax.

**Important:** If there is animosity among children and a will contest is possible, I prefer the concept of using a trust during your lifetime. When a trust operates smoothly during your lifetime, the arrangement is harder to overturn after you're gone. Furthermore, property in a trust does not have to go through the probate process, the way property in an estate must. If the parties want a prenuptial arrangement, I also prefer such a trust—along with a prenuptial agreement that sets forth how the surviving second spouse is to be provided for.

**Reason:** Trusts are more difficult to overturn in most states than prenuptial agreements, which are technically contracts that may be attacked on the grounds of fraud, nondisclosure of all assets or undue influence. If the estate is more than the exclusion amount, an estate tax return must be filed and an estate plan is needed. This exclusion amount will rise each year to $1 million in 2006 and thereafter. Estate taxes can be avoided if the individual is married and the gross estate is worth no more than the exclusion amount. Thus, the solutions presented above must tie in with an estate plan to minimize estate taxes.

**More from Stanley Hagendorf...**

## Avoid Challenges to Your Will

**•Use a living trust to handle the estate.** The longer the trust is in operation, the less likely a challenge will be successful.

**•Videotape the situation surrounding the signing of the will,** to show that you are competent.

*Trap:* A no-contest clause disinherits anyone who contests the will. But—such clauses are invalid in many states and are useless if nothing is bequeathed to the person in the will.

*Caution:* If anyone is disinherited in the will, the document should explain why. Be sure that the explanation is factually correct.

*Example:* A child has not been in contact for 10 years.

## Estate Planning Trap

A dangerous trap faces those who plan to use wills, trusts and other legal devices to distribute valuable assets to heirs. If an attorney makes a mistake when drafting legal documents, so that much of an estate goes to the IRS instead of to heirs as intended, the heirs cannot sue the attorney for malpractice under the laws of New York, Maryland and several other states. This is because the heirs lack "privity" with the attorney who made the mistake—he wasn't working for them, so they can't sue him. *Safety:* Research the laws of your state that apply to estate planning malpractice. If "privity" is an issue, create it by having your heirs pay part of your estate planning attorney's fee and have the attorney agree in writing that he is working for them as well.

Seymour Goldberg, Esq., CPA, senior partner, Goldberg & Goldberg, PC, 666 Old Country Rd., Suite 600, Garden City, NY 11530. Mr. Goldberg is author of *How to Handle an IRS Audit* and *Pension Distributions: Planning Strategies, Cases and Rulings*, both published by the *CPA Journal.*

## Inheritance Snatcher

Review your will to make sure you're not leaving anything to a relative in a nursing home whose stay is paid for by Medicaid or to anyone who might be in that position in the near future. *Trap:* Inheritances received by Medicaid recipients may be taken by the government in whole or in part. *Self-defense:* Redo your will so the inheritance goes to someone else, such as a child of the patient. The child can use the money to provide his/her hospitalized parent with "extras."

Sidney Kess, attorney and CPA, 10 Rockefeller Plaza, Suite 909, New York 10020. Over the years he has taught tax law to more than 600,000 tax professionals. Mr. Kess is consulting editor of *Financial and Estate Planning* and coauthor of *1040 Preparation, 2000 Edition*, both published by CCH Inc.

 **Estate Planning Tactics From Attorney Martin Shenkman**

Martin Shenkman, Esq., estate attorney and financial planner, Teaneck, NJ. Mr. Shenkman is author of *The Beneficiary Workbook* and The *Complete Book of Trusts*, both published by John Wiley & Sons, Inc.

### What Beneficiaries Need to Know...Your Checklist

It's impossible to prepare oneself for the *emotional* loss experienced upon the death of a loved one. But we can do advance planning to minimize the financial and legal impact of a death in the family.

*Key:* Knowing what we have to do in the event a death occurs. *Most important...*

**•Straighten things out with your loved ones before anyone dies.** *Talk to your parents and/or spouse about your concerns...*

•What is it that they want? Have funeral arrangements been made? Do they want the family business kept intact?

•Have they taken the necessary actions to put their affairs in order (made a will or trust, named beneficiaries of life insurance policies and retirement plans)?

•If they have a will, is it up-to-date?

•Do they know about *your* finances? Do your parents know that you have a greater need for an inheritance than your sister? There's no law that says bequests must be equal. What's important is that your parents meet their beneficiaries' needs.

Talk things over with your brothers and sisters so that everyone knows where the others stand. This is a touchy issue, so an extra measure of tact is required.

•**Get organized now.** When someone dies, one of the big problems for beneficiaries is locating the things necessary to settle the estate. *Make sure you know before the death occurs where to find the following documents and information...*

•Will

•Trusts

•Deeds (if any)

•Safe-deposit boxes (location of boxes, contents and keys)

•Life insurance policies

•Funeral and burial instructions

•Names and addresses of creditors and debtors

•List of assets and where they are located

•List of all advisers—attorney, accountant, insurance agent, stockbroker

### ACTION STEPS

When someone dies, you may be overcome by emotion. *Still, certain actions should be taken as soon as possible...*

•**See to funeral and burial arrangements.** If there was no planning before death, then the arrangements are up to you.

•**Get copies of the death certificate.** These are necessary to change the title on most of the person's assets—cars, bank accounts, etc. The number of copies needed depends on the number of assets involved.

•**Give the original will to an attorney.** He/she will start probate proceedings (the legal process for settling an estate)—unless adequate steps have been taken to avoid probate.

*Note:* The attorney may already be in possession of the will if he prepared it.

•**Apply for benefits.** For example, a spouse or minor child is entitled to a $225 allowance from Social Security. A widow (and some divorced spouses) may also be entitled to Social Security benefits based on the deceased spouse's earnings. Call 800-772-1213. If the person died from a work-related injury or occupational disease, see whether worker's compensation will provide benefits to a widow or minor child. Also check with the Veterans Administration if the deceased received an honorable discharge (there may be burial and other benefits available). Call 800-827-1000.

•**Cancel the lease.** If your parent or loved one rented a home, cancel the lease after clearing out the furnishings.

•**Inform insurance companies.** File life insurance claims for any policies on the person's life, and request that the insurers send you Form 712, *Life Insurance Statement* (a statement about the life insurance that must be filed with the estate tax return). Make sure the car insurance company continues to cover the person's car until it's sold or transferred to a beneficiary. Make sure the homeowner's policy continues to provide adequate coverage for the person's things until removed from the home.

•**Notify companies the person did business with.** Cancel credit cards, and close charge accounts. Tell airlines to transfer frequent-flier miles (in accordance with the will or to the primary beneficiary).

•**Gather assets.** This doesn't mean piling them all together. It means getting a list of all the assets at the time of the decedent's death, along with copies of statements, deeds, etc. This information is needed for probate. It's also essential for filing federal and state estate tax returns, if required.

•**Review IRAs.** If the surviving spouse is the beneficiary, decide whether to roll an IRA over to the surviving spouse.

•**Get good advice—***and get it now.* The money you pay to attorneys and other advisers to resolve issues up front can be much lower than if you deal with problems after a person's death.

More from Martin Shenkman...

# The Truth About Living Wills

A living will can't force your doctor to do what you wish. While it is a legal document that puts you on record as wishing to refuse life-sustaining treatment and relieves doctors and hospitals of potential liability for following your wishes, a living will can't change your doctor's religious or ethical feelings, which might be counter to your request.

*Self-defense:* Speak with your primary doctor to make sure he/she agrees to abide by your living will. If he will not promise to do so, find another doctor. Be sure your living will gives your agent authority to move you to another hospital.

# The Five Wishes Living Will

Peter J. Strauss, Esq., a partner in the law firm Epstein Becker & Green, PC, 250 Park Ave., New York 10017, and Fellow of the National Academy of Elder Law Attorneys. He is coauthor of *The Elder Law Handbook—A Legal and Financial Survival Guide for Caregivers and Seniors*. Facts On File.

The US Supreme Court has acknowledged that competent adults have the right to refuse medical care, even when such refusal can lead to death. But to be legally effective, the court said, a request of this kind must be stated clearly and unequivocally.

*Caution:* If the request is not put in writing, loved ones may have to go to court to have it enforced.

*On the horizon:* A new, gentler and more effective way to give instructions regarding respirators, feeding tubes, etc.

## LIVING WILLS AND HEALTH CARE PROXIES

There is often confusion about what kind of legal document is needed to carry out a person's wishes about his/her death. There are *two* key documents...

●**Living will**—or health care declaration—outlines the type of care a person does and does not want.

●**Health care proxy**—or health care power of attorney—designates someone to speak on a person's behalf should he become unable to do so himself.

*Prepare both documents.* The health care proxy allows the person named—the agent—to express the medical care wishes of the person who signed the document.

The living will tells the agent what the ill person would say regarding medical care if he could speak.

This ensures that the wishes of the person who signed the living will—not necessarily in accord with the agent's wishes—are the ones to be observed by the doctors.

The will supplies legal support to your agent. The fact that the type of medical care a person wants has been put in writing, in a legal document, helps to relieve any guilt an agent might feel about authorizing or declining drastic measures.

In some states one document can include *both* a living will and health care agent designation. In other states separate documents are required. Check with a local elder law attorney to find out exactly what is needed.

## THE FIVE WISHES LIVING WILL

A new type of living will is currently used in Florida. Developed by The Commission on Aging With Dignity, the *Five Wishes Living Will* is a plain-language document that details the type of medical treatment a person is to be given in case of terminal illness or injury where death is expected.

The document includes more than just instructions about respirators, feeding and hydration tubes.

It also outlines how a person wants to be treated by caregivers when in a hopeless medical situation. He may specify that he wants to have his hand held and to be cared for with cheerfulness, not sadness.

The biggest departure of a *Five Wishes Living Will* from a traditional living will is that it provides an outlet for expressing *feelings*. For instance, it gives a person a chance to tell family members one last time how much they were loved.

## FIVE WISHES ACROSS AMERICA

Look for Florida's *Five Wishes Living Will* in 33 states and the District of Columbia...

- Arizona
- Arkansas
- Colorado
- Connecticut
- Delaware
- DC
- Georgia
- Florida
- Hawaii
- Idaho
- Illinois
- Iowa
- Louisiana
- Maine
- Maryland
- Massachusetts
- Michigan
- Minnesota
- Mississippi
- Missouri
- Montana
- Nebraska
- New Jersey
- New Mexico
- New York
- North Carolina
- North Dakota
- Pennsylvania
- Rhode Island
- South Dakota
- Tennessee
- Virginia
- Washington
- Wyoming

People who live in states that did not formally enact this new living will can have it executed as a supplement to that state's recommended form.

For a copy of the *Five Wishes Living Will* write to The Commission on Aging with Dignity, Box 1661, Tallahassee, Florida 32302. *Cost:* $4.

**Note:** There are other documents available for use nationwide, including living will and proxy forms available for $5 from Choice In Dying, Inc., Box 97290, Washington, DC 20077-7205 (800-989-9455).

***Making it legal:*** To make a *Five Wishes Living Will* legally effective, you must sign it in the manner prescribed by state law. Check with a lawyer.

## LETTING OTHERS KNOW

Even though a health care proxy/living will is properly executed according to state law, it won't be effective unless the right people know it exists.

Doctors and loved ones should be told when the documents are signed. They should be sent copies, or told where they can find the will.

***Pocket it:*** I have my clients keep a miniature copy of their health care proxy in their wallets in case of a sudden medical emergency.

# 15

# Very, Very Personal

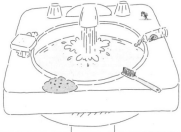

## How to Make Sex Fun And Fulfilling...Again

Sexual desire dwindles for many reasons, including marital strife, chronic pain, work demands, financial trouble and performance anxiety.

Whatever the cause, a flagging libido means more than missing out on a terrific source of pleasure. It can harm self-image...nip a budding romance...and even bring a long-term relationship to the breaking point.

Here's how to revivify your sex life...

●**Don't assume that a decline in libido is inevitable.** Many people unwittingly set the stage for libido problems by anticipating that their sex drive will diminish with age. In fact, age has little to do with it.

*Recent study:* Researchers at Duke University in Durham, North Carolina, followed a group of men from their mid-40s to age 70. During this 25-year span, only one-third of the men reported a decline in libido. The other two-thirds reported either no change—or an increase in libido.

Sexual desire is *not* some mystical force that slowly ebbs. It's something that can be nurtured.

●**Rule out medical causes.** Any severe illness—especially one that causes pain—can curb desire for a time. But a libido that stays low for longer than three months is likely to stem from a physical illness, such as...

●**Hypothyroidism.** An underactive thyroid gland can cause low energy, sluggishness, weight gain and malaise.

●**Depression.** It can cause crying jags, lack of appetite, poor concentration, sleep disturbance and, of course, sadness.

●**Testosterone deficiency.** Too little testosterone gives men enlarged breasts, reduced muscle tone and diminished beard growth.

●**Diabetes.** It can cause impotence as well as reduced libido.

Anthony Pietropinto, MD, attending psychiatrist at St. Luke's–Roosevelt Medical Center in New York City. He is coauthor of *Not Tonight, Dear—How to Awaken Your Sexual Desire.* Doubleday.

If you're having libido problems, it's a good idea to be examined by a doctor. In many cases, libido returns once an underlying illness has been treated.

●**Watch out for troublesome medications.** Diminished libido can be a side effect of many common drugs...

●**Blood pressure drugs,** especially *propranolol* (Inderal) and other beta-blockers.

●**Antidepressants,** especially *fluoxetine* (Prozac) and other serotonin-reuptake inhibitors.

●**Oral contraceptives,** especially Ortho-Novum, Lo/Ovral, Norinyl and others that contain *progesterone*.

If you notice a loss of libido while taking one of these drugs, alert your doctor. In most cases, there's an equally effective drug that doesn't affect sexual desire.

●**Rein in unrealistic expectations.** Do you expect rapture each time you make love? Do you expect sex with a longtime partner to be as exhilarating as when you first met?

If you set impossibly high standards for each sexual encounter, you're setting yourself up for disappointment. Repeated letdowns lead eventually to diminished desire.

Consider the origin of your sexual assumptions. Novels and motion pictures tend to portray every sexual encounter as a transcendent experience.

In reality, sexual encounters are subject to the varying moods, energies and interests of real people. In the real world, sex ranges from glorious to not-so-good.

Determine what you can realistically expect from sex...and what *you* need to feel satisfied. Share your thoughts with your partner...and work toward meeting the needs of both of you.

If a particular encounter is a flop, don't assume that all future encounters will turn out bad, too. Remind yourself of other encounters that did turn out well.

●**Relive erotic experiences from your past.** Each day, take a few minutes to summon erotic feelings.

Sit down in a quiet room, and visualize a sexual encounter that you recall as having been particularly arousing. Don't feel guilty if it features an old flame—no one but you has to know.

Focus on the pleasure you felt. Tell yourself that your next sexual encounter can be equally gratifying.

*Helpful:* Keep a sex diary. Record sexual ideas, sexual conversations, sexual fantasies—and any physical feelings that accompany them.

Chart sexual activity, too. Include the frequency of sex, who took the initiative and what you liked or disliked.

Periodically review your diary. Look for patterns to learn what sparks desire...and what inhibits it.

●**Take frequent fantasy breaks.** If you're feeling tame, you might simply imagine yourself heading home with a favorite movie star after attending the Oscars. But feel free to think about whatever it is that triggers your libido—no matter how unusual or taboo.

When you're ready, share a fantasy with your partner. Start by talking about plots and characters. If it seems appropriate to do so, act out your fantasy—complete with costumes and props.

Role-playing a fantasy can be confined to the bedroom...or it can start hours or even days in advance of the eventual sexual encounter. Anything goes, as long as you're both agreeable.

*Caution:* It's okay to imagine that your partner is someone else, but it's best to keep that part of the fantasy to yourself.

●**Break out of familiar routines.** For established couples, boredom is the single biggest libido-killer.

To keep sex interesting, make love at unexpected times and places. Try out new positions and techniques...wear erotic garments...and create a suggestive setting with music, candles and incense.

Sex that's truly spontaneous can be a terrific turn-on.

# Easy Route to a Better Sex Life

Allow yourself small pleasures regularly—such as a hot bath or a movie matinee—so you and your partner can relax and enjoy sexuality. Schedule at least one hour a week just for you and your spouse. Do not watch TV at night—play a board game, read out loud or do something else to bring yourselves closer. Do not discuss anger-provoking issues near bedtime. If you're always too tired to make love, try setting the alarm for 90 minutes after you fall asleep or for one hour earlier in the morning and make love then. And don't worry about frequency. *Quality matters more than quantity.*

*Secrets of Better Sex* by Joel Block, PhD, clinical psychologist, Human Sexuality Center, New Hyde Park, NY. Simon & Schuster.

# Impotence: New Treatment And Prevention

Arthur L. Burnett, MD, director of the Male Consultation Clinic at Johns Hopkins University School of Medicine in Baltimore. He has written extensively about impotence, including a recent article in *Geriatrics,* 7500 Old Oak Blvd., Cleveland 44130.

Nowadays it seems you can't open a newspaper without reading about Viagra, the new impotence drug.

As the first FDA-approved oral medication for the treatment of impotence, Viagra—the trade name for *sildenafil*—*does* represent a breakthrough.

Until Viagra's arrival, the vast majority of the estimated 30 million American men with impotence suffered in silence. Either they were too embarrassed to seek help...or they thought little could be done to help them.

But Viagra is *not* the only available treatment for impotence—more accurately called erectile dysfunction.

### WHAT GOES WRONG?

The physiology underlying erections is complex. Upon sexual arousal, a man's brain, spinal cord and peripheral nerves send nerve signals to his penis. These signals trigger the release of *nitric oxide* and *cyclic guanosine monophos-*

*phate (GMP),* "chemical messenger" molecules that cause blood vessels in the penis to dilate.

As a result of blood vessel dilation, the spongy chambers inside the penis (the *corpora cavernosa*) become engorged with blood...and the penis stiffens.

Many things can derail this process. Sometimes the culprit is anxiety, depression, lack of desire or another psychological problem. In four out of five cases, however, there's a *physical* reason for erectile dysfunction...

●**Cardiovascular disease.** The same fatty deposits that form in coronary arteries often form inside arteries in the penis. If penile arteries are blocked, blood cannot fill the corpora cavernosa—and the penis remains flaccid.

●**Diabetes.** Elevated blood sugar levels can impair penile circulation and damage the nerves that carry impulses between the brain and the penis.

●**Injury.** Damage to the spinal cord or to genital tissue can disrupt circulation and/or critical nerve pathways. One common cause of such injuries is prostate surgery.

●**Testosterone deficiency.** Without the correct amount of testosterone, a man's libido is weak. If a lack of testosterone is found through a blood test, testosterone-replacement therapy may solve the problem.

Since the health problems that underlie some cases of erectile dysfunction can be life-threatening, it's crucial that they be properly diagnosed and treated. Any man troubled by erectile dysfunction should phone his doctor to schedule a physical exam.

### THE PILL SOLUTION

Recent studies have shown Viagra to be helpful for 70% of men who are troubled by erectile dysfunction—*regardless of what's causing the problem.*

***How it works:*** Viagra creates strong, long-lasting erections by blocking the breakdown of nitric oxide and cyclic GMP.

The pill is taken about an hour before sex. The boost in sexual response lasts four to six hours.

For many men, the result has been truly remarkable. Some have been able to enjoy sex for the first time in decades.

## WHEN VIAGRA DOESN'T WORK

If penile blood vessels are so occluded that blood cannot flow into them, or in cases of significant nerve damage—Viagra cannot help.

One in 10 men is unable to tolerate Viagra's side effects—headaches, indigestion, facial flushing and subtle visual disturbances. For some men, Viagra makes everything look blue for several hours.

Viagra is off-limits to men who take *nitroglycerin* or another nitrate-containing drug for heart disease.

## OTHER TREATMENT OPTIONS

Older treatments for erectile dysfunction may have been overshadowed by Viagra, but they're still worth considering...

•**Penile injections.** Using a fine needle, a man injects the prescription medication *alprostadil* or another vasodilator into the base of his penis about 15 minutes before sex. The resulting erection can last up to an hour.

Injection therapy works for about 90% of men who try it. It's often a good bet for men with nerve damage and other problems that render Viagra useless.

While the injections themselves cause surprisingly little pain, 50% of men who use injection therapy experience pain in the penis afterward—but this problem can easily be remedied by adjusting the medication.

•**Penile suppositories.** A tiny suppository containing alprostadil is inserted in the urethra about 15 minutes before sex. It's effective in about 40% of cases.

One in three men who use the suppository experience some discomfort in the penis, and 3% to 4% have slight bleeding, dizziness or low blood pressure.

•**Vacuum devices.** An airtight plastic cylinder is placed over the penis, and then the air is pumped out. The reduction in pressure causes an erection by facilitating the flow of blood into the penis. The cylinder is removed, and a rubber band placed around the base of the penis helps maintain the erection.

The device works nearly all the time. However, it's cumbersome, interferes with spontaneity and can reduce sensation.

•**Penile prostheses.** Surgical implantation of a semirigid material into the penis can make it permanently erect. Or a surgeon can implant a hydraulic chamber that can be pumped up and emptied via a little pump in the scrotum.

Eighty-five percent of patients are satisfied with the outcome.

## PSYCHOLOGICAL HELP

Even in cases of erectile dysfunction caused primarily by a physical problem, psychological disorders like anxiety and depression can complicate matters.

In some cases, erectile dysfunction stems from marital conflict. Here, too, drug therapy may restore erections—but it won't address the underlying problem. Viagra is *not* an aphrodisiac.

Satisfactory sex involves mind *and* body. Men with erectile trouble may want to consult a sex therapist as well as a physician.

## AVOIDING POTENCY PROBLEMS

Make lifestyle changes that lower your risk for the diseases that lead to erectile dysfunction.

Limit your consumption of dietary fat while boosting your intake of fruits and vegetables... get regular exercise...avoid smoking...and practice meditation or take other steps to alleviate psychological stress.

If you have high cholesterol, high blood pressure, diabetes or any other disease that can contribute to erectile dysfunction, be sure to get effective treatment.

# Natural Treatment for Impotency

Natural alternatives to Viagra for treating impotence include extracts of ginkgo leaves or ginseng root. They are available at drugstores and health food stores. Consult your physician before trying either remedy. These are the dosages I would discuss. *Ginkgo:* 40 mg extract, three times a day. Don't use it if you take aspirin or blood thinners. *Ginseng:* 100 mg to 200 mg extract daily. Men using ginseng should have their blood pressure monitored regularly. Don't use it if you drink caffeinated beverages regularly or take other stimulants. And be patient—it may take several months to see results.

Adriane Fugh-Berman, MD, a medical researcher based in Washington, DC, and author of *Alternative Medicine: What Works.* Williams & Wilkins.

# Vasectomies Do Not Affect Sex

Semen contains less than 5% sperm—the rest is fluids from the seminal vesicles and prostate. Vasectomies stop only the flow of sperm. They should not affect sexual desire or performance. *Caution:* Some sperm can remain in semen for up to 30 ejaculations after a vasectomy, so continue using birth control until it is confirmed that there is zero sperm. A simple lab test can determine when semen no longer contains sperm. Vasectomy reversal is possible, with up to a 90% success rate.

Jonathan Jarow, MD, male fertility specialist, Johns Hopkins Medical Institutions, Baltimore.

# Oral Sex Trap

Yeast infections are far more common among women who receive cunnilingus. *Theory:* Infection-causing yeast are found in the mouths of up to half of all adults…so oral sex may be an effective means of transmitting it to the vagina. Brushing and flossing help reduce yeast levels in the mouth…as does rinsing with antiseptic mouthwash.

Judith Seifer, PhD, RN, past president, American Association of Sex Educators, Counselors and Therapists, Box 238, Mount Vernon, IA 52314. She is cocreator of the *Better Sex Video Series*.

# Better Condom Selection

Unlubricated condoms significantly increase the risk of women developing first-time urinary-tract infections. The problem is 30 times more likely.

Betsy Foxman, PhD, associate professor, department of epidemiology at the University of Michigan School of Public Health, Ann Arbor. Her study was published in *Epidemiology*.

# You Can Boost Fertility Without Drugs or Tricky High-Tech Procedures

Sherman J. Silber, MD, director of the Infertility Center of St. Louis. He is author of *How to Get Pregnant with the New Technology.* Warner Books.

For certain couples, fertility drugs and high-tech medical tests and procedures are the only path to parenthood short of adoption.

But too many infertile couples jump the gun, seeking these costly, emotionally draining interventions when they could get pregnant *on their own* if they tried certain natural strategies.

### WHY INFERTILITY IS RAMPANT

In men, fertility peaks around age 18—then slowly declines. In women, fertility also peaks around age 18—but drops off sharply after age 30.

By her early 30s, a woman's fertility has dropped twenty-fold. This means that up to 28% of *perfectly fertile* women in their 30s are unable to conceive even after a year of trying.

***Implication:*** Most couples should resort to fertility testing and treatments only after an entire year trying to get pregnant.

### TIMING IS OF THE ESSENCE

To boost the chance of conception, couples must time sexual intercourse to coincide with ovulation.

Some women try to predict ovulation by recording changes in body temperature. Individuals who use this system often believe that body temperature rises just before ovulation.

But the rise in body temperature typically occurs *the day after* ovulation—a time of sharply diminished fertility. Temperature tracking is actually a better recipe for birth control than for conception.

***More reliable:*** Pinpoint the date of ovulation via an ovulation test kit. Using such a kit—sold in drugstores for about $40—a woman employs a chemically treated dipstick to check her urine for *luteinizing hormone* (LH).

A color change in the dipstick signals a surge of LH. That means ovulation is imminent. In most cases, it's best to have intercourse the first night after the LH test is positive.

### HOW TO HAVE SEX

Some couples think it's a good idea for the man to "save up" his semen by avoiding sex (or masturbation) until his partner reaches her time of maximum fertility.

But sperm counts reach a plateau after only two or three days of abstinence. There's no benefit in waiting any longer.

In fact, the longer sperm remains in the man's body, the less vigorous it is—and the less capable it is of fertilizing an egg.

***Bottom line:*** Having sex every other day is usually best.

Woman-on-bottom positions are most likely to result in conception. These positions promote retention of semen for longer periods of time than do other positions.

To further promote semen retention, women should remain supine for 30 minutes following intercourse.

### GET IN SHAPE

Body weight doesn't affect male fertility. But women who are even slightly over their ideal weight often have trouble getting pregnant.

***Reason:*** Fat cells absorb estrogen and release it slowly, blunting the spike in levels of *follicle-stimulating hormone* (FSH) that initiates egg development early in the menstrual cycle.

On the other hand, women who are too thin tend to ovulate erratically—or not at all.

For maximum fertility, women should strive to be as close as possible to their ideal body weight.

***Important:*** Women should be sure to get 400 micrograms of *folic acid* every day. A deficiency of this B-vitamin can cause miscarriage or fetal abnormalities.

### CONTROL STRESS

Psychological stress can significantly lower a woman's fertility. This isn't surprising, given the central role the brain plays in the menstrual cycle.

***Example:*** Ovulation is initiated when a brain structure called the hypothalamus produces *gonadotropin-releasing hormone* (GNRH). This hormone causes the pituitary to release LH.

Stress can inhibit ovulation altogether, something that's familiar to any woman who has ever missed her period during a particularly stressful time.

Stress can also cause uterine contractions, which can keep a fertilized egg from implanting.

It's impossible to will yourself to be relaxed—especially if you're worried about getting pregnant. But it's helpful to acknowledge any anxiety you might be feeling...and take steps to curb it.

One way to relax is to take a brisk 30-minute walk four or more days a week. You might also look into meditation, progressive muscle relaxation or another relaxation technique.

Romantic evenings together should definitely be a part of your conception program.

### FERTILITY ROBBERS

●**Alcohol** can interfere with ovulation and sperm production. Men and women alike should limit alcohol consumption to two drinks a day.

●**High temperatures** can interfere with sperm production.

Some doctors believe that boxer shorts, which tend to keep the scrotum cooler than briefs, are better for fertility. This has never been proved. Just in case, men should avoid any article of clothing that holds the testicles tightly against the body.

It's also a good idea for men to avoid hot baths, saunas, etc.

●**Medications** can affect fertility in men and women. That goes for prescription and over-the-counter (OTC) drugs.

With the exception of OTC supplements such as *DHEA* and *androstenedione*—which are toxic to the reproductive systems of both sexes—it's unclear precisely which drugs reduce fertility.

For this reason, it's best to avoid all drugs except those that are truly necessary.

•**Smoking** can have a devastating effect on female fertility. In addition to starving egg-producing follicles of oxygen, tobacco smoke —even "secondhand" smoke—can cause chromosomal errors that lead to miscarriage.

# Mammogram Trap

Mammograms often give false-positives, indicating the presence of a breast tumor when none really exists.

***Recent finding:*** One in two women who undergo annual mammograms over a 10-year period can be expected to have at least one false-positive mammogram.

In addition to needless anxiety, false-positives lead to additional testing and even to infection and scarring from needless biopsies.

Women should realize that most positive results do *not* mean breast cancer.

***Helpful:*** Make sure your doctor has previous mammograms available for comparison.

Joann G. Elmore, MD, MPH, associate professor of medicine and epidemiology, University of Washington School of Medicine, Seattle. Her study of mammograms among 2,400 women 40 to 69 years of age was published in *The New England Journal of Medicine,* 10 Shattuck St., Boston 02115.

# Chemotherapy Before Breast Cancer Surgery

Breast cancer patients often benefit from chemotherapy *before* surgery. In a recent study, 80% of patients who underwent pre-op chemo had their tumors shrink by at least 50%. Some women who had been slated for mastec-tomy (breast removal) were able to have a less disfiguring lumpectomy instead. In 36% of the women, the tumor disappeared completely.

Bernard Fisher, MD, director of research, division of human oncology, Allegheny University of Health Sciences, Pittsburgh. His five-year study of 1,523 breast cancer patients was published in the *Journal of Clinical Oncology,* Curtis Ctr., Independence Square West, Suite 300, Philadelphia 19106-3399.

# New Pap Smear Testing

Pap smears are sometimes misread. Each year, 500,000 American women are told that their Pap smears are normal when they're really abnormal. *Result:* These women fail to get treatment for cervical cancer in its earliest, most treatable stages. *Good news:* The FDA recently approved *Papnet,* a computerized retesting method that identifies at least 7.1 times as many "false negatives" as manual rescreening.

Klaus Schreiber, MD, associate professor of pathology, Albert Einstein College of Medicine, Bronx. For more information on Papnet, call the manufacturer at 800-727-6384

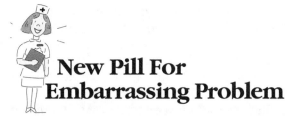

# New Pill For Embarrassing Problem

About 17 million people in the US have overactive bladders. Most are women. The new prescription drug *tolterodine tartrate*, sold as *Detrol*, helps control urinary urgency, frequent urination and urinary incontinence in people with overactive bladders. Clinical trials report fewer significant side effects than with other drugs currently used.

Alan Wein, MD, professor and chairman, division of urology, Hospital of the University of Pennsylvania, Philadelphia.

# How to Win the New Personal-Ads Game When Looking for Mr. or Ms. Right

Judy Kuriansky, PhD, clinical psychologist and host of *Love Phones,* the nationally syndicated radio call-in show. She is author of four books on relationships, including *The Complete Idiot's Guide to Dating.* Alpha Books.

What are the best places to run a personal ad? Focus first on personal ads in publications that you read regularly. If a magazine or newspaper attracts you, it will probably attract people like you and people whom you will like.

The personal ads on the Internet are also useful. Search for sites by typing in the word "dating" or "personals." From there you'll find a subset of people looking for others who share their interests.

### What are the ingredients of an ad that attracts a good match?

Many people have trouble writing personal ads because they try too hard. The result is often stiff and formal.

Before placing an ad you've written, read it into a tape recorder. Play it back. It should sound fast, snappy, honest and sincere. You want your ad to get noticed, but you don't want to attract those who are attracted to the wrong version of you—or somebody you've invented.

Run your ad by your friends. Ask them if it truly reflects your best qualities—without going overboard. Look at past ads. Find some ads you like...and change words so that they fit you.

### What's the best way to answer an ad that requests a phoned-in response?

Many ads today ask you to call a number and leave a telephone message on a voice-mail system.

Speak honestly and freely, as if to a good friend. But if you're at all nervous about leaving a message, prepare your script first. Then rehearse so you can read it naturally into the phone when the time comes.

Be confident. Push past shyness. Focus on what you're looking for and why you're an ideal person to meet. Avoid saying "Uhhh"...or putting yourself down.

### How do you do a background check on people who answer the ad?

Ask for the person's work number. Call to find out if it is really a business and if the person actually works there. Keep in mind that some people may ask their friends to pose as phony employers.

Also, if the person mentions that he/she loves certain activities, such as yoga or going to the gym, you can find out where he goes and see if the locations really exist.

### What about asking for a photograph before you meet?

This is a must. Ask for a full-body shot and not just a head shot.

***Reason:*** Not only do you want to see what the person looks like, but you also want to see if the photo looks dated or doctored.

### What's the best strategy when you speak directly to someone who responded to the ad?

Just be yourself, but prepare in advance to talk about things that interest you most. Speaking passionately will inspire your response.

Ask questions that can't be answered by a simple yes or no.

***Example:*** Don't ask, "Do you like movies?" Ask, "What's the last movie you saw that you really liked and why?"

The idea is to get the person talking so you can learn more about him.

### When is the right time to meet in person?

Probably after you've had two or three phone conversations.

When you finally agree to meet face to face, meet during the day, in daylight, in a public place—restaurants work well...for lunch...or a coffee shop. Consider bringing a friend for safety and feedback.

Define a limited meeting time for a painless parting in case it doesn't go well.

Always end with appreciation. Never give false promises to call if you have no intention of doing so. Simply say you are busy for weeks ahead.

# How To Be Happily Single

Xavier Amador, PhD, associate professor of psychology at the College of Physicians and Surgeons, Columbia University, New York, and director of the Diagnoses and Evaluation Center at Columbia University and the New York State Psychiatric Institute. He is psychology and health contributor to NBC's *Weekend Today* Show and coauthor of *Being Single in a Couples' World: How to Be Happily Single While Looking for Love,* The Free Press.

Only a generation ago, wanting to be married was a given. Single women had little social or economic status. And men were encouraged to start families.

Now both men and women can enjoy financial independence, a rich social life, travel, love, sex and even children without being married.

But psychologically, most people cling to the belief that to be single is to be sad. Centuries-old stereotypes and biases haven't caught up with the realities of being single today…

• Too many widows and widowers retire from the social scene, allowing themselves to completely become isolated instead of forging new connections.

• Most single people say their worst fear is to end up alone. That response cuts across all ages and both sexes. *Reality:* You are not alone just because you aren't married.

Being single can be wonderful and fulfilling, but only if you understand and are able to counter the forces that can make you feel bad about it.

In my 15 years as a therapist, unmarried patients—divorced, widowed or never married—have repeatedly lamented the frustrations of singlehood. I slowly began to realize that most of their problems resulted from *attitudes,* both others' and their own, about the unmarried state.

I was single myself at the time and identified strongly. So with a colleague, I wrote a book about it—*Being Single in a Couples' World.* We identified many ways single people could improve their lives by identifying the obstacles and striving to remove them.

### POWERFUL SCRIPTS

Year after year, we buy into two codes that have been pressed into our consciousness…

• The cultural marriage script. This has been imposed by society and long tradition.

From religious tenets to fairy tales, married people are described as respectable, responsible and mature. They're the ones who live happily ever after. What light does that throw on the unmarried? The flip side of that coin is that when people are single, they are considered suspect, irresponsible and immature.

• The personal marriage script. This script stems from childhood lessons about intimacy and marriage that direct you to feel, think and act in ways that make singlehood either a joy or a misery.

If you're single or have single friends or children, consider revising your personal marriage script. Assess your feelings about the unmarried. How do they affect your self-image and behavior toward others?

You may have to question beliefs you've held for a lifetime. Challenging your negative biases is critical to feeling confident about yourself and your ability to count with others. Then you can address the cultural marriage script and help your loved ones start to free themselves of rigid, outdated notions.

Suppose you do want to be married. Fine, but don't obsess about it. If you focus on the prize, you won't recognize the single person's precious gifts of friendship, autonomy and time alone. Being clear about why you're single and more at peace with who you are will make you not only happier but also more open to love.

### APPROACHING SINGLEHOOD AS A NEW COUNTRY

Learning to fit in without giving up your identity as a single person involves four stages, very much like the ones immigrants feel upon reaching new shores…

• **Alienation.** You're a stranger in a strange land. You barely speak the language. You ask, "Why don't I belong?"

●**Assessment.** You look for ways to fit in. You may reinvent yourself positively or fall into a bad marriage.

●**Acceptance.** You learn that you're part of a large minority. You develop a more realistic understanding of how the world has changed for singles in recent decades.

●**Assimilation.** You shed your feelings of failure for being single. You live in the present, enjoying your freedom.

### HELPING FRIENDS AND FAMILY ACKNOWLEDGE YOUR NEEDS

Single people often feel ignored by couples and by previously single friends who have entered romantic relationships. Problems...

●The couples play host but won't visit.

●The couples presume their movie and restaurant choices are more valid than the single person's.

●The couples feel free to cancel plans at the last minute.

The best way to stop feeling marginalized is to present your point of view. Without anger, explain to your friends and family that you feel they're not taking your feelings into account.

Cite several examples...and say how you would have preferred them to communicate and behave. People who care about you will tune in to you. It works 99% of the time.

Here are the four "E"s to becoming more visible to coupled loved ones...

●**Examine your needs.** What can you realistically expect to get out of your relationship with this previously single person?

●**Empathy check.** Rather than taking it personally or feeling rejected, put yourself in your coupled friend's shoes. Is your friend feeling guilty about letting you down, angry because of pressure from you to spend more quality time together, defensive from criticism or possibly overwhelmed from demands of the new relationship?

●**Express your needs.** When you're both not stressed, communicate what you learned from your empathy check.

●**Expect to compromise.** Accept that your relationship, which you value, will never be exactly the same as before. How far can each of you go toward meeting the other's needs?

### COMMUNICATING WITH YOUR SINGLE ADULT CHILD (OR PARENT)

Many singles feel tormented by parents who keep asking when they'll tie the knot. And parents aren't the only culprits.

Adult children may pester a widowed parent to remarry. Yes, you can mention marriage to your loved one occasionally, provided that you...

●Remain sensitive to how he/she feels about this issue.

●Don't assume everyone is desperate to get married or remarried.

●Shun thoughts that unmarried people are "losers."

●Rejoice in your loved one's school and job success, outside interests, vacations and friendships—not only dating accomplishments.

●Avoid blaming ("You're too picky"). It leaves everyone demoralized and the single person no closer to resolution.

---

**More from Dr. Amador...**

# Avoiding Friendly Fire

I call barrages of pro-marriage messages from loving relatives or friends "friendly fire."

Often they confuse their own hopes and aspirations with the single person's.

These assaults stem from blind adherence to the cultural script and a failure to empathize. *How well-meaning friends and relatives blow it...*

●Greeting the single person with "Are you seeing someone?"

●Fixing the single person up on blind dates against his/her wishes.

●Sending a check to a dating service without permission.

If you've gone too far, tell your loved one that you want to start afresh. Admit that you've applied your own standards to his life and want to update them. Ask how you can be more supportive. Listen to the answers and follow up. Breaking old habits is worth the effort and will pay off.

# Myth: Loving Couples Never Ever Fight

James L. Creighton, PhD, a psychologist in Los Gatos, CA, who specializes in conflict resolution. He is author of *How Loving Couples Fight* (Aslan Publishing) and coauthor of *Getting Well Again* (Bantam).

It is a myth that happy couples never fight. In fact, they regularly disagree with each other.

What sets loving couples apart is that they disagree in loving ways. They don't let disagreements turn into nasty battles. And their "fights" seem to strengthen, rather than hurt, their relationships.

Handling conflict in a healthy way is a skill that can be learned.

### ACCEPT CONFLICT AS NORMAL

Trying to ignore disagreements or bury resentments doesn't get rid of them. It only allows them to grow below the surface. When we face conflict and deal with it openly, it's easier to let it go and move on. *Steps to take...*

●**Express what you feel, not what you think.** Couples who fight lovingly start by talking about how they feel, not about what they think is "wrong" with their partner.

They frame arguments by saying, "I'm hurt/angry/frustrated" rather than, "You're rude/sloppy/a jerk."

When one spouse does something that bothers the other, he/she says so immediately. But he describes the specific behavior—not his interpretation.

*Example:* "I was upset when you didn't return my call" expresses how the person feels. "I'm mad because you're inconsiderate" expresses what the person thinks.

It's tempting to blame your negative feelings on the other person's inadequacies. Resist this urge.

Attacking or accusing may make you feel temporarily powerful. But it erodes trust, creating emotional fallout that is very difficult to clean up.

●**Listen—rather than talk—your way out of conflict.** When someone is upset, the natural reaction is to try to talk him out of it. We do this by making excuses for the person...or trying to come up with solutions to the problem...or pointing out all the reasons why there's no need to be upset. But this response implies that the other person doesn't have a right to his feelings. So talking often makes matters worse.

In reality, all it takes to stop the person from being angry is to acknowledge how he feels.

*Key to effective listening:* After your partner has finished speaking, summarize the feelings and ideas that were just expressed. Don't evaluate whether those words are right or wrong...and don't try to "fix" anything. Just repeat what you've heard.

When you're first learning this technique, it can feel artificial or even patronizing—but it works very effectively.

Many of the couples I work with get around this by using the five-minute rule. Either partner can invoke this rule at any time.

*How it works:* One person has five minutes to speak without interruption. Then the other person has five minutes. If you can't decide who should start, flip a coin. Sometimes you both may need another turn to speak.

By the end of the second round, both people have usually gotten most of their frustration out of the way and can start discussing the problem more constructively.

### FIGHT FAIRLY

Happy couples follow several unspoken rules that keep their small arguments from escalating into big ones...

●**Stick to the issue.** If he's mad because she's not ready to leave at the agreed-upon time, that's the subject the loving couple talks about.

They don't get sidetracked by accusations, such as, "You don't care how I feel" or, "One of us has to live in the real world."

They also don't keep bringing up past grievances. If an issue keeps coming up over and over, they'll talk about it—but not as a way of punishing each other when they're arguing about something else.

●**Don't hit below the belt.** Loving couples don't try to hurt each other by attacking sensitive areas, such as weight, job status, etc.

●**Don't drag other people into it.** Don't say things such as, "I'm not the only person who feels this way. Your sister and brother do, too."

Trying to bolster your side of the argument by bringing up someone else not only escalates the fight but also poisons your partner's relationship with that person.

Some couples find it helpful to make these rules explicit—and remind each other gently if one of them breaks a rule.

Don't turn these reminders into occasions to gloat. A simple reminder, such as, "Remember, we agreed not to do that" usually is enough.

***Important:*** The best time to agree on rules is right after a fight, when you've cooled down enough to talk reasonably. The memory of the fight you just had—and how unpleasant it was not to be following the rules—will motivate you to do things differently.

### HUDDLE TO SOLVE PROBLEMS

Sometimes just hearing each other out helps partners understand one another's point of view—and resolves the conflict. When that's not enough, happy couples work together to find a better way of dealing with the issue.

*Problem-solving steps...*

●Agree on what the problem is.

●Brainstorm alternative solutions.

●Agree on a solution that best meets your needs and those of your partner.

●Agree on a way to put the solution into practice.

●Evaluate how well the solution is working.

# Couples Communication

Men usually like to talk side to side...women, face to face. So a man may want to discuss important subjects while driving in a car, while a woman may prefer to wait until they get where they are going. Women should not be put off by men who tend to move away from face-to-face conversation—and each sex should be aware of the other's preference.

*The First Five Minutes: How to Make a Great First Impression in Any Business Situation* by Mary Mitchell, president, Uncommon Courtesies, business-communication consultants, Philadelphia. John Wiley & Sons.

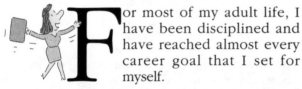

# Diet, Nutrition and Exercise

## Take-It-Off-and-Keep-It-Off Diet Magic from Professor of Law and Political Science

**F**or most of my adult life, I have been disciplined and have reached almost every career goal that I set for myself.

***Examples:*** I was a law clerk for Supreme Court Justice Stevens...I was the first woman to run a presidential campaign...I became a tenured professor at Harvard Law School...I was the first female editor of *Harvard Law Review*...I have written four books—and I'm only 45 years old.

Yet I haven't been able to resist a pastry—a weakness that caused my weight to balloon several years ago by 40 pounds.

Then I realized that I could use the same disciplined strategies that helped me succeed in my career to lose weight and keep off the pounds.

### CHANGING YOUR MIND

My wake-up call came several years ago in the dressing room of a clothing store. I was 40 years old, and 40 pounds overweight. I had been a size 10 before my son was born a few months earlier, but I had grown to a size 14.

I had been on diets for most of my life, but I was still heavier than I wanted to be.

In that dressing room, I decided that losing weight was not just important—it was going to be my top priority. I knew that I had the power and determination to do it.

I decided I would approach my diet the same way I approached everything else in my life—as if it were a career objective. In just five months, I lost the 40 pounds.

Like many adults, I used to approach dieting with the mind-set of a teenager. I ate the latest fad diet foods...set my weight-loss goals too high...restricted my calories too much...

---

Susan Estrich, JD, a professor of law and political science at the University of Southern California and a syndicated newspaper columnist. She is author of *Making the Case for Yourself: A Diet Book for Smart Women*. Riverhead.

bought all the trendy weight-loss gadgets…and overexercised—*and burned out.*

I threw common sense to the wind. I risked my health and sanity to lose a few pounds, only to gain them back.

***The secret of weight loss:*** Any healthful diet will work if you stick to it. The key is getting your mind to go along with your diet. How you think about dieting and exercise is more important than what you eat and how you feel.

### MY BIG DIETING ADVANTAGE

At work, you assess a situation critically. You do some research, brainstorm strategies, set reasonable goals and come up with a plan.

When the plan goes awry, you adjust it. You don't give up. You don't blame others—at least not if you want to succeed. Instead, you take responsibility and move forward.

***Example:*** I used to blame my weight on my lack of discipline. That was ridiculous because I am nothing if not disciplined at work.

•**Make a contract with yourself.** Declare your weight-loss intentions—in writing, as if you were writing a memo or a contract outlining the terms of a project.

Start with a 21-day commitment. Why 21 days? Because that's how long experts say it takes for a new behavior pattern to take root.

Memos and contracts are good because they are binding. What you declare on paper you are obligated to accomplish. Memos also make you think out whether your goals are reasonable and achievable.

### THE DIET CONTRACT

•**Mission statement.** Describe what you agree to do over the next three weeks.

***Example:*** I promised to follow a low-calorie diet for 21 days. I promised to devote one hour every day, for each of the 21 days, to exercise. I even promised to mark the scheduled hour on the days of my calendar right away.

The diet you choose to follow isn't important as long as it is healthful and low in calories—but not less than 1,200 calories a day.

Your attitude is the key to success, not the specific diet.

•**Planning statement.** Devise a statement that covers how you plan to cope with hazardous situations—parties, office birthday cakes and family gatherings.

***Example:*** I promised myself to plan in advance for every event that involves eating over the next 21 days. I wrote that I considered my diet a valid and legitimate reason to decide not to go somewhere.

•**Reward clause.** We often eat the wrong foods in an attempt to reward ourselves. Or we do it because we have nothing better to do with our time.

***Helpful:*** Make a list of acceptable rewards—other than food—that you would enjoy almost as much as you progress through the next 21 days.

***Example:*** After one week on my diet, I rewarded myself with a new book. After two weeks, a massage.

•**Evening eating component.** Most of us break our diets at night, eating 70% of our calories after 5 pm. Devise strategies for circumventing junk-food eating.

***Example:*** I made a promise to myself to stop eating by 8:30 pm on weekdays and 9:30 pm on weekends.

•**Cheating clause.** A promise not to cheat doesn't mean much. But a promise to cheat only after giving the situation thought has a chance of acting as a deterrent.

***Example:*** I promised to write down why I was going to eat a muffin or chips or cookies before eating them. In most cases, writing down my answers gave me just enough time to catch myself and give up the craving.

•**Nonderailment clause.** We've all cheated on diets and let slipups ruin our days or diets. Make that reaction unacceptable behavior.

***Example:*** I wrote that if I cheated, I would not use it as an excuse to abandon my diet. When I strayed, I resumed my strict adherence to the 21-day plan as if I had never cheated.

The 21-day diet is just the beginning of a weight-loss regimen. Continue on the course…and remind yourself of your goals. Your workplace skills will prod you to lose the weight—and keep it off.

## Very Effective Weight-Loss Strategies

•**Restaurants:** Avoid the *10-minute* problems—the first 10 minutes with the bread basket staring at you and the last 10 minutes with dessert.

*Skip breads altogether.* Have a tomato juice or shrimp cocktail instead. For dessert, have sorbet...fruit...or cappuccino with skim milk. *Best:* Have an apple...low-fat yogurt...or some other healthful snack before you go out.

•**Travel:** Do not eat desserts until the last day of your trip. If you eat them earlier, you are likely to do it throughout the entire trip.

*Airports:* Stay away from newsstands—they stock high-sugar snacks. *Better:* Bring your own fruit.

•**Watching TV:** Don't snack in front of the TV—sip hot or cool liquids instead.

*Effective strategies wherever you are:* Resist cravings for 10 minutes—they may go away. *Also:* Avoid going longer than three or four hours without a healthful snack or meal. Eating at regular intervals will keep your blood sugar stable and keep cravings at bay.

Stephen Gullo, PhD, president, Institute for Health and Weight Sciences, 16 E. 65 St., New York 10021, and author of *Thin Tastes Better: Control Your Food Triggers Without Feeling Deprived.* Dell.

# Secrets of the Diet Masters

Anne M. Fletcher, MS, RD, registered dietitian and former executive editor of *Tufts University Diet & Nutrition Letter.* She is author of *Eating Thin for Life: Food Secrets & Recipes from People Who Have Lost Weight & Kept It Off* and *The Thin for Life Daybook,* both published by Houghton Mifflin/Chapters.

People who lose weight and keep the pounds off for longer than three years are true diet experts. To learn their eating and exercise secrets, I surveyed 208 women and men whose average weight loss was 64 pounds.

Here's what they said works...

•**Drink a glass of water before eating.** There really is no metabolic reason why drinking water should make you shed pounds.

But to my surprise, two out of every three people I questioned told me they make a serious effort to drink water to control their weight.

While downing a glass of water (eight to 10 ounces) won't necessarily stem the craving for a candy bar, the water will fill you up. Having a glass of water before or between meals leaves less room in your stomach and is likely to help you eat smaller portions.

If water is not appealing, drink sparkling water with lemon or lime...or flavored sparkling water...or even diet soda.

When you feel hungry or have a craving between meals, try drinking a glass of water and waiting 20 minutes to see if the desire to eat passes. If not, have a *small* amount of the item you desire—along with a big glass of water.

•**Kick the red meat habit.** For years, health experts have been telling us to get less of our protein from meat—particularly steaks and burgers, which tend to be high in total fat and the saturated fat that is associated with heart disease.

The people I interviewed cut back dramatically on red meat. Most told me they eat little or no red meat, with more than half indicating that at most they eat meat once or twice a week. Instead of meat, they favored poultry, seafood and legumes—all of which are lower in fat and calories.

From a nutritional standpoint, there is no reason to shun lean meats. But red meat seems to be associated with past unhealthy ways of eating that maintainers want to avoid.

*Helpful:* Think of meat as a condiment rather than as the main course. When you eat red meat, your portion should be no bigger than a deck of cards.

Substitute a three-ounce portion of skinless poultry, fish or shellfish for meat. On other nights, have a meatless pasta dish...or a vegetarian meal consisting of a hearty bean soup or rice and beans.

*Example:* A filling, tasty combination is rice, seasoned canned beans and salsa. Mix and warm, then top with some reduced-fat cheese or fat-free sour cream.

●**Eat low-fat and fat-free foods carefully.** There is evidence suggesting that when some people see the words "low-fat" or "fat-free" on food labels, they eat much more.

The diet masters consume reduced-fat foods carefully, watching their portion sizes. Given a choice between two similar foods with similar calorie values, they tend to choose the one with less fat but they consume it in a portion equal to the regular one.

*Helpful:* The next time you reach for a bag of low-fat chips or cookies, read the label and parcel out only the amount listed as a "serving size." Then put the bag away. Also, compare labels of reduced-fat and regular versions of the same foods to see if there really is that much of a difference.

*My rule of thumb:* If there is no more than a two- to three-gram fat difference and no more than a 25-calorie difference per serving, the reduced-fat item probably doesn't have much of an edge.

To stick to reasonable portions of all snack foods, have a piece of fruit along with each snack or sweet.

●Keep track of what you eat. Most diet masters do not obsessively weigh and measure the foods they eat. But they do track their consumption occasionally.

Some count calories or keep track of food groups, while others keep food diaries, writing down the foods they eat as the day progresses.

Keeping a food diary pinpoints where your extra calories are coming from if you get stuck at a plateau while losing weight. It also makes you stop and think before grabbing a handful of snacks.

*Helpful:* Buy yourself a lined notebook or a weight-loss journal. For one week, write down what you eat, the amount and the total calories in the portion. There is no need to count sugar-free beverages or gum.

Women trying to lose weight should stick with 1,200 to 1,500 calories a day...for men, the daily caloric intake should be 1,500 to 2,000 calories.

●**Don't let exercise become boring.** Exercise is a cornerstone of successful weight con-

trol. Most diet masters told me that they exercise at least three times a week, with 25% of them working out five or six times weekly. Many of them had more than one way to keep physically fit.

*Example:* Six out of 10 people engage in at least two different forms of exercise, such as walking and light weight training. Some change their exercise with the season—outdoor cycling in the summer and aerobics in the winter.

Others vary their exercise within a workout session. Spending 45 minutes on a treadmill is boring, but spending 15 minutes on each of three different pieces of equipment is more bearable.

*Helpful:* Since exercise goals that are too rigorous are usually short-lived, start small, start easy and do a form of exercise that you enjoy.

Begin by walking for 15 to 20 minutes, the top form of exercise among diet masters. After a few weeks, increase to 30 minutes, and on alternate days, ride your bike or lift light weights.

*Important:* Give yourself a break—schedule some days off from exercise each week, and don't feel you have to keep increasing your exercise to benefit. That's a good way to get hurt or discouraged.

# #1 Heart Attack Trigger

Many heart attacks are triggered by a fatty meal. Researchers have found that heart attacks are most likely to occur in the six hours following consumption of a meal *high in fat,* regardless of the source of the fat.

Recent studies have shown that fatty foods increase the blood level of a substance that encourages the formation of blood clots and makes arteries stiffer, constricting blood flow.

*Prevention:* Men and women who have not had heart attacks should eat meals with less than 20 grams of saturated fat. A "killer meal" would be, for instance, a prime beef hamburger (20 grams), plus french fries fried in beef tallow (10 grams) and one cup of premium ice cream (20 grams).

William P. Castelli, MD, medical director of the Framingham Cardiovascular Institute and former director of the Framingham Heart Study, Framingham, MA.

# Better Eating on the Road

When eating at fast-food restaurants, buy a grilled chicken sandwich without mayonnaise. Avoid sauces, gravies, butter and other fatty toppings and dressings. Use mustard or salsa as condiments. Be sure to get at least half the day's food from breakfast and lunch. Eat less in restaurants—most portions are twice what you need. If going out for a big meal, eat vegetarian the rest of the day.

Georgia Kostas, RD, nutrition director, Cooper Clinic, Cooper Aerobics Center, Dallas.

# The Mediterranean Diet

The Mediterranean diet is even more healthful than experts had realized. The diet— rich in bread, cereals, fruits, vegetables, canola oil, nuts and olive oil and low in red meat, butter and cream—has long been credited for the low rates of heart disease among people living along the Mediterranean Sea. In a recent study, researchers found that the diet not only helped prevent heart disease, but also cut cancer risk by 61%.

Michel de Lorgeril, MD, researcher and cardiology consultant, Laboratoire de Physiologie, Centre Hospitalo-Universitaire, Saint-Etienne, France.

# Young Kids Need Fat

Infants and toddlers should not be placed on a restricted-fat diet. Restricting fat intake to 30% of total calories makes sense for most adults. But fat restriction in kids age five or under impairs their physical and intellectual growth and visual acuity…and may even raise their risk for heart disease later in life. *Prudent approach:* Let children eat what they want until age five. After that, see that they gradually reduce their fat intake throughout the remainder of their childhood and teen years.

Bruce A. Watkins, PhD, professor of lipid chemistry and metabolism, Purdue University, West Lafayette, IN.

# Men Need Calcium, Too

After age 50, men should consume 1,200 mg of calcium per day. In a recent study, men took calcium supplements to boost their daily intake from 700 mg to 1,200 mg.

**Result:** They experienced significantly reduced rates of bone loss.

Some men may need a supplement to meet the 1,200 mg level, but food sources of calcium are preferred. Sources include low-fat milk and yogurt and green, leafy vegetables.

Bess Dawson-Hughes, MD, chief, Calcium and Bone Metabolism Lab, Jean Mayer US Department of Agriculture Human Nutrition Research Center on Aging, Tufts University, Boston.

# Whey Is Nutritious

The clear liquid that pools inside containers of yogurt is nutritious. *Whey* is rich in vitamins, minerals, carbohydrates and protein. Stir it back into the yogurt before eating.

Leslie Bonci, RD, MPH, assistant director of nutrition, Center for Digestive Health, Allegheny General Hospital, Pittsburgh.

# Foods that Relax You

Annemarie Colbin, certified health education specialist and founder of the Natural Gourmet Cookery School in New York City. Ms. Colbin is author of the chapter "Food for Relaxation" in *The Big Book of Relaxation.* The Relaxation Company. She is also author of *Food and Our Bones: The Natural Way to Prevent Osteoporosis.* Plume.

You probably know that foods rich in carbohydrates and fiber—and *free* of hydrogenated fat (the fat in fried foods, margarine, shortening)—help you stay healthy. But—did you know the same foods also help your mind and body relax?

Steamed vegetables, fruits, whole-wheat bread, brown rice, polenta or oatmeal help you relax by providing your body with a source of energy that is steadily metabolized and continuously absorbed—and by stimulating the relaxing brain chemical serotonin.

When these foods are consumed with some protein—fish or chicken—they leave you feeling calm and focused.

### FOOD MYTHS

Refined sugar and alcohol seem to have a relaxing effect on the body. In fact, they often make you sleepy. But don't be fooled.

After the initial ease of tension, the effects of alcohol wear off, leaving many people tense and angry.

The same is true for sugar. After an initial sugar "rush"—the surge that leaves you feeling temporarily alert and clear-headed—many people feel exhausted.

They typically crave more sugar to get them going again, and a cycle of highs and lows becomes a way of life.

### RELAXING FOODS

To keep your energy in balance and feel tension-free, eat a variety of the following healthful foods...

●**Breakfast.** Start your day with a small piece of fish with dark rye bread, or with an organic egg on whole-grain toast or oatmeal cooked with raisins and cinnamon and topped with toasted sunflower and pumpkin seeds.

The protein/carbohydrate combination will leave you feeling relaxed and focused—unlike a high-fat, high-sugar breakfast (a donut or muffin), which may create a need for caffeine and more sugar as the morning wears on.

In general, I don't recommend eating dairy products. Among other things, they tend to make some people feel heavy and congested.

●**Lunching out.** Have a sandwich on whole-wheat bread or pita, an English muffin or rye toast.

*Great fillers:* Thinly sliced natural meats like turkey, chicken breast or roast beef...a dab of mustard or a bit of mayonnaise...and vegetables like lettuce, tomato, onion, grated carrots or sprouts.

Another good lunch option is soup—anything with dried beans or peas—such as split pea, lentil, Yankee bean or black bean. Also

good are hearty vegetable soups and chicken soup, served with bread and salad.

If your goal is to be alert and energetic, have more protein and fewer carbohydrates for lunch.

*Good choice:* Broiled fish or grilled chicken and a side salad. Avoid dessert.

*Poor choice:* Pasta and green salad—it's likely to leave you feeling relaxed and ready for a siesta, not raring to go.

●**Lunch at home.** Mash avocado with a little salsa and eat it on whole-wheat pita bread. Mash canned salmon or sardines with some lemon juice, chopped onion and celery and spread on rye crackers.

*One potato:* A great low-fat, relaxing side dish or snack is a baked yam or sweet potato. To keep yams on hand, bake six at a time in a 400-degree oven for one hour—but don't wrap or puncture the skin. Store them in the refrigerator and serve cold, sliced and steamed, grilled or pan-fried.

●**Dinner out.** For a good night's sleep, choose pastas (skip the heavy Alfredo sauce), polenta, rice dishes, cooked vegetables, salads, curries, baked or broiled fresh fish...and other dishes that are low in protein and high in complex carbohydrates.

*Dessert:* Something fruit-based, like sorbet. Avoid chocolate, which contains caffeine and sugar.

●**Dinner at home.** A high-fiber vegetarian dinner cooked at home will relax you and give you the nutrients you need.

*Good choices:* Brown rice, barley, polenta, kasha, bean soups, green vegetables like broccoli, baked yams or squash, salad.

*Dessert:* Something sweetened with fruit juice, barley malt or maple syrup (which has the added benefit of being high in calcium).

### FOODS TO AVOID

Some foods and drinks stimulate the nervous system and cause tension and insomnia—whether they're consumed in the morning or at night. *To stay relaxed, avoid...*

●**Caffeine.** Caffeine-containing foods and beverages include sodas, chocolate, teas—even green tea—and some over-the-counter and prescription medications.

●**Alcohol.** It's OK to have a glass of wine occasionally with dinner, but alcohol every day can interfere with sleep and cause mood swings.

●**Sugar.** When you crave something sweet, try a dessert sweetened with fruit juice, grain malt or maple syrup. Chamomile tea with honey is relaxing. Another of my favorite sweets is Bananas Vermont…

*4 bananas, ripe but firm*
*1 tbsp. unsalted butter*
*1 tbsp. maple syrup*
*2 tbsp. water*

Peel bananas, cut once in half across, then cut each piece in half again lengthwise. Melt the butter and pour into a 9" x 14" baking pan. Arrange the bananas in it, turning once to get a little butter on the other side. Mix water and maple syrup and drizzle over the bananas. Broil five minutes, or until bananas soften. Four pieces per person. Serves four.

# Feel-Full Snacks That Are Only About 150 Calories Each

Barbara Rolls, PhD, professor of nutrition and head of the Laboratory for the Study of Human Ingestive Behavior at The Pennsylvania State University, University Park.

Snacking in the evening is one of the chief culprits in weight gain. Here are healthful snacks that are roughly 150 calories each…

### ANGEL FOOD CAKE

Top one slice of angel food cake with one cup of whole fresh strawberries and two tablespoons of light, nondairy whipped topping.

### BAKED APPLE

Peel an apple one-quarter down from the top. Core it, and place two teaspoons of brown sugar in the center. Sprinkle with cinnamon. Microwave on high in a small, covered bowl for two to three minutes.

### CARROTS, CELERY AND DIP

Place 15 prewashed baby carrots and a sliced stalk of celery on a plate. Dip them into three tablespoons of nonfat ranch dressing.

### FRUIT AND POPCORN

Two and one-quarter cups of fresh air-popped popcorn—plain or lightly salted. Enjoy with one-half an apple and one cup of grapes on the side.

### FRUIT SMOOTHIE

Use a blender to mix four ounces of light yogurt…one-quarter cup of nonfat milk …three-quarter cup of frozen or fresh strawberries, sliced…one-third of a banana…and one cup of ice. The banana will give any smoothie a rich, filling texture.

### MILK AND COOKIES

Have three-quarter cup of nonfat milk and eight *bite-sized,* reduced-fat chocolate chip cookies.

### OAT CEREAL WITH MILK

Mix three-quarter cup of toasted oat cereal with three-quarter cup of nonfat milk.

### TOMATO SOUP

One and one-quarter cups of tomato soup made with water. Also have three saltine crackers.

# Is Milk Truly Good for You?

Neal Barnard, MD, president and founder of the Physicians Committee for Responsible Medicine, 5100 Wisconsin Ave., Washington, DC 20016. His most recent book is *Foods that Fight Pain.* Harmony.

Nutritionists, doctors and public health officials have long recommended low-fat and nonfat varieties of milk and other dairy products as good sources of calcium and other key nutrients.

Most health experts continue to recommend milk. But studies have begun to link milk consumption with a range of childhood and adult illnesses.

Milk's most vocal critic, Dr. Neal Barnard, explains why he's now convinced that milk isn't good for adults—or children.

### CANCER

Preliminary evidence suggests a connection between *galactose*, a sugar found in milk, and ovarian cancer. Another compound found in milk, *insulin-like growth factor 1* (IGF-1), has been linked to cancer of the breast, kidney and prostate.

In a study published recently in the journal *Science*, Harvard researchers found that men with high levels of IGF-1 in their blood were four times more likely than men with low levels to develop prostate cancer.

The possibility that IGF-1 is carcinogenic is especially alarming because many dairy cattle are now being treated with *bovine growth hormone* (BGH) to boost their milk output.

Milk from BGH-treated cattle has twice as much IGF-1 as milk from untreated cattle.

*Trap:* Milk producers are not required to indicate on package labels whether the cows from which the milk came were treated with BGH.

### DIABETES

More than 90 studies have now implicated milk as a major cause of juvenile (type I) diabetes. This disease strikes one in every 500 children. It is lifelong—and life-threatening.

The trouble starts when *bovine albumin* passes into the bloodstream. For most children, this milk protein is apparently harmless. But roughly one of every five children is sensitive to it.

Once it enters the bloodstream of an allergic child, bovine albumin stimulates the body to produce antibodies. By a quirk of nature, the same antibodies that attack bovine albumin also attack insulin-producing cells located in the pancreas.

In a 1992 study published in *The New England Journal of Medicine*, University of Toronto researchers found that diabetic children had six times more antibodies to bovine albumin in their blood than nondiabetic children did.

### ANEMIA

Milk can cause anemia by interfering with iron absorption...and/or by triggering internal bleeding.

*At special risk:* Children. The American Academy of Pediatrics now recommends that children under age one not drink milk.

In a study conducted recently at the University of Iowa and published in the journal *Pediatrics*, the stools of infants fed milk contained five times as much blood as stools from children fed formula.

The researchers concluded that the amount of iron lost was "nutritionally important."

### MILK AND OSTEOPOROSIS

Many women drink milk because they think the calcium it contains will reduce their risk for osteoporosis. But there is growing doubt that milk really does protect the bones.

The ongoing Harvard Nurses' Health Study of 78,000 women has found that women who drink three glasses of milk per day are no less likely to develop osteoporosis than women who drink no milk at all.

### GOING MILK-FREE

Given the potential health risks associated with milk, I feel that it's prudent to get your calcium from beans and green, leafy vegetables like broccoli, kale and collard or mustard greens.

Three or four daily servings of beans and/or leafy greens provide more than enough calcium for most people.

To ensure that you get enough, you can add calcium-fortified orange juice to your diet.

If you love milk and cannot imagine giving it up, consider switching to soy milk or rice milk. These products don't taste exactly like cow's milk, but many people who try them like them.

They work on breakfast cereals and in coffee. They're now widely available in supermarkets.

# Snack-Food Heaven?

David W. Freeman, editor, *Bottom Line/Health*, Boardroom Inc., Box 2614, 55 Railroad Ave., Greenwich, CT 06836-2614.

Have you tried olestra? It's the fat substitute used in Frito-Lay's Wow brand snacks. I tried some Wow potato chips the other day. They tasted just like regular potato chips but with none of the usual artery-clogging, waist-expanding fat.

The idea of guilt-free snacking seemed too good to be true. Sure enough, when I did a little research, I found that olestra is too good to be true.

The problem with olestra is twofold according to Meir J. Stampfer, MD, a Harvard researcher who has emerged as a leading critic of the fake fat.

First, since olestra passes through the body undigested, people who eat it sometimes suffer cramps and/or diarrhea.

Second—and much more ominous—is the fact that olestra can deplete the body of crucial fat-soluble vitamins. To counteract this tendency, olestra-containing snacks are fortified with vitamins A, D, E and K.

But those are not the only fat-soluble vitamins affected by olestra. Olestra also depletes the body of *carotenoids*, antioxidant compounds that have been shown to play a role in reducing the risk for heart disease, stroke, cancer and the retinal disorder, macular degeneration.

Stampfer estimates that over the next decade, olestra consumption could cause each year up to 9,800 additional cases of prostate cancer...32,000 additional cases of coronary artery disease...7,400 additional cases of lung cancer...and 390 additional cases of macular degeneration.

Frito-Lay maintains that olestra is safe. The FDA seems to agree. Following hearings in Washington, DC, the agency ruled that the fake fat can remain on the market.

But until olestra has a longer track record for safety, I'll be watching carefully from the sidelines.

---

# Soda Drinkers Beware!

Sweetened soft drinks weaken bones. As part of a preliminary study, people drank five cans of nondiet soda daily for three months. *Result:* They absorbed less calcium and excreted more phosphorus than others—depriving their bodies of important bone minerals. *Problem:* Soft drinks take the place of more healthful foods. *Self-defense:* Drink no more than two cans a day. *Much more healthful:* Fruit juice...nonfat milk...water.

Forrest Nielsen, PhD, director of the US Department of Agriculture's Human Nutrition Research Center in Grand Forks, ND.

---

# Walk and Live Longer

To lengthen your life—*walk*. Men who walked more than two miles a day were almost half as likely to have died during a 12-year period as men who walked less than one mile a day. The earlier you establish a walking habit, the more you reduce your risk of cancer and heart disease in later life.

Robert Abbott, PhD, professor of biostatistics, University of Virginia School of Medicine, Charlottesville, whose study was published in *The New England Journal of Medicine*.

---

# Everyday Stretches to Keep You Flexible: Do Them Anytime...Anywhere

Bob Anderson, a fitness consultant based in Palmer Lake, CO. Widely regarded as the country's leading authority on stretching, Mr. Anderson is the author of *Stretching* and *Stretching at Your Computer or Desk,* both published by Shelter Publications.

Aerobic exercise is essential for staying healthy. But walking, cycling, swimming, etc., are *not* enough.

In order to stay limber and surefooted, you must stretch your muscles. Regular stretching is especially crucial during and after middle age. Middle-aged muscles that go unstretched gradually lose flexibility.

Reduced flexibility interferes with your ability to carry out your everyday activities. It also raises your risk for injuries that occur as a result of falls, pulled muscles, etc.

***Good news:*** You do *not* have to enroll in a yoga class or follow some complicated routine. All you must do is squeeze a few stretches into your daily routine.

These eight stretches can be done anytime, anywhere—while working at the office, waiting in line, talking on the telephone, reading a magazine, etc. They can be done separately or in combination with each other.

***Caution:*** Stretches should be gentle and slow. The goal is to ease tension in tight muscles— not to achieve total flexibility in a single session.

### SHOULDERS AND UPPER BACK

Interlace your fingers, then straighten your arms in front of you with palms facing away.

Hold the stretch for 10 seconds. You should feel a pleasant sensation of tautness in your arms, upper back and shoulder blades.

### NECK AND SHOULDERS

Raise your shoulders upward toward your ears until you feel tension in your neck and shoulders. Hold for five seconds, then let your shoulders drop back to their normal position. Repeat twice more.

This stretch can be done standing or seated. It should be used at the first sign of tension in your shoulders or neck.

### INNER THIGHS AND GROIN

Stand with hands on your hips. Point your feet straight ahead, a little more than shoulder-width apart.

Bend your right knee slightly, letting your left hip drop toward the ground. Hold for 10 seconds, then repeat with the left knee and right hip.

### CHEST AND BACK

Place your palms on your lower back just above your hips, with your elbows back and loose thumbs pointing forward.

Gently press forward, lifting your chest slightly until you feel tautness in your lower back and upper chest. Hold for 15 seconds.

### UPPER TORSO

Place your hands shoulder-width apart against the wall at chin level (or grasp a handy shelf or the top of a filing cabinet). Bend your knees, and lower your head between your arms. Keep your hips directly above your feet. Hold for 15 seconds.

You should feel tension in your neck, shoulders, arms and upper back.

### TRICEPS

Stand with knees slightly bent. With your left hand, gently pull your right elbow behind your head until you feel the stretch in your right shoulder and the back of your upper right arm. Hold the stretch for 10 seconds, then switch arms and repeat.

Be careful not to hold your breath or to overstretch.

### HAMSTRINGS AND LOWER BACK

Sit in a firm chair. Grasp your upper left leg with both hands, just above the back of the knee. Gently pull your bent leg toward your chest. Hold for 10 seconds, feeling the tension in your left thigh and lower back. Switch legs and repeat.

If you spend long hours at a desk, this stretch is great for relieving back tension.

### PELVIC REGION

While standing in front of a desk, place your right foot against the edge of the desk. Bend your right knee until you feel a gentle stretch in the inside of your left leg. Hold for 15 seconds, then switch legs and repeat.

This stretch is tailor-made for talking on the phone.

---

# Psychological Strategies to Help You Stick with Your Exercise Regimen

Carolyn Scott Kortge, a Eugene, OR, journalist and race walker—and a student of Buddhist meditation. The winner of silver and bronze medals at the US National Masters Championships in 1992, she is the author of *The Spirited Walker: Fitness Walking for Clarity, Balance and Spiritual Connection*. Harper San Francisco.

---

Walking for as little as 20 minutes a day greatly reduces your risk for several deadly ailments, including heart disease and cancer.

These remarkable benefits of walking ought to be motivation enough for all of us to lace on a pair of sneakers and begin a program of daily strolls.

Sadly, many people derive so little pleasure from walking that they never launch a walking program. Those who do often lose interest after a matter of weeks or months...and give up.

***Good news:*** Many reluctant walkers find they're able to stick with a regimen by performing mind-focusing mental exercises as they move along.

Called *mindful walking,* this exercise–meditation combination helps people stick with a regimen by distracting them from the negative thoughts that make them want to stop.

***Examples:*** "This is too hard"..."I'd rather be watching TV"..."I'll never get in shape"..."I should have done so-and-so."

Mindful walking also confers long-lasting psychological benefits, including reduced anxiety and depression and a heightened sense of tranquility.

Try these four mental exercises on your next walk (or run). You might try one for five or 10 minutes, then switch to another. Experiment until you find the exercise or combination of exercises that proves especially effective.

### FOUR-STEP BREATHING

This simple exercise makes you more aware of your body's movements...and makes your stride more relaxed and fluid.

***What to do:*** As you walk, focus your attention on your breathing. Inhale slowly and deeply, silently counting—one count for each step—"in, two, three, four" as you do.

Then exhale for four counts—one per step—saying, "out, two, three, four."

One foot will always land on an even count, the other foot on an odd count.

After doing four-step breathing for a minute or two, add a visual element. Imagine that each exhalation inflates a perfectly spherical balloon attached to your mouth. Each inhalation deflates the balloon.

If your concentration wavers, your invisible balloon will lose its roundness. You'll need to focus again to get it to return to its original shape.

People who try this exercise are often amazed at how difficult it is to sustain the necessary mental focus. What's the secret? Practice, practice, practice.

### THREE-STEP BREATHING

Since your feet will be constantly switching from even to odd counts, this exercise takes even more concentration than four-step breathing. It's even better at focusing your mind.

***What to do:*** Inhale deeply for three steps as you silently count "in, two, three." Then exhale for three steps while counting "out, two, three."

Hold this "one, two, three" tempo for a few minutes, then add the imaginary balloon.

Practice three-step breathing until you can sustain it for five minutes at a time.

### POSITIVE SELF-TALK

It's only natural to engage in mental self-talk while walking. The challenge is to replace negative self-talk with positive self-talk.

***What to do:*** Watch carefully for the first sign of fatigue or boredom. As soon as you hear negativity creeping into your inner monologue, take a deep breath and remind yourself, "I'm doing something that's good for me, so I'm going to keep going."

Next, repeat a positive phrase over and over again—one syllable per step.

***Examples:*** "I am strong"..."I give thanks" ..."Yes I can."

Whenever you start feeling fatigued, take that deep breath, and repeat these favorite phrases to yourself.

If your mind wanders, gently steer it back to your affirmation.

### INTERVALS

This is a great way to practice positive self-talk and enhance your aerobic workout at the same time.

After 10 minutes of easy walking, pick a building, a street lamp or another landmark about two minutes' walk away. Pick up the pace until you reach the landmark, then slow down to catch your breath. Pick another landmark and start over again.

# Cardiovascular Exercise

How *hard* you exercise may matter more for cardiovascular health than how much. In a study of recreational runners, only levels of HDL—"good" cholesterol—were found to respond better to distance than speed. Blood pressure, total cholesterol and body fat are all affected more positively by the intensity of exercise than by the amount.

Paul Williams, PhD, life sciences division, Lawrence Berkeley Laboratory, Berkeley, CA, whose study was published in *Archives of Internal Medicine*.

# Exercise Opportunities: Use Anything...Anywhere

Porter Shimer, author of 10 books on health and fitness, including *Too Busy to Exercise*. Storey Books.

Here are ways to make your own exercise opportunities...

•**Anything that has weight can be lifted**— phone books...portable TVs...table lamps.

•**Exercise your muscles against each other isometrically**...when forced to sit for long periods.

*Example:* Brace yourself by putting your palms on your thighs just above your knees and try to lean forward with slightly bent arms, held rigid.

•**Do horizontal exercises...**when you have a chance to lie down.

*Examples:* Lie on one side, with one hand propping up your head and the other in front, slowly raise your top leg as far as you comfortably can, hold for five seconds, lower slowly and repeat nine times. Then switch sides and repeat the set.

•**Don't just stand there** waiting for the bus or train—walk.

•**Never ignore a flight of stairs at home or elsewhere.** Stair climbing is such good exercise that people pay good money for machines that duplicate this motion.

•**Carry your own luggage.**

•**Burn off calories with courtesy.** Small active acts of politeness—like holding elevator doors...opening car doors...approaching people so you can speak quietly rather than holler to them—add up, little by little, to a gain in physical fitness...and help you make new friends.

•**Don't be embarrassed if you look a little odd exercising.**

*Example:* When people see you in the act of lifting yourself up by pressing with your palms on the armrests of your bus seat, explain it is an exercise to develop your triceps.

# 17

# Natural Healing

## Dr. Andrew Weil Tells How to Strengthen Your Immune System

The immune system is one of the most important keys to good health. Made up of a complex interaction of blood cells, protein molecules and organs, it helps to protect the body from infection, foreign substances and cancer cells that arise spontaneously—or that come from the environment.

The immune system also is involved in the daily maintenance and repair of tissues. A strong immune system can protect us. A weak immune system increases our vulnerability to disease.

### THE IMMUNE SYSTEM'S ROLE

The immune system is not perfect. An increased vulnerability to infections and other diseases indicates the immune system is weakened. An overactive immune system can cause allergies or mistakenly attack itself, leading to asthma, ulcerative colitis, rheumatoid arthritis, and other diseases.

The immune system can analyze experiences with germs, remember them and pass them on to future generations of cells. By fortifying our immune systems, we improve the likelihood of strengthening immune response when an infection or foreign body tries to invade.

Whatever steps you take to boost your immune system, always discuss them first with your doctor.

### BOLSTERING IMMUNE RESPONSE

**•Avoid indiscriminate use of antibiotics.** Antibiotics are powerful medications that are used to fight bacterial infections. But they should be reserved for situations in which the immune system cannot stop an infection or when an infection takes hold in a vital organ.

---

Andrew Weil, MD, director of the Foundation for Integrative Medicine, University of Arizona and founder of the Center for Integrative Medicine in Tucson. He is author of *Spontaneous Healing* and *8 Weeks to Optimum Health*, both published by Fawcett.

267

Using an antibiotic at the first sign of infection prevents the immune system from having an opportunity to deal with it and emerge stronger. Overuse of antibiotics also encourages bacteria to develop into stronger strains that are resistant to drugs.

***Better than antibiotics:*** The next time you feel you're getting sick, cut down on unnecessary expenditures of energy. Go to bed early, delay plans, drink lots of water and allow others to care for you. A little rest goes a long way to alter the course of an illness and provide an extra energy boost for the immune system.

●**Eat the right foods.** Data show that many seemingly benevolent factors in our food can either help or harm our immunity.

***Examples:*** The red and purple pigments in berries and grapes appear to enhance the immune system and boost defenses against cancer. Polyunsaturated fats, such as safflower oil and margarine, have been shown to produce "free radicals"—unstable oxygen molecules—that can aggravate inflammation and produce immune system disorders.

*Better...*

●Eat fatty acids that favor immune defenses. This means minimizing intake of polyunsaturated oils and instead using monounsaturated fats, such as olive and canola oils.

●Eat less protein and more carbohydrate-rich foods, such as vegetables, fruits and fibrous grains. Proteins are complex molecules that, eaten in excess, drain energy reserves as the body breaks them down. Additionally, the remnants of protein that has been metabolized can irritate the immune system.

●Reduce intake of foods of animal origin, specifically meat, poultry and dairy. Oftentimes, animals are raised on steroids and antibiotics.

●**Eat natural substances that boost the immune system.** *Examples...*

●***Certain mushrooms,*** such as shiitake, dried maitake and enokidake or enoki—found in Asian groceries—have innate properties that boost the immune system and help fight disease.

●***Echinacea,*** a wildflower native to the plains of North America, has been extensively studied for its immune-enhancing properties.

***Usage:*** I use one dropperful of echinacea tincture four times a day...or two capsules of freeze-dried extract four times a day for colds, flu and sore throats. It can also be used to build immunity in the absence of infection. Here, I halve the adult dose and alternate two weeks on, two weeks off.

●***Astragalus*** preparations are produced from the root of this plant. It has antiviral and immune-boosting properties...and it can be purchased in any health food store.

***Usage:*** Two capsules, two times per day... or as the product label directs.

●**Take a daily mix of vitamins.** In addition to the important nutrients contained in fruits and vegetables, you can boost immunity by taking antioxidant supplements. These nutrients block chemical reactions and neutralize free radicals that cause tissue damage. All vitamins should be taken with food. I recommend the following to my patients...

●1,000 to 2,000 mg C.

●400 to 800 international units (IU) natural E. You'll want to look for d-alpha tocopherol plus other tocopherols.

●200 micrograms selenium. It is better if taken at the same time as the vitamin E dose.

●25,000 IU mixed carotene tablet. It should contain alpha- and beta-carotenes, lutein and lycopene.

●100 mg coenzyme Q.

●One B-100 complex tablet.

●**Maintain good oral health.** Many people are surprised to learn that the mouth can harbor hidden infections that take a toll on the immune system.

***Helpful:*** Maintain good oral hygiene by brushing and flossing at least twice daily. You should have your teeth and gums examined at least twice a year in order to detect any areas of hidden infection.

It is also critical to avoid any major dental work during periods of illness, as procedures like root canal can trigger serious illness if your body's defenses are down.

●**Boost your energy reserves.** Training the body to use energy more efficiently can improve cardiovascular health, general stamina and mental health and, most important, strengthen the immune system.

***Goal:*** Work up to at least 30 minutes of aerobic activity five times a week. To avoid boredom, I recommend varied activities—jogging, swimming, cycling, race-walking, jumping rope.

If a period of exercise does not increase your heart rate or stimulate your breathing, you're not working hard enough.

●**Add exercises that improve mental and emotional health to your daily routine.** All body systems are interconnected, especially with the nervous system. These connections primarily take the form of chemical messengers called *peptides*, which carry communication between cells. Just as grief can depress the immune system, joy can enhance it.

I encourage people to pursue meaningful connections in their lives, such as spending time with family, with a pet or in the community, hiking or lunching in the park.

Putting energy into positive states and connections can resolve negativity and boost immunity.

---

# Cut Your Risk of Cancer By Two Thirds

J. Robert Hatherill, PhD, a research scientist in the environmental studies program at the University of California in Santa Barbara. He is author of *Eat to Beat Cancer*. Renaissance Books.

---

Can changing your diet eliminate your risk of developing cancer? That proposition—the centerpiece of a book called *The Breast Cancer Prevention Diet* (Little, Brown)—caused a firestorm of controversy.

Critics of the book, written by television correspondent Bob Arnot, MD, argue that nothing can eliminate the danger of cancer altogether. They're right. No diet, supplement or drug can *guarantee* you won't get cancer. But you *can* do a great deal to protect yourself.

Diet is now believed to be a factor in approximately 60% of all malignancies—with smoking, heredity and viral infections accounting for the rest.

Theoretically, an effective anticancer diet should be capable of cutting your cancer risk by roughly two-thirds.

## NO QUICK FIX

The most compelling demonstrations of cancer risk reduction come from *population studies*. These experiments compare the incidence of certain diseases among different groups of people.

More than 200 such studies have been completed. Among other things, these studies show that cancer rates are much lower in developing nations than in the US.

Citizens of developing nations tend to eat *very* differently than the average American. The average American eats lots of fatty and/or highly processed foods. In developing countries, people eat mostly fruits, vegetables and grains.

## WHAT TO AVOID

It's now well established that eating less dietary fat can cut your cancer risk. Dietary fat clearly raises the risk for breast, colon and prostate cancers.

In addition, you must avoid foods known to raise cancer risk—and boost consumption of foods that lower the risk…

●**Minimize consumption of beef, pork, poultry and fish.** These foods can be concentrated sources of dioxin, polychlorinated biphenyls (PCBs) and other potent carcinogens.

These compounds sap the body's cancer-fighting ability…and trigger genetic mutations that can lead to cancer.

●**Wash produce thoroughly.** If peeling is not an option, use VegiWash or another produce wash. Whenever possible, buy organic.

●**Drink more water.** Drinking eight eight-ounce glasses of water a day helps flush carcinogens out of the body.

●**Consume more dietary fiber**—in the form of fresh fruits, vegetables and whole grains. Fiber speeds the passage of feces through the intestines, reducing the amount of time any carcinogens present in the body remain in contact with body tissues.

●**Avoid processed foods.** Potato chips, baked goods and other processed foods tend to contain lots of trans fatty acids, refined sugar and/or sodium. Animal studies have linked each of these substances to cancer.

## A SHIELD AGAINST CANCER

From the standpoint of cancer avoidance, virtually all fruits, vegetables and grains are beneficial. But certain plant foods are special —because they contain cancer-preventing compounds.

Eight plant foods are particularly rich sources of these *phytochemicals.* They should be eaten every day.

•**Onions and garlic.** The same sulfur compounds that give these herbs their characteristic aromas protect cells against oxidative damage. That's the first step in the cancer process.

Onions and garlic also block the formation of *nitrosamines.* These potent carcinogens are formed in the stomach following consumption of cured meats and other nitrate-containing foods.

•**Crucifers.** Broccoli, cauliflower, cabbage and brussels sprouts are rich sources of potent anticancer compounds known as *glucosinolates.*

Crucifer consumption has been linked with reduced risk for lung and colon cancer.

•**Nuts and seeds.** In addition to antioxidants, nuts and seeds contain *protease inhibitors.* These compounds help block the growth of blood vessels that tumors need to obtain nutrients from the bloodstream.

•**Whole grains.** Oats, wheat and other grains contain fiber that helps isolate cancer-causing compounds and remove them from the body.

Flaxseed, rye and millet are rich in *lignans.* These compounds act as weak estrogens, helping stymie the growth of breast cancer and other malignancies that are often estrogen-dependent.

•**Legumes.** Beans, peas and lentils are rich in fiber and *saponins,* compounds that block tumor growth by inhibiting DNA synthesis. Soybeans are the most potent anticancer legume.

•**Fruits.** In addition to vitamin C—a potent antioxidant—citrus fruits contain cancer-fighting compounds known as *monoterpenes* and *glutathione.*

*Ellagic acid*—in blackberries, strawberries and raspberries—binds to carcinogens and thereby deactivates them.

•**Tomatoes.** Tomatoes get their red color from *lycopene,* a phytochemical that blocks the formation of carcinogens. Lycopene appears to be especially effective at preventing prostate cancer.

*Important:* Lycopene is more easily absorbed from cooked tomatoes than from raw tomatoes.

•**Umbellifers.** Carrots, parsley, celery and the spices cumin, anise, caraway and coriander are rich sources of phytochemicals.

The *carotenoids* in carrots are strong antioxidants.

Compounds found in celery boost the action of the carcinogen-deactivating enzyme *glutathione S-transferase.*

---

# Herbal Remedies: Secrets Of Greater Effectiveness And Safer Use

Ethan Russo, MD, clinical assistant professor of medicine at the University of Washington School of Medicine in Seattle. He is author of *The Handbook of Psychotropic Herbs.* Haworth Press.

---

People often assume that because herbs are "natural," they pose little risk. Not true.

Some herbs are too toxic for medicinal use. Even some that are generally safe can cause liver or kidney damage.

And like drugs, herbal remedies can react dangerously with certain drugs or foods.

How can you use herbal remedies for maximum safety and effectiveness? In a recent interview, physician-herbalist Dr. Ethan Russo set down these guidelines...

•**Avoid herbs known to be dangerous.** Given their inherent dangers, it's best to avoid chaparral, comfrey, life root, germander, coltsfoot, sassafras and ephedra (ma huang).

•**Don't be misled by wild claims.** Federal law forbids herbal remedy manufacturers from saying their products offer outright cures.

But manufacturers often tout their products as providing relief from a ludicrously wide range of ailments.

Take manufacturers' claims with a grain of salt. The best manufacturers often make no health claims for their products.

●**Seek reliable information.** The average doctor knows little about herbs. The same is true for the average druggist.

Health food store clerks may sound knowledgeable, but their information often comes from herbal remedy manufacturers—hardly a source of unbiased information.

The most reliable source of information on herbs is *The Complete German Commission E Monographs: Therapeutic Guide to Herbal Medicines,* American Botanical Council/$176.50.*

●**Work with a knowledgeable practitioner.** For referral to an herb-savvy medical doctor in your area, contact the American Botanical Council at 512-926-4900...or see its Web site at www.herbalgram.org.

*Alternative:* See a naturopathic physician. In addition to basic medical training, naturopaths have extensive instruction in the safe use of herbs.

For referral to a naturopath in your area, contact the American Association of Naturopathic Physicians at 206-298-0125.

●**Buy only standardized formulations.** Standardized herbal extracts have been formulated to provide the active ingredient or ingredients at a specific concentration. That way, you're assured the product is both potent and safe to use.

Look for the word "standardized" or the words "German standards" on the label.

●**Follow label directions carefully.** Like drugs, herbs work best at specific dosages. Take only the recommended dosage, and be sure to take the herb with or without meals, water, etc.—as indicated.

●**Don't mix herbs and drugs.** Herbs can boost the potency of certain medications. If you're taking a prescription drug, don't begin taking any herbal extract until you've checked with a physician or naturopath.

*Your library may have this book. If not, it can be ordered from the American Botanical Council...or via an on-line bookseller.

If a doctor has prescribed a drug for you, let him/her know about any herbal remedies you're already taking. He may need to adjust the dosage.

*Common herb–drug interactions include...*

●**Saint-John's-wort and *fluoxetine*** (Prozac). The combination can raise brain levels of the neurotransmitter serotonin. "Serotonin syndrome" can cause delirium and other dangerous symptoms.

●**Ginkgo biloba and anticoagulants.** Like aspirin, *warfarin* (Coumadin) and other anticoagulants, ginkgo thins the blood. Taken along with an anticoagulant, ginkgo can cause internal bleeding.

●**Watch out for allergic reactions.** Introduce herbs one at a time. Don't add a second herb until you've taken the first for an entire week without experiencing any symptoms of an allergic reaction—rash, upset stomach, dizziness or headache. If you experience any of these symptoms, stop taking the herb at once. Try taking it again one week later. If symptoms return, stop taking the herb for good.

*Caution:* If you become short of breath after taking an herb, call for an ambulance at once.

●**Don't take herbs during pregnancy.** Ginger, garlic and other herbs that are popular as foods are generally okay. But other herbs can cause serious problems for pregnant women.

It's also best to check with a doctor before giving any herbal remedy to a child under age 12.

---

# You Don't Have to Put Up With Fatigue Anymore

Erika T. Schwartz, MD, an internist in private practice in Armonk, NY. She is author of *Natural Energy: From Tired to Terrific in 10 Days.* Putnam.

---

You've tried getting more sleep. You've tried exercising and taking other steps to control psychological stress. Yet you're still feeling tired and run down. You know it's unwise to prop yourself up with caffeine. But what else can you do to boost your energy levels?

Once anemia, heart disease, thyroid disease, hepatitis, mononucleosis and other medical causes of fatigue have been ruled out, the average physician is at a loss as to what to do next.

"You'll just have to learn to live with it," he/she might say. Or, "Well, you *are* getting older."

Not true. These nutrition-based strategies can be very effective...

### DRINK MORE WATER

Many cases of fatigue can be traced to the *mitochondria,* the microscopic "power plants" inside each cell of the body.

Mitochondria synthesize *adenosine triphosphate* (ATP), a high-energy molecule that's used throughout the body as a source of energy. But the chemical reactions that yield ATP also make free radicals and other toxins as by-products.

To flush out these toxins, the body needs at least 64 ounces of water a day. Less than that, and mitochondria are apt to become "clogged" with toxins, becoming inefficient at pumping out ATP.

### RECONSIDER SALT

For many people with high blood pressure, salt deserves its status as a dietary no-no. But in healthy individuals, moderate salt intake boosts energy levels.

Salt helps the body hold on to the water it takes in. By boosting water retention, salt helps keep mitochondria free of toxins and functioning properly.

As long as your blood pressure is normal, it's safe to boost your intake of chicken stock, miso soup, salted nuts and other unprocessed sources of salt whenever you feel fatigued.

### EAT SMALL, EAT OFTEN

Eating three big meals a day puts your blood sugar (glucose) levels on a roller coaster. Low glucose can cause fatigue.

Eating every three hours helps keep your energy up by steadying your glucose levels.

Your goal should be to consume a mix of protein and fiber at each meal. Because fiber-and protein-rich foods are digested slowly, they provide a steady, reliable source of energy.

Eat plenty of vegetables, brown rice, multigrain bread, grilled chicken or fish, nuts and dried fruits.

### ENERGY-BOOSTING SUPPLEMENTS

Three nutrients are of proven value in the treatment of chronic fatigue...

•**L-carnitine.** This amino acid helps transport fatty acids into mitochondria, where they're used to make ATP.

L-carnitine is found in lamb, beef and other meats, but you'd have to consume impossibly large amounts of these natural food sources to get the 1,000 mg of L-carnitine needed each day to boost your energy.

Ask your doctor about taking the prescription L-carnitine supplement *Carnitor.* The typical dosage is three or four 330-mg tablets a day.

•**Coenzyme Q10.** This antioxidant enzyme acts as a catalyst to "spark" synthesis of ATP.

Organ meats are the best source of coenzyme Q, but you'd have to eat far too much to get the recommended 100 mg of coenzyme Q10 per day.

Coenzyme Q10 is sold over the counter in powder or gel form. The gel is more easily absorbed. The typical dosage is two 50-mg gelcaps a day.

•**Magnesium.** This mineral is needed for ATP synthesis. Unfortunately, chocolate, caffeine, soft drinks and highly processed foods tend to deplete the body of magnesium. As a result, magnesium deficiency is common in the US, and fatigue is a symptom of magnesium deficiency.

***At special risk:*** Diabetics, people who consume lots of caffeine and people who take diuretic drugs.

Good sources of magnesium include wheat bran...brown rice...spinach...kale...chicken ...turkey...pork...apricots...and curry powder.

Ask your doctor about taking a magnesium supplement, too.

# Use Music to Heal The Body...and Strengthen The Mind

Don Campbell, classical musician, composer and lecturer in Boulder, CO, and founder of the Institute for Music, Health and Education. He is author of *The Mozart Effect: Tapping the Power of Music to Heal the Body, Strengthen the Mind, and Unlock the Creative Spirit.* Avon Books.

Even music lovers tend to take music for granted. We know that a pleasant tune can lighten a gloomy mood, and an arrangement of favorite selections can create a pleasant dinner atmosphere or provide an evening's entertainment and delight. *But music can do much, much more...*

• It has an almost magical power to reach into our minds and bodies.

• It can act as a stimulant, helping us to think more sharply and work more productively ...or it can act as a relaxant, creating a place of safety and beauty to ease the tensions of the day.

• It can even aid recovery from surgery and serious disease.

*Best of all:* The power of music is available to anyone, nearly anytime.

## WHAT MUSIC CAN DO

Although much of the power of music remains mysterious, researchers continue to learn about its effects on the mind and body.

By stimulating the auditory nerves, sounds create brain messages that ripple through the body, influencing muscle tone, equilibrium and joint flexibility. The organized sounds of music literally *orchestrate* physical activity into strong, coherent rhythms. If you have exercised to music, you have a sense of this.

But music also impacts physiology on a deep, basic level. The human heartbeat is especially attuned to sound—changes in tempo and volume act as natural pacemakers. Breathing slows down or speeds up along with the music.

*Important:* The cells of your body respond to music. A study at Michigan State University found that just 15 minutes of listening could increase levels of immune chemicals—vital to protect against disease. Release of cortisol (the "stress hormone") dropped by up to 25%.

Music has a direct effect on the function of the brain. It can slow down and equalize brain waves to create a meditative state...or it can energize brain waves, quickening the thinking process and enhancing creativity.

## HEALING HARMONIES

Increasingly, doctors and hospitals tap the healing power of music to ease pain. A study of 408 patients with severe headaches and neurological disorders reported that those who listened to concert music for six months needed less medication than a control group who didn't listen to music.

Patients who listened to just 15 minutes of slow, rich, soothing music before surgery required as much as half the usual dose of sedatives and painkillers after the operation. Lutheran Hospital, in Denver, provides a 24-hour video channel of images and fine music to help patients relax and heal faster.

If you are planning surgery, spend a few days beforehand rehearsing for recovery.

Choose an album of slow and beautiful baroque or classical music. Each day, listen to the album while lying down with your eyes closed. Imagine the operation being over—and yourself comfortable and healing well.

Bring your own portable cassette or CD player (with earphones), and ask to have the nurse turn it on when you are brought to the recovery room. Then you will awaken to soothing, healing harmony.

## SOUNDS AGAINST STRESS

The well-known ability of music to reduce tension and ease anxiety has been confirmed by scientific studies. A paper in the *Journal of the American Medical Association* reported that when surgeons listened to their favorite music while operating (classical compositions, jazz and folk songs were chosen), their blood pressure was lower, their pulse was slower and they could think more quickly and accurately.

Often, it's hard to let go of work stresses when the day is done. *Helpful:* Use music as a "bridge." As you drive home, play refreshing classical music instead of listening to the chatter of talk shows on the radio.

If you're especially keyed up, slow, meditative selections are best.

If you commute by bus or train, a portable cassette player with earphones can create a stress-reducing island of tranquillity that will leave you calm and centered when you arrive home.

### PUTTING MUSIC TO WORK

Not only does music create a more pleasant work environment, it boosts productivity, too. Ninety minutes of light classical music increased copyediting accuracy by 21% in a University of Washington study. Efficiency rose nearly 20% after a nine-month office music program at Mississippi Power and Light.

On your own, you can use music to improve alertness, think more clearly and increase your creativity.

If you must deal with new material or master new skills, get into a state of alert relaxation that accelerates the learning process by listening to baroque music for five to 10 minutes.

*Examples:* The sonatas and concertos of Johan Sebastian Bach, Georg Philipp Telemann and Antonio Vivaldi (as well as *Music for the Mozart Effect*, Volume 2, Spring Hill Music, 800-721-2177/ $16.98 CD, $10.98 cassette).

To activate your brain and raise your attention level, high-frequency sounds are most effective. Try turning down the bass on your sound system, and turning up the treble. Choose a piece of music with lots of violins, and listen for a few minutes when you need to be energized.

*Examples:* The Mozart violin concertos (and *Music for the Mozart Effect*, Volume 1, Spring Hill Music, 800-721-2177/$16.98 CD, $10.98 cassette). These are especially effective to "wake up" your brain after lunch, when you may be feeling especially sluggish.

### CHOOSING WISELY

Music is largely a matter of taste—selections you don't enjoy are unlikely to be very helpful. But to gain the broadest benefits, it pays to experiment and expand your acquaintance with the whole spectrum of sounds.

The music of Mozart, in particular, has been linked to energizing, healing, creative effects. The key may be its purity and clarity. The compositions of this genius are complex enough to be engaging, but not distracting …the emotions they arouse are invigorating but not overwhelming. Their lightness and vitality inspire creativity.

*Other kinds of music can have other powers…*

●Gregorian chant uses the natural rhythms of breathing…it is excellent for quiet study, meditation and deep relaxation.

●Big-band, pop and top-40 selections inspire movement, engage emotions and create a sense of well-being.

●Jazz, blues and Dixieland can uplift and inspire, releasing deep joy and sadness.

●Romantic classical pieces—Robert Schumann, Peter Ilyich Tchaikovsky, Frederic Chopin, Franz Liszt—emphasize expression and emotion. They enhance sympathy, compassion and love.

●Impressionist music evokes dreamlike images and can unlock your imagination. *Examples:* Claude Debussy and Maurice Ravel.

# How Doctors Stay Well With Sickness All Around All Day Long

Michael Janson, MD, a general practitioner in private practice in Barnstable, MA, and president of the American College for Advancement in Medicine, a professional nonprofit medical educational organization. He is author of *The Vitamin Revolution in Health Care.* Arcadia Press.

Doctors provide the best of their science-based knowledge about health and disease to their patients. But many of them hold off recommending alternative treatments that they themselves use.

Here's what many doctors I know believe for themselves…and how they take care of themselves to limit the likelihood of illness. Consult your doctor to be sure this advice is *right for you.*

●**Vitamin supplements are essential to replenish cells with nutrients.** More than 60% of doctors say that they take supplements regularly even though they don't recommend them to their patients.

There's no question that a balanced diet is key to keeping your body functioning at its optimum level.

However, a variety of factors influence the value of nutrients in our daily diets. Factors include genetic makeup...pollution...overprocessed foods...and stress. Stress robs the body of important immune-boosting nutrients.

Vitamin supplements enhance a healthy diet and offer protection against the many factors that negatively influence our food supply and health.

*What I recommend to my patients:* In addition to a multivitamin/mineral, I tell patients to take 50 to 100 mg of vitamin B6...400 to 800 mcg folic acid...2,000 mg vitamin C...and 6 to 15 mg of natural beta-carotene, daily.

●**Vitamin E can protect against heart disease.** According to a recent survey, 80% of doctors said they took vitamin E.

Numerous studies have shown that vitamin E can protect the circulatory system against the consequence of cholesterol deposits. Those deposits can lead to clogged arteries—and to atherosclerosis.

Therapeutic doses range from 400 to 1,200 international units (IUs) per day of natural E (d-alpha-tocopherol).

*Caution:* If you are taking anticlotting medications (for example, Coumadin or aspirin), you should consult your doctor before starting to take vitamin E. Its natural anticlotting properties may cause too much of that effect in your blood.

●**Niacin and glucosamine sulfate** can reduce joint pain and cartilage degeneration associated with osteoarthritis—without the side effects of anti-inflammatory drugs.

Osteoarthritis—which is a degenerative joint condition that affects about 80% of people older than age 70—is effectively treated with anti-inflammatory medicines.

But these medications can cause troublesome and sometimes serious side effects for many of the patients who take them.

That's why niacin (vitamin B3) and glucosamine sulfate turn out to be an effective alternative for most of my patients.

Niacin has many uses in the body, including helping to maintain normal mental functions, energy in the cells, digestion and healthy skin.

Glucosamine sulfate is a natural compound found in connective tissue and cartilage that contributes to joint strength. Supplements help to repair joint cartilage and relieve pain within four to eight weeks.

*Doses:* For my patients, I recommend two 500-mg glucosamine sulfate tablets twice daily and/or two 500-mg niacinamide tablets twice daily.

●**Headaches can be effectively managed through massage and diet.** Many of my colleagues ask their spouses or partners to massage their temples or necks after the working day or they get periodic professional massages.

*Reason:* Massage can help to relieve headaches that may be caused by muscle tension in various parts of the body. In fact, many pain clinics use massage as part of an overall program to treat tension headaches.

Your diet can play a large role in the onset or exacerbation of headaches—particularly processed, sugary foods, which cause blood sugar levels to fluctuate.

*What you can do:* Before you reach for an over-the-counter pain reliever, examine the foods you've been eating. Get rid of heavily processed foods, which often contain nitrates, white flour and sugar. Satisfy your cravings for sweets by eating fruits.

Standardized extracts of the herbal medicines feverfew (25 to 50 mg two to three times daily) or ginkgo biloba (60 mg twice a day) can also reduce the frequency and intensity of headaches without the rebound effect of medicines. (As with all herbs, pregnant women may need to take special precautions.)

●**Stress management can help lower and maintain blood pressure.** Many doctors are hesitant to discuss breathing and visualization exercises because they are still considered unconventional in most medical practices. But many others believe that they are key to lowering blood pressure and keeping it down, with or without medications.

*Example:* Sit in a comfortable position, and place one hand on your abdomen. While envisioning a warm, comfortable place, breathe in and out slowly, pushing your hand out each time you inhale. Do this for at least five minutes, three to four times daily.

275

It's also important to go to bed in a calm state. Read a relaxing book or listen to relaxing music just before bed.

●**Exercise has positive effects on more than two dozen chronic health problems,** ranging from rheumatism to diabetes. It's usual for doctors to recommend physical activity.

But has your doctor told you the reasons behind those recommendations? And how much exercise you should be doing?

Studies have demonstrated that regular exercise can improve cardiovascular health, including lipid levels, heart rate and blood pressure, and reduce breast cancer risk in women younger than age 40 by more than one-third.

Researchers have also demonstrated increases in strength and bone and muscle mass, by as much as 170% among individuals over age 80.

*Best routine:* Walk briskly at least four to five times every week. *Aim:* Three miles in 45 minutes.

Go as fast as you can without getting out of breath—but work up a sweat. Strength-training three times weekly is a valuable addition.

---

# Antiaging Strategies for Your Body And Mind

David W. Johnson, PhD, assistant professor of physiology at the University of New England College of Osteopathic Medicine in Biddeford, ME. He is the author of *Feel 30 for the Next 50 Years.* Avon Books.

The aging process starts earlier than many people realize. Even if you're only 35 years old and have no symptoms of disease, microscopic damage is already occurring in the cells of your major organs.

But progressive damage to the body can be delayed. A multipronged program reduces the risk for heart disease, cancer and other major ailments.

It also slows the rate at which people develop "normal" problems of aging, such as hearing loss, vision loss, memory problems, etc.

### ANTIOXIDANTS

As you may already know, antioxidants are compounds that deactivate *free radicals,* highly reactive molecules that attack cell membranes, proteins and even our DNA.

Free radicals have been implicated in heart disease, cancer and dementia.

Recent evidence suggests that free radicals are also responsible for the gradual decline of the immune system, which leaves older people increasingly vulnerable to infection. So far, four antioxidants seem to be especially beneficial...

●**Carotenoids.** These fat-soluble antioxidants help protect cell membranes.

To boost carotenoid levels in your body, eat more sweet potatoes and other red and yellow vegetables...and take a supplement containing 50 mg of mixed carotenoids every other day.

●**Vitamin E.** This fat-soluble antioxidant has been shown to protect the heart and brain... and to enhance the immune system.

It's hard to get enough vitamin E from grains and other food sources without also getting too much fat. For this reason, it's best to rely on a supplement. The usual dosage is 200 international units (IU) per day.

●**Vitamin C.** This water-soluble antioxidant—found primarily in citrus fruits—protects parts of cells that vitamin E and carotenoids can't reach. The usual dosage is 500 mg every other day.

●**Selenium.** This mineral, found primarily in seafood and liver, plays a pivotal role in neutralizing free radicals. Yet many Americans are deficient in selenium. The usual dosage is 200 micrograms (mcg) every other day.

In addition to these antioxidants, it's often a good idea to take supplements of folic acid (1 mg per day)...coenzyme Q (50 mg per day)... and zinc (20 mg per day). Discuss the matter with your doctor.

### A STRONG BODY

Why do people tend to get weaker and more easily fatigued as they grow older? For most of us, it's simply that our muscle mass has gotten smaller.

Aging-related muscle shrinkage is known as sarcopenia. Most cases of *sarcopenia* result not from the passage of time, but from disuse—lack of exercise, in other words.

In addition to maintaining strength and vigor, physical activity lowers the risk for heart disease, diabetes, osteoporosis, depression and certain types of cancer.

Exercise also helps prevent hip fracture, which can be debilitating for older people.

For decades now, doctors have been urging their patients to get regular aerobic exercise. That includes running, fast walking, bicycling, swimming and other activities that raise your pulse for an extended period of time.*

Aerobic exercise is essential, but we now know that strength training (weight-lifting) is equally important.

Use free weights (dumbbells, barbells, etc.) or exercise machines to build muscle in your arms, legs and torso.

Start with a weight that you can lift eight times in rapid succession. The last two repetitions should cause a burning sensation in your muscles. Pause for three minutes, then do another set. Gradually work your way up to three sets of 15 reps.

### A SOUND MIND

The same antioxidants that help prevent heart disease and cancer—vitamin E in particular—also seem to prevent aging-related changes in the brain.

There's no indication that antioxidants improve thinking ability. But research on a family of cognition-enhancing compounds known as *nootropics* (Greek for "mind turning") has shown that these compounds can improve memory in certain individuals.

Two nootropics—each sold over the counter—seem especially beneficial...

•**Ginkgo biloba.** This herbal extract has been shown to improve memory and to

*Your goal in doing aerobic exercise should be to raise your heart rate to 50% to 80% of its maximum for at least 20 minutes a day, at least three days a week. To calculate your maximum heart rate, subtract your age in years from 220.

shorten reaction times. It works in both healthy individuals and in those with Alzheimer's disease or another form of dementia.

***Typical dosage:*** 100 mg twice a day.

•**Phosphatidylserine.** This compound, derived from plants, helps stabilize cell membranes in the brain and facilitates communication between brain cells (neurons).

Researchers have noted improvements in attention, memory and concentration in individuals who take phosphatidylserine on a daily basis.

***Typical dosage:*** 100 mg twice a day.

"Use it or lose it" applies to the brain as well as to the muscles. Solving complex problems, memorizing things and otherwise giving your brain a workout seem to stimulate neurons to form new connections.

This process helps compensate for the neurons that die or become dysfunctional each day.

If your daily life involves little short-term memory skills, add "memory games" to your routine.

***Example:*** After watching the nightly news on television, see how many of the stories you can recall. Have a family member keep track of how you do.

### HOW ABOUT HORMONES?

As estrogen and testosterone levels dwindle, so does sex drive.

Falling levels of human growth hormone (hGH) cause muscle wasting.

Declines in the hormone DHEA have been linked to declining energy levels, memory loss and reduced immunity.

Hormone-replacement therapy can restore vitality for some people—particularly older people whose levels have dropped significantly. But it requires close medical supervision.

That's true for hGH, DHEA, testosterone and estrogen. Used unwisely, hormone replacement can promote growth of prostate cancer and breast cancer.

### ANTIAGING HELP

If you'd like to find a physician who can tailor an aggressive antiaging program specifically for you, contact the American Academy of Anti-Aging Medicine at 773-528-4333.

# Antioxidant Therapy

Jeffrey Blumberg, PhD, professor of nutrition and chief of the Antioxidants Research Laboratory at Tufts University in Boston.

By now, you've probably heard about *free radicals* and the harm they do to the human body.

Free radicals are thought to contribute to cancer, cataracts, heart disease, Alzheimer's disease and other chronic ailments.

You may also know that *antioxidants*—found in food and nutritional supplements—help minimize free radical damage.

But many people are still confused. Leading antioxidant researcher Dr. Jeffrey Blumberg clears up the confusion...

### WHAT ARE FREE RADICALS?

Free radicals are molecular fragments created when the body burns oxygen...or when it's exposed to "insults" like tobacco smoke or sunlight.

Free radicals react eagerly with other molecules in a process known as *oxidation*. Antioxidants neutralize free radicals by scavenging and destroying them before they reach the other molecules.

There's growing evidence that an antioxidant-rich diet helps stop free radical damage. How can you be sure you're getting enough antioxidants? The best strategy is to eat a variety of fruits and vegetables—five to nine servings per day. Taking antioxidant supplements may also be a good idea.

*Caution:* Although antioxidant supplements do seem to enhance a well-rounded diet, they are not a substitute for such a diet.

### KEY ANTIOXIDANTS

Scientists have just begun to identify the thousands of antioxidants found in foods. So far, five seem especially important...

•**Vitamin C** helps prevent heart disease by blocking oxidation of cholesterol and other fatty substances in the blood. It also blocks the effects of *nitrites*, carcinogens found in bacon and other preserved meats.

Sources of vitamin C include citrus fruits, cantaloupe, strawberries, peppers, tomatoes and broccoli. A one-cup serving of cantaloupe or broccoli contains about 100 mg of vitamin C.

*Daily supplement:* 250 to 1,000 mg of vitamin C. Studies have shown that the incidence of heart disease—as well as of cataracts and cancer—is significantly lower among people whose vitamin C intake falls within this range.

*Caution:* Vitamin C pills can cause diarrhea. To avoid trouble, start at 250 mg per day, and increase the dosage gradually over several weeks. Do not take more than 1,000 mg per day without a doctor's supervision.

The beneficial effects of vitamin C have been demonstrated in numerous scientific studies. In 1998, however, scientists at the University of Leicester in England published a study that suggested that vitamin C supplements could *raise* the risk for cancer.

The English researchers found DNA damage—a harbinger of cancer—among individuals who took 500 mg of vitamin C each day for six weeks.

This study cannot be taken seriously. It contained insufficient detail for other researchers to evaluate the methodology.

In addition, the authors never subjected the study to peer review, the process in which weaknesses in methodology are often detected.

*Most telling:* Other researchers who tried to replicate these findings didn't get the same results.

•**Vitamin E** fights heart disease by preventing oxidation of LDL (bad) cholesterol...blocks sunlight-induced oxidation of skin cells...and helps prevent cataracts.

One study suggested that vitamin E may slow the progression of Alzheimer's disease. Other studies suggest that it enhances the clot-preventing power of aspirin, suggesting that the aspirin–vitamin E combination might be a good idea for many heart patients.

Sources of vitamin E include vegetable oil...almonds and other nuts...and especially wheat germ.

Because good sources of vitamin E tend to be high in fat, it's hard to get enough E from food without getting too much fat. Vitamin E supplementation is therefore widely accepted to be a good idea.

*Daily supplement:* 100 to 400 international units (IU) of vitamin E.

Most studies showing the protective effects of vitamin E supplements have used *dl-alpha-tocopherol*, the synthetic form of the vitamin. The natural form—*d-alpha-tocopherol*—costs more but is somewhat more potent.

●**Beta-carotene and other carotenoids** help prevent heart disease, stroke, cataracts and cancer of the breast, cervix and stomach.

Carotenoids also block development of lung cancer—at least when taken by nonsmokers.

In the mid-1990s, Finnish and American researchers discovered that smokers who took high-dose beta-carotene supplements seemed to be at *increased* risk for lung cancer.

In light of these studies, heavy smokers should avoid beta-carotene supplements. Studies involving nonsmokers have not found beta-carotene or any other carotenoid to be toxic.

Sources of beta-carotene and other carotenoids include cantaloupes, apricots, carrots and squash and other red and yellow fruits and vegetables...broccoli...and green, leafy vegetables.

*Daily supplement:* 15,000 IU of beta-carotene—for nonsmokers only.

Preliminary research suggests that other carotenoids may be even more protective than beta-carotene...

●*Lycopene* seems to reduce the risk for prostate cancer.

●*Lutein* and *zeaxanthin* seem to guard against age-related macular degeneration, a potentially blinding retinal ailment.

●**Selenium** boosts the disease-fighting power of other antioxidants. In several recent studies, people who took a selenium supplement had a substantially reduced risk for lung and prostate cancer.

Sources of selenium include Brazil nuts and seafood (especially mackerel, oysters, tuna and shrimp).

*Daily supplement:* 200 micrograms (mcg) of selenium. Higher doses can cause loss of hair and fingernails and possibly nerve damage.

●**Flavonoids** have been linked to reduced risk for heart disease and stroke—and possibly cancer.

Sources of flavonoids include onions, apples and grapes...green and black tea...and red wine.

Several flavonoid supplements are now on the market, including pine bark extract and grape seed extract. But until the effectiveness of these supplements has been demonstrated in clinical trials, it's probably a good idea to depend upon food sources of flavonoids.

# Garlic and Your Health

John Milner, PhD, professor and head of the department of nutrition at Pennsylvania State University in University Park. Dr. Milner chaired a recent major conference on the health benefits of garlic in Newport Beach, CA.

Recent studies conducted in the US, Europe and China suggest that garlic can lower cholesterol levels...fight bacterial and viral infections...prevent cancer ...and boost memory.

How strong is the evidence? Could you benefit by adding more garlic to your diet...or by taking garlic pills?

### GARLIC VS. CHOLESTEROL

As proponents of garlic are quick to point out, numerous studies suggest that regular consumption of garlic—one clove a day or the equivalent in supplement form—cuts serum cholesterol by 7% to 15%. Garlic seems to be particularly helpful at reducing LDL (bad) cholesterol.

Other studies suggest that garlic has little or no effect on cholesterol levels.

*Example:* A study conducted at the University of Bonn and published in *The Journal of the American Medical Association* showed that cholesterol levels remained unchanged even when garlic oil equivalent to four to five cloves of garlic was consumed on a daily basis for 12 weeks.

What explains the inconsistency of the studies? It may be that only some people respond to garlic. It's also possible that garlic interacts with the other foods in one's diet.

Another possible explanation for the inconsistency may be the fact that the studies have used various garlic preparations. Some have used unprocessed garlic. Others have used a garlic extract—which might or might not have the same biological activity as whole garlic.

### GARLIC VS. CANCER

Research suggests that garlic can help prevent a variety of malignancies...

•**Stomach cancer.** In a 1984 study conducted in China, people who ate garlic regularly had an unusually low rate of this potentially deadly cancer.

•**Colon cancer.** A 1994 study of women in Iowa found that the incidence of colon cancer was 50% lower among those who consumed the most garlic.

•**Prostate cancer.** A 1997 study conducted in Oxford, England, found that men who consumed garlic two or more times per week were one-third less likely than other men to develop prostate cancer.

If garlic does protect against cancer, the explanation may lie in the sulfur compounds it contains.

Some laboratory studies have demonstrated that these compounds block the synthesis of carcinogens known as *nitrosamines*. In the absence of sulfur, the digestive process leads to the formation of nitrosamines each time nitrates and nitrites are consumed. Nitrates and nitrites are found in preservatives and in beets, spinach and certain other foods.

Garlic also stimulates the body to synthesize *glutathione*. In addition to deactivating certain carcinogens, this natural antioxidant protects cell membranes against damage caused by renegade molecules known as free radicals.

Recent studies suggest that it might be possible to derive cancer chemotherapy drugs from garlic.

In one recent study, a garlic derivative called *S-allylmercaptocysteine* inhibited the growth of human prostate tumors that had been transplanted to mice.

In another study, a garlic extract called *diallyldisulfide* inhibited the growth of human breast cancer cells.

### HOW TO EAT GARLIC

There is no *proof* that garlic can reduce cholesterol, lower cancer risk or do anything else to protect your health. But given the evidence in garlic's favor—plus the fact that the only downside to garlic consumption is bad breath—it makes sense to include some in your diet.

One to three grams of garlic per day—the equivalent of one clove—should be enough.

If you cook with garlic, be careful to preserve the potentially beneficial sulfur compounds. To do this, peel garlic, chop or crush it and then let it stand for 15 to 30 minutes before cooking. This "waiting period" facilitates chemical reactions that yield the biologically active compounds.

If you don't like the taste or smell of garlic, deodorized supplements are available. These products contain compounds similar to those found in raw garlic.

---

# Natural Remedies For Headache Pain

Alexander Mauskop, MD, associate professor of clinical neurology at the State University of New York in Brooklyn and director of the New York Headache Center in New York City. He is coauthor of *The Headache Alternative: A Neurologist's Guide to Drug-Free Relief.* Dell.

Which medication works best for headache pain? *That depends on the type of headache...*

•**Migraines** are usually treated with *sumatriptan* (Imitrex), *zolmitriptan* (Zomig) or another "triptan" drug.

•**Tension headaches** are usually treated with anti-inflammatory drugs like *ibuprofen* (Motrin) or *naproxen* (Aleve).

•**Cluster headaches** are usually treated with sumatriptan or inhaled oxygen.

These treatments are reliable and safe for occasional use. But when patients start to use headache medication more than twice a week, stomach upset and other side effects become a serious concern.*

*See a doctor at once if your headache is accompanied by confusion, convulsions or loss of consciousness...pain in the eye or ear...slurred speech, numbness, blurred vision or trouble walking...fever or nausea.

For this reason, headache sufferers should be sure to ask their doctors about trying non-drug approaches as well.

### DIETARY MODIFICATION

Chronic headaches often have their origins in food sensitivities. To identify the food or foods underlying your pain, try this elimination diet...

•**For one week,** keep a list of all foods and beverages you consume. Be sure to include seasonings.

•**For the next 30 days,** avoid all foods and beverages you consumed during the 24 hours preceding each headache you had during the week.

•**After 30 days,** reintroduce suspect foods one per meal. Before eating the food, take your resting pulse. Twenty minutes after eating, take your pulse again.

If your pulse after eating is 10 beats or more per minute faster than your pulse before eating, you may be sensitive to the food you've just reintroduced. Avoid the food for another 30 days.

If you remain sensitive to this food for several months, eliminate it permanently.

### NUTRITIONAL SUPPLEMENTS

Headaches occur less frequently in individuals whose intake of certain key nutrients is adequate. *Ask your doctor about taking...*

•**Magnesium** (400 mg a day). This mineral has no effect on tension headaches but is moderately effective against migraines and cluster headaches.

*Most effective:* Slow-release or chelated magnesium tablets. They're better absorbed than conventional tablets.

•**Fish oil or flaxseed oil** (15 g per day). These oils are rich in omega-3 fatty acids, which have been associated with reduced migraine frequency and severity.

•**Lecithin** (200 mg a day). This protein—sold as a powder that can be mixed into beverages—reduces symptoms of cluster headaches.

•**Vitamin B-2** (riboflavin). Megadoses of this B vitamin—400 mg a day for two to three months—have been shown to reduce the frequency and severity of migraines.

Megadoses should be taken only under a doctor's supervision.

### ACUPUNCTURE

Acupuncture works against tension and migraine headaches. Typically, the patient undergoes weekly or twice-weekly sessions for 10 weeks, followed by monthly "maintenance" sessions.

For the name of an acupuncturist in your area, contact the American Academy of Medical Acupuncture at 800-521-2262.

*Caution:* Make sure the acupuncturist uses disposable needles.

In many cases, headaches can be prevented via acupressure, the self-help variant of acupuncture. Try these techniques at the first sign of pain...

•**Press your thumbs against the hollows between the muscles in the neck**—just below the base of the skull and in line with your ears. Hold for two minutes. Breathe deeply throughout.

•**Use your thumbs to press the upper inside corners of the eye sockets.** Hold for one minute while breathing deeply.

•**Use your right thumb to press on the top of the fleshy mound between your left thumb and index finger.** Hold for one minute while breathing deeply. Switch hands and repeat.

### ENVIRONMENTAL FACTORS

To avoid the eyestrain that triggers some headaches, be sure to have adequate lighting for the task at hand.

*Trap:* Fluorescent bulbs often produce a barely perceptible flicker that can cause headaches. If there's a chance fluorescent flicker is behind your headaches, switch to incandescent bulbs.

*Important:* Have a professional eye exam once a year. Straining to compensate for poor vision can cause headaches.

Mold, dust mites and fungi can trigger headaches. To eliminate these airborne irritants, install exhaust fans in your bathroom and kitchen...and a dehumidifier in your basement or any other damp area. Indoor humidity should stay between 35% and 40%.

Use scent-free hypoallergenic soap and non-aerosol sprays.

Some headaches are triggered by chronic low-level exposure to carbon monoxide (CO). Never leave a car idling in an attached garage. Consider installing a CO detector in your home.

### HERBAL REMEDIES

Feverfew can reduce the frequency and severity of migraines. If you'd like to try this herb, chew two fresh or freeze-dried leaves a day...or take 125 mg of dried feverfew that contains at least 0.2% parthenolide.

There's no evidence that herbal remedies are effective for tension or cluster headaches.

### MASSAGE THERAPY

Massage has been found to reduce pain caused by tension and migraine headaches—but not cluster headaches.

For referral to a massage therapist in your area, contact the American Massage Therapist Association at 847-864-0123.

### BIOFEEDBACK

By using devices that measure muscle tension and blood flow, biofeedback teaches you to relax tense muscles...and boost blood flow to your scalp. Each technique can ease headache pain.

For adults, 10 or more 30- to 60-minute sessions may be necessary. Children typically need only five or six.

To find a biofeedback therapist in your area, send a self-addressed, stamped, business-sized envelope to the Biofeedback Certification Institute of America, 10200 W. 44th Ave., Suite 310, Wheat Ridge, CO 80033.

### EXERCISE

Aerobic activity is beneficial for people with chronic headaches. Adding a *mantra*—a word repeated over and over to focus the mind—enhances the effect.

*Caution:* Exercising during a headache tends to intensify the pain.

### FOR PERSISTENT HEADACHES

If nondrug therapies fail to work within three months, consult a headache specialist.

For a list of specialists in your area, phone the National Headache Foundation (NHF) at 888-643-5552...or send a self-addressed, stamped, business-sized envelope to the NHF at 428 W. St. James Pl., Chicago 60614.

# Controlling Chronic Pain With Magnetic Therapy

Ronald Lawrence, MD, president, North American Academy of Magnetic Therapy, 28240 West Agoura Rd., Suite 202, Agoura Hills, CA 91301. He is coauthor of *Magnet Therapy: The Pain Cure Alternative*. Prima Publishing.

Do magnets have healing power? Alternative practitioners have long said yes, and recent studies suggest that they may be right.

In a recent study published in the *Archives of Physical Medicine and Rehabilitation*, researchers at Baylor College of Medicine in Houston found magnets to be more effective than sham magnets at blocking pain caused by post-polio syndrome.[*]

In the controlled study, 76% of patients treated with a magnet got pain relief. Only 18% treated with a sham magnet got relief.

### GROWING BODY OF EVIDENCE

In other studies, magnets have proven effective against...

•**Fibromyalgia.** Researchers at Tufts University School of Medicine in Boston showed that magnets help relieve muscle pain caused by this mysterious condition.

In the study, patients who slept on magnetic mattresses experienced greater pain relief than patients who slept on ordinary mattresses.

•**Diabetic neuropathy.** In research conducted at New York Medical College in Valhalla, magnetic foot pads were more effective than nonmagnetic foot pads at relieving numbness, tingling and pain associated with this diabetes-related problem.

Evidence suggests that roughly 80% of chronic pain sufferers could benefit from magnetic therapy. That's true for virtually any form of pain.

### HOW MAGNETS RELIEVE PAIN

When held against the skin, magnets relax capillary walls, thereby boosting blood flow to the painful area.

[*]This syndrome, marked by leg pain, affects up to 20% of polio sufferers later in life.

They also help prevent the muscle spasms that underlie many forms of pain—apparently by interfering with muscle contractions. And—they interfere with the electrochemical reactions that take place within nerve cells, impeding their ability to transmit pain messages to the brain.

Of course, chronic pain *can* be controlled with aspirin and other over-the-counter and prescription painkillers. But unlike pain medications, magnets do not carry any risk of side effects.

### SELECTING MEDICAL MAGNETS

Medical magnets come in a dizzying range of shapes, sizes and strengths. They range in price from about $5 all the way to $900.

It's usually best to start with one or several coin-shaped magnets made of the rare earth metal *neodymium-boron*. For most applications, these "neo" magnets work just as well as—and cost less than—other magnets. *Cost:* About $10 each.

Magnetism is measured in *gauss*. A typical refrigerator magnet is about 10 gauss. That's too weak to penetrate the skin—and unlikely to be helpful for anything more than a minor bruise.

Medical magnets range in strength from 450 gauss to 10,000 gauss. The higher the gauss, the better the pain relief.

Since magnets aren't always helpful, it's best to purchase yours from a company that offers a money-back guarantee of at least 30 days.

For a free list of magnet manufacturers and their phone numbers, contact the North American Academy of Magnetic Therapy (see previous page for address).

### PUTTING MAGNETS TO WORK

The magnet should be affixed to the skin directly over the painful area. Some people use ordinary adhesive bandages to affix the magnets. But *Transpore*—a paper tape made by 3M—works better. It holds well, and it doesn't pull the hairs from the skin when it's removed.

If the magnet fails to provide relief within a few days, reposition the magnet over the nearest acupuncture point. To locate these points on the body, consult a book on acupuncture.

If repositioning the magnet fails to bring relief within 30 days, odds are it's not going to

work. Switch to another type of magnet...or speak with your doctor about using painkilling medication or another conventional approach.

•**Aching feet.** Magnetic insoles can relieve foot pain and the achy feeling in the legs after you've been standing all day.

•**Arthritis.** If pain is limited to your fingers, a neo magnet taped to the affected joint should do the trick. Or—you can wear a magnetic wristband.

For fibromyalgia or for arthritis pain throughout the body, a magnetic mattress is usually best. If the $900 cost is too much for you, opt for a magnetic mattress pad. *Cost:* $250 to $500.

•**Back pain.** Place four magnets about 1.5 inches on either side of the spine, two per side. If applying and removing several magnets proves troublesome, use a three- to four-inch ceramic strip magnet...or a magnetic back brace.

•**Headache.** Tape magnets to your temples...or to the back of your head, just above the neck. Or—use a magnetic headband.

•**Tennis elbow**. Use a magnetic band around the elbow. The same band also relieves hand and arm pain caused by repetitive strain injury.

# Alzheimer's Help

Rocking chairs help relieve symptoms of Alzheimer's disease.

***Recent study:*** After rocking for at least 80 minutes a day for six weeks, many Alzheimer's patients felt less depressed and anxious. Those who rocked the most experienced the greatest improvement.

***Theory:*** Rhythmic rocking triggers the release of endorphins, natural compounds that relieve pain and improve mood.

Nancy M. Watson, RN, PhD, assistant professor of nursing, University of Rochester School of Nursing, Rochester, NY. Her two-year study of 25 nursing home residents 72 to 95 years of age was presented at a recent meeting of the Eastern Nursing Research Society.

# Natural Remedies from Jamison Starbuck

Jamison Starbuck, ND, a naturopathic physician in family practice and a lecturer at the University of Montana, both in Missoula. She is past president of the American Association of Naturopathic Physicians and a contributing editor of *The Alternative Advisor: The Complete Guide to Natural Therapies and Alternative Treatments.* Time Life.

## Drug-Free Solutions to Digestive Problems

•Do you use Tums, Tagamet or another acid-reducing medication more than once a month?

•Are you avoiding certain foods—even healthful foods like beans and vegetables—because they cause stomach upset?

•Do you frequently experience belching, flatulence or a bloated feeling after meals?

•Do your bowel movements tend to occur less frequently than once a day?

If you answered "yes" to any of these questions, your digestion may need improving.

The keys to proper digestion are a good supply of digestive juices...a healthy gut lining...and lots of beneficial bacteria in the stomach and intestines. Without these three things, you're likely to develop a sour stomach, belching, flatulence, abdominal pain and/or constipation.

Digestive juice is made up of hydrochloric acid from the stomach lining, enzymes from the pancreas and bile from the gallbladder. When enough hydrochloric acid is present, digestive juice is highly acidic. Without enough acid, the stomach becomes distended and crampy. In many cases of low acidity, digestive juice and partially digested food are forced upward into the esophagus, resulting in the pain of heartburn.

Studies show that almost 50% of people over age 50 have too little acid. Yet many physicians continue to prescribe antacids for indigestion. Antacids often do curb the pain, and they may be fine for occasional use. But regular, long-term use of antacids is unwise.

Antacid "abuse" can result in nutritional deficiencies, especially of calcium and magnesium. These minerals—essential for keeping bones strong—are properly absorbed only under conditions of high acidity.

Antacids can also cause a range of side effects, including headache, depression, insomnia, impotence and even liver damage.

A better approach is to improve your digestion naturally. Gobbling food under stressful conditions—while driving, during a meeting, etc.—lowers the production of stomach acid. On the other hand, 60 seconds of relaxation at the start of a meal—deep breathing, meditation or simply saying grace—brings a marked increase in secretions.

Since it gives food a "head start" on the digestive process, thorough chewing can be very helpful. So can the use of "bitters." Available at health food stores, bitters is a tincture made of gentian, wormwood, white horehound, anise and/or other herbs. Ten to 15 drops on the tongue at the start of a meal stimulates the vagus nerve. That's the nerve responsible for telling the stomach to start digestion.

Good digestion also requires a large population of healthy bacteria. I often urge my patients to take a daily pill containing one billion live bacteria...or a daily cup of plain yogurt that contains "active cultures."

If digestive trouble has led to a peptic ulcer or gastritis, *deglycyrrhizinated licorice* (DGL) can be helpful. Studies have shown that DGL can be just as effective as Tagamet or Zantac in the treatment of these problems.

DGL is sold at health food stores. It can be safely used for up to six weeks. The typical dosage is two to four 400-mg tablets a day, taken between meals.

**More from Jamison Starbuck...**

# Migraine Relief... Migraine Avoidance Strategies

Migraine headaches affect more than 26 million Americans. As anyone who has ever had a migraine headache can attest, the pain and other symptoms can be very severe—severe enough to disrupt family life and career...impair self-esteem...and destroy intimate relationships.

Migraines usually begin with an *aura*. This is an odd sensation or sensations—disorientation, seeing halos around lights, sensing odd smells, etc. Then come nausea and even vomiting as severe pain creeps up the shoulders, neck and head.

Medical doctors often prescribe *sumatriptan* (Imitrex) or *rizatriptan* (Maxalt) for their patients with migraines. While these drugs work quickly to reduce pain by constricting dilated blood vessels, they do nothing to prevent migraines. And they can be extremely dangerous for individuals at risk for heart and circulatory disease.

I take a different approach to migraine, looking for an underlying imbalance in health. When this imbalance is corrected, migraines occur less and less frequently—or disappear altogether.

What sort of imbalances am I talking about? I've seen migraines associated with hormonal imbalances caused by hysterectomy or the use of birth-control pills...allergic reactions to foods, animals or chemicals...gallbladder disease and other digestive problems...severe emotional stress, such as the loss of a loved one, divorce, being fired or a recent move.

Migraine sufferers can play an important role in their own recovery. In many cases of recurrent migraines, it can be helpful to write out a detailed "time line" of your headaches. Include everything that might have even the slightest connection to your headaches—events, location, medications, dietary habits, sleep patterns, family members and pets. Start from the time of your first migraine and go up to the present date.

In preparing this time line, you may notice a connection between some aspect of your life and your migraines. Often it's something simple. Once I treated a 12-year-old boy whose migraines were continuing despite the fact that he had seen several headache specialists—and despite the fact that he was taking huge doses of painkilling medication.

After examining this boy and reviewing his history, I realized that his headaches had begun around the time that he started drinking

lots of soft drinks. Within 10 days of giving up soft drinks, he was pain-free.

It's sometimes possible to stop a migraine simply by administering a deep massage to the shoulders and neck at the first sign of pain. Applying ice or a cold compress afterward can further the relief. Some patients find that sitting with their feet in hot water and a cold compress on their neck reduces headache discomfort dramatically.

For pain relief, homeopathic remedies are also helpful. Consider trying *bryonia* for migraines associated with dry mouth, excessive thirst and irritability...and when any sort of movement is unbearable. *Gelsemium* can help when a migraine involves dull pain, apathy, listlessness and sleepiness. With either remedy, I usually tell my patients to take a 6C potency—two pellets every four hours as needed for pain.

---

**Jamison Starbuck on Muscle Ache Remedies...**

# Getting Relief from Mysterious Muscle Pain

Do you have chronic muscle pain, especially in the neck and shoulders and around joints? Are you bothered by poor sleep, daytime fatigue and listlessness? If so, you may be suffering from fibromyalgia. Three to five million Americans have this mysterious ailment. Eighty percent are women between 35 and 60 years of age.

Fibromyalgia wasn't recognized as a disease until 1990. The cause of the disorder is still unknown, and many doctors remain unaware of the "diagnostic criteria" used to identify it. These consist of muscle pain on both sides of the body for a minimum of three consecutive months...along with pain in at least 11 of 18 "tender points," including at the knees and elbows, the base of the neck and skull and other areas as well.

Fibromyalgia can be *very* tricky to diagnose. No blood test is available to confirm the diagnosis. And since it affects muscle (soft tissue) rather than bone, X rays are not useful. Not surprisingly, many cases go undetected. If you think you might have fibromyalgia, it's important to consult a health-care practitioner who is well acquainted with the condition. Look for someone who can recite the diagnostic criteria and who has treated at least a handful of cases. If you need help finding a qualified practitioner, contact The Fibromyalgia Network, Box 31750, Tucson, Arizona 85751. 800-853-2929.

Since no single drug alleviates all symptoms of fibromyalgia, medical doctors often use several. If you work with an MD, you may be given prescriptions for a muscle relaxant, a sedative and an antidepressant. These drugs can cause nasty side effects, including nausea, bowel changes, dry mouth and headaches. To control these problems, doctors often prescribe additional medications—which can cause side effects of their own. As you might imagine, this approach to treatment isn't always successful.

Many cases of fibromyalgia can be controlled simply by eliminating meat, dairy products, refined sugar, hydrogenated fats and alcohol. These foods aggravate symptoms by robbing the body of inflammation-fighting essential fatty acids.

If you have fibromyalgia, consider switching to a diet rich in fish, seeds, soy and grains. If one month of this semi-vegetarian diet causes symptoms to abate, you might want to make the dietary change permanent.

In my practice, I've noticed a strong correlation between fibromyalgia and the health of the patient's adrenal glands. In simple cases, fibromyalgia pain and lethargy can be eliminated by boosting adrenal function with Siberian ginseng (*Eleutherococcus senticosus*). One teaspoon twice daily of a 1:1 alcohol extract of dried herb—available in health food stores—is safe for most people, but check with your doctor first.

Another remedy that often helps alleviate trigger point tenderness is a combination of magnesium and malic acid (malate). This one-pill combo—available at health food stores and some drugstores—improves the health of muscle tissue. It's safe for most people—but, again, check with your doctor.

Although fibromyalgia is a physical ailment, many sufferers make matters worse by "overdoing" things. I give patients this advice—learn to

leave some projects unfinished, and use the time you free up to do something nice for yourself. You can always finish the project later.

---

# Essential Secret of Kicking Addictions

Addiction to alcohol, tobacco or drugs destroys lives—those of the addicts and those of their friends and family. Short of incarceration, the only way to stop addictive behavior is to *decide* to stop. Typically, this decision comes after months or years of internal debate. If you've reached this point, I offer several suggestions that might prove helpful...

• **Make a commitment—in writing.** Pick a quit date. Write that date on a piece of paper, along with a written vow to quit, and post it somewhere highly visible. Your vow will be a guidepost, especially in the midst of your journey, when the going gets tough—as it inevitably does.

• **Line up people who will support your decision to quit.** Choose individuals you respect but with whom you have no strong emotional ties. For most people, that means a doctor, clergyman, therapist...and/or maybe an ex-smoker or ex-drinker. Explain your plan, and meet with your support "team" regularly during the withdrawal period. Spend recreational time with people who encourage your decision to quit—which may mean you'll have to make new friends.

Books can be a big help. One book that my patients find particularly valuable is Doug Althauser's *You Can Free Yourself from Alcohol & Drugs,* New Harbinger.

• **Eat according to a schedule.** Eating on a regular basis helps curb your cravings—by keeping blood sugar levels relatively constant. Large swings in blood sugar levels are known to trigger intense cravings—for tobacco and alcohol as well as for food.

I usually advise my patients fighting addictions to eat three meals a day. Each meal should include a small amount of lentils, peas, soybeans or another source of protein. Fresh vegetables and fiber-rich foods like rice, barley, baked potatoes and whole grains are also important during withdrawal. These foods are digested at a slow, steady pace, so they help keep blood sugar levels constant.

**•Consider taking vitamin supplements and herbal remedies.** Vitamin pills don't make quitting easier. But certain vitamins do reduce withdrawal symptoms. I typically recommend 100 mg each of vitamins B-3, B-5 and B-6...400 micrograms (mcg) of vitamin B-12...800 mcg of folic acid...400 international units (IU) of vitamin E...and 1,000 mg of vitamin C, but consult with your doctor. These supplements should be taken with food on a daily basis.

Herbs, too, can be helpful—especially for people trying to give up smoking. Giving up cigarettes often causes a transient, but aggravating, cough and/or lung congestion. A tea made of mullein, marshmallow root, coltsfoot and peppermint helps keep the lungs clear.

Buy an ounce or two of each herb at a health food store. Mix them in a jar, and use two teaspoons of the herb mix per eight ounces of boiling water. Three cups daily during the first two weeks of quitting should help keep your lungs healthy.

People addicted to alcohol or drugs often benefit from taking milk thistle capsules. This herb helps curb the achy, flu-like symptoms that often strike during withdrawal.

I generally recommend 200 mg to 400 mg of milk thistle to be taken on a daily basis for the first month after the quit date. Watch out—people with a history of liver disease or who are taking a medication that affects the liver should consult a doctor before taking milk thistle.

---

**Jamison Starbuck's Ear Infection Treatments...**

# Ear Infections—Antibiotics and Alternatives

By age three, 75% of children develop at least one ear infection—known among doctors as *otitis media*.* Even with "good" medical care, many of these kids wind

*The term "otitis" comes from the Greek words "ot" (meaning ear) and "itis" (meaning inflammation of). "Media" is the Latin word for middle.

up enduring ear pain, fever and irritability—again and again.

Pediatricians often treat ear infections with amoxicillin or another antibiotic. Antibiotics are highly effective at killing infectious bacteria. Yet some pediatricians are prescribing these powerful drugs for teething-associated ear pain and other problems not caused by bacterial infection—when antibiotics are useless.

Giving antibiotics for anything other than a bacterial infection is bad medicine. Overuse of antibiotics causes bacteria to become resistant to antibiotics, making infections very difficult to treat.

I've successfully treated hundreds of children with ear infections. Antibiotics are seldom necessary, since most kids respond to alternative approaches.

First, a bit about anatomy. The middle ear is a pea-sized cavity between the eardrum and the eustachian tube, which links the middle ear to the throat. The eustachian tube opens and closes as necessary to regulate air pressure within the middle ear.

Congestion stemming from a cold or an allergic reaction often causes the eustachian tube and surrounding tissues to swell. Swelling can interfere with the eustachian tube's activity, sometimes resulting in a slight partial vacuum in the middle ear. When that happens, bacteria and/or other microbes from the nose and throat are drawn into the middle ear, causing otitis media.

A child's risk of developing otitis media can be minimized by breast-feeding for at least four months. Breast milk contains infection-fighting antibodies. Avoiding exposure to tobacco smoke is another good strategy. Smoke can cause delicate tissues of the nose and throat to swell, increasing the risk for otitis media.

For children who do develop otitis media, I've found that homeopathy is often the best approach. Homeopathy involves the use of tiny doses of natural medicines to stimulate the body's self-healing powers.

To find a licensed homeopath near you, call the National Center for Homeopathy (703-548-7790)...or visit the American Association of Naturopathic Physicians web site at www.naturopathic.org. You can also get referrals from parents whose children with ear infections have been successfully treated using homeopathy.

Since allergic congestion often sets the stage for otitis, I always consider food allergies when treating children with ear infections. Dairy foods are often the culprit. I urge parents to remove all dairy products from the child's diet for at least one month—and to continue without dairy if ear infections seem to abate.

Other effective treatments for ear infection include applying alternating hot and cold compresses on the scalp behind and below the ear...and administering ear drops made from garlic and the herbs *mullein* and *Saint-John's-wort*. These drops are available at health food stores.

Parents who are troubled by repeatedly having to take a child to the doctor for a suspected ear infection may want to learn to use an otoscope. With this lighted viewing scope—available for less than $100 at drugstores—you can peer into the ear and tell whether the child has an ear infection. Ask your pediatrician to show you how to use it.

# Drug-Free Remedies for Constipation, Bloating and Other "Irritable Bowel" Problems

Geoffrey Turnbull, MD, associate professor of medicine, Dalhousie University and Queen Elizabeth II Health Sciences Center, both in Halifax, Nova Scotia. He is coauthor of *IBS Relief—A Doctor, a Dietitian and a Psychologist Provide a Team Approach to Managing Irritable Bowel Syndrome*. Chronimed Publishing.

Are you frequently constipated? Do you suffer from abdominal pain, bloating and/or other digestive problems?

If so, you may be among the estimated 30 million Americans who suffer from irritable bowel syndrome (IBS).

IBS is not dangerous. However, the symptoms it causes can make life very unpleasant.

While there's no cure for IBS, nine out of 10 cases can be controlled via simple lifestyle strategies. Sadly, only half of all IBS sufferers ever consult a doctor.

**TELLTALE SYMPTOMS**

IBS typically strikes during one's twenties or thirties. The most common symptom is pain in the lower abdomen.

The pain often becomes intense during a bowel movement, then subsides...only to recur a few minutes later.

***Caution:*** Abdominal pain that lingers after a bowel movement could be a sign of colitis, colon cancer or another serious ailment.

Other IBS symptoms include...

●**Constipation...or episodes of loose bowel movements.** These episodes typically occur every few weeks or so and last a few days.

A change in bowel habits that persists for weeks may indicate colitis, Crohn's disease or some other serious disorder.

●**Abdominal bloating or swelling.** This typically gets worse during the day, then disappears at night.

●**Sensation of incomplete emptying after having a bowel movement.**

●**Mucus in the stool.** Contrary to what many people think, mucus in the stool is not necessarily a sign of serious disease. Mucus mixed with blood, however, is often symptomatic of colitis.

If you're having any troublesome bowel symptoms, see a doctor right away. He/she should take a full history and conduct diagnostic tests to rule out more serious problems.

To augment any IBS treatments recommended by your doctor, consider trying the following self-help strategies...

**DIET MODIFICATION**

The first step in controlling IBS is to drink lots of water—at least eight eight-ounce glasses per day. It's also essential to adopt a diet that includes...

●Six to 11 daily servings of whole-grain bread, whole-wheat or bran cereal, brown rice or pasta.

●Three to five daily servings of vegetables.

288

• Two to four daily servings of fruit.

• Two or three daily servings of nonfat milk, yogurt or cheese.

• Two or three daily servings of meat, poultry, fish, eggs, beans or nuts.

These dietary guidelines help ensure that you get all necessary nutrients and enough dietary fiber.

The body needs at least 20 g of fiber a day to regulate bowel function. The average American gets only eight to 10 g.

### RETHINKING EATING HABITS

IBS often goes hand in hand with bad eating habits.

*Examples:* Skipping meals...eating too fast...overeating...and/or substituting burgers, fries, potato chips and other fatty foods for more wholesome foods.

To minimize IBS symptoms, plan sufficient time for meals...eat fast food no more than once a week...eat three meals a day...and eat only until full.

Pay particular attention to how much you eat at parties and family gatherings. Overeating is often encouraged at these events.

*Healthful snacks:* Wheat bran muffins, whole-wheat crackers, cereal, fresh or canned fruit, pretzels, baked potatoes, rice or pudding.

### AVOIDING TRIGGER FOODS

IBS symptoms often arise following the consumption of certain foods. "Trigger" foods vary from person to person. Common ones include...

• Raw vegetables.

• Cooked vegetables—brussels sprouts, corn, broccoli, cauliflower, cabbage, onions and sauerkraut. (Cooked potatoes, beets, asparagus, green beans, peas, spinach, squash and zucchini are generally safe.)

• Beans and lentils.

• Cantaloupe, honeydew melon and unpeeled apples. (Peeled apples, oranges, nectarines, peaches, pears, ripe bananas, grapefruit and kiwi are generally safe.)

• Beer.

• Coffee, tea and other beverages that contain caffeine.

To pinpoint your trigger foods, keep a food/symptom diary for two weeks. After each meal, use blue ink to record all the foods and beverages you just consumed. Include amounts and how each food was prepared.

Use red ink to record any symptoms that occur.

At the end of the two-week period, review your diary. Notice if any food or foods might be causing your symptoms.

*Good news:* In many cases, it's possible to continue eating a trigger food *without* experiencing IBS symptoms—if you eat smaller quantities...drink extra water...consume more fiber...and/or avoid eating other trigger foods at the same time.

### STRESS REDUCTION

Psychological stress causes muscles to tighten and raises heart rate and breathing rate. It also triggers the release of stress hormones.

Collectively, these physiological changes disrupt the delicate rhythm of the digestive system.

Stress reduction is often highly effective at controlling IBS. In some instances, all that's required is daily exercise—perhaps just a 20-minute walk.

Other effective stress-reducing strategies...

• **Make a stress list.** Jot down all the sources of stress in your life. Rate each on a scale from 1 (not upsetting) to 10 (extremely upsetting).

Put an "A" beside acute stresses tied to specific events. Put a "C" beside *chronic* stresses, situations that have no foreseeable end.

Chronic stresses with high numerical ratings are the ones you should work hardest at alleviating.

• **Keep a stress diary.** For two weeks, record any bowel symptoms, along with the stresses of the day and how they could have affected you.

• **Try deep breathing.** Sit up straight. Place one hand on your stomach, the other on your chest. Inhale through your nose as you force your stomach out. Then exhale through your mouth, pulling your stomach back in.

• **Be more assertive.** One of the most common sources of stress is a lack of assertiveness. Someone asks you to do something and you agree to do it—even though you lack the time or inclination to do it.

Next time someone tries to get you to do something you'd rather not do, become a "broken record." Restate your wishes, word for word, in response to each attempt at persuasion.

# Anti-Diarrhea Root

Annemarie Colbin, certified health education specialist and founder of the Natural Gourmet Cookery School in New York City. She is the author of four books, including *Food and Our Bones: The Natural Way to Prevent Osteoporosis.* Plume.

Southerners are only too familiar with kudzu. This hardy vine—imported from Japan a century ago to control soil erosion—has flourished in the warm climate, spreading relentlessly over gardens, lawns and houses.

It turns out that the root of this pesky plant has medicinal value. Cooked into a thick broth, it soothes and relaxes the gastrointestinal tract, providing relief from indigestion, heartburn and diarrhea.

Kudzu can also help relieve psychological stress. There's even some evidence that it relieves cravings for alcohol.

Unlike conventional drugs, kudzu provides relief without causing unpleasant side effects. Over-the-counter diarrhea remedies, for example, sometimes lead to constipation.

Kudzu starch is sold in health food stores as kuzu—its Japanese name. Pure kuzu is a lumpy white powder. If it's sold as a fine powder, it may be adulterated.

It costs $4 to $5 for 3½ ounces.

***To prepare kudzu broth:*** Mix one tablespoon kuzu with one cup cold water until completely dissolved.

Cook on medium heat, stirring continuously. The mixture will thicken and turn clear upon boiling.

Remove from heat, then add natural soy sauce (shoyu or tamari) to taste—about one tablespoon. Shoyu and tamari are available at health food stores.

Eat up to one cup of kuzu broth a day until symptoms ease.

***Important:*** If discomfort is severe—or lasts more than two days—consult your doctor.

# How to Keep Emotional Stress from Harming Your Heart

James Blumenthal, PhD, professor of medical psychology at Duke University School of Medicine in Durham, NC. His recent study on heart disease and psychological stress was published in the *Archives of Internal Medicine,* 515 N. State St., Chicago 60610.

Heart patients have been told again and again to stop smoking, cut down on dietary fat and get regular aerobic exercise. As it turns out, these familiar strategies simply aren't enough to ensure cardiac health.

In a recently completed five-year study, Duke University researchers determined that psychological stress plays a far bigger role in heart disease than had been thought.

The researchers found that diseased hearts often experience oxygen starvation (ischemia) during periods of stress, just as cardiac ischemia often occurs during intense exercise.

In addition to causing heart-related chest pain (angina), ischemia can trigger a heart attack. In the Duke study, heart patients who experienced cardiac ischemia during a mental stress test were *twice* as likely as other heart patients to have heart attacks or heart problems requiring cardiac surgery.

***Good news:*** The additional risk can be minimized via stress-management training.

### MENTAL STRESS TEST

In a standard exercise stress test, heart activity is monitored—usually via an electrocardiogram—as the patient walks or runs on a treadmill.

In the mental stress test used in the Duke study, heart activity was monitored as patients performed challenging mental tasks, such as solving a tough math problem.

Although mental stress tests aren't a routine part of cardiac care, many cardiologists can administer such a test to patients who request it.

If the mental stress test reveals stress-induced ischemia, consider enrolling in a stress-reduction program.

In the Duke study, people who completed a four-month stress-management course sharply reduced their risk for ischemic episodes and heart attacks.

### STRESS MANAGEMENT

Formal stress-management courses are now offered by many hospitals. If you would like to participate in such a program, be sure that it's designed specifically for heart patients.

If such a program is not available in your community, you can devise a stress-management program for yourself.

*Important:* Effective stress management involves three distinct sets of skills...

•Learning to achieve a state of deep muscle relaxation.

•Cultivating skills for coping with stress. This is often called "stress resilience."

•Avoiding situations that cause stress.

### 5-5-15 RELAXATION

Twice a day, find a quiet, comfortable place to sit. Take a deep breath, then let it out. Relax as fully as possible.

Extend your arms in front of you. Make a tight fist with each hand. Keep your hands tightly clenched for five seconds, then let the tension out halfway. Hold for five more seconds.

Now relax your hands completely for 15 seconds. Notice how tension drains from your hands...and is replaced by a sensation of comfort.

Tense your biceps for five seconds, bending your arms at the elbows. Then let the tension out halfway for five seconds. Now relax your upper arms completely for 15 seconds. Focus on the growing sense of relaxation.

Use this same 5-5-15 approach to relax muscles in the rest of your body...

•**Arms.** Tense your wrists, bending your hands back and extending your fingers upward. Let the tension out halfway, then relax completely.

•**Neck.** Tense your neck muscles by bringing your head forward until your chin touches your chest.

Let the tension out halfway, then relax completely. Let your head hang comfortably as you concentrate on the relaxation spreading through your neck muscles.

•**Shoulders.** Tense your shoulders by shrugging them as high as possible. Let the tension out halfway, then relax completely, letting your shoulders drop.

•**Back.** Tense your back by pulling your shoulders back as far as possible. Let the tension out halfway, then relax completely.

•**Scalp and forehead.** Wrinkle your forehead and hold for five seconds. Release halfway, then relax your scalp and forehead completely.

•**Eyes.** Close your eyes as tightly as possible. Let the tension out halfway, then relax completely.

•**Tongue.** Tense your tongue by pressing it against the roof of your mouth. Let the tension out halfway, then let your tongue, neck and jaw relax completely.

•**Chest.** Take an enormous breath, inhaling through your nose. Hold it for five seconds, then exhale through your mouth.

•**Abdomen.** Tighten your stomach muscles, then let the tension out halfway, and then relax completely.

•**Buttocks.** Tense your buttock muscles, then let the tension out halfway. Then relax completely. Focus on the feelings of heaviness and relaxation.

•**Thighs.** Extend your legs six inches above the floor and tense your thigh muscles. Let the tension out halfway, then relax your thighs completely.

•**Feet and calves.** Dig your toes into the bottoms of your shoes, then relax your toes halfway. Then relax your toes completely.

*To conclude:* Inhale slowly through your nose until your lungs are full. Hold for five seconds. Then exhale slowly through your mouth, silently repeating the word "relax" or "calm" as you do so.

### STRESS RESILIENCE

Regular exercise, low-fat food, adequate sleep and satisfying relationships are all important factors in coping with stress.

There are also specific coping techniques you can use...

•**Learn to recognize your own unique stress response.** Using a diary, note the times and places you feel nervous, frustrated or impatient. Try to pinpoint the precise cause or causes of each stressful episode.

•**When stress occurs,** take immediate action. If it's convenient to do so, start doing your relaxation exercises. If doing so is inconvenient, try altering your thought patterns.

*What to do:* Whatever the cause of your distress—a traffic jam, rude sales clerk, etc.—try to view the situation realistically.

Avoid the words "should" and "ought." Saying or even thinking either one can be a major contributor to stressful feelings. Instead, strive to adopt a more realistic reaction.

*Example:* "I wish I weren't stuck in this traffic jam, but there's nothing I can do about it."

### STRESS AVOIDANCE

Do you find yourself standing on a long line at the bank every Friday—and getting upset by it? Try banking when lines are short.

Bothered by frequent telephone calls? Let your answering machine take the calls…or take your phone off the hook.

*Also helpful:* Frequent vacations. Sometimes even a three-day weekend can reduce stress levels dramatically.

# Peanuts vs. Heart Disease

Peanuts work as well as olive oil to protect against heart disease.

People with mildly elevated cholesterol whose cholesterol-lowering diets included peanuts and peanut butter, and others who used peanut oil, achieved an 11% drop in total cholesterol and a 14% to 15% drop in LDL or "bad" cholesterol.

Those were the same results that were achieved by people using an equal amount of olive oil in their diets. The results are better than those from classic low-fat diets, which can also decrease HDL or "good" cholesterol.

*Penny Kris-Etherton, PhD, RD, professor of nutrition, Pennsylvania State University, University Park, whose study comparing five types of diets was presented at the 1998 Experimental Biology meetings in San Francisco.*

# Heart Doctor's Stop-Smoking Plan

•**Write down the day you will quit**—between two and four weeks from the day you decide—and keep the date in sight.

•**Pick a nonworking day to quit**—to limit stress.

•**For seven days, record every cigarette smoked.** Number each, and write when you smoked it and why.

•**See which cigarettes you smoked from habit and boredom,** and drop them first. Work toward dropping the harder ones.

•**Start walking or bike riding regularly.** Fight smoking urges by brushing your hair or playing with a rubber band.

•**Take it one day at a time**—most withdrawal symptoms end within four weeks.

*Heart Fitness for Life: The Essential Guide to Preventing and Reversing Heart Disease by Mary McGowan, MD, director, Cholesterol Management Center, New England Heart Institute, Manchester, NH. Oxford University Press.*

# Cabbage Leaves For Arthritic Joints

*Michael Van Straten, ND, DO, a naturopath and acupuncturist in private practice in London. He is the author of Home Remedies: A Practical Guide to Common Ailments You Can Safely Treat at Home Using Conventional and Complementary Medicine. Marlowe & Company.*

Cabbage leaves contain powerful anti-inflammatory compounds. Applied to arthritic joints, these compounds are remarkably effective at relieving both pain and swelling.

Arthritis sufferers often rely on over-the-counter anti-inflammatory drugs like *ibuprofen* (Advil) for relief of their symptoms. But prolonged use of these drugs can cause stomach pain and even bleeding ulcers.

Using cabbage leaves instead helps reduce

the amount of medication needed. And cabbage seems to work more effectively than topical creams marketed for arthritis relief.

***What to do:*** Use a rolling pin or knife handle to bruise one or two large, outer, dark-green leaves from a head of a green cabbage.

Warm the leaves in a microwave, steamer or oven, then wrap them around the joint. Cover with a towel. Leave in place for 15 minutes.

The compress should be applied once daily for mild inflammation, two or three times a day for severe inflammation.

Warm cabbage leaves can also be used to curb inflammation resulting from tennis elbow, sprains or other minor injuries. Apply ice and elevate the injured limb to curb the initial swelling. Then apply the cabbage leaf compress two or three times daily until pain and swelling subside.

Odd as it sounds, women with painful breast cysts—as well as nursing mothers with inflamed, cracked nipples—can also get relief from cabbage leaves.

Line the cups of a bra with bruised cabbage leaves. Leave in place for an hour a day. It's not necessary to warm the leaves.

# Herbal Help for PMS

Varro E. Tyler, PhD, professor emeritus of pharmacognosy at Purdue University in West Lafayette, IN. He is author of *Herbs of Choice: The Therapeutic Use of Phytomedicinals.* Haworth Press.

Folklore has it that monks used the peppery fruit of the chasteberry bush (*Vitex agnus-castus*) to suppress their sexual desires.

Today chasteberry is used by women as a natural remedy for premenstrual syndrome (PMS) and other ailments caused by hormone imbalances.

Support for the use of chasteberry comes from a distinguished panel of German scientists, who recently completed a lengthy review of research on herbal remedies.

The panel recommended chasteberry for bloating, headache, depression and other symptoms of PMS…for menopausal hot flashes… and for painful breasts.

Chasteberry acts on the pituitary gland, a pea-sized gland located at the base of the brain. In turn, the pituitary gland signals the ovaries to restore a normal balance of the hormones estrogen and progesterone.

If you'd like to try chasteberry, consult your doctor to be sure that your symptoms stem from a hormone imbalance.

For PMS, chasteberry should generally be taken from the onset of symptoms until the beginning of the menstrual period.

For other problems, chasteberry can be taken continuously for up to six months. The usual dose is 20 mg per day. To avoid side effects—typically, mild gastrointestinal problems such as nausea—take chasteberry with meals.

***Caution:*** Chasteberry should be avoided by women who are pregnant or on hormone therapy.

Chasteberry is available in health food stores as a liquid extract or in capsule form.

# The Herb for the Eyes

David Winston, an herbalist certified by the American Herbalists Guild, and dean of the Herbal Therapeutics School of Botanic Medicine in Washington, NJ.

During World War II, British pilots observed that night vision was better among those who regularly ate bilberry jam. Subsequent research showed that bilberry, a cousin of the American blueberry, benefits a variety of vision disorders.

Besides boosting night vision, bilberry can be used to slow the progression of *retinitis pigmentosa* (RP). This hereditary eye disorder begins with night blindness and leads eventually to total blindness.

Bilberry also strengthens capillary walls within the retina. That's good news for people with diabetic retinopathy or macular degeneration.

***Important:*** Bilberry is most useful in *preventing* and *slowing* visual degeneration. It won't restore vision already lost.

Bilberry is rich in potent antioxidants called *anthocyanosides*. These compounds speed production of a retinal pigment called *visual purple*. Bilberry extract is standardized to contain 25% anthocyanosides.

Diabetics and others who wish to take bilberry as a preventive measure can take one 160-mg capsule daily. The capsules are sold at health food stores.

Or you can eat fresh blueberries—cooked enough to break down the skin. That allows the active components to be absorbed.

Eat a cup of berries daily—in pancakes…or as syrup or sauce. If you've been diagnosed with diabetic retinopathy, RP or macular degeneration, ask your doctor about taking two or three bilberry. At these doses, no adverse effects have been reported.

takes three weeks to be ready, so be sure to make a batch in advance.

***What to do:*** Mix one teaspoon of cayenne powder with one pint of soy oil in a bottle made of dark glass or opaque plastic. Let the contents blend for three weeks, shaking the bottle daily.

Using a dropper, rub three drops onto the soles of your feet or your hands. Wash your hands before touching your eyes.

***Caution:*** Use cayenne only on unbroken skin. If irritation occurs, run cool water over the affected skin…and stop using cayenne.

Cayenne is sold in small spice bottles at grocery stores. However, it's more potent and less costly when purchased in bulk from a health food store.

Soy oil is sold in supermarkets and health food stores.

# Red-Hot Relief for Cold Feet and Hands

Andrew L. Rubman, ND, director of the Southbury Clinic for Traditional Medicines in Southbury, CT.

You may know that a cayenne pepper extract called *capsaicin* (Capzasin) can be used topically to relieve arthritis pain. But cayenne can also be used to keep feet and hands warm in cold weather.

People whose extremities tend to be uncomfortably cold when they venture outdoors often rely upon thick insulation and/or heat-generating chemical gel packs. But cayenne powder—one-eighth of a teaspoon sprinkled into each shoe and/or glove—acts *internally* to help the body generate heat. That's a more effective way to stay warm.

***How it works:*** Water-soluble components in cayenne dilate capillaries in the skin surface, producing an immediate sensation of heat. Within 15 minutes, oil-soluble compounds reach deeper tissues, generating warmth for hours.If you're planning to spend several hours in the cold, consider using cayenne liniment instead of cayenne powder. Liniment

# Kidney Stone Avoidance Secrets

Your risk of developing kidney stones can be reduced by drinking more fluids. But what you drink makes a big difference.

***Recent study:*** Water, wine and caffeinated and decaffeinated coffee and tea all lowered kidney stone risk. Grapefruit juice increased risk.

Gary C. Curhan, MD, ScD, nephrologist and epidemiologist, Harvard Medical School, Boston. His study of 81,093 healthy women 40 to 65 years of age was published in the *Annals of Internal Medicine*, Sixth St. at Race, Philadelphia 19106.

# How to Keep Your Bladder Very Healthy

Jerry G. Blaivas, MD, clinical professor of urology at Cornell University College of Medicine and a urologist in private practice, both in New York City. He is author of *Conquering Bladder and Prostate Problems,* Plenum, and four professional books on urology-related topics.

Bladder trouble affects one out of every three people over the age of 50. While we can't stop the aging process, there are ways to reduce the risk for urinary pain, bladder cancer, infections, etc.

## FLUID INTAKE

Many health-conscious people make it a point to drink at least eight glasses of water each day. That's the level recommended by many doctors.

*Reality:* If you eat a wholesome diet and have no obvious bladder problems, drinking that much brings no real health benefits. And that level of fluid intake can lead to the inconvenience of having to go to the bathroom a dozen or more times a day.

*Bottom line:* Most people can safely let their thirst determine how much they drink. However, boosting fluid intake is often beneficial to people suffering from any of three conditions…

**1. Dark or discolored urine.** Dark, concentrated urine can be a sign of dehydration or kidney infection. If boosting your fluid intake does not lighten your urine, consult a doctor.

*Warning sign:* Red or bloody urine. Unless you've recently eaten beets—which can tint your urine red—see a doctor at once. You may have an infection…or even cancer.

Vitamin supplements and certain oral medications can give urine an orange or bluish hue.

**2. Urinary tract infections (UTIs).** Though they're usually thought of as a women's problem, UTIs are also a problem for men. They're caused by *E. coli* and other infectious bacteria.

**3. Kidney stones.** Fluids help prevent kidney stones from recurring by lowering the concentration of the stone-forming minerals calcium and oxalates in urine.

In each of these three cases, it's prudent to boost your daily fluid intake to eight eight-ounce glasses of water, juice or other nonalcoholic beverages. That's 64 ounces daily.

Boosting your fluid intake will help prevent UTIs by flushing infection-causing bacteria from the bladder. Doing so will also reduce your risk for kidney stone recurrence.

## LIFESTYLE STRATEGIES

Certain lifestyle habits can also play a role in the prevention and treatment of bladder problems.

•**Bladder cancer.** Smoking is now thought to cause half of all cases of bladder cancer. The best way to avoid bladder cancer is to avoid smoking.

Blood in the urine or a burning sensation upon urination can be the first symptoms of bladder cancer. See a doctor at once.

•**Urinary tract infections.** Like some cases of bladder cancer, UTIs are characterized by a burning sensation upon urination…and an almost constant need to urinate. Sometimes the urine turns bloody.

Even without treatment, UTIs generally clear up within a couple of weeks. Yet the symptoms they cause can be extremely unpleasant.

*To reduce your risk:* Have a large glass of water, cranberry juice or another beverage before *and after sex.* That promotes urination, which helps rid your urinary tract of bacteria.

Cranberry juice's high acidity inhibits growth of bacteria that cause UTIs.

Cranberry juice also triggers the formation of a mucus-like barrier along the bladder wall. This slick surface keeps bacteria from adhering.

Since warm water is a perfect breeding ground for bacteria, take showers instead of baths.

Tampons and diaphragms can also put you at risk. Any woman who is infection-prone should consider switching to feminine napkins and/or another form of birth control.

Some people find that vitamin C supplements seem to reduce the frequency of UTIs. Too much vitamin C, however, can cause kidney stones. If you take vitamin C, do not exceed 1,000 mg per day.

*Caution:* Although UTIs are rarely serious for women, in men they often indicate urinary blockage, nerve damage or a sexually transmitted disease.

Each of these possibilities requires a doctor's care.

•**Incontinence.** Most cases of urine leakage are caused by spasmodic contractions of the bladder or problems with the urinary sphincter. That's the muscular ring surrounding the base of the bladder, where it connects with the urethra (the tube that carries urine out of the body).

In many cases, it's possible to prevent incontinence via regular use of specialized pelvic muscle exercises called *Kegels*. Kegels work for both men and women.

*What to do:* Several times each day, squeeze your muscles as though you were trying to stop a bowel movement...and then squeeze the muscles it takes to stop urine in midstream.

A urologist can recommend many other non-surgical approaches to incontinence. If these fail, surgery is usually effective.

### THE STRESS CONNECTION

Aging men have a nearly universal complaint—a weak urine stream. What causes the problem? In men, two of three cases stem from muscle tension in the prostate, which narrows the urethra and inhibits the flow of urine.

*To strengthen the urine stream:* Use yoga or another stress-reduction technique to help reduce muscle tension.

Reducing psychological stress may help relax these prostate and urethra muscles that can cause blockages that weaken urine flow. If these measures fail, a urologist can offer other ways to correct prostate problems.

# Common Conversions

| To convert | to | multiply by |
|---|---|---|
| acres | hectares | .4047 |
| bushels | hectoliters | .3524 |
| centimeters | inches | .3937 |
| cubic feet | cubic meters | .0283 |
| cubic meters | cubic yards | 1.3079 |
| cubic yards | cubic meters | .7646 |
| feet | meters | .3048 |
| gallons | liters | 3.7853 |
| grains | grams | .0648 |
| grams | grains | 15.4324 |
| grams | ounces avdp | .0353 |
| hectares | acres | 2.4710 |
| hectoliters | bushels | 2.8378 |
| inches | millimeters | 25.4000 |
| inches | centimeters | 2.5400 |
| kilograms | pounds ap or t | 2.6792 |
| kilograms | pounds avdp | 2.2046 |
| kilometers | miles | .6214 |
| liters | gallons | .2642 |
| liters | pints (dry) | 1.8162 |
| liters | pints (liquid) | 2.1134 |
| liters | quarts (dry) | 9081 |

| To convert | to | multiply by |
|---|---|---|
| liters | quart (liquid) | 1.0567 |
| meters | feet | 3.2808 |
| meters | yards | 1.0936 |
| metric tons | tons (long) | .9842 |
| metric tons | tons (short) | 1.1023 |
| miles | kilometers | 1.6093 |
| millimeters | inches | .0394 |
| ounces avdp | grams | 28.3495 |
| pecks | liters | 8.8096 |
| pints (dry) | liters | .5506 |
| pints (liquid) | liters | .4732 |
| pounds ap or t | kilograms | .3782 |
| pounds avdp. | kilograms | .4536 |
| quarts (dry) | liters | 1.1012 |
| quarts (liquid) | liters | .9463 |
| square feet | square meters | .0929 |
| square meters | square feet | 10.7639 |
| square meters | square yards | 1.1960 |
| square yards | square meters | .8631 |
| tons (long) | metric tons | 1.0160 |
| tons (short) | metric tons | .9072 |
| yards | meters | .9144 |

# 18

# Education Smarts

## Ben Kaplan Attended One of America's Great Colleges *Free*... How Your Kids Can, Too

**P**arents of students who are planning on attending college find the prospect of paying for a college education today daunting, as tuition costs continue to rise.

*Example:* The cost of attending Harvard —including room and board—is in excess of $32,000.

Unless the school's financial aid office is especially generous, many students will have to take out loans and assume onerous postgraduate financial burdens...or not attend at all.

An often-overlooked source of financial aid is merit-based scholarships that are not offered by universities. In the following paragraphs, Kaplan tells how he won nearly $90,000—

enough to cover virtually all of his Harvard tuition.

### SECRETS OF FINDING FREE MONEY

These strategies can help any student, regardless of grade-point average, win scholarship money...

●**Make a long list of scholarship opportunities.** Most students apply for only a handful of scholarships, usually the ones their guidance counselors recommend. But the more money you seek, the more money you have a chance of winning.

I applied to about 30 different groups...and began the process in my junior year of high school. Each scholarship has a different deadline, and it usually takes one to three months to find out if you've won. Your school's scholarship library and guidance counselor are good places to start to create a list of groups.

---

Benjamin Kaplan, who won nearly $90,000 in scholarship money from about two dozen different organizations before and after being accepted at Harvard University in 1995. An economics major from Eugene, OR, he graduated this year.

But don't stop there. I got permission to visit other high schools in my area and looked in their libraries and on bulletin boards outside guidance counselors' offices. Most merit-based scholarships are not specific to particular high schools, and by visiting other schools, I was able to combat the imperfect flow of information often associated with scholarship contests.

Recently, the Internet has been a gold mine of scholarship information, in particular http://www.finaid.org, which is affiliated with the National Association of Student Financial Aid Administrators.

***Important:*** Don't ignore scholarships that seem relatively small. A $300 award may seem like nothing compared with a five-figure annual tuition bill. But the small awards add up.

I found that most of the books on scholarships in bookstores weren't particularly helpful. Many of them focused narrowly on scholarships for students whose parents work for certain companies or funds offered by specific colleges.

***Important:*** You don't have to inform most scholarship organizations that you've applied to other groups and have been awarded money. However, telling them may be a good strategy early on in your search because winning other awards enhances your credibility.

● **Know what each scholarship group wants.** Each scholarship organization defines its own selection criteria. Custom-tailoring your materials to fit these criteria is critical.

Many organizations favor student leaders or students who perform community service. Other groups look for students who have exceptional talents—writers, scientists, athletes or musicians.

Know what scholarship groups are looking for so that you can tailor your application appropriately. The selection process for a particular scholarship is often designed to yield an "ideal" candidate. You should tweak your materials to appeal to that ideal.

***Strategy:*** Most organizations will supply a list of past winners upon request. Contacting these past winners is valuable—you can often gain inside information about particular contests that extends far beyond published judging criteria.

● **Pick and choose the scholarships that are right for you.** Merit-based scholarships can be divided into three categories...

● The first group selects students based on the performance of a specified task (writing, artwork, speeches, etc.).

● The second category judges on the basis of past achievements (extracurricular activities, academics, etc.).

● The final category is a hybrid of the previous two.

Most scholarships fall into the second or third category and are based on a standard format—an essay, a grade transcript, a description of extracurricular activities and recommendation letters.

***Helpful:*** Try to pick essay topics that fit the requirements of a broad range of scholarships. This allows you to recycle essays and saves enormous amounts of time and energy. After creating this generic material, customize it to fit each scholarship. Rethinking passages means improvements in your writing as you edit.

The essay should always relate a personal experience or speak in a personal voice, since most submitted essays are wooden and dry. The essays need to be tight, without any spots that drag. The last thing you want to do is bore the judges.

Write long—perhaps 25% longer than the word limit—then force yourself to pare down the essay. Essays should get across who you are and what you are most passionate about.

● **Make sure your transcript and letters of recommendation capture the real you.** Transcripts are straightforward—but they can be spruced up.

***Example:*** My principal gave me permission to have listed on my transcript honors and awards that I had won in both school- and nonschool-related activities. This allowed me to place special emphasis on my most compelling achievements.

Recommendation letters are important. Play an active role in how they take shape. Meet with teachers and others whom you want to write letters. Give them a written summary of your goals and achievements. Communicate the central themes of the application so they can be reflected in the recommendations.

***Helpful:*** Get as many letters as you can. People who know you in different contexts will often have different perspectives, and the more perspectives the better. You'll be able to choose which letters to include with different scholarship packages.

**Example:** My journalism adviser wrote a letter about my work on the school newspaper to an organization that emphasized teamwork. For an organization that sought out individual initiative, a different teacher stressed the community service program I had developed.

# Excellent Educations For Much, Much Less

Edward Custard, former college admissions officer and president of Carpe Diem ETC, an education consulting firm, Box 183, Sugar Loaf, NY 10981. He is editor of three college guides, including *The Best 311 Colleges, 1999.* Princeton Review.

The average cost of a college education is at an all-time high—and is expected to rise at about 5% annually. Here are top colleges whose annual tuitions are below the average...

### CALIFORNIA

•**University of California/*Berkeley.*** The intellectual flagship of California's formidable public system, Berkeley is highly competitive. More than 95% of its freshmen were in the top 10% of their high school classes. Though it is a huge state school, more than half the classes have fewer than 24 students. *Tuition:* In-state/$4,354...out-of-state/$13,338. 510-642-3175.

### GEORGIA

•**Georgia Institute of Technology/*Atlanta.*** Top-notch engineering school—without the mega-competitive admissions profile of MIT or Cal Tech. Most people don't realize this is a public school. *Tuition:* In-state/$5,604 ...out-of-state/$9,225. 404-894-4154.

### ILLINOIS

•**University of Illinois/*Urbana-Champaign.*** Highly rated engineering school that also has a first-rate computer science program.

It was the training ground of Marc Andreessen, cofounder of Netscape. The school also gets high marks for its biology and business programs. *Tuition:* In-state/$4,746...out-of-state/$11,838. 217-333-0302.

### MARYLAND

•**University of Maryland/*Baltimore County.*** This up-and-coming branch of the state university system has 8,500 students. The school has a banner computer graphics program including a collaboration with Silicon Graphics, a state-of-the-art technology company. *Tuition:* In-state/$4,046...out-of-state/$8,518. 800-862-2482.

### MISSOURI

•**Truman State/*Kirksville.*** This school of 6,050 students has one of the nation's most thorough liberal arts core programs. Among the top programs are business, biology and English. The average class size is 16 students. *Tuition:* In-state/$3,544...out-of-state/$6,344. 660-785-4114.

### NEW JERSEY

•**Rutgers University/*New Brunswick.*** This State University of New Jersey excels in psychology, nursing and English and has a highly rated performing arts school. *Tuition:* In-state/ $4,562...out-of-state/$9,286. 732-445-3770.

### NEW YORK

•**Cooper Union/*New York City.*** What could be cheaper than tuition that is absolutely free? At this arts, engineering and architecture school, grades, talent and creative portfolios are what get students admitted. 212-353-4100.

•**State University of New York/*Geneseo.*** This less-famous branch of the SUNY system is cloistered away in this small town 30 miles south of Rochester. *Tuition:* In-state/$3,400 ...out-of-state/$8,300. 716-245-5571.

### NORTH CAROLINA

•**University of North Carolina/*Chapel Hill.*** Known for its athletic program, this college also is an academic powerhouse that is set in a bucolic college town. *Tuition:* In-state/ $2,262...out-of-state/$11,428. 919-966-3621.

### TEXAS

•**University of Texas/*Austin.*** This campus with 50,000 students is located in a beautiful town known for music and nightlife. Excels in liberal arts, business and communications. *Tuition:* In-state/$3,128...out-of-state/$9,616. 512-475-7399.

### WASHINGTON STATE

•**University of Washington/***Seattle.* This urban campus with a view of Mt. Rainier has a population of 35,000 students. Business, biology and psychology are the most popular majors, but there are 13 undergraduate colleges overseen by a 3,500-member faculty. *Tuition:* In-state/$3,638...out-of-state/$12,029. 206-543-9686.

---

# New World of College Financial Aid: How to Get Your Full Share

Kalman A. Chany, president of Campus Consultants Inc., a fee-based firm that assists families in maximizing financial aid eligibility, 1202 Lexington Ave., Suite 327, New York 10028. He is author of *Paying for College Without Going Broke, 1999 Edition.* Random House.

---

Most parents need financial help when they are paying for their children's college educations. Unfortunately, many parents are not familiar with the best ways to apply for and receive financial aid.

*Result:* They pay more out of their own pockets and enroll their children in colleges that they can *afford*—rather than colleges that are ideal for their children.

Here are the most common mistakes people make when applying for financial assistance from a college...

*Mistake:* **Assuming that you're not eligible for financial aid.** Many people don't apply because they believe they are not eligible if they earn more than $75,000 a year or own their own homes...or they've heard that their neighbors applied and were turned down.

*Reality:* There is no real income cutoff. Sometimes families with incomes in excess of $125,000 receive financial aid. Financial aid is awarded based on a complex formula that fac-

tors in many variables, including the number of members in the household, the number of children in college and the age of the oldest parent.

*Mistake:* **Failing to do any advance planning for the application process.**

*Reality:* Eligibility is determined by taking a snapshot of your family's financial situation. If you are applying for your child's freshman year of college, the year that is scrutinized is from January 1 of your child's junior year in high school to December 31 of his/her senior year. Any financial transactions you make during that year could help—or hurt—your child's chances of getting aid.

*Example:* If you had accumulated some stock investments to pay for college and sold them during the first half of your child's senior year in high school, the capital gains on the stock would increase your income and reduce your eligibility for aid.

To give your child the best chance of receiving financial aid, you must plan to accelerate income into earlier years and minimize discretionary income items during the key tax years that affect your eligibility for aid.

*Mistake:* **Missing the deadlines.** Many people believe that the time to apply for financial aid is after the child has been accepted to a college.

*Reality:* It's crucial to apply for aid at the same time that your child is applying to colleges. There is a limited amount of aid available, and priority is given to those who meet the deadlines. Extensions are rarely granted.

The best source of information about deadlines is the school itself. Be certain to find out if the material is to be *postmarked, received* or *processed* by the deadline.

*Mistake:* **Not keeping track of the process.** Many families simply fill out the financial aid forms and hope for the best. They are not assertive enough and do not keep track of things. They also don't check in with the colleges.

*Reality:* You have to assume that things are going to go wrong. Check with the school, and make certain it has everything it needs. Find out if there is anything else you could send to improve your chances. Make photocopies of all the forms in case you are asked any questions.

*Important:* Although instructions on the application forms will tell you not to send them by certified mail, I recommend you do so for your own protection. If your forms are lost or misplaced, the processing center or the college may try to claim that you never filed them. Using certified mail/return receipt requested gives you proof of mailing and delivery.

### Mistake: Assuming the college will help you get the most financial aid possible.

*Reality:* It's important to understand that the college is apportioning a pot of money…and demand exceeds supply. Therefore, it is not in the school's best interest to help you figure out how to maximize your child's financial aid.

### Mistake: Assuming financial aid packages are set in stone.

*Reality:* It is often possible to negotiate a better package than the one you are initially offered by the college. One of your strongest bargaining chips could be a better financial aid package from a comparable school.

You might say, *I'd really love to have my child attend your school, but the money is an issue. We've been offered a much more generous package from College X.* Be honest about this, though, since you may be asked to provide a copy of that package.

*Trend:* The first offer that any college makes to parents is often not its best offer. The college wants to see if you will blink—and it is leaving itself room for bargaining. College officials will deny this vehemently…but every year, I see colleges change the amounts of their awards.

### Mistake: Rejecting student loans when they're offered as part of a package.
Many parents say, *I don't want my child to borrow or to have debt when he/she graduates from school.* Meanwhile, these parents have thousands of dollars in outstanding credit card debt.

*Reality:* Student loans are great deals and compare favorably with other borrowing options.

*Example:* The need-based student loans (Perkins Loan and subsidized Stafford Loan) charge no interest and do not require repayment of principal until the student leaves school.

*Better:* Take the student loans, use current income to pay off other debt and then, if you want to pay the student loans off in a lump sum after graduation, you can do so with no repayment penalty. In this way, you might save hundreds—or even thousands—of dollars in interest.

### Mistake: Being unaware of other attractive borrowing options.

*Reality:* Even if they don't qualify for need-based student loans, virtually all students qualify for *unsubsidized* Stafford Loans. The colleges' financial aid offices can tell you how to apply for these loans.

*How they work:* Although the child is charged interest while in school, it is at an attractive rate based on the 91-day Treasury bill plus 1.7%. The rate is set each year at the end of June.

Some colleges have their own loan programs, which may have very attractive terms. There is also the federal Parent Loans for Undergraduate Students (PLUS) program, which allows you to borrow the total cost of education less any aid offered.

*Example:* If the tuition costs $25,000 and your child is getting $10,000 in financial aid, you can borrow up to $15,000.

*To maximize your aid package:* Take out a Perkins Loan first, then a Stafford Loan, then a PLUS Loan.

### Mistake: Failing to understand the implications of every financial decision you make during the years you are seeking aid.

*Reality:* From January 1 of your child's junior year in high school to January 1 of his junior year in college, any decision you make could ruin the chances for aid the next year. *Common mistakes:*

- Withdrawing funds from a pension.

- Taking capital gains on securities.

- Overpaying state and local taxes so that you receive a large refund the following year.

*Note:* Widowed or divorced parents who remarry during a child's college years are sometimes unpleasantly surprised to find that the income of the new spouse is factored into the financial aid formula.

# Be Careful What You Say When Applying For Financial Aid

Dianne Van Riper, assistant inspector general in the Office of the Inspector General at the US Education Department, Washington, DC. The Office responds to questions about how best to answer financial aid applications. 800-433-3243.

Stretching the truth to maximize financial assistance is riskier than most parents or students realize.

The penalty includes paying back up to three times the amount of aid you received and fines as high as $10,000 per lie. Cheats also may be arrested and charged with a felony.

Here are the most common ways that parents and students get into trouble on financial aid applications...

*Trap:* **Using a dishonest college consultant.** College consultants may charge several hundred dollars to help parents negotiate the student aid application maze. While most consultants are honest, a sizable minority are willing to bend or break the rules for clients.

When you sign the financial aid application that a consultant has prepared, you are legally certifying that you have reviewed the information, and it is accurate.

***When choosing a consultant:*** Beware of those who "guarantee" to win your child student aid. There are so many variables in which students are—and are not—awarded aid that guarantees are impossible.

Read and review the application instructions with the consultant. They're surprisingly clear and easy to understand. If you don't understand some of the instructions, call the college financial aid officer.

*Trap:* **Underreporting household income.** By law, colleges are required to verify the incomes that are claimed by 30% of the students who applied for financial aid. They usually do this by requesting copies of the families' tax returns.

But currently, the US Education Department has the authority to check *all* applications by matching them against the original tax data you provided to the IRS.

*Trap:* **Claiming your child isn't your dependent.** An independent child's student aid is based on his/her income, which can be meager.

There are very explicit requirements for a student to be declared independent. Applicants can access these rules from college financial aid offices...or at the US Education Department Web site, www.ed.gov.

There are also rules for orphan or ward-of-the-state status.

*Trap:* **Claiming more dependents than you actually have.** Many cheats say they have more children than they actually do, to increase the amount of aid they receive. This information, too, will soon be checked against actual tax returns.

*Trap:* **Falsely claiming that the child lives with the lower-earning parent,** if you and your spouse are divorced.

*Trap:* **A married college student who claims to be single or divorced** so that his spouse's income isn't figured into the student aid calculation.

*Trap:* **Falsely claiming that there are more members of the household in post-secondary education** than are actively enrolled.

# The New Education IRAs

Anyone with young children or grandchildren who is eligible to set up an Education IRA should take advantage of this opportunity. The income limits are modified Adjusted Gross Income up to $95,000, or $150,000 in a joint return, with a contribution phase-out for AGI between $95,000 and $110,000, or $150,000 and $160,000 on a joint return. *Contribution limit:* A total of $500 per child per year.

***Tax benefit:*** Earnings accumulate tax free, and there will be no tax on withdrawal providing the money is used for qualified education expenses.

If you have more than one child (or grandchild), set up an Education IRA for each.

If you decide not to use the IRA for one child—he wins a scholarship, for example—you can turn the money over to another child.

***Trap:*** If the money is not used (or rolled over into another education IRA) by the time the child is 30, the beneficiary will be taxed on the earnings and owe a 10% tax penalty.

Even so, the tax-deferred inside buildup on an Education IRA makes it worthwhile.

Gregory F. Jenner, national director of tax policy for Coopers & Lybrand LLP, 1900 K St. NW, Washington, DC 20006. Mr. Jenner is a former tax counsel of the Senate Finance Committee and was a special assistant to the Assistant Secretary of the Treasury for tax policy during the Bush Administration.

# Tuition-Saving Secret

Save thousands of dollars in tuition by shopping for "bargains" among a large group of schools.

Most parents and their children research only five schools. But many of the nation's 3,000 colleges are offering merit-based discounts to qualified applicants. *Better:* Look into at least 20 schools.

***Example:*** If your child graduates in the top third of his/her class, you can negotiate lower tuition at many schools—in some cases up to 50% off.

Raymond Loewe, president of College Money, a fee-based financial planning service that specializes in counseling parents on paying for college, 112B Centre Blvd., Marlton, NJ 08503.

# Smart College Prep Tactics from Consultant Adam Robinson

Adam Robinson, cofounder of the Princeton Review SAT preparation course and a private consultant in New York. He is author of *What Smart Students Know.* Crown Publishing.

## Start Early to Get into an Elite College

To get into an elite college, one passion is better than a half-dozen interests. These colleges look at extracurricular activities—so pursue an interest for as many summers as you can. *Surprising:* Your achievements may win you scholarships that pay more than a summer job. *Other useful summer activities:* Build vocabulary by learning at least five words a day—10 is better. Spend time preparing for advanced-placement courses and for the SAT-IIs (formerly called Achievement Tests) that you will be taking. *Summer before senior year:* Start such time-consuming tasks as obtaining college applications...and writing college essays.

**More from Adam Robinson...**

## SAT-Boosting Magic

The best way to practice the SAT is to use paper and pencil, not computer versions.

***Reasons:*** The closer the practice is to the real thing, the more it can help your score. A computer screen makes it hard to go back and forth, as you can with the printed versions... and you don't have the scratch paper right there, as you do with the actual test.

***Best practice test:*** *10 Real SATs*, published by The College Board, is available at most bookstores.

You don't need to take expensive courses—but it is important to get test-taking guidance from an experienced teacher or older students who did well on the tests.

# Better SAT Preparation

Don't expect miracles by taking SAT prep courses. The courses tend to focus on general commonsense test-taking strategies. They are better at helping students who *already* have good scores than students whose scores need a big lift. Best resource for improving SAT Verbal scores independently—*Up Your Score* by Larry Berger, Workman/$9.95. Best resources for improving scores on the math test—*SAT Success* by Joan Carris, Michael R. Crystal, Peterson's / $14.95 and the *SAT Math Workbook* by Brigitte Saunders, et al, Arco/$10.95.

*Behind the Scenes: An Inside Look at the Selective College Admission Process* by Edward Wall, partner, Gibbs and Wall, education counselors, Byfield, MA, and former dean of admissions, Amherst College. Octameron Associates.

# When to Put Off College

Don't let kids take a year off between high school and college unless they have very specific plans and goals that will truly contribute to growth. Many organizations offer internships, foreign language study or other formal yearlong programs for students between high school and college.

*Information:* City Year (617-927-2500)... Dynamy Internship Year (508-755-2571)...Time Out Associates (617-698-8977).

*Signs that a student might benefit from a year off:* Inertia sets in during his/her senior year...he shows strong interest in doing something very different from what he has done so far.

*Caution:* Don't expect a year off to get him into a better college. The year off is much more likely to change his expectations about which college will make the best fit.

Arthur Mullaney, president of College Impressions, counselors to prospective college students, and editor of *College Impressions*, Box 665, Canton, MA 02021.

# Better Private-School Selection

Ask school administrators how much time is reserved for basic subjects....and about other areas that concern you. Ask to see the class schedules. School officials may shade their comments in a particular direction, but schedules show the real priorities.

*Bad Teachers: The Essential Guide for Concerned Parents* by Guy Strickland, educational researcher, Sherman Oaks, CA. Pocket Books.

# Computer Literacy In Your Later Years

Become computer literate through Senior-Net, the national nonprofit organization dedicated to bringing computer literacy to older adults. SeniorNet operates more than 140 learning centers nationally. It offers low-cost instruction in subjects ranging from a basic introduction to computers to classes in software applications for genealogy, investing, tax management, business, the Internet and more.

*Contact:* SeniorNet at 121 Second St., 7th Fl., San Francisco 94105. 415-495-4990.

Patricia Robison, information technology consultant, Andersen Consulting, 1221 Avenue of the Americas, New York 10105.

# 19

# Making the Most of Your Leisure Time

## How to Host a Dynamite Dinner Party

Speaking as a veteran guest and host of hundreds of dinner parties, I have learned what works and what doesn't.

While it may sound nice to be casual about entertaining, the laid-back host can wind up with guests who hate each other by the end of the evening.

To avoid social disasters and ensure that the evening will be easy for you and memorable for your guests, you need to plan ahead.

### BEFORE THE DINNER

•*Number of guests.* It depends on your budget, table capacity and the mood you're looking for. Though my dining room table seats 10 comfortably, I like doing dinners for eight. The conversation is more cohesive, and the meal service and cleanup are more manageable.

Invite enough people so that if one couple cancels, the evening won't be dull.

Think through all of the contingencies. It's not just a number—it's your evening.

•*Whom to invite.* For that special dinner party, you might start your list with a Key Guest.

This is the person or couple you want to get to know better, owe a return invitation, need to entertain for business reasons or want to welcome to the neighborhood.

Offer your Key Guest a few possible dates. Then build your guest list around the Key Guest's availability.

List 10 or 12 others who would interact well with the Key Guest. These are people whose personalities your Key Guest would enjoy or who might be of professional help to him/her. Fill the remaining seats with friends with whom you yourself like spending time.

***Important:*** Don't forget to ask if anyone has special dietary needs.

Letty Cottin Pogrebin, author of eight books, including *Getting Over Getting Older*, Berkley. She is a founding editor of *Ms.* magazine and current president of the Authors Guild.

**Risk:** Don't assume that people who are in the same profession will have things in common. Not all lawyers get along. Folks in business, theater, politics or architecture are often more competitive than convivial. Invite *personalities*—not *careers*.

●*What to serve.* During the cocktail period, offer hors d'oeuvres, not just nuts or olives. Otherwise your guests will starve waiting for dinner.

Forty-five minutes to an hour for cocktails allows enough time for get-acquainted chitchat and latecomers' arrivals. For example, in New York City, it's common for guests to arrive 30 minutes late.

Consider keeping a bottle of flavored vodka in the freezer and champagne in the fridge. Guests appreciate being offered something special as an aperitif along with the usual wine and liquor. Stock up on club soda. It's a surprising favorite.

If the hors d'oeuvres were substantial, start dinner with the entrée. Personally, I prefer to begin with a light appetizer or soup, since a first course extends the table time and builds camaraderie.

The easiest main course is a one-dish meal requiring no tricky timing—a stew, paella, casserole or curry paired with rice or orzo.

Add a crusty peasant bread, green salad and a simple dessert, such as individual tarts and chocolate-dipped strawberries.

**Warning:** Running short of food is worse than having leftovers. Err on the side of excess with both food and drink. And—regardless of the menu, stock both red and white wine.

### DURING DINNER

●*Seating.* Make place cards with the names on both sides—and written big enough so guests across the table can read them. Analyze everyone's strengths and interests before you place their cards at the table. A thoughtful seating plan will enhance the social experience for everyone.

**Examples:** If you want your Key Guest to hear about a friend's consulting service, place your Key Guest between you and your friend. You then will be able to steer the conversation to that subject if your friend doesn't.

Put singles side by side if you foresee romantic possibilities. But don't be a slave to the boy-girl arrangement.

●*Conversation.* Most people chat easily during the first part of the meal, properly turning to the dinner companions on either side.

But after the friendly tête-à-têtes peter out, you may need to reinvigorate the conversation among the entire group. *Ideas for catalytic intervention...*

●*Provocative question* for the whole table to address. *Examples:* "What do you wish your parents had taught you?"..."How do you relax?"

Stimulating queries give people something to chew on besides the chicken. They also ensure that everyone at the table has a chance to be heard.

The late novelist Bernard Malamud used to ask wonderfully intense questions, such as, "If you could live your life over again, what would you do differently?"..."If you could instantly possess any body of knowledge in the world, what would it be?" Inevitably, the ensuing discourse was many cuts above the usual social small talk, and Malamud's guests always left the dinner party feeling enriched and enlightened.

●*Express your point of view* on a current issue—the more controversial, the better.

●*Have your guests introduce themselves,* saying what most interests or excites them at the moment. Don't ask what they do. It is boring and embarrasses people who are out of work and makes some homemakers feel ill at ease. What you want to get at are people's *passions*.

A publisher I know is a consummate host at his many business dinners.

As soon as everyone unfolds their napkins, he does a round of introductions. He describes his guests with superlatives they could not use about themselves, thereby providing information that greases the conversational gears during dinner.

After the main course, he asks everyone to talk about new developments in their lives or fields of expertise. I always leave these evenings with marvelous up-to-the-minute bulletins on innovations in medicine, science, finance, law, travel—you name it.

**Risk:** Timing is everything. Some people resent having their tête-à-têtes interrupted for group discussion. Be sensitive. When the table is humming with bonhomie, leave well enough alone.

### AFTER DINNER

•*Keep a record.* Write down who was there and what you served so you won't repeat the guest mix—or menu—next time. I've eaten the same food five times at a friend's house. It makes me feel like a cog in an assembly line.

•*Network.* After his business dinners, my publishing friend sends out a name and address list with a note saying something like, "Here's who you met last night in case you'd like to keep in touch." Guests find this welcome gesture facilitates new personal and client relationships.

•*Debrief.* Pay attention to comments after the fact. "Sorry I ate so many hors d'oeuvres—I was starved" might mean the cocktail hour was too long. "That guy next to me was some talker!" tells you to be wary of motormouths.

•*Luxuriate.* Enjoy the afterglow of successful hospitality. Good food and great conversation is a gift for mind and mouth, and its deepest satisfaction belongs to the giver.

## Better Bicycling

When climbing a hill on a bike, mentally break it into small pieces. Find a landmark ahead of you, and focus on riding to it. Then set a new goal.

•**Use a gear that balances the climb between your legs and lungs.** Breathe deeply while pedaling.

•**Keep rest stops to two minutes or less.** Straddle the bike while resting—do not get off completely.

•**Ride as far right as is comfortable, and stay highly aware of your lane position.** Be prepared to "take the lane" by riding in the middle of the lane if it would be unsafe for cars to pass—especially at tops of hills and on blind curves to the right.

•**Use low gears when appropriate** so you can sit while climbing.

*Donald Tighe, director of education, League of American Bicyclists, Washington, DC.*

# For Happier Kitchening

*Nicholas Baxter, Lund Baxter Enterprises, a catering company, 692 Greenwich St., New York 10014.*

Great hosts take care of their cooking equipment and are prepared for surprise guests.

### CARING FOR EQUIPMENT

•**Knives.** The brand matters less than how well you take care of the blades. Best way to sharpen knives—rub them vigorously against a *sharpening steel* after every use.

*To store knives to keep them sharp...*

•Vertical rack cut into a work surface. Slits cut into a countertop or attached to the end of a counter allow knives to hang freely.

•Magnetic strip attached to the side of a counter or wall. This keeps the cutting edge of blades from being rubbed repeatedly against a hard surface every time you take them out.

•If you store knives in a freestanding, angled butcher block, slip knives into their slots with the sharp side up.

Wash the sharpening steel periodically with vinegar to remove grease buildup. Then rinse and dry.

•**Plastic scraper.** Buy the one favored by bakers to scrape the curved surfaces of bowls. It has one straight edge and the rest is curved. It's inexpensive and tends not to shred or break as long-handled rubber models do.

•**Cutting boards.** Own two boards. Mark each of the four sides for meat, poultry, fish and vegetables with an indelible marker.

*Aim:* Reduce cross-contamination.

A plastic board is easier to clean, but make sure that it is not rock hard. Otherwise it will blunt knives.

Also consider different color boards for different purposes.

Cleaning up carefully after preparing meat, fish or chicken is critical.

*Helpful...*

•**Plastic and wooden boards.** Rinse off in a solution of five parts water to one part bleach for regular cleaning...use a one-to-one solution for stubborn stains. The juice of one lemon to a cup of salt gives the board a pleasant smell and is slightly abrasive. Putting boards in a dishwasher will warp them.

•**Butcher block.** Coat the surface with a combination of kosher salt and lemon juice. Then scrub with a firm brush—to leach out residues in the wood.

•**Bowls.** Cooking is easier if you prepare each recipe ingredient listed—peeling, cutting, beating, grating—and in the exact quantities called for before you start cooking. That's why you always need plenty of bowls. I have at least four medium-sized and a dozen small bowls that are made of glass and stainless steel.

### ENTERTAINING ON SHORT NOTICE

Maintain a pantry that holds classic items. Core staples in my home kitchen...

•**Refrigerator.** Lemons, limes, onions, herbed oils, cooked chicken or smoked salmon...and a selection of cheeses.

•**Freezer.** Pizza bases, frozen berries, ice cream or pound cake.

•**Shelves.** Pasta—in several shapes and sizes, cans of diced tomatoes, artichoke hearts and anchovy filets.

From this pantry, I can produce the following meal in 30 minutes...

•**Appetizer.** Bruschetta-style pizza. Cut pizza base into strips or pieces...top with diced cooked chicken or salmon. Heat 10 minutes...drizzle with herbed oil.

•**Main course.** Pasta in artichoke sauce. Dice onions and sauté for five minutes. Add tomatoes, anchovies and artichokes. Cook for 10 minutes. While the sauce is cooking, prepare pasta.

•**Dessert.** In the microwave or on the stove top, warm the frozen berries with cinnamon, nutmeg and lemon zest to taste. Serve over ice cream...or on its own...or over a simple store-bought pound cake.

# Vicki Rovere's Secrets Of Thrift Shopping

Vicki Rovere, lecturer and author of *Worn Again, Hallelujah! A Guide to NYC's Thrift Shops & Other Treasure Troves*. Vicki Rovere, 339 Lafayette St., New York 10012.

For a more enjoyable, productive experience, know why you are shopping at a thrift shop. Other than saving money, people shop in thrift stores for a variety of reasons, including...

•**Treasure hunting.** Hoping to make an unexpected discovery.

•**Collecting.** The search for specific types of items, such as Hawaiian shirts, Barbie dolls, cast-iron toys.

### STRATEGIES

•**Choosing a store.** Some are neatly laid out, with clothes arranged according to size. Others are a jumble of tables heaped with merchandise for shoppers to root through. Most stores specialize—clothing...appliances, etc. *Key:* Find the type of store that suits your shopping personality and needs.

•**Clothing.** Classic or trendy? There are two philosophies for buying thrift shop clothing. Some shoppers buy only classics. Others enjoy having fun with new fashions, especially those they wouldn't want to buy at retail prices in a department store.

•**Comparison shop.** If you are looking for a particular item, know what it costs new, so you can be sure you're getting it for a bargain.

*Example:* I once bought a broken ice crusher at a thrift shop. Later, I discovered I could have bought a new one for only a little more...and saved repair costs, too.

•**Cannibalizing appliances.** Thrift shops are great for finding replacement parts for broken items.

*Example:* I recently bought an electric blender after my blender's glass top broke. Because the one I bought had a burned-out motor, I got it for a fraction of what I'd have paid for a replacement top alone.

•**Keep going back.** Most thrift shops receive new merchandise constantly, so go back regularly.

Store employees, especially at smaller thrift shops, will often keep an eye out for the type of merchandise favored by a regular customer.

• **Bargaining basics.** Most thrift stores frown on haggling. Prices are already cut to the bone.

The Salvation Army and Goodwill stores have firm policies to discourage dickering.

*My theory:* It never hurts to try. If I'm refused, so be it.

*Helpful:* Find something wrong with the item—a missing button, a stain—and ask for a "damaged item discount." Also ask for volume discounts.

*Example:* One store sells clothing for $1.25 per pound, with a minimum of 25 pounds.

• **Learn to mend.** You will then be able to buy and rescue what are otherwise wonderful garments that have been discarded.

*Examples:* Embroider a design over a tear or stain…patch a problem with a decorative piece of fabric…redye the entire garment a dark color.

• **Wear tight clothing when shopping.** Many thrift shops do not have dressing rooms for trying on clothing. Wear leotards, tights, even bicycle shorts so you can try on clothing right there in the aisle.

# Buying and Selling Collectibles on the Internet

Malcolm Katt, an antiques dealer. He is also owner of Millwood Gallery, which specializes in Nippon and Packard porcelain, 50 Shingle House Rd., Millwood, NY 10546.

The volume of business on the Internet's collectible auction markets has exploded in the last few years, and for very good reasons. *Collectible trading on the Internet gives you…*

• Secure, anonymous, cheap and effortless access to collectors all over the world.

• The chance to view pictures of the thousands of items that are for sale in your special field of collecting—no matter how quirky it is.

• The opportunity to make a few extra dollars—or a few thousand.

• A fascinating entrance to the information superhighway—if you're not there yet.

• The possibility of developing friendships through E-mail exchanges with other collectors.

If you're a serious collector, you may have to go on-line. It has been estimated that within the next five years, 50% of all collectible sales will take place over the Internet.

*Fact:* The world's largest Internet trading service, eBay, was started in September 1995 as a way to help its founder's girlfriend sell her collection of Pez dispensers. (The company went public in September 1998. The founder became a billionaire—in only three years!)

### BUYING AND SELLING ON-LINE

*The most popular Internet auction sites are…*

• www.eBay.com
• www.boxlot.com
• www.ehammer.com
• www.skybid.com
• www.AuctionIt.com
• www.AuctionUniverse.com

eBay is the biggest by far. At last report more than 1.2 million people have used eBay to buy and sell merchandise in more than 1,500 categories—from Beanie Babies to books. Every day there are more than 12 million "page views," that is, viewings by potential buyers checking out wares.

*What does it cost?* On-line auction companies typically charge an "insertion fee" for listing an item and a commission based on the selling price.

On eBay, the top insertion fee is $2, and the commission is up to 5% when items are sold.

There are several software programs available to help sellers manage on-line selling.

*Example: Auction Assistant 2* by Blackthorne Software provides eBay sellers with low-cost/high-featured software to automate the tasks of listing and maintaining auctions. *Cost:* $59.95 (www.blackthornesw.com).

*To be a buyer on-line:* Register at one of the auction sites. Simply fill out an on-line application that includes your name and mailing address. It is not necessary to reveal your Social Security or credit card number. *Details...*

- You are described on-line only by a code name you have selected.

- The highest bidder is notified by E-mail and contacted by the seller to arrange payment.

- Payment is made directly to the seller by check or money order.

### SAFEGUARDS

The buyer has the ability to verify the seller's honesty by checking a "feedback" rating. So, you can avoid dealing with individuals whose ratings raise questions.

Sellers receive positive, negative or neutral comments from previous buyers.

On eBay, if a seller has too many negative comments, he/she can be terminated from using the service.

Keep in mind that reputable sellers give the buyer the opportunity to return the item if unsatisfied for a valid reason.

On-line escrow services for expensive items are also available.

There is no fee to view, bid and buy on-line. The seller pays the insertion fee and commission. Buyers typically pay for postage and insurance.

### BUYER BEWARE

Just like written descriptions, a photo seen on a small screen does not always reveal damage or problems that the seller has overlooked.

Remember that buying on-line is no different from buying in person. Often the seller is ignorant of what he is offering or is purposely deceitful. As always, *buyer beware.*

# Common Gardening Mistakes

Planting in the wrong place...judging the plant by the size it is when you bring it home from the nursery, not the size it will reach at maturity...buying plants not suitable for your area's climate and soil...not thinking of sun needs...failing to properly prepare the soil—healthy soil is alive with nutrients and microorganisms, so plants grow almost effortlessly. Improve soil health by eliminating weeds, tilling, adding organic matter, aerating and, if necessary, building raised beds.

Marsha M. Harlow, Master Gardener in San Antonio.

# Home Video Secrets from A Professional Filmmaker

David Irving, chairman of the prestigious undergraduate film department at New York University. He is a filmmaker who has made six feature films and more than a dozen documentaries.

Think through the scenes before you tape. In the film business, every aspect of a movie that is about to be shot is thought through and plotted out in "preproduction." Think ahead about the story you want to tell on video and the audience you'll be telling it to.

*Example:* If it's a birthday party, think about the scenes you'll want in the video—kids arriving, opening presents, games, blowing out candles, eating the cake, etc. Make a "shot list"—outlining these different scenes.

- **Open with an "establishing shot."** This tells the viewer what the video is about and starts the narrative progression.

*Example:* For the birthday party, you may want an initial shot of the decorated room before the kids arrive.

- **Use "bump shots" to vary the rhythm and pace of your video.** While you might be able to watch your child in the bathtub for 10 minutes, most viewers are more than happy with just a few seconds.

*Helpful:* Use what I call "bump shots." Tape the 10-minute bathtub scene—but create change and variety. Turn the camera on for five or 10 seconds, turn it off, move to another position, tape for another five or 10 seconds, etc.

Eight slightly different 10-second shots of bath time are far easier to watch than minutes on end from one angle.

- **Keep the camera moving.** Every viewer's eye is highly trained now—even if they don't know it. We need to be engaged. Otherwise, we get bored easily.

While you may not have the skills of a professional, you can at least keep the viewer's interest by panning the camera slowly from left to right—or by zooming in slowly for a close-up and zooming out for a wide shot.

---

# Casino Sports Betting: One Of the Best Casino Bets

Stanford Wong, a professional gambler who has written 12 books on casino betting. He is coauthor of *The Complete Idiot's Guide to Gambling Like a Pro.* Alpha Books.

---

Many visitors to Las Vegas or Lake Tahoe casinos overlook one of the best values that Nevada has to offer—wagering on professional sports contests.

### ADVANTAGES OF SPORTS WAGERING

While certain casino games may offer better odds on a given bet, a casino sports bet provides far more bang for your entertainment dollar—hours of enjoyment for a single wager.

*Example:* In a typical bet on a football game, you risk $11 to win $10. That extra dollar represents the casino's commission. It gives the house an advantage of 4.5%—more than twice as much as the house edge against a smart blackjack or craps player.

But in the space of a single football game, you might play up to 300 hands of blackjack. Over the same period of time, you would be placing much more of your bankroll at risk.

### OTHER ADVANTAGES

• Free seat near a big-screen television, with complimentary drinks.

• The ability to follow—and bet on—more than one professional sport at a time, thanks to multiple screens.

• The satisfaction of a wager that rewards skill over pure luck.

### TYPES OF BETS

There are two basic forms of sports gambling. Both involve the creation of a *betting line.*

That is designed to make a bet on either team equally attractive.

A casino always seeks to balance the amount of money bet on two opposing teams so as to guarantee a house profit through its commissions, no matter which team wins.

In football and basketball, you will generally see the betting line stated as a *point spread*—simply called the *spread.*

The point spread gives the underdog extra points to make the wager as fair as possible. A bet on the underdog wins if the underdog beats the favorite outright—or if the favorite wins by less than the spread.

*Example:* Let's say the Chicago Bulls were favored to beat the Los Angeles Lakers by six points. Let's say you like the Lakers, who proceed to lose, 94–89. You would win your bet because the Lakers lost by less than six points.

In baseball, the betting line is usually expressed as a *money line.* This penalizes people who bet on a favorite by forcing them to bet a lot to win just a little.

*Example:* Let's say the odds of the New York Mets beating the Los Angeles Dodgers are 8–7. If you bet on the Mets, you must bet $8 to make a profit of $5. If you bet on the Dodgers, you must risk $5 to win $7.

People who like long shots can play a *parlay,* a bet involving two or more games. If any of your teams lose, you lose the bet. But if they all win, you can earn a large profit for a relatively small wager.

A two-team parlay usually pays off at 13 to 5—that is, a winning $10 bet will return a total of $36, which is a $26 profit plus the original wager. A three-team parlay usually pays 6–1.

*Drawback:* The house advantage is higher than for a single-game bet—about 10% for a two-team parlay...more than 12% for a three-team parlay.

*Teaser:* One popular parlay variation is the teaser, in which there are more attractive point spreads for each of the games you play. To compensate, teasers pay off at lower odds than standard parlays.

*Bad sports wager:* The future book. You bet on a team to win the World Series or the Super Bowl, often months before the outcome is known. This amounts to an interest-free loan to the casino, and the house advantage is usually high.

### STRATEGIES

Sports bettors can gain an advantage by learning new information about a team or players that most other people don't have yet.

*Example:* A late-breaking report on ESPN about an injury.

But advance, or "inside," information is not essential to showing a profit. By doing your homework and avoiding certain traps, you can win at sports betting with the same basic data that everyone else has.

### TO IMPROVE YOUR CHANCES

●**Football.** In September, early in the football season, look for teams that are overrated because of their previous year's performance—and bet against them.

*Example:* Football teams coming off outstanding campaigns that led them to the Super Bowl. By fall, their personnel will have changed and their motivation may not be quite as intense.

As a result, the point spreads in their favor will likely be larger than they actually should be, especially in exhibition games and the first game or two of the regular season.

*The play:* Take the points, and bet the underdogs against the defending champions.

●**Basketball.** In NBA basketball, home teams win approximately 60% of their games, a fact reflected in the point spread. But in certain situations, the home advantage or road disadvantage may be less significant than usual.

*Example:* A seasoned veteran team coming off a home winning streak is more likely to continue to win when going on the road. Even if it loses, it may beat the spread by losing by fewer points than the point spread against it.

*The play:* Bet the hot veteran team, particularly on the first game of a road trip.

●**Baseball.** The dominant factor in baseball is the pitcher. *Key statistics…*

●A pitcher's win–loss percentage—the higher, the better.

●His earned run average—the lower, the better.

But before investing in a star hurler, check his recent performance. Most newspapers include statistics for a pitcher's last three games.

If he is in a slump, you might be wise to wait for a good performance, then bet on him the next time.

# Roulette Odds

There is no system that can improve your odds in roulette. For every dollar you bet, you can expect to lose 5.3 cents on every spin of the wheel.

*One bet that is worse than all the others:* The house edge on the five-number bet—betting that the 0, 00, 1, 2 or 3 will come up—is 7.9%. This means you'll likely lose 7.9 cents on the dollar per spin rather than the standard 5.3 cents.

*Best strategy:* Play blackjack instead.

Michael Orkin, professor of statistics at California State University at Hayward and author of *Can You Win? The Real Odds for Casino Gambling, Sports Betting, and Lotteries.* W.H. Freeman.

# Victor Boc's Winning Poker Strategies

Victor Boc, former professional poker player who competed in the World Series of Poker for seven consecutive years. He is author of *How to Solve All Your Money Problems Forever: Creating a Positive Flow of Money into Your Life,* which gives his personal finance lessons learned from playing poker. Perigee.

Poker skills that took me years to figure out will raise your odds of winning higher pots.

●**Put the odds in your favor.** You don't have to be a mathematical genius to be a good poker player, but the more you know about the odds, the better you will do.

Let's say it will cost $10 to make the final bet in a hand that has a $100 pot. Before putting in your $10, calculate the odds of winning.

*Strategy:* Let's say you need a club on the last card to get a flush that will almost certainly win the pot.

Subtract from 13 the number of clubs that are face up on the table and in your hand. Then divide the result into the number of cards you don't see. If you see 24 cards, the number of cards you don't see is 28 (52−24).

As long as your chances of winning are better than one in 10, you should make the bet.

Over time, your wins will more than offset your losses.

•**Cultivate a reputation as a relatively loose player.** You'll make more money if people think you bluff more than you do.

People are more likely to call your bets if they suspect that you're trying to bluff with a bad hand. The key to making big money at poker is to be sure that your opponents pay to stay in the game—and see your winning hands.

*Strategy:* Every so often, you should make a big bet when you don't necessarily have the best hand. This investment will subtly advertise that your bets don't always mean what they seem to mean.

Your opponents will get the message—and eventually you'll get more of their money.

*Warning:* One of the worst things you can do is to earn a reputation as a tight player. If other players know that you only bet heavily when you have a sure winner, good players will stop paying to stay in. And you'll make a lot less money than if they had contributed to the pot.

•**Play a rush.** A "rush" is a lucky streak, and it happens to everybody. It is always temporary—but long-term winners know how to exploit it while it lasts.

*Strategy:* When the cards are going your way, press your advantage. Play as if you expect to win. Bet more heavily. As opponents start to fear you, consider bluffing.

If you're too cautious during this kind of streak, you may make only half as much as you should, and that can mean the difference between a winning and a losing night.

Once you lose three or four hands in a row, the streak is over. Return to your normal playing style or else you risk giving back quickly all that you just made.

•**Have a sense of who's winning and who's losing—and by *how much*.** You need to know approximately how you're doing at all times. You don't want to lose too much.

But more important, you need to know how your opponents are doing.

*Reason:* Players who are winning a lot typically bluff more. Big losers tend to bluff less. Good players know this and can use this knowledge against their opponents.

Assess the value of the chips each player has. In most cases, you'll have more success bluffing out a big loser rather than a big winner.

Don't agonize when you're bluffed out. All great players fold early only to learn that the winner bluffed.

If you called every time an opponent played his/her hand as if it was better than yours, you would lose more than you would win.

The worst players never believe that anyone's hand is better until they see the evidence for themselves. Besides, some pots are too small to be worth the risk.

*Signs of a bluff:* Players who bet too quickly or who display too much bravado.

# How to Protect Yourself Against Poker Cheats

Ken Flaton, a professional poker player and recent winner of the $500,000 first prize in the US Poker Championship. He has won many other tournaments, including the Seven-Card Stud Championship at the World Series of Poker.

If you are sure that you are one of the best players at the table—but you are losing consistently—you may be playing in a rigged game. Signs of trouble in games outside of well-monitored casinos...

•If you lose a fabulous hand, such as a high full house, more than once on the same night.

•If some players always seem to know how good your hand is—they call when you're bluffing and fold when you have a great hand.

•If a player bets inappropriately and then beats you.

### COMMON POKER SCAMS

•*"Cool" decks.* These are prearranged decks designed to produce a specific outcome.

These cool decks are usually introduced into a game after there has been a distraction, such as someone spilling a drink.

Or they emerge after a rest break or a player's trip to the bathroom.

***Self-defense:*** If you already suspect the dealer of cheating, watch him/her carefully after a "diversion." Also, never assume, after a break, that your great hand is a winner.

•***Marked cards.*** Nothing gives a cheater more power than a deck with cards that are identifiable from the back. A well-marked deck can be purchased at almost any local card-game supply store or at a professional magic shop.

***Self-defense:*** When it's your turn to deal, review the cards by holding the deck with the backs of the cards up. Riffle through the cards with your thumb. If you see a pattern of dots, dashes or other irregular designs, that's evidence of foul play.

•***Shuffling tricks.*** A card "mechanic" can fix a deck while shuffling the cards. He can do this by using an overhand shuffle—cards are held the long way across the palm while the other hand shifts several cards at a time—instead of the standard riffle shuffle.

***Self-defense:*** Watch shuffles closely. Request that all players shuffle cards face down so there's less chance of tricks.

•***Partnerships.*** Sometimes two players are in collusion. They may gang up against you by repeatedly raising to force you out of the pot...or they may signal each other to indicate what they have or what they need from the deck.

***Self-defense:*** Get out of the game right away.

•***Games with chips.*** Sometimes players cheat in seemingly small ways—for example, by not putting in their entire bet or taking an extra chip out of the pot when they make change.

***Self-defense:*** If you get suspicious, closely examine the person's bet to make sure it is correct. Do this several times so that the cheater knows he is being watched.

# Better Video Poker

To find out how well a machine pays, locate the one-coin payout schedule list on the far left side. Then scan down to the full house and flush. Play only machines that pay nine coins for a full house and six for a flush—they have a 99.6% payback. The best-paying machines also have a royal flush maximum-coin payoff of 4,000 coins or, more rarely, 4,700 coins. *Better playing:* Do not play quickly or with two hands. That will not lead to more payouts...and you will probably make more mistakes.

*Casino Gambling Made Easier* by Gayle Mitchell, casino seminar leader, Phoenix, Webster Research/Information Services Group, 888-208-7117.

# 20

## Your Car

## Auto Dealers' Dirty Tricks: Now You Can Beat Them At Their Own Game

While car buyers are becoming savvier and sharper shoppers—car dealers are also becoming sharper. They have some tricks that get even knowledgeable customers to pay more than they should.

***Trap:*** **The salesperson agrees to one price—but the financing department uses a higher one to figure the payments.** Everyone knows that it's smart to find out what the dealer paid for the car before starting to negotiate the price.

Yet you may still wind up paying more than you should if you're like many people and finance the purchase through the dealership.

Financing department personnel are paid commissions on what they sell you. If they can sell you a loan whose rate is higher than it needs to be, they receive a higher commission.

*Some* dealers boost interest rates by using "rate factors" that produce a payment that is from 50 cents to several dollars a month higher than the payment a standard factor would produce.

Other dealers use factors that include credit life, accident and health insurance whether you ask for them or not.

***How to determine what your payment should be:*** Buy a mortgage loan payment book, which is available at most bookstores. Look up the payment for a loan—at whatever interest rate you are going to pay and for whatever length of time your car loan will last.

***Example:*** Say it is a four-year loan at 8%. The book will tell you that the payment is $244.13 per month. Take that number and remove the decimal point. Then put a decimal point and a zero in front of it. Your factor is 0.024413. Say you

Michael Flinn, a former sales and leasing specialist with a new-car dealership in New York. He is author of *How to Save Big Money When You Lease a Car.* Perigee Books.

are financing $15,000 at 8% for four years. Multiply 15,000 by 0.024413. The result is 366.195. Round it up to 366.20, put the dollar sign in front of it, and that is what your payment should be. Check that figure against the dealer's figure to make sure nothing has been added that you didn't ask for.

***Important:*** Make sure the numbers from the dealer and from the payment book involve the same interest rate and time period.

### Trap: Double-dipping on preparation fees.

As a savvy buyer, you want to negotiate a price slightly above the dealer's cost for the vehicle. A reasonable amount is 2% to 3% above the dealer's cost on readily available cars. Cars in short supply command a premium.

The salesperson agrees—but says you forgot to include the dealer's other costs and fees in your calculations. Some of these fees, such as destination charges and national advertising costs that the dealer pays, are probably legitimate. "Prep fees" are not. A prep fee—often $100 to $250—is built into the car's price. Thus, if the salesperson tacks it on, he/she is trying to get you to pay it twice.

***Exceptions:*** A prep fee is appropriate if you have something special done to the car… and for some European cars.

***Self-defense:*** Ask the dealer to outline the fees he's talking about. Don't tell the salesperson you're on to the prep fee scam when he first mentions it—or when you first notice that he's written it down.

Instead, wait until the last minute—just before signing the contract—and then tell him you've just noticed it and want it taken out. Most will give in if you persist and make it seem as if it is a deal-breaker.

### Trap: The hard sell on after-market packages.

A car dealer's profit margin on a new vehicle can be razor thin with a knowledgeable customer. But the margin on "dealer add-ons," or "after-market packages," is typically significant. The most common of these packages are…

• The *protection package*, which usually involves rustproofing, fabric guard and paint shield.

• The *decor group*, which normally means taped-on striping plus special floor mats or mud flaps.

Many smart car shoppers are aware that these packages are overpriced. But that does not mean that the salespeople won't still try to get you to pay.

***Examples:*** The salesperson might tell you that these options have already been installed and can't be avoided. He might offer a big discount on the options. He might even try to slip them into the contract without mentioning them.

Don't give in. Check the contract before you sign to make sure these after-market packages haven't been added on without your consent. And don't fall for "big discounts." The margin is huge, and the discounts are small.

Don't confuse these dealer add-ons with factory options packages.

Factory options packages include stepped-up sound systems, sunroofs, cruise control, air-conditioning, etc.—and are usually a good deal *when they're discounted* as part of a special options package.

### Trap: Give the customer a great deal on the new car—but steal the trade-in.

Most new-car buyers trade in their old cars. The most a dealer will pay for a trade-in is its wholesale value. But it can be quite difficult to determine the actual wholesale value of your car. Many used-car price guides are inaccurate.

Dealerships take advantage of this and offer new-car buyers far less than the going rate on their trade-ins—50% to 80% of wholesale value. In fact, most dealerships now make more from their used cars than they do from their new cars.

***Self-defense:*** Sell your car on your own. But if that is too much trouble, take your trade-in to two or three used-car lots before you buy your new car and ask what they would offer you for it. If you get two or three offers that are within a few dollars of each other, you have probably gotten the wholesale price of your car. If you want to check a book for your car's wholesale or "actual cash" value, consult the *Black Book*, published by National Auto Research, a division of Hearst Media Corporation. It is the book the pros use because its prices are based on what cars like yours were bringing at auction the previous week in your region.

Unfortunately, you can't buy the *Black Book* at your local drugstore or bookstore. You can, however, stop at your local car dealership and ask to see it.

## Car-Buying Know-How from Ashly Knapp

Ashly Knapp, CEO of AutoAdvisor, Inc., a fee-based information and car-buyer's service based in Seattle. For more information, go to www.autoadvisor.com.

## Self-Defense Against Tricky Car Ads

A car ad has one goal—to lure you onto the dealer's lot. And some dealers may bend the truth a bit, if that will hook you.

*Common tricky ad claims—and how to guard against them...*

***Trap #1:* "The lowest price on year 2000 models."** The ad lists a great price—but not the word "new."

***Reality:*** By February, rental companies will start returning their year 2000 fleets to dealers—cars that might have 10,000 aggressively driven miles on them.

Also, in most states, dealers may legally advertise demo cars as new—even after thousands of miles.

***Self-defense:*** Look for the word "new" in every ad. And check the odometer before buying.

***Trap #2:* "Car priced only 1% above invoice."** Some dealers add on a "documentation fee," as high as $400, or use other accounting tricks.

***Self-defense:*** Look up the invoice price.

***Best:*** Edmund's prices at www.edmunds.com.

Also, be sure to negotiate in dollars, not percentages.

***Trap: #3:* "All cars are in stock."** Dealers want you to think they have the exact car you want. But they rarely do.

***Self-defense:*** Shop around. Never let a salesperson convince you to buy what you don't want. If what you want isn't on the lot, consider placing a factory order and waiting three months.

***Caution:*** Ads that boast low prices on "loss leaders" can be very misleading. A dealer advertises a super-low price, but customers may find it applies to literally *one* vehicle, which was already sold.

***Trap #4:* "Free sunroof," or other option.** Dealers never give anything away. If they "throw in" a $900 sunroof, they're giving you a discount in the shape of a sunroof.

***Self-defense:*** Don't be lured by free offers.

***Trap #5:* "Lease a car for only $399 a month"—or another low price.** Low monthly payments may mean a big chunk of money up front.

*Other sneaky lease tricks...*

● **Low annual mileage restriction.** Most Americans drive 15,000 miles a year. Yet many leases have hefty penalties above 9,000 or 12,000 miles.

***Key:*** Know how much you drive.

● **Long lease term.** A lease should not be longer than 36 months. At the end of that term the vehicle is still valuable to the dealer as resale. This may mean a better deal for you up front.

The best deals apply to a vehicle with minimal options. If you try to change it—you may blow the deal.

***Trap #6:* "Zero-down lease."** The word "down" may apply only to money put down against the price of the car. It doesn't rule out "start-up fees," including deposits, acquisition fees or taxes—usually $1,500 or more.

***Self-defense:*** Always expect to put down some cash up front.

Remember, too, that the more you finance, the more you pay in interest.

---

**More from Ashly Knapp...**

## How to Use the Internet to Save Money on a New Car

The Internet has become a convenient, free resource for people looking to save money on a new car. But some sites are better than others.

## RESEARCHING CARS

● Visit automakers' sites. Almost every car-maker has a Web site to promote its models. Most sites can be found by typing the company's name—or some form of it—on your screen.

*Examples:* Typing in www.gm.com or www.toyota.com will access the General Motors or Toyota site.

Company sites display color photos of cars and list available options and color choices. They also include dealer listings, manufacturer prices and sometimes finance options.

● Compare features by accessing sites that provide direct feature comparisons of makes and models.

*Examples:* www.compare.net and www.excite.com/autos.

● Use a search engine when you have narrowed your choices to a particular model. Search engines such as Infoseek or Yahoo! allow you to access newspaper and magazine reviews.

*Example: Detroit Free Press* (www.freep.com) and www.thecarconnection.com have especially sharp car reviews.

## CHECKING DEALER COSTS

There are several sites that provide price information for specific makes and models. These sites will usually give you suggested retail prices...and what the cars cost the dealers. Try to get as close as you can to cost, but remember dealers often get lower prices after discounts from automakers. To find dealer costs...

● Edmund's (www.edmunds.com), which prints the most thorough reports.

● Kelley Blue Book (www.kbb.com) makes a great double check.

Both are based on their print price guides. Armed with this information, you should be able to bargain more effectively with a dealer. While the dealer invoice price is a good place to start, buyers need to understand that dealers also have costs that are not reflected in the invoice price.

*Example:* Different dealers have different costs of operation...and receive different compensation after the vehicles are sold. So, while all dealers pay the same to buy a car, they have different costs to sell the car.

No Web site tracks these cost differences. So buyers need to exercise caution when bargaining with dealers.

## STRATEGY

To achieve the best price, go to Web sites like...

● www.autobytel.com
● www.autovantage.com
● www.carpoint.msn.com

Then use the quotes/prices from these sites as your starting point with your neighborhood dealers.

## BUYING CARS

You can rarely buy a new car directly over the Internet, but you can initiate the transaction, then meet face-to-face with the dealer to complete the purchase.

---

**And Finally from Ashly Knapp...**

## Lease Surprise

If you're unsure whether to lease again or to buy a new car, you can often take your time deciding by extending your current lease for six or 12 months—without penalties—even if your lease contract doesn't mention this option. Your monthly payments will stay the same. Call your lease administrator for an extension. *Important:* Check that the car's residual value—its worth at the end of the lease—continues to decline during the extension period.

---

# Car-Buying/Leasing Savvy from W. James Bragg

W. James Bragg, CEO, Fighting Chance, a fee-based information service for new-car buyers, 5318 E. Second St., Long Beach, CA 90803. He is author of *Car Buyer's and Leaser's Negotiating Bible*. Random House.

## Shrewd Car-Buying Strategy

When given the choice, *dealer financing* may be a better deal than a lump-sum rebate.

*Example:* If you were to finance $18,000 over 48 months at a standard 8.5%, after taking a

$750 rebate, your monthly payment will be $425. But if you accept a dealer's 3.9% financing, your monthly cost will be only $406.

***Caution:*** Financing is just one element of a good deal. Before looking at monthly payments, do careful price research…set a target price that is close to the dealer's cost…get nondealer financing approved to have a basis for comparison.

**More from W. James Bragg…**

## Smart Car Buying

Consider buying a car at the end of your lease period if the purchase price in the contract is lower than the car's current retail market value. That makes the car a bargain. It can also pay to buy the car if the leasing company will negotiate on price—offer $500 above the car's wholesale value.

***Also:*** Consider buying if the car is in such condition that you will incur big end-of-lease charges for excess mileage or wear and tear.

To find out what a similar used model is selling for in your area, visit dealerships and compare prices, check classified ads and refer to the *Kelley Blue Book.*

**Better Leasing from W. James Bragg…**

## Car-Leasing Smarts

If leasing a car the second time around, remember that leasing companies love repeat customers. They should be willing to waive charges for such items as security deposits and lease acquisition fees if you lease from them a second—or third—time.

# Smart Car-Selling Strategy

Sell your car yourself to get $500 to $1,500 more than you would on a trade-in. Start fixing it up one month before you plan to buy a new car. *How:* Replace bald tires with good used ones. Flush the cooling system so no rust shows when the radiator cap is opened. Remove inside ornaments and steering-wheel wrapping. Have a body shop fix obvious nicks and scratches. Have a mechanic inspect the car and document its condition. Show potential buyers the mechanic's paperwork so there is less worry about defects or needed repairs.

*How to Sell Your Car and Make More Money* by Ralph Hoffmann. StarWay Inc.

# Buy a European Car Overseas/Get a Free Vacation

C. Van Tune, editor-in-chief of *Motor Trend*, 6420 Wilshire Blvd., Los Angeles 90048. He has test-driven and reviewed cars for more than 18 years and a few years ago purchased a car abroad.

If you're shopping for a European luxury car, you can save 5% to 10% off the price if you agree to pick it up at the carmaker's factory abroad.

The savings can amount to thousands of dollars—more than enough to pay for a European vacation as you drive the car to a port to be shipped home. The carmaker will even help you plan the trip.

C. Van Tune, editor of *Motor Trend,* bought a BMW 540i in Germany and had it shipped back to the US, saving $6,000—or 10%—off the car's price. He outlines the process below.

What you need to know before paying for a car here and picking it up abroad…

●**Any authorized US dealer can handle the purchase.** You pay for the car here, pick it up in Europe, drop it off at a shipping point, fly home and the car is delivered to your dealer about five weeks later…then you pick it up. US dealers that provide this service are BMW, Mercedes-Benz, Porsche, Saab and Volvo.

Most dealers require a wait of about two to three months to ensure that the model and options you've selected will be available.

***Helpful:*** Call the manufacturers' toll-free numbers for brochures that describe their European delivery programs in detail. That way, you can determine whether to take advantage of a tour package or make your own plans with a travel agent. Be sure to make flight arrangements after you have a date to pick up your car.

*Caution:* Some European delivery programs don't operate year-round.

• **Calculate savings carefully.** All car transportation costs—including the cost of transportation from a US port to your car dealer—are included.

Some carmakers offer free insurance and registration while you're abroad. However, you are responsible for state, local and any luxury taxes that may apply.

You also must pay for your own travel costs, including flights, meals, accommodations, gas and tolls. But the money you save by picking up the car abroad may cover all of your costs.

The best way to determine your savings is to have the dealer calculate your expenses.

*Key:* How long you plan to travel abroad.

*Deposit:* Most dealers require a deposit of $1,000 or more at the time you sign your order. You might not be entitled to a refund if you change your mind about buying the car. Full payment is due before you depart. The dealer then fills out the necessary paperwork and forwards it to the factory abroad.

If you can't make the trip abroad after ordering, the car will be shipped to your dealer for pickup. Or you can purchase one off the lot of your local dealership. If you decide you don't want the vehicle after all, you may lose your deposit.

• **Ask the dealer about styles that are not in stock.** In some cases, US dealers sell out of certain popular styles.

*Example:* When the Porsche 911 Turbo was out of stock at many dealers here, it could be ordered through overseas delivery.

Also ask about savings on options. Some options are less expensive when you pick up the car in Europe than if you had bought the car in the US.

*Example:* Buying a sunroof for your Saab 9-3 will add $1,110 to the price in the US...but it will cost an extra $1,055 if you take European delivery.

*Caution:* Options, such as mobile phones, radios and CD players, cannot be installed overseas. You must wait for your domestic dealer to do that work once the car arrives in the US. There is no additional charge when the installation is done back here.

• **Travel discounts**—and packages on lodging and airfares...

• Some carmakers team up with airlines to offer airfare discounts of 20% or more.

• Some carmakers also offer you free or discounted hotel accommodations that can trim your travel budget significantly.

Such packages typically include lodging at first-rate resorts and driving itineraries that will give you a chance to drive your car on high-speed highways and winding mountain roads.

*Example 1:* Mercedes offers discounted fares on Continental, Lufthansa and SAS Airlines. The discounts can save you at least 10% to 20% off standard fares. Mercedes also has put together a five-day, four-night package with stopovers at luxury hotels in Germany's scenic Black Forest, Innsbruck and Munich for $1,000 per couple.

*Example 2:* Saab provides your first night's stay free at a hotel outside its factory in Trollhattan, Sweden. They also provide breakfast and dinner for two.

• **Have your dealer assess drop-off restrictions and fees.** You may be required to pick up the car at a specific European factory. Some companies, including BMW and Volvo, will let you choose a different city. But you will be charged a fee by a trucking company to transport your car from the factory to your desired city.

You need to select the city where you will drop off the car to be shipped to the US. Some firms will let you choose among 15 to 20 drop-off points without paying a fee. Others may specify a drop-off location and charge a fee if you leave your car somewhere else.

The car company will assume responsibility for dents in shipping, and the vehicle is covered under the standard warranty program if there are engine troubles or system problems.

## Auto Expert Art Spinella Discusses...

Art Spinella, vice president, CNW Marketing/Research, which provides auto buying and leasing data to corporate clients, Box 744, Bandon, OR 97411.

## Buying a Used Car

It's fine to shop at used-car superstores, but do not necessarily buy there.

Superstores like CarMax and AutoNation USA let you see a big selection of used cars in a no-pressure atmosphere.

Computer printouts detail mileage and options on cars you are considering.

*Downside:* Superstores will not negotiate price. And they charge about 1% more than franchised dealers do for similar cars.

*Strategy:* Take the superstore's printouts to a local dealer and try to get a better deal. You may even get a lower-mileage car, since many of those go first to franchised dealers.

---

**More from Art Spinella...**

## New Car-Leasing Strategy

Tailor your lease. This lets you decide how long to keep a car.

*Example:* Mercedes-Benz lets customers lease for any length of time between 24 and 60 months. Someone might start leasing a convertible in the spring and keep it for 27 months to have it through three summers.

*Caution:* Leases longer than three years can be a poor deal, since most warranties end after three years and maintenance costs rise.

---

# Head Restraints Make a Difference

Check the built-in head restraints before buying a new car. The higher they are, the more protection they provide in a crash. When you drive, the headrest should reach as close to the top of your head as possible and touch the back of your head. *Best system available:* Active head restraint/seat systems on some new BMWs and Saabs, which move to protect your head and neck in the event of a crash. *To protect yourself in your current car:* Adjust the headrest to make it high enough to touch the back of your head, but not your neck. Keep the seat back as close to vertical as possible. *Most at risk:* Tall people, whose heads roll back over the top of the restraints in a crash.

David Solomon, editor, *Nutz & Boltz,* Box 123, Butler, MD 21023.

# Transfer Your Car Lease

To get out of a car lease without paying substantial surrender charges, try to find someone with good credit to take it over. If your leasing agreement allows a transfer, you may have to pay only a few hundred dollars in early termination paperwork fees.

*Alternative:* Try convincing the dealer to let you upgrade. The dealer may agree if you have been leasing a high-demand vehicle and have kept it up well. Car dealers that do a lot of leasing will usually be more flexible than ones that do few leases.

James Hall, vice president, AutoPacific Inc., automotive marketing consultants, Detroit.

---

# Keep Your New Car Looking New

To keep a new car looking new keep it garaged if at all possible, so acids from bird droppings and tree sap do not damage the fresh paint. If these substances get on the car, remove them with soap made for washing cars.

• **Wait at least 30 days** after the car's built date before using a car cover or taking the car through a commercial car wash.

• **Do not wax or polish the car for at least 60 days.** When you do wax or polish it, use a good-quality car wax or polish that does not contain abrasive cleaning agents. Polish the car once every four months to keep it shiny.

Dan Seigel, president and CEO, Earl Scheib Paint & Body, Beverly Hills, CA.

---

# Most Common Auto-Repair Scams...and How to Avoid Them

Arthur P. Glickman, coauthor of *Avoiding Auto Repair Rip-Offs.* Consumer Reports Books.

---

• **Automatic transmission repair scam.** The mechanic claims he/she cannot determine the cause of your car's shifting problem until he tears the transmission down—and then tells you it needs to be completely rebuilt at a cost of $500 to $3,000. As proof, he shows you small metal shavings in the transmission fluid.

***Reality:*** Minor shifting problems are often caused by other, less-expensive problems elsewhere in the engine, and some shavings are normal.

***Self-defense:*** Practice routine transmission maintenance. Have a mechanic check the transmission fluid and clean and replace the screen and filter regularly. Get two written estimates before approving any major transmission work.

●**Brake repair scam.** After luring you in with a lowball $59 brake special, the mechanic tells you that your car needs a complete brake job. *Including:* Replacing the calipers, rotor pistons and wheel cylinders. *Cost:* Upward of $500.

***Self-defense:*** Get a second opinion. Get a written measurement of the pad wear, and compare this with what the owner's manual says indicates a need for new pads. Avoid low-price service specials.

●**Coil spring repair scam.** Coil springs, which help support the car body, should last the life of the car.

***Self-defense:*** Ask for a written measurement of the distance between the ground and the bottom of the car. *Reason:* Unless it's significantly less than what the owner's manual says it should be, you don't need new coil springs.

●**Steering repair scam.** A customer who responds to a low-cost front-end alignment special is brought into the service bay where his car is up on the lift. The mechanic wiggles a wheel, causing it to wobble, and says this proves you need new ball joints. He may even say there's a danger of your wheel or wheels actually falling off.

***Reality:*** A little wobble is normal in such circumstances.

***Self-defense:*** Have the shop give you a written measurement of the wear and looseness of the ball joint stated in thousandths of an inch or millimeters and compare this with the allowances listed in the owner's manual.

After a California law was passed requiring such information on all invoices, ball joint sales dropped 85%.

●**Shock absorber replacement scam.** To prove you need new shocks, the mechanic pushes down on one corner of the car, which then bounces up and down a few times.

***Reality:*** This proves absolutely nothing.

***Self-defense:*** Unless you've noticed severe body sway, front-end dip when braking and a bouncing rise, you probably don't need new shocks.

●**Body shop insurance scams.** Body repairs paid for by insurance companies are often done with substandard parts, may be incomplete and might involve kickbacks, fraud and forced discounts to the insurer.

***One problem:*** It's difficult, if not impossible, to do such repairs adequately for what the insurance company will pay—and so the repair shop cuts corners.

***Self-defense:*** Insure your car with a reputable agency that will give you a choice of body shops...compare the estimate to the final bill to make sure everything it said it was going to do was actually done.

# Here's How To Win the Car-Repair Game

Robert Krughoff, president of the Center for the Study of Services/Consumers' Checkbook, a nonprofit group that evaluates body shops, auto insurance companies and many other types of service firms, 733 15 St. NW, Washington, DC 20005.

●**Get your car towed to the garage of your choice.** If your car is immobile, have it towed to a body shop you trust for an estimate.

If your car needs only minor repairs, it is probably fine to get an estimate from an insurance company drive-in claims center and have the repairs done at almost any shop the company recommends.

But for major repairs, be sure to get the estimate and repairs from a body shop you have checked out thoroughly.

●**Choose an advocate mechanic.** Some insurance companies give customers a list of body shops from which to choose. They're not all the same. What you want is a competent body shop. Your local or state consumer agency can tell you if there have been any complaints made.

Your best bet is a shop where the estimator is articulate. Such a personality will come in handy if you need the person to be your advocate during a dispute with the insurer over needed parts or repairs.

•**Don't let the insurer send you to a lousy body shop.** If your insurer won't pay what your preferred shop wants to charge and steers you to another shop that will do the work for less...

•Check the shop with your local or state consumer agency to see if complaints for consumer fraud have been lodged against it.

•Request that you be given a warranty on the repairs, both from the car-repair shop and your insurance company.

•**Don't sign off on your claim until the work is completed.** Often, wrecked cars sustain more damage than initially thought. Should the body shop find hidden damage in the course of repairs, you want to be able to go back to your insurance company on firm legal footing and demand an increase.

•**Know when your car is totaled.** If your car is damaged so badly it needs engine parts, chances are it should be totaled and the insurer should pay for a replacement vehicle of the same value.

# What to Do When Your Alternator Light Comes On

If the alternator light comes on while you are driving, turn off as many electricity-using devices as possible and keep driving to the next service station. Do not turn the engine off—the electrical system may be unable to restart the car. *Caution:* If the alternator *and*

temperature lights come on, *do not* keep driving—stop as soon as possible. Then shut off the engine. When both lights are on, the water pump may have stopped working. That can rapidly lead to serious engine damage.

Mary Jackson, lecturer on car care and automotive literacy, Boulder, CO, and author of *Car Smarts*. John Muir Publications.

# Changing Antifreeze

Annual cooling-system flushing is no longer needed—thanks to better cooling systems and longer-lasting antifreeze. Today's antifreeze may need to be changed only every two to five years. Follow the manufacturer's recommendation. Consider a long-life antifreeze (dyed bright orange instead of the traditional green). You may be able to double the time between cooling-system flushes with the long-life product. *Caution:* Do not expect to get five years or 150,000 miles from after-market long-life products. They may last that long in new cars—but only if installed within the first 3,000 miles of engine use.

David Van Sickle, director of automotive and consumer information, American Automobile Association, Washington, DC.

# Keep Your Car from Sailing Away

If you are planning to buy a sport-utility vehicle or luxury car or sports car, beware of the recent increase in car thefts in and near US port cities.

***Reason:*** These cities provide easy access to waterways, allowing professional thieves to ship stolen cars by boat to another location quickly.

***Self-defense:*** If you're in the market for a high-end car, consider installing an "electronic antitheft immobilizer," an option on many of the latest vehicle models. These units disable a car's engine when the ignition is turned off, making theft nearly impossible.

Kim Hazelbaker, senior vice president of the Insurance Institute for Highway Safety, 1005 N. Glebe Rd., Arlington, VA 22201.

## Don't Be Caught Off Guard

After a car accident, find people who saw what happened and ask exactly what they saw. Take down their phone numbers for the police and your insurance company.

Wait for police before moving your car—but drive to the shoulder if you are in traffic and the car is not leaking anything. When talking to the other driver, do not stand between your cars. When police arrive, give them all the facts you can. Mention any pain you feel. Keep your own records of the accident—have a pen, notepad and disposable camera in your glove compartment.

Sharon Park, communications manager, Chartered Property Casualty Underwriters Society (CPCU), Box 3009, Malvern, PA 19355.

## Oil Additives: A Waste Of Money

Oil additives do not work. They can damage a car engine by upsetting the balance of additives already in engine oil. This can increase engine wear, harm fuel economy and increase emissions.

Michael McMillan, PhD, manager, General Motors Research and Development Center and Fuels and Lubricants Department, quoted in *Nutz & Boltz,* Box 123, Butler, MD 21023.

# Zodiac Signs

| Sign | Symbol | Sign | Symbol |
|---|---|---|---|
| • **Capricorn**/December 22–January 19 | *Goat* | • **Cancer**/June 21–July 22 | *Crab* |
| • **Aquarius**/January 20–February 18 | *Water Bearer* | • **Leo**/July 23–August 22 | *Lion* |
| • **Pisces**/February 19–March 20 | *Fish* | • **Virgo**/August 23–September 22 | *Virgin* |
| • **Aries**/March 21–April 19 | *Ram* | • **Libra**/September 23–October 22 | *Scales* |
| • **Taurus**/April 20–May 20 | *Bull* | • **Scorpio**/Oct. 23–November 21 | *Scorpion* |
| • **Gemini**/May 21–June 20 | *Twins* | • **Sagittarius**/Nov. 22–December 21 | *Centaur* |

# Anniversary Gifts

| Traditional | Modern | Traditional | Modern | Traditional | Modern |
|---|---|---|---|---|---|
| • 1st ....Paper | Clocks | • 9th ...Pottery, Willow | Leather | • 25th....Silver | Silver |
| • 2nd...Cotton | China | •10th...Tin, Aluminum | Diamond Jewelry | • 30th....Pearl | Diamond |
| • 3rd....Leather | Crystal, Glass | •11th...Steel | Fashion, Jewelry | • 35th....Coral | Jade |
| • 4th ...Books | Appliances | •12th...Silk, Linen | Pearls | • 40th....Ruby | Ruby |
| • 5th ...Wood | Silverware | •13th...Lace | Textiles, Furs | • 50th....Gold | Gold |
| • 6th ...Candy, Iron | Wood | •14th...Ivory | Gold Jewelry | • 55th....Emerald | Emerald |
| • 7th ...Wool, Copper | Desk Sets | •15th...Crystal | Watches | • 60th....Diamond | Diamond |
| • 8th ...Bronze, Pottery | Linens, Laces | •20th...China | Platinum | • 65th....Diamond | Diamond |

# Birthstones and Flowers

| Month | Stone | Flower | Month | Stone | Flower |
|---|---|---|---|---|---|
| • January | garnet | snowdrop or carnation | • July | ruby | water lily or larkspur |
| • February | amethyst | primrose or violet | • August | sardonyx or carnelian | poppy or gladiolus |
| • March | aquamarine or bloodstone | violet or jonquil | • September | sapphire | morning glory or aster |
| • April | diamond | daisy or sweet pea | • October | opal or tourmaline | hops or calendula |
| • May | emerald | hawthorn or lily of the valley | • November | topaz | chrysanthemum |
| • June | pearl, agate, alexandrite | rose | • December | turquoise or lapis lazuli | holly or narcissus |

# 21

# Self-Defense

## Hidden Dangers That May Be in Household Products

Federal regulations that govern the labeling of consumer products are woefully inadequate. Consequently, it can be difficult for consumers to find out precisely which products contain potentially dangerous or questionable ingredients or contaminants—and which are safe.

*Here's how you can protect yourself...*

### POTENTIALLY DANGEROUS PRODUCTS—AND SAFER ALTERNATIVES

•**Frankfurters.** The *nitrite* preservatives in many frankfurters may interact with *amines*, which occur naturally in meat and fish, to form cancer-causing compounds called *nitrosamines*.

Some franks also may be contaminated with the potentially carcinogenic pesticides *benzene hexachloride, Dacthal, dieldrin, DDT* and *heptachlor*...and with residues of powerful hormones.

*Safer:* "Nitrite-free" franks or—better still—tofu franks.

•**Bug killers.** Many household pesticides contain *propoxur*, a compound that may be both carcinogenic and neurotoxic.

*Safer:* Brands that use *pyrethrum* or another natural, herbal pesticide instead of propoxur.

•**Cat litter.** Many brands contain *crystalline silica*, an eye and lung irritant and suspected carcinogen.

*Safer:* Litter made of a natural ingredient, such as pulverized paper.

•**Flea collars.** Many flea collars contain the pesticide propoxur.

Samuel S. Epstein, MD, professor of occupational and environmental medicine at the University of Illinois School of Public Health in Chicago and chairman of the Cancer Prevention Coalition, 520 N. Michigan Ave., Suite 410, Chicago 60611. www.preventcancer.com. He is author of *The Politics of Cancer Revisited.* East Ridge Press.

*Safer:* Flea collars made with natural, herbal pesticides.

● **Air fresheners.** Some aerosol brands contain *orthophenylphenol*, a skin irritant and possible carcinogen. This is potentially dangerous because tiny aerosol droplets are readily inhaled deep into the lungs.

*Safer:* Solid air fresheners made with plant-based scents.

● **Hair conditioners.** Some brands contain formaldehyde and the potentially carcinogenic dye FD&C Red #4.

*Safer:* Natural, plant-based conditioners.

● **Hair dye.** Some black and dark brown hair dyes may be linked to several kinds of cancer, including nonHodgkin's lymphoma, multiple myeloma and leukemia.

*Safer:* Hair dyes that substitute plant-based substances, such as henna, for the synthetic dyes.

● **Laundry detergents.** Many brands that contain washing soda are caustic. Some brands may also be contaminated with a potential carcinogen called *1,4 dioxane*.

*Safer:* Vegetable-based detergents or laundry soap.

● **Makeup.** Many cosmetics contain talc, titanium dioxide and/or the preservative BHA—all of which are potentially carcinogenic. In addition, lanolin found in many brands may be tainted with DDT.

*Safer:* All-natural, plant-based cosmetics.

● **Moth repellents.** These often contain *naphthalene*, a neurotoxin, or *dichlorobenzidine*, a volatile compound that is a possible carcinogen.

*Safer:* Cedar blocks, chips and sachets.

● **Paint strippers.** Aerosol strippers often contain *methanol*, a neurotoxin that is also a skin and eye irritant…along with *methylene chloride*, a potential carcinogen.

*Safer:* Get rid of old paint by sanding or scraping it off. To avoid inhalation of dust, wear a respirator mask.

● **Shaving creams.** Some brands contain the preservative BHA…along with *triethanolamine* and/or *diethanolamine*, which are nitrosamine precursors.

Others contain Blue #1 and other potentially cancer-causing dyes.

*Safer:* Natural brands—especially those that are applied with a brush.

● **Talcum powder.** Talc may irritate the lungs and has been linked to ovarian cancer.

*Safer:* Products made with cornstarch.

● **Toothpaste.** Many popular brands of toothpaste contain Blue #1 and saccharin, both of which may be carcinogens.

*Safer:* Natural toothpaste without fluoride.

● **Weed killer.** Some brands contain sodium *2,4-dichlorophenoxyacetate* (2,4-D), a potential carcinogen and neurotoxin.

*Safer:* "Weed whackers" or other tools for cutting rather than poisoning weeds.

● **Whole milk**—including whole-milk products, such as cheese and milk chocolate.

Milk fat may contain the potentially carcinogenic compounds DDT, *dieldrin*, *hexachlorobenzene* and/or *heptachlor*.

In addition, milk products are sometimes tainted with antibiotic residues. Some of these residues may cause allergic reactions. Others, particularly bovine growth hormone, are suspected of causing breast, prostate and other cancers.

Ingestion of these antibiotic residues may also promote growth of potentially dangerous antibiotic-resistant bacteria inside the body.

*Safer:* Organic skim milk, especially brands labeled "bovine growth hormone-free."

# Make Sure Your Water Is Safe to Drink

Timothy McCall, MD, a New York City internist and author of *Examining Your Doctor: A Patient's Guide to Avoiding Harmful Medical Care*. Citadel Press.

Tap water can be contaminated with hundreds of potentially harmful substances. Experts—including doctors—disagree on the risk. It's naive, though, to dismiss the potential for harm.

Most Americans get their drinking water from a municipal water system. If you do, ask your local water utility for a copy of the *municipal drinking water contaminant analysis.* Utilities are required by law to test their water on a regular basis—and to make test results available to the public.

But there's a problem with relying solely on these analyses. Lead can leach into water from pipes and faucets in your home—after the water leaves the utility. To find out if your water contains lead, you can arrange to have it tested. The cost is usually around $40.

There are two other potential problems with the contaminant analyses provided by local water utilities. First, they give only a "snapshot" of toxins. A transient contamination might not be evident at the time the water was tested. Second, hundreds of harmful chemicals aren't looked for at all.

If your water comes from a private well—or if you're worried about your community's water system—consider having it tested not only for lead, but also for other heavy metals, pesticides, nitrates and bacteria. A battery of tests generally costs less than $200, but shop around. Even among certified labs, the price varies quite a bit. One lab, National Testing Laboratories (800-458-3330), offers an extensive battery of tests for $149.

If you need help locating a certified water-testing lab, contact your state's water-quality department—or the EPA's Safe Drinking Water Hotline (800-426-4791). Watch out for outfits offering free water testing. They're usually trying to sell you a filtration system that you might not need.

You could invest thousands of dollars testing your water for every conceivable contaminant. I don't think that's practical—or affordable—for most people. I recommend that you test only for the most likely contaminants. Call your local health department and ask what sorts of contaminants are common in your area. If tests reveal—or if you suspect—particular pollutants, choose a water-purification system to deal specifically with those problems.

●**Carbon filters** remove bad taste, chlorine and some hazardous organic compounds. They're ineffective against viruses and bacteria.

●**Reverse osmosis filters** remove a large array of potentially toxic minerals, heavy metals and infectious microorganisms. They're expensive, though, and waste a lot of water.

●**Distillation filters** remove lead, microbes and most man-made contaminants. They're ineffective against *volatile organic compounds* like benzene and chloroform, which have been linked to cancer.

For more information about water-filtration systems, contact the National Sanitation Foundation (800-673-8010).

Bottled water is a potential solution, of course, but be wary. Some is less healthful than good municipal tap water. Given the high cost of premium brands, a home purification system may be a better deal in the long run.

Be careful, though. Virtually all bottled water lacks fluoride and many home filtration units remove fluoride. Children may need another source of this tooth-protecting element.

# Smart Crime Prevention Strategies From Sgt. Kevin Coffey

Sgt. Kevin Coffey, a member of the Los Angeles Police Department and president of Corporate Travel Safety, a firm that conducts seminars for large corporations on travel safety, 4371 Park Fortuna, Calabasa, CA 91302. He is narrator of *"Lies, Cons and Stolen Briefcases,"* an audio-cassette program about reducing the risk of becoming an airport crime victim. Magellan's Travel Gear.

## Home Security Without the Big Bad Alarm-System Price Tag

Homes with alarm systems are less than half as likely to be burglarized as homes without alarms. But not everyone can afford the thousands of dollars that top-of-the-line security systems command.

It is possible to have home security without spending a fortune on an expensive alarm system. Here's what I've learned about home

327

security on the cheap—and what I've done in my own home...

●**Consider a low-cost alarm system.** Do-it-yourself systems are sold through home centers and are simple to install and operate.

Most turn on a home's lights—or set off an alarm—when they sense motion in or around the house.

*Example:* A basic X-10 system can cost as little as $100 or $200. Unless your area or possessions dictate a particularly high level of security, a low-cost system such as this may be all that you need.

*Reason:* Most home break-ins are committed by kids—not by "professionals." These people are looking for a low-risk, quick score. So even a low-end security system is usually enough to do the job.

Don't be scared off by the do-it-yourself component. Installation requires little more than plugging the unit in. And if you ever move, you can take it with you.

●**Simple audio deterrents work.** Most effective—motion detectors that imitate the sound of a dog barking when someone nears your door. I have one of these devices myself.

*Beware:* Some brands sound so artificial that even the first-time burglar won't be fooled. But a few are convincing.

Listen to the product before buying to be sure the pitch and length of the barks can be varied and that they sound real, not tinny or mechanical.

*For apartment and condominium dwellers:* Motion-detecting alarm systems could cause problems because of the amount of traffic passing through.

*Better:* A CD-ROM disk that slides into your computer and simulates the sounds of people talking inside.

●**Ask a neighbor to take in your newspaper.** Most people cancel their newspaper delivery when they travel. Unfortunately, burglars know this. Some dishonest newspaper delivery people work with burglars to target travelers' homes. I prefer to trust neighbors... they're inexpensive, too.

●**Secure the common points of entry.** Steps to take around the house to limit easy entry...

●**Doors.** Replace hollow-core doors with solid-core or metal doors. Don't use doors that have windows.

●**Windows.** More than 35% of burglars enter through windows—and almost always first-floor windows. Make sure that the exterior of your house is lit well and that the windows aren't hidden from view behind shrubs or trees.

●**Sliding glass doors.** Make sure the door can't be lifted out of its track from the outside. Drill a hole in the upper track above where the door rests when closed. Insert a screw, protruding down far enough so that the door still can slide, but can't be raised out of its track.

Prevent the door from being slid open from the outside. The most cost-effective measure is to cut a broom handle to rest in the door's track. Don't worry about a thief breaking the door glass. A big pane of glass like this would make too much noise for most burglars' tastes.

●**Garage doors.** If you have an electric door opener, it's usually possible to pry the door open.

*Better:* Get a garage door with drop bolts that go down into the cement of your garage floor, preventing such entries. Home-product stores have inexpensive drop-bolt systems that can be attached to existing doors.

If you buy a new electric door, look for one that has a "code tumbler," which will prevent thieves from using their unit to open your door.

Or for about $60 you can retrofit an older door with this technology—something I recently did with my own garage door.

●**Pet doors.** These are a popular way for kids to break into homes. The best solution is to get a motion-detector system designed for pet-door safety. You put a small device on your pet's collar, which allows it silent entry. If anyone else enters through the opening, an alarm sounds.

---

**More from Sgt. Kevin Coffey...**

# How Not to Be a Hotel Crime Victim

Most hotels have taken steps to tighten security. But that hasn't stopped criminals from creating new opportunities in lobbies, hallways and rooms. *Steps to take to avoid becoming a victim...*

●**Avoid hotels with room locks** that are operated by traditional metal keys. No matter how new-looking the lock may be, you are vulnerable.

*Reasons:* Guests often forget to turn in the room keys. Despite hotel claims to the contrary, most hotels won't change a lock until several copies of its key are missing. One could be in the possession of a criminal. Keys from departing guests who put them on the hotel counter could be picked up by criminals before hotel employees even notice the keys.

*Best type of hotel door lock:* One that is operated by a card with a magnetic strip on the back. The strip allows the code to be automatically reprogrammed whenever a guest checks out, so your lock is as secure as possible.

*Second-best type of lock:* The punch-card style. The cards can be reprogrammed easily, so one that falls into the wrong hands can be rendered worthless.

●**Stay in rooms near the elevator...** between the fifth and eighth floors. Lower floors are at greater risk of break-ins. Above the eighth floor can be risky, too, since not all local fire departments have ladders that can reach above that height.

Rooms near the elevator can provide additional safety. They have the greatest amount of foot traffic, so criminals have less time to attempt a break-in unnoticed. Also, with more people around, a shout for help is more likely to be heard.

Rooms at the ends of halls are less safe. There's typically less traffic in the corridor, and they're often near the stairs. Intruders can count on them for a quick escape.

●**Watch your valuables when you check in.** Hotel lobbies are not safe. Keep briefcases and laptop computers on the counter...or between your legs and the counter.

●**Give your room a quick security sweep.** Lock the doors to the balcony. Lock the door to the adjoining room. With the door open, check the closet, the bathroom and anywhere else large enough to fit a person.

●**Use the safe-deposit boxes at the front desk**—if the one in your room needs a key. The only safe in-room boxes are the type that allow guests to program their own combination using electronic buttons.

Verify any unexpected hotel employees who visit your room. If someone calls up and says he/she is a hotel employee about to come to your room, call the front desk to confirm his identity.

---

# The Best Ways to Protect Against Crime

Sanford Strong, president of Sanford Strong Corp., which teaches life-or-death decision making to corporate executives and their families in 18 countries, Box 600280, San Diego 92160. He is a 20-year veteran of the San Diego Police Department and author of *Strong on Defense: Survival Rules to Protect You and Your Family from Crime*. Pocket Books.

---

Most people panic when confronted by a criminal, and they make costly mistakes. To avoid harm, there are defense and survival techniques that can help you and your family.

What to do if you are confronted by the new, dangerous criminal...

### CRIME ON THE STREET

People think they will come up with the right response when confronted by a criminal. But—that doesn't happen in real life. Panic sets in, and most people react emotionally, not rationally. Unless you have made survival decisions ahead of time, odds are you will be paralyzed with fear and unable to respond in a way that will help you.

*Important:* Think about yourself as a crime victim. Visualize how you should react.

*Best response:* Be the most willing, compliant victim the robber has had all day. Give him/her everything immediately—your wallet, watch, car keys, etc.

Then immediately bolt and run. If you can't run because you're cornered or restrained— scream, yell, make as much noise as possible. Screaming attracts attention and helps block out everything else and focuses you on what must be done. Don't plead or beg.

*Important:* Most crimes start in public or semipublic places. While you may be injured if you run or resist, it's better to be injured in a public place than in an isolated area that is hard to see from public areas. The worst crimes occur when the victim is moved to a second location—what I call crime scene #2.

### CRIME IN YOUR CAR

It is rare for men or children to be abducted during carjackings, but it is very common for women to be taken away.

If you are taken in a car crime, there is only one solution—cause the car to crash as soon as possible to avoid even worse crimes being committed at a remote site.

**Don't wait until you are traveling at high speeds.** Crash the car in your driveway...the shopping mall parking lot...in front of the store.

If you are not the driver, force him to crash. Don't grab the steering wheel—gouge his eyes. Not sure you can do this? Remember what's at stake at the second crime scene. You could do it to save your child—do it to save yourself.

If you are fearful that gouging his eyes or causing a crash will prompt him to shoot you, remember that someone who would shoot a victim in a public spot would shoot in a remote spot. Don't risk it later, when there will be no one to help.

*Example:* When a woman was carjacked in Atlanta, she tried to calm the man down with words. Instead he forced her onto a highway while becoming increasingly violent. When he threatened to kill her, the woman realized her only option was to crash the car. She slowed to 40 mph and plowed into an exit sign and a tree. Her seat belt saved her from serious injury. The assailant, who was on parole, was injured in the crash and fled, but he was caught soon afterward.

### CRIME IN THE HOME

The most dangerous crime situation is the armed home intruder. The rate of serious injury from armed intrusions is 35%, compared with 10% for armed robbery on the street.

During a real-life home intrusion, it is rare for parents to be able to save their children because parents are the first to be attacked. The best chance for children to survive is to know how to escape on their own—and get help.

*Strategy:* Practice a family escape-and-survive drill. This could include using rope to climb

from a window. The aim is to teach your children how to escape and get help.

Walk the family through every room in the home, even bathrooms without windows and walk-in closets. You want to teach children not to make the mistake of going to a room from which escape is impossible. You also want to establish an escape path from every room where escape is possible.

Next, train the children in what to do when they do escape. Establish which neighbors the children should run to.

***Important:*** Don't assume your kids are too young for escape-and-survive lessons. You can teach children as young as four or five years old without traumatizing them. Deal with it matter-of-factly, and be prepared to answer their many questions.

Don't count on one 15-minute session to drive home the lesson. Getting children to leave their home and their parents—even to get help—is tough. Actively rehearsing the escape-and-survival plan gives children the psychological permission to leave and get help.

# Safer Living Alone

A Personal Emergency Response System (PERS) can be a lifesaver for an older person who lives alone. These small, light systems worn as a pendant or bracelet have an emergency alarm button and a two-way voice communication system.

When the wearer pushes the button, a trained employee at the PERS company calls back, usually within a minute. If the caller does not reply, the employee calls the local rescue squad, telling them where to find the key to the caller's house. That information is on file along with other data, including names and phone numbers of family members or neighbors and relevant medical information.

A PERS is not appropriate for people who are not mentally alert and may forget to press the button or repeatedly press it unnecessarily. *Cost:* About $50 for installation and $30 per month. *Nationwide PERS companies include...*

- Link to Life (888-337-LIFE).
- Pioneer Medical Systems (800-234-0683).
- Response Ability Systems, Inc. (800-564-1508).

You can also get information about a PERS by calling your local or state agency on aging.

*Sue F. Ward, secretary of the Maryland Department of Aging, 301 W. Preston St., Suite 1007, Baltimore 21201.*

# Terrorism Self-Defense

*William McCarthy, PhD, president, Threat Research, Inc., security consultants to international businesses, 7600 Admiral Dr., Alexandria, VA 22308. He is former commander of the New York City Police Department bomb squad.*

*Benjamin Weiner, president, Probe International, Inc., economic and political consultants, 1047 Sunset Rd., Stamford, CT 06903. He is a former US diplomat and has traveled to every corner of the globe.*

Threats against personal safety are rising at home and abroad. Two leading security experts explain what you can do to avoid becoming a target…

### STAYING SAFE IN THE US
### William McCarthy, PhD, *Threat Research, Inc.*

- **Be alert to the risks.** Don't automatically adopt an "it can't happen here" mentality. The threat of terrorist violence in the US still is low. But the terrorist threat does exist—as the World Trade Center bombing made clear.

*Best advice:* Live your life as usual, but increase your awareness of what is going on around you. You stay alert to traffic when you cross a street—maintain that same sense of alertness whenever you're away from your home.

- **Watch your surroundings as you walk down the street or enter a building.** Be aware of the people and events around you. Don't let others see you daydreaming. Let your behavior demonstrate your awareness to others. The more alert you are to what is going on around you, the better your defenses against everything from street crime to terrorist violence.

- **Avoid points of vulnerability.** Explosive devices inflict the most damage to the perimeter of the target.

When you enter a building—to be safer—put as much brick-and-mortar as possible between you and the outside walls. Don't linger in the lobby. Pass through as quickly as possible.

The area of greatest danger is near the big plate glass windows of buildings, stores and airports. Most victims aren't killed by the blast, but by flying glass and other debris. Wherever you are, never lean against an outside glass window. If possible, keep a reinforced cement column between you and the glass.

- **Beware of mail bombs.** These are the most insidious weapons terrorists use. They were the weapon of choice of the Unabomber. Although he is safely in prison, bombs are still sent through the mail.

*Warning:* A mail bomb is set off by opening it. People know that. Yet I'm amazed by the number of people who get a suspicious letter or package and open it.

*Best advice:* If you get a suspicious package at home or at work, don't open it. Consider a package suspicious if…

- It is addressed to someone at your firm who doesn't exist.
- It carries a return address with which you aren't familiar.
- It carries excessive postage.
- It is stained.

*Very important:* If anything makes you suspicious of a letter or a parcel, leave it unopened, clear the area and call for help.

- **Never be embarrassed about calling the police.** People would rather live with fear than risk calling the police for a false alarm. If it is a false alarm, no harm is done—but if there is a bomb, failing to call the police can hurt or kill.

*Best advice:* If you notice a suspicious package or object in your workplace, make an immediate effort to find out how the package got there. If you don't get an answer that satisfies you by the end of the day, call the police. Don't go home for the night without resolving your worry.

*Warning:* Never remain in the vicinity of an unattended package or suitcase left in a public area. If you see someone walk away from a suitcase or other package, politely remind him/her that he left the object unattended. If the person doesn't return to retrieve the package or if there is no one around, call the police. In Israel, if you walk two steps away from a package, I guarantee someone will challenge you.

### STAYING SAFE OVERSEAS
#### Benjamin Weiner, *Probe International, Inc.*

●**Think carefully about where you go.** With increased travel worldwide and reduced border vigilance, no place is safe from terrorism.

*Example:* There was no political reason why Muslim terrorists would attack a target in Kenya. They wanted to attack a symbol of the US, and the embassy in Nairobi was convenient.

*Reducing the risk:* Some countries pose greater risks than others. A country may be an avowed foe of the US or something may be going on now that makes a country a high-risk place to visit.

Keep up with current events so you know the latest political, economic and social hot spots. Your travel agent or business travel department should know the latest State Department warnings on areas to avoid…or contact the US State Department at 202-647-5225…or the embassy or nearest consulate of the country.

*Helpful:* The Internet has numerous sites with up-to-date travel intelligence. Travel warnings from the State Department are available at http://travel.state.gov/travel_warnings.html.

●**Plan *when* to go.** Terrorist acts are most likely to occur on days that have symbolic meaning to the people involved. Take into account religious holidays, ethnic observances and national days. Learn important days in countries you'll be visiting, and plan your itinerary around them. If your travel agent doesn't have this information, contact the local representative of the country.

●**Be a security-smart traveler.** Airports are a favorite target for terrorist attacks, so spend as little time in them as you can. Join one of the airline clubs. This will provide you with a relatively safe place to wait for your flight. Travel light, with everything in one or two bags. Carry luggage on board, so you can avoid the baggage-claim area. That gets you out of the airport faster.

●**Be as inconspicuous as possible.** Whether you're a tourist or a business traveler, avoid anything that makes you stand out in the crowd. Don't wear or do anything that would cause people to give you a second glance.

*Best advice:* Dress quietly. Wear a business suit or sports clothes in muted tones. Don't wear religious symbols. Avoid clothing with logos of American colleges or sports teams. Don't call attention to yourself by wearing flashy jewelry or an expensive watch.

*Helpful:* Your luggage should not have any American symbols or logos of American companies. It must have an ID tag, but put your identification into the holder backward. If the luggage is lost, the tag will be taken apart to learn your identity. Otherwise, anyone looking at your ID tag will see only a blank card.

●**Be a street-smart traveler.** Avoid street demonstrations and political gatherings, even in countries where anti-American violence is rare. Anything can happen when passions get inflamed.

Be polite and soft-spoken wherever you go. Offensive language or rude behavior makes you stand out in a crowd. Try to visit high-profile tourist attractions during off-peak hours—especially in destinations where terrorist groups are known to operate. That will not only help keep you safe, it will let you see the sights when the crowds are the thinnest.

---

# Protect Yourself With Immunization

William Schaffner, MD, chairman of the department of preventive medicine at Vanderbilt University Medical School in Nashville.

---

Polio, diphtheria and other childhood scourges have mostly disappeared in the US, thanks mainly to large-scale vaccination programs.

Adults tend to think of getting immunized only before traveling abroad—to guard against "traveler's diseases" like typhoid or cholera.*

*The Centers for Disease Control and Prevention in Atlanta (888-232-3228) offers a free 24-hour hotline to tell you exactly which shots are recommended for your destination.

But vaccine-preventable illnesses can be just as deadly…and they're all around us.

### INFLUENZA

Every few years, an influenza epidemic strikes the US. The typical epidemic causes 10,000 to 40,000 deaths, mostly among people age 65 or older.

Flu shots are up to 40% effective at preventing the disease. If you do get influenza despite being vaccinated, your illness should be less severe…and less likely to lead to pneumonia or another serious complication.

A new shot is needed each fall, to guard against the specific strains of influenza expected to circulate the following winter.

***Who needs the vaccine:*** Everyone age 65 or older…younger adults who have heart, lung or kidney disease or a metabolic disease like diabetes…and women who will be pregnant during flu season (December through April).

Flu shots are also a good idea for cancer patients and other individuals with compromised immunity…health-care workers…people caring for elderly relatives…and anyone who simply wants to avoid the aches, fever and inconvenience of the flu.

*Caution:* Individuals allergic to eggs should not get this vaccine. It contains egg proteins.

### PNEUMOCOCCAL DISEASE

Pneumonia and other illnesses caused by *pneumococcus* bacteria kill 40,000 Americans a year. Half of this number would be saved if everyone at risk got the pneumococcal vaccine.

It is unclear how long the protection from a single shot lasts. For those who are especially vulnerable to pneumococcal disease, including the immune deficient and the elderly, revaccination is recommended.

***Who needs the vaccine:*** Official guidelines call for immunization at age 65, but some experts suggest lowering the age to 50. That's when the incidence of pneumococcal disease rises.

The pneumococcal vaccine is also appropriate for people at risk for influenza…people with sickle-cell anemia…and anyone who has lost his/her spleen.

*Caution:* Postpone vaccination if you're pregnant.

### HEPATITIS B

This liver infection can be spread sexually or via contact with contaminated blood. It strikes 300,000 Americans a year. Roughly 25% of these develop chronic hepatitis B, which can lead to cirrhosis or liver cancer.

Three injections are given over a six-month period. This regimen confers lifetime immunity in over 90% of those who get it.

***Who needs the vaccine:*** All young adults who weren't immunized in childhood…and all health-care workers. The vaccine is also recommended for every sexually active person who is not in a long-term monogamous relationship.

Some experts think all adults and children should get the hepatitis B vaccine.

### MEASLES-MUMPS-RUBELLA

Thirty percent of measles and mumps cases occur in adults who did not have these diseases in childhood and/or who were not fully immunized.

Measles is more severe in adults than in children. It can lead to serious complications such as pneumonia.

Two shots, given one month apart, confer lifetime immunity to all three diseases in 99% of those who get the shots.

***Who needs the vaccine:*** The measles-mumps-rubella vaccine is vital for health-care workers and those who travel abroad if they have not had a documented case of measles, mumps or rubella and didn't get the double-shot vaccination.

*Caution:* Do not get immunized if you're pregnant or anticipate becoming pregnant within three months.

### CHICKEN POX

One in 10 adults has never had chicken pox (varicella), and the disease is far more serious in adults than in children. A vaccine against chicken pox became available three years ago.

Two injections are given, four to eight weeks apart. The vaccine is about 95% effective.

***Who needs the vaccine:*** Anyone who never had chicken pox or who is uncertain as to whether he had chicken pox. Immunity to chicken pox is especially important for teachers, health-care workers and others in close contact with children.

*Caution:* Postpone vaccination if you're pregnant or may become pregnant within the next month.

### TETANUS

There are only 50 or so cases of tetanus in the US each year, but the illness is almost always fatal. Fortunately, the tetanus vaccine confers total protection.

Almost everyone gets vaccinated in childhood, but protection wanes. Only half of adults have full immunity.

*Who needs the vaccine:* Everyone age 15 or older should get a tetanus booster every 10 years.

### HEPATITIS A

Hepatitis A strikes 140,000 Americans a year. It's caused by consuming food or water that is contaminated with human waste.

For lifetime immunity, two injections given six months apart are required.

*Who needs the vaccine:* Get vaccinated at least one month before traveling to any undeveloped region.

Vaccination is also a good idea if hepatitis A is endemic in your area. To find out if it is, call your local health department.

## Phone Card Caution

Avoid phone card scams at public phones by looking for a pay phone in which you swipe the card rather than punch in numbers. Be super-cautious at all punch-in pay phones. Don't answer a ringing phone in a busy public place. Make your own call on another phone that is not ringing by punching in your numbers. If it was an electronic thief who placed the call on the ringing phone, your number can be stolen if you use the same phone.

Beware of shoulder surfers who hover behind or beside you to spot the numbers you use. Shield your hand as you enter the numbers because scammers use binoculars and video cameras with long-range lenses to snare numbers from a distance.

John Heath, AT&T, 295 N. Maple Ave., Basking Ridge, NJ 07920.

## Pickpocket Self-Defense

Beware if someone shouts "thief." Crooks yell to trick people into showing where their money is—people instinctively feel for their wallets or purses. Watch out for sudden jostling in lines at museums and train and bus stops. Do not carry a wallet in a back pocket. If using a shoulder bag, wear the strap diagonally across you. Be especially wary on Fridays, Saturdays and days before holidays—crooks are extra-active then because people tend to have extra cash.

John Owens, editor-in-chief, *Travel Holiday,* 1633 Broadway, New York 10019.

## Protect Your Winnings

If you win a large cash award from a lottery, sweepstakes or casino, protect your privacy and money immediately.

*Reason:* Winners are targeted by scam artists, thieves and curiosity seekers.

*Smart moves:* Get an unlisted phone number…subscribe to Caller ID to screen calls…forward your mail to a post office box…hire an estate-planning attorney to negotiate with the sponsor and a financial planner to help manage your prize wisely.

*Important:* Decline interviews that put you in the public eye.

John Featherman, editor, *Privacy Newsletter,* Box 8206, Philadelphia 19101.

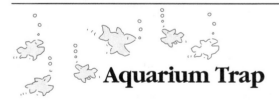

## Aquarium Trap

Tropical fish owners sometimes develop red nodules on their hands and arms. "Fish tank granuloma" occurs when a tank-dwelling microbe called *Mycobacterium marinum* enters the body through small cuts in the skin.

*Problem:* While relatively harmless, the ailment is often misdiagnosed as anything from cat scratch fever to tuberculosis. *Self-defense:* Don rubber gloves before placing your arms in a fish tank.

John Ryan, MD, consultant senior lecturer, department of accident and emergency medicine, Royal Sussex County Hospital, Brighton, England.

## Toilet Self-Defense

Close the toilet lid before flushing. The fine mist that is created by the swirling water can spread disease-causing *E. coli* bacteria to nearby toothbrushes.

In a recent study, one in five toothbrushes was contaminated with *E. coli* from toilets.

Charles Gerba, PhD, professor of microbiology, University of Arizona, Tucson.

## For Greater Elevator Safety

Do not press your floor number until all strangers press theirs. Stand with your back against an elevator wall to minimize your exposure to muggers and pickpockets. At your floor, check the corridor before leaving the elevator—*do not get out if you see a stranger.* Be especially careful in the basement—the most hazardous part of an apartment building.

Ira Lipman, president, Guardsmark, Inc., one of the world's largest security services companies, Memphis.

## Safer Driving

If a deer jumps in front of your car, gently press the horn while braking. Do not try to swerve.

*Also:* Don't try to scare off deer with headlights—they are attracted to the lights and can fixate on them, especially if you flash your high beams.

***Worst times of day for car/deer collisions:*** Early morning and early evening—when deer are active.

AAA Foundation for Traffic Safety, 1440 New York Ave. NW, Suite 201, Washington, DC 20005.

## Auto Life Saver

Always carry an object capable of breaking your car's window glass should you get caught in a flash flood or drive into deep water.

***Good choice:*** An automatic center punch, sold in any hardware store. The tool will break the glass simply by pressing the pointed end against the window. A tire iron, jack handle, heavy-duty flashlight or hammer will also do the job.

***Helpful:*** Keep the object where it is readily accessible, such as in the glove compartment or taped under the driver's seat.

David Solomon, editor, *Nutz & Boltz,* Box 123, Butler, MD 21023.

## E-Mail Self-Defense

Internet virus warnings are often phony. Viruses can do damage, but many Internet postings are scams, gags or misinformation. *Example:* A threatening chain letter claiming that a virus will infect your computer if you do not forward the letter to 10 people within 45 minutes. An E-mail *without* an attachment cannot infect a computer with a virus. But *E-mail with attachments* can. *Dangerous clues:* E-mail from unknown sources...attachments with long file names. Immediately delete these items. *Do not open them.* Find out about many hoax virus messages at the Computer Virus Myths page, http://www.kumite.com/myths. And be sure to run antivirus software...get the latest patches for both antivirus and E-mail programs...and update them regularly.

Mark J. Estren, PhD, technology columnist and consultant, McLean, VA.

# Kids' Basic Internet Rules

• *Don't* give out any personal information without a parent's permission.

• *Don't* arrange to meet anyone in person without your parents present.

• *Don't* believe everything people tell you on-line.

• *Don't* respond to any obscene or threatening messages.

• *Do* keep your own language clean and appropriate—messages can be traced back to you.

• *Do* tell your parents if something or someone on-line makes you uncomfortable.

Ann Orr, senior editor, *Children's Software Revue*, 44 Main St., Flemington, NJ 08822.

# Computer Crime Self-Defense

M.E. Kabay, PhD, CISSP, director of education, International Computer Security Association, 1200 Walnut Bottom Rd., Suite 3, Carlisle, PA 17013.

Most of the damage that is caused to business computing systems is the work of employees with access to those systems who are dishonest...angry...careless...or untrained. *Self-defense...*

• **Thoroughly check references and backgrounds** before hiring information technology employees. Provide ongoing training and security awareness programs for these employees.

• **Enforce a formal policy that bars employees from giving out** *any* **unauthorized information about the company's computer systems.** And—name one person to be responsible for all outside contacts regarding the company's computing systems. As part of this policy, require the manager to verify all outside requests for information before answering any questions.

*Aim:* To foil computer hackers who break into computer systems using information obtained from the company's own employees. They often get the information they need by simply calling and asking questions about the system, posing as service personnel who need the information to make "remote" repairs.

• **Continuously update the company's network software.** Using outdated network software creates another window of opportunity for outside hackers to invade your company's computing systems.

*Helpful:* Subscribe to the Computer Emergency Response Team-Coordination Center (CERT-CC) advisories about computer hacker activity, and install software patches whenever the reports indicate a need.

CERT-CC (available on-line at www.cert. org) studies Internet security vulnerabilities, provides incident response services to sites that have been the victims of attack and publishes security advisories to help businesses improve computer security.

# Index